Now You're Talking!

Discover the World of Ham Radio

First Edition

EDITED BY

Jim Kearman, KR1S
Joel P. Kleinman, N1BKE
Larry D. Wolfgang, WR1B

PRODUCTION STAFF

Michelle Chrisjohn, WB1ENT
Sue Fagan
Jodi Morin, KA1JPA
Steffie Nelson, KA1IFB
David Pingree
Joe Shea
Deborah Strzeszkowski
Mark Wilson, AA2Z

COVER ARTWORK

Bev Rich

The American Radio Relay League, Inc.
Newington, CT 06111

This book may be used for Novice and Technician exams given up to July 1, 1993.

Foreword

Amateur Radio is a very exciting avocation to many people all over the world. It provides a medium through which people in all walks of life can share a common interest. Amateur Radio also has many faces and can be seen differently by each person. To some just the ability to talk to people of diverse cultures is what drew them to Amateur Radio. For some it provides an important communications link home from remote parts of the earth (and beyond). The Amateur Radio Service enjoys access to the radio waves with very few restrictions. This has given many electronics experimenters an opportunity to dabble at the forefront of communications technology that they would not otherwise have.

I call it an avocation because to many of us it is much more than just a hobby. My own entry into Amateur Radio was in 1963 at the age of 12. Little did I know that it would play such an important role in my future life. During my college career I was employed by the university planetarium as a technician. The hands-on experience with soldering iron and volt meter that I acquired in my Amateur Radio activities got me that job. Later when applying for a job teaching physics at a technical college I was turned down until they found out I was a "ham." The ability to teach practical electronics learned through Amateur Radio, as well as physics, gave me the edge over the other candidates. The practical technical experience I have gained through Amateur Radio has continued to serve me well throughout my professional career.

The climax of my Amateur Radio activities (so far) has been the operation of SAREX-2 from aboard the Space Shuttle Columbia. Between December 2 and December 10, 1990 I was able to communicate with over 100 people on voice, and nearly 1000 on packet radio! Imagine the excitement of talking to Amateur Radio operators all over the world from earth orbit. It was indeed the ultimate DXpedition!

The Federal Communications Commission and the ARRL have now provided even more ways than ever before to enter this continually changing "hobby". With the new laws in place you can choose an entry-level license that best suits your current level of expertise. Depending upon your interests, you can also choose a license that either stresses the technical or traditional aspects of Amateur Radio. Whatever direction you decide to take you will enter a worldwide fraternity that will never cease to provide new challenges. Best of luck, and see you on the air!

73,

Ronald A. Parise, WA4SIR

Preface

Welcome! If you are reading these lines, chances are that you would like to join the more than two million people in every corner of the globe who call themselves radio amateurs, or "hams." They have earned the very special privilege of being able to communicate directly with one another, by radio, without regard to the barriers that so often interfere with our understanding of the world. Whether across town or across the sea, hams are always looking for new friends; so, wherever you may happen to be, you are probably near someone—perhaps a whole club—who would be glad to help you get started.

Most of the active radio amateurs in the United States are members of the American Radio Relay League. ARRL has been the hams' own organization for more than 75 years, providing training materials and other services and representing its members nationally and internationally. *Now You're Talking!* is just one of the many ARRL publications for all levels and interests in Amateur Radio. You don't need a ham license to join. If you're interested in ham radio, we're interested in you. It's as simple as that!

David Sumner, K1ZZ
Executive Vice President

Newington, Connecticut
March 1991

Contents

Two Tracks To Your First Ham Radio License

Until recently, the Novice license was the entry route for most newcomers to Amateur Radio. The Novice license exam covers basic theory and regulations and a 5-word-per-minute (WPM) Morse code test. Novices are allowed to operate code on four high-frequency (HF) bands, where world-wide communication is possible, without satellites or repeater stations. Novices are also allowed to use voice on one HF band and two higher-frequency bands used mostly for local communications. Other privileges include radioteletype and computer-to-computer communications on certain bands.

The Technician class license was usually the next step up for many radio amateurs. The Technician license formerly required the same Morse-code exam as the Novice license, and a slightly more difficult exam covering electronics and radio theory and Federal Communications Commission (FCC) rules and regulations. Technician licensees were automatically given the same operating privileges as Novices, *in addition* to full privileges on the amateur VHF and UHF bands.

Effective February 14, 1991, however, FCC removed the Morse-code requirement for obtaining a Technician license. The theory and rules and regulations examination remains unchanged. Now Technician licensees have all the VHF and UHF privileges formerly granted to Technicians, but *not* the HF prvileges granted to Novices. Those Novice-band privileges can be earned, however, by any code-free Technician licensee who passes a 5-WPM code test. (Previously licensed Technician-class operators retain all of their privileges.)

Any holder of a new Technician license who passes the code test is issued a *Certificate of Successful Completion of Examination* (CSCE) and is immediately granted Novice operating privileges on the HF bands. Novices who upgrade to Technician within two years of the expiration of their Novice licenses are also automatically granted Novice privileges when they pass the Technician exam.

How To Use This Book

You're about to begin an exciting adventure: a fun-filled journey into the world of Amateur Radio. *Now You're Talking!* is *the* study guide to help you reach your goal. This book introduces you to basic radio theory in an easily understood style. You'll also learn Federal Communications Commission (FCC) rules and regulations—just as the FCC requires. You will learn enough to pass your Novice *or* Technician written exam with ease. But we in the American Radio Relay League care much more about you and your future in Amateur Radio than to stop there! We won't abandon you once your new "ticket" is in hand.

Now You're Talking! is also a pathway to a successful beginning after you've passed your license exam. In this book you'll find the practical knowledge needed to become an effective communicator. We all hope you will take enough pride in the achievement of earning your license to be a considerate communicator as well.

But that's all a few weeks and a few pages down the line. To ensure your success and head you in the right direction toward your first on-the-air contact, here's how to use this book to your best advantage.

Now You're Talking! has been designed and written by a staff with a great deal of experience, backed by decades of Amateur Radio tradition. This book provides everything you'll need to learn—and understand—what you should know to operate an Amateur Radio station. We explain all the rules and regulations required of Novice and Technician candidates, not only to pass the test, but to operate properly (legally) once your license is hanging proudly in your shack.

SELF STUDY OR CLASSROOM USE?

We designed *Now You're Talking!* both for self study and for classroom use. An interested student will find this book complete, readable and easy to understand. Read carefully, and test yourself often as you study. Before you know it, you'll be ready to pass that exam!

Why deprive yourself of the company of fellow beginners and the expertise of those "old-timers" in your hometown, though? *Now You're Talking!* goes hand-in-hand with a very effective ARRL-sponsored training program run by over 6000 volunteer instructors throughout the United States. If you would like to find out about a local class, just contact the Educational Activities Department at ARRL Headquarters—we'll be happy to assist.

Hams are very social animals who derive a great deal of pleasure from helping a newcomer along the way. The most effective learning situation is often the one you share with others. There are knowledgeable people to turn to when you have a question or problem. You can practice the Morse code with fellow students, and quiz one another on basic electronics concepts.

It doesn't matter if you're studying on your own or joining a class. Use *Now You're Talking!* to study for your Novice or Technician exam and you'll be on the air in no time at all.

USING THIS BOOK

Now You're Talking! leads you from one subject to the next in a logical sequence that builds on the knowledge learned in earlier sections. It presents the material in easily digested and well-defined "bite-sized" sections. You will be directed to turn to the question pool in Chapter 12 (and 13 if you're preparing for the Technician exam) as you complete a section of the material.

This review will help you determine if you're ready to move on. It will also highlight those areas where you need a little more study. In addition, this approach takes you through the entire question pool. By the time you complete the book, you will be familiar with all the questions used to make up your test. Please take the time to follow these instructions. Believe us, it's better to learn the material correctly the first time than to rush ahead, ignoring weak areas and unresolved questions.

Every page of this book presents information you'll need to pass the exam and become an effective operator. Pay attention to diagrams, photographs, sketches and captions; they contain a wealth of information you should know. You'll also find a few anecdotes and "mini-articles" (called Sidebars) that will help put the tradition of Amateur Radio in perspective. Our roots go back to the beginning of the 20th Century, and our community service continues even as you read this.

Start at the beginning. Chapter 1 summarizes the fun you will have when you earn your license and join the thousands of other active radio amateurs. Chapter 2 explains the need for international and national regulation. It describes the regulating bodies and the relevant sections of Part 97 of the FCC Rules and Regulations.

Chapter 3 breaks basic radio theory into well-defined sections. Each section builds on the previous material to explain the theory you'll need to answer the questions in Chapters 12 and 13.

Study these sections one at a time. Be sure to follow the instructions at specific places in the text that direct you to study the actual test questions. This is the best way to determine how well you understand the most important points. The text explains the theory in straightforward terms, so you shouldn't have any problems. Don't be afraid to ask for help if you don't understand something, though.

If you're participating in an official ARRL-registered class, you'll have the chance to ask the experts for help. Ask your instructor about anything you are having difficulty with. You may also find it helpful to discuss the material with your fellow students. If you're not in a class and run into snags, don't despair! The Educational Activities Department at ARRL Headquarters will be happy to put you in touch with an Amateur Radio operator in your area who can help answer your questions.

Chapters 4 and 5 cover some basic components and circuits. You will also learn how to connect various pieces of equipment to form an Amateur Radio station.

Chapter 6 offers some guidelines to help you select the equipment you'll need to set up your own radio station. Chapter 7 gives you all the information about antennas that you'll need to pass your exam and get started in Amateur Radio. Full construction details are provided for several simple antennas suitable for Novice or Technician operation.

Chapter 8 will help you assemble an effective Amateur Radio station. After your license arrives from the FCC and your station is set up, Chapter 9 leads you through those first few contacts. How do you know when to operate on what band? Where do you turn to make contact with a specific foreign country or faraway state? How do you establish contact in the first place and what do you say? What sorts of activities will you want to become involved with on the air? Chapter 9 has the operating information to make you feel at ease on the air. Chapter 10 will help you identify and solve the problems you are most likely to encounter as a new ham.

All these chapters cover information necessary to pass the exam and the practical information you'll need to make your ham radio experience enjoyable. Study the material presented in this book and follow the instructions to review the exam questions. You'll cover small sections of the text and a few questions at a time. Review the related sections if you have any difficulty, and then go over the questions again. In this way you will soon be ready for your exam. Before you know it, you'll be on the air!

Most people learn more when they are actively involved in the learning process. Turning to the questions and answers when directed in the text helps you be actively involved. If you wish, you can mark the correct answers in the question pool. This will reinforce the material in your mind. Make an asterisk or check mark in the left margin next to the correct answer. Then you can cover those marks with a slip of paper when you want to review later. Paper clips make excellent place markers to help you find your spot in the text, the question pool and the answer key.

If You Decide to Learn the Code

Chapter 11 lets you in on a little secret. The Morse code is not only easy to learn; it can be so enjoyable that you may become "addicted." You should read this chapter before beginning to learn the Morse code. People try to learn the code by many different methods. The code cassettes in *Your Introduction to Morse Code* teach you the Morse code at your own pace. You should rewind the tape to review any characters that give you difficulty. The technique used with these tapes also makes it easy to increase your speed once you've learned the code.

After reading Chapter 11, begin studying the code and theory in "parallel"; that is, split your study time between daily sessions with the code and study sessions with the text. Move ahead at a pace that allows you to master the material. You do have to keep moving, however. Don't allow yourself to stay on one section too long, even if you have to come back and review later.

———— THE NOVICE TEST ————

The FCC requires two licensed hams to give a Novice exam. If you're taking a class, you'll have no problem in locating two experienced hams to administer the code test and written exam. Who may give the Novice test? Sections 97.513 and 97.515 of the FCC rules list the qualifications for the two people who administer a Novice test. Both Novice examiners must:

1) hold a current General, Advanced or Amateur Extra class operator license issued by the FCC;

2) be at least 18 years of age;

3) not be related to the applicant;

4) not own a significant interest in, or be an employee of, any company or other organization engaged in the manufacture or distribution of equipment used in connection with Amateur Radio transmissions, or in preparation or distribution of any publication used in preparation for obtaining an Amateur Radio license. An employee who can demonstrate that he or she does not normally communicate with that part of an organization engaged in such manufacture or publishing is eligible to be a volunteer examiner, however;

5) never had their Amateur Radio station or operator's license revoked or suspended.

The code test requires you to show your ability to send and receive the Morse code at 5 words per minute. Here is a simple way to estimate code speed: Five characters make one word, with punctuation and numerals counting as two characters each. You must know the 26 letters, 10 numerals and the basic punctuation marks: comma, period, question mark, double dash (= also called $\overline{BT}$) and fraction bar (/ also called $\overline{DN}$). You must also know some common procedural signals (prosigns): $\overline{AR}$ (the + sign, also used to mean "over" or "end of message") and $\overline{SK}$ ("clear; end of contact"). For further details on the code test, see Chapter 11.

For the written exam, you must answer 30 questions about Amateur Radio rules, theory and practice. Your test questions will be drawn from the pool of more than 350 questions. Most VECs (including the ARRL/VEC) agreed to use the question pool printed in Chapter 12, beginning on July 1, 1990. The question pool includes the multiple-choice answers that most VECs have agreed to use.

The question pool is divided into nine subelements. Each subelement is further divided into blocks, with one question to come from each block. Your test must include one question from each of the 30 blocks. Your examiners may select the questions, or they may contact the Educational Activities Department at ARRL Headquarters for a printed exam. Your examiners could simply go through the question pool printed in Chapter 12 and have you answer the chosen questions right from the book. (Provided you have not marked the correct answers beforehand!) The passing grade for an amateur license is 74%, so you will need 22 or more correct answers out of the 30 questions on your exam to pass the test. (Another way of putting this is that you may have as many as eight incorrect answers and still pass!)

The questions must be used exactly as printed (and as reproduced in Chapter 12 of this book). Novice examiners may use their discretion about the examination format. This opens several possibilities for the examiners. The exam could be multiple-choice, true-false, or essay type. They may even conduct your test on an oral "interview" basis, with the examiners asking the questions and the applicant responding. The examiners aren't *required* to use the multiple-choice answers printed with the questions in Chapter 12, but we highly *recommend* it, and most examiners use this format.

THE TECHNICIAN TEST

Since January 1, 1985, all US amateur exams except the Novice have been administered under the Volunteer-Examiner Program. Novice exams do not come under the regulations involving Volunteer-Examiner Coordinators (VECs).

To qualify for a Technician-class license, you must pass Elements 2 and 3A. *You do not have to pass Element 1A (5-WPM code test).* If you already hold a valid Novice license, then you have credit for passing Elements 1A and 2 and will not have to retake those elements.

The Element 3A exam consists of 25 questions taken from a pool of more than 250. The question pools for all amateur examinations are maintained by a Question Pool Committee selected by the Volunteer Examiner Coordinators. The FCC allows Volunteer Examiners to select the questions for an amateur exam, but they must use the questions exactly as they are released by the VEC that coordinates the test session. If you attend a test session coordinated by the ARRL/VEC, your test will be designed by the ARRL/VEC, and the questions and answers will be exactly as they are printed in Chapter 13.

BEFORE YOU TAKE YOUR TEST

Before you go to take your exam, fill out an FCC Form 610. (Chapter 2 has full details about how to fill out this form.) After you complete the test, your examiners grade it. When you pass all the exam elements required for the license, the examiners complete the Administering VE's Report on the front of the form and the Certification section on the back, indicating that you passed all required elements.

A completed Novice-license application goes directly to the FCC in Gettysburg, PA. Applications for the other license classes go first to the administering VEC, then to the FCC. Now comes the hard part! It may take as long as six weeks for your license to arrive in the mail. The FCC staff processes your application along with the thousands of other 610 forms they receive each month.

If you need help in locating someone to administer the Novice test, drop a note to the Educational Activities Department at ARRL Headquarters. For a schedule of Volunteer Examiner test sessions in your area, write to the ARRL/VEC office. We can put you in touch with examiners and clubs in your area.

Give *Now You're Talking!* a chance to guide you the way it was intended—by following these instructions. You'll soon be joining us on the air. Each of us at the American Radio Relay League Headquarters and the entire ARRL membership wishes you the very best of success. We are all looking forward to that day in the not-too-distant future when we hear your signal on the ham bands. 73 (best regards) and good luck!

Chapter 1

Discovering Amateur Radio

How did you first hear about Amateur Radio? That evening news report about the Amateur Radio operators who relayed messages after the San Francisco earthquake? The funny-looking antenna in your neighbor's yard? A birthday greeting via Amateur Radio from your uncle who lives clear across the country? Or maybe you heard about hams who talked to astronaut Ron Parise during a space-shuttle mission.

Obviously, you know something about amateur (ham) radio; you have this book. But you want to know more. *Now You're Talking!* will introduce you to the wonderful hobby of Amateur Radio. It will answer your many questions on the subject, and lead you to your first license.

WHAT CAN I DO AS A HAM?

Ham radio offers so much variety, it would be hard to describe all its activities in a book twice this size! Most of all, ham radio gives you a chance to meet other people who like to *communicate*. That's the one thing all hams have in common. You can communicate with other hams in your area with a simple hand-held radio. You can talk to hams all over the world in many ways. The most popular way is by bouncing your signal off the ionosphere, a layer in the upper atmosphere. Other hams like to use the OSCAR satellites. OSCAR means *Orbiting Satellite Carrying Amateur Radio*. Hams have

designed and built almost two dozen OSCARs since 1961. If you like a challenge, you can even bounce your signals off the moon. It's possible to contact other hams in over 100 countries by this method, as strange as it sounds!

How do you talk to these other hams? Well, you can use voice of course, but there are other ways as well. The oldest form of radio communication is the Morse code. You don't have to know the code to become a ham anymore, but many hams enjoy using this funny language.

Maybe you've tried computer-to-computer conversations over the telephone lines. As a ham, you can have similar conversations with other hams around the world. The best part is, you don't have to pay for the call!

Maybe you're interested in photography or video. Many hams have television equipment, including color. Hams led the way in *slow-scan television*, which lets you send color photographs, slides and artwork to other hams thousands of miles away.

If you like to work on electronic circuits, ham radio gives you the chance to build your own transmitters and receivers, and actually use them to talk to other people. Even if you'd just like to plug in a radio and go on the air, you might enjoy building some part of your station, from scratch or from a kit.

Unlike shortwave or scanner listening, Amateur Radio doesn't make you sit on the sidelines. When East and West

Germany became one country, hams didn't have to learn about it from the TV news: they talked directly to hams in both places!

Most people would like to do something to help their communities. Ham radio operators provide communications for marathons and parades, and lend a hand during emergencies. Earthquakes and hurricanes don't happen very often, fortunately, but hams still provide assistance every day. Through telephone patches, mobile hams report traffic accidents and disabled cars. Other hams working from home relay messages across the country and around the world. Imagine talking to a missionary operating a battery-powered station deep in the Amazon jungle, or a sailor attempting an around-the-world solo journey!

Ham radio operators are proud of their hobby. That's why you see so many license plates with ham call signs. Communicating on the air isn't all we do, though. We get together at club meetings, *hamfests* and conventions. To welcome newcomers we sponsor thousands of classes each year to help anyone who's interested join our great hobby.

TWO PATHS TO CHOOSE FROM

There are five classes of Amateur Radio license in the United States. All US amateur licenses have 10-year terms and are renewable. In the US, licenses are issued by the Federal Communications Commission (FCC). There is no license fee. Although you can take the exams and start right out at the highest class, most beginners enter Amateur Radio with either the Novice or Technician license.

There are several differences between the two entry-level licenses, in exams and operating privileges. They are described in the following sections. To pass the Novice license exam, you're required to know Morse code, but there's no code exam for the Technician license. No matter which path you choose, this book has all the information you need to pass the written exams.

The Novice License

To receive a Novice license you have to pass a 30-question written exam in basic electronics theory, FCC regulations and operating practices. You also have to copy the international Morse code at 5 words per minute (WPM).

Novice licensees are granted a wide range of privileges on several amateur bands. Some of these bands are mainly useful for local communications, but others offer the ability to talk to other radio amateurs around the world, without the use of satellites (we'll tell you more about satellite communications later). The Morse code and many abbreviations such as "Q signals" are understood internationally. This makes the code ideal for communicating with hams in foreign countries. Plenty of stations in other countries operate in the Novice bands. Quite a few Novices have even contacted hams in more than 100 different countries. Chapter 2 has more information about Novice-license privileges.

The Novice exam can be given by a pair of General, Advanced or Extra-class amateurs. For help learning the code we recommend *Your Introduction to Morse Code*, a package of two audio cassettes that teach you the code, letter by letter. When you know the code, the tapes give you practice at 5 WPM, the same speed used on the Novice exam.

The Technician License

If you aren't interested in learning the Morse code right now, the Technician license is for you. To receive a Technician license you have to pass the same 30-question written exam as for the Novice license, plus an additional 25-question exam. The additional exam covers the same subjects, but in more detail.

Technician licensees are granted full amateur privileges on the extensive VHF, UHF and microwave amateur bands, including Amateur Radio satellite bands. Yes, with a Technician license you can talk to other amateurs around the world via satellite! Technician licensees can use the popular 2-meter band, where thousands of amateur-owned repeater stations provide solid communications over large areas.

If you start out as a Technician and then decide you'd also like to use the high-frequency Novice bands, all you have to do is pass a 5-WPM Morse code exam. Your new privileges will begin the day you pass the exam. There is enough Morse code activity on the Technician bands to help you if you decide to learn the code. Chapter 2 has more information about Technician-license privileges.

The Technician license exam (and all other amateur license exams except the Novice) are given by teams of

Volunteer Examiners. Thousands of exam sessions are held each year, so you shouldn't have to travel far or wait long to take one. Write to ARRL for information on exam sessions near you.

WE COME FROM ALL WALKS OF LIFE

Having fun communicating and experimenting. That's what Amateur Radio is all about. That's why people from all walks of life become hams. Young or old, we all enjoy the thrill of meeting and exchanging ideas with people from across town or from the other side of the earth. The excitement of building a new project or getting a circuit to work properly is almost beyond description.

Carm Prestia is a diamond-in-the-rough police sergeant, patrolling a bustling university town tucked away in the mountains of Pennsylvania. By night, he packs a .38-caliber Police Special to protect thousands of his fellow townspeople. By day, he wields a soldering iron in pursuit of the world's greatest hobby: Amateur Radio.

"I love to talk to people on the radio," Carm explains as he unstraps his portable radio from his uniform belt. "I talk all night at work, but I still go home and fire up the ham gear."

Carm's shack (hams all over the world affectionately call this room their "shack") is in a corner of his basement. His equipment table holds a transmitter for sending and a receiver for listening. His radio gear works with an antenna outside, above his backyard. Carm can talk with a friend in the next town one minute and with a ham halfway around the world in Australia the next.

Each Amateur Radio station has its own distinctive call sign. The Federal Communications Commission (FCC) issued Carm his call sign, WB3ADI.

Ham radio operators are so proud of their call signs that the two often become inseparable in the minds of friends. Barry, K7UGA, of Arizona has worked (talked with) thousands of hams on the air. Many of them didn't know that his last name is Goldwater or that he was a United States senator. King Hussein of Jordan is also a ham, known simply as JY1 to all his on-the-air friends.

AGE IS NO BARRIER

Age is no barrier to getting a ham license and joining in the fun. There are hams of all ages, from five years to more than 80 years. Michelle Allen, an "A" student from New Haven, Indiana, received her Novice license at the age of 12. Known to her ham friends as KA9FUL, she spends a lot of her time (aside from school and sports) on the radio.

Then there's Gary Lieb, KA6DLE, of Ventura, California, who was licensed at age 10. Every morning before school, he got on the air and made several contacts. In just a few months, Gary spoke (using Morse code) with hams in Switzerland, Sweden, Canada, Japan and all over the United States. Each time he contacted a new place, he looked it up on the map to find its exact location. Ham radio was a big help in Gary's study of geography. Gary does admit that he had a small advantage in learning about Amateur Radio. His father, Jerome, is WA6GSA, and his older brother, Adam, is WA6JGK.

Of course, young people aren't the only ones who are active radio amateurs. Involved in many hobbies, Evelyn Fox of Merrimac, Wisconsin, plays contract bridge with her AARP (American Association of Retired Persons) group on the 40-meter band.

Evelyn was over 75 years old when she became interested in Amateur Radio. That didn't stop her from taking on the job of learning radio theory and the international Morse code. She found the theory a pleasant challenge. She joined a club, attended its classes, and became WB9QZA. Not bad for someone who knew nothing about electronics when she first got started.

"BREWING IT" AT HOME

Ham radio operators pop up in some of the least expected places. Dr Peter Pehem, 5Z4JJ, is one of Africa's flying doctors. He works out of a small village on the north slope of Mount Kilimanjaro in Kenya. Pete has been bitten by an OSCAR bug, but can't do anything about it while on medical duty. But he can and does attack it with great pleasure when he's off duty.

Somebody gave Pete an old radiotelephone, a vacuum tube and some coaxial cable. The doctor added empty aspirin tins and a quartz crystal from his airplane radio. Right out there in the African bush, he fired up a homemade transmitter, built on the aspirin tins. Then he talked to the world through OSCAR, the Orbiting Satellite Carrying Amateur Radio.

Pete proved something with his homemade gear: You don't need a shack full of the latest commercial equipment to have fun on the air. New hams find this out every day. Tom Giugliano, WA2GOQ, of Brooklyn, New York, contacted 26 states using a pre-World War II transmitter and receiver. He used a simple homemade wire antenna. Other hams have bridged the oceans to contact hams in Europe and Japan using simple equipment running less than 1 watt of power. As a Novice, you'll be permitted 200-watts peak envelope power (PEP) output on the HF bands. That's more than enough to contact other hams around the world. Technicians who have passed a 5-WPM code test have the same privileges. On the VHF, UHF and microwave bands, Technicians are allowed to use 1500-watts output, although that much power is rarely needed or used.

There was a time, many years ago, when no commercial equipment was available. The earliest hams, beginning more than 75 years ago, tried to find more efficient ways of communicating with each other. All early radio sets were home-brew (homebuilt) and were capable only of communication over several miles. Some transmitters were nothing more than a length of copper wire wrapped around an oatmeal box, attached to a few other basic parts and a wire antenna. Often the transmissions were one-way, with one transmitting station broadcasting to several receive-only stations. Over the years, hams have continually looked for ways to transmit farther and better. They are constantly developing and advancing the state of the art in their quest for more effective ways of communicating.

PEERING BACK THROUGH TIME

It all started on a raw December day in 1901. Italian inventor and experimenter Guglielmo Marconi launched the Age of Wireless from an abandoned barracks at St John's, Newfoundland. He listened intently for a crackling series of buzzes, the letter S in international Morse code, traversing the 2000 miles from Cornwall, England. That signal was the culmination of years of experimentation. News of Marconi's feat stimulated hundreds of electrical hobbyists to build their own "wireless" equipment. They became the first hams.

Later, Marconi set up a huge station at Cape Cod that was unlike anything today's ham has experienced. Marconi's 3-foot-diameter spark-gap rotor fed 30,000 watts of power to a huge antenna array suspended from four 200-foot towers on the dunes at South Wellfleet, Massachusetts.

By 1914, Marconi had set up a station and antennas for daily transmission across the Atlantic. And Amateur Radio operators all over America were firing up their own homebuilt transmitters. Soon, several hundred amateurs across the country joined Hiram Percy Maxim in forming the American Radio Relay League (ARRL), based in Hartford, Connecticut. These amateurs set up a series of "airborne trunk lines" through which they could relay messages from coast to coast. If you're interested in learning more about the history of Amateur Radio, you'll enjoy *200 Meters and Down* by Clinton B. DeSoto. *Fifty Years of ARRL* is also an interesting account of the ARRL's first half century. *From Spark to Space* looks at 75 years of ARRL and Amateur Radio history. All three books are available from your local ham radio dealer or directly from ARRL.

There were more hams experimenting all the time. Commercial broadcasting stations began to spring up after World War I. This brought a great deal of confusion to the airwaves. Congress created the Federal Radio Commission in 1927 to unravel the confusion and assign specific frequencies for

The state-of-the-art in amateur gear has come a long way since the days of "Old Betsy," Hiram Percy Maxim's own spark-gap transmitter. Spark-gap transmitters were the very first type of radio transmitters, used in the early 1900s.

specific uses. Soon amateurs found themselves with their own frequency bands.

Continued experimentation over the years has brought us tubes and transistors. Equipment has grown smaller and more sophisticated. In the early days of radio communications, equipment was large and heavy. Sometimes it would take a roomful of equipment to accomplish what can now be done with the circuitry in a tiny box.

——WE PITCH IN WHEN NEEDED——

Traditionally, amateurs have served their countries in times of need. During wartime, amateurs have patriotically taken their communications skills and technical ability into the field. During natural disasters, when normal channels of communication are interrupted, hams provide an emergency communications system. Practically all radio transmitters operating in the United States provide some public service at one time or another. Hams don't wait for someone to ask for their help; they pitch in when needed. They provide communications on March of Dimes walk-a-thons, help plug the dikes when floods threaten and warn of approaching hurricanes. Hams bring assistance to sinking ships, direct medical supplies into earthquake zones, and search for downed aircraft and lost children.

Amateur Radio operators recognize their responsibility to provide these public-service communications. They train in various ways to be effective communicators in times of trouble. Every day, amateurs relay thousands of routine messages across the country. They send many of these messages through "traffic nets" devoted to developing the skill of sending and receiving messages efficiently. (A net is a gathering of hams on a single frequency for some specific

purpose. In this case the net's purpose is to "pass traffic" —relay messages.) This daily operation helps prepare hams for real emergencies. Also, each June thousands of hams across the country participate in the ARRL Field Day. They set up portable stations, including antennas, and use emergency power. These operating events help hams to test their emergency communications capabilities and to help them identify problems that could arise in the event of a disaster.

MAYDAY—WE'RE GOING DOWN

Hams often provide relays for ships that run into trouble on the high seas. A huge, destructive wave struck the 35-foot yacht *Gambit* while it was sailing in the South China Sea. The force of the wave smashed the porthole glass and broke the main boom. The crew suddenly found their ship adrift and taking on water.

Fortunately, the yacht's captain, Dean Pregerson, WH2ABD, is a ham, and he had a radio on board. He quickly put out a distress call on the 20-meter amateur band. Hams in Hong Kong, Japan, Indonesia and Guam heard his call. Tony Armstrong, VS6AG, notified Hong Kong Marine Search and Rescue Center. The hams on Guam alerted the

US Air Force base there. Hams in Hong Kong kept in constant touch with the sinking yacht while search planes and ships combed the area. After more than 18 hours of continuous searching, the rescuers found the ship and saved the crew.

IN QUAKES AND FLOODS: HAMS ARE THERE

In September 1985 a massive earthquake rocked Mexico City, and a smaller but just-as-terrifying aftershock hit two days later. Amateur Radio operators across North America sprang into action. Thousands of inquiries came in to ARRL Headquarters and to individual hams across the country. Friends, relatives and business associates worried about people in the affected area.

Why did they choose to ask Amateur Radio operators to help them? Over the decades, hams have volunteered their services in times of emergency to relay vital information to and from stricken areas. The September 1985 quakes in Mexico knocked out most means of communications. Especially in rural areas, Amateur Radio was the only way news of the disaster could reach the rest of the world. Hundreds of Amateur Radio operators spent days and nights seeking news of individuals and conditions in certain areas. They went back to their regular routine of working and spending time with their families only after workers restored regular communications channels.

In October 1989, an earthquake struck the San Francisco area. With local power and telephone communications knocked out, San Francisco hams went to work. Using amateur stations that fit in briefcases, they relayed messages between residents and their worried relatives and friends outside the stricken area. These tiny stations included a hand-held Amateur Radio transceiver, a lap-top computer and a radio modem called a TNC.

When towns and cities in the Fargo, North Dakota and Moorhead, Minnesota area were threatened by flooding, members of the Red River Radio Amateur Club were ready. Portable transceivers in hand, radio amateurs patrolled sandbag dikes and riverbanks, reporting on the flood's progress. When one dike started leaking at the bottom and was undermining the sand bags, Amateur Radio was used to call in the Army Corps of Engineers.

Radio amateurs help out even when the emergency is outside the US. In September 1989, Hurricane Hugo did terrible damage to island nations in the Caribbean, and Puerto Rico. Most of the islands were completely cut off from the main-land; all normal means of communication were destroyed. Through volunteer Amateur Radio networks, shipments of relief and medical supplies were coordinated. Island residents were able to contact loved ones on the mainland and other islands. Amateur Radio "jump teams" even sped to the affected areas to help restore communications.

NO BARRIERS TO ENJOYING HAM RADIO

Amateur Radio holds no roadblocks for people with disabilities. Many people who are unable to walk, see or talk are able to enjoy their Amateur Radio hobby, conversing with friends in their home town or across the world. Some local ham clubs even take classes to a home to help a person with a disability discover ham radio.

Although unable to leave his bed, Otho Jarman was able to earn his ham license. Bill Haney, WA6CMZ, helped Otho learn the code and pass his Novice exam through such a club program. Bill spent one hour each week teaching Otho the code, and in seven weeks he passed his Novice exam. Other members of the Barstow (California) Amateur Radio Club helped Otho put his station together. They obtained equipment for him and constructed antennas.

Soon, Otho, WB6KYM, was on the air talking with hams in Mozambique, Nicaragua and Puerto Rico. He could communicate with the world from his bed. Sixteen years earlier, at age 22, Otho had broken his spine when he dove into a reservoir to rescue a drowning child. Although interested in Amateur Radio for years, he had not had an opportunity to learn about it until the club came along. Now he monitors local frequencies from 7 AM to 10 PM, often just chatting or giving directions to motorists.

"Amateur Radio can take a disabled person out of his living room, out of his bed or out of his wheelchair, and put him in the real world," Otho says.

The Courage Center, of Golden Valley, Minnesota, sponsors the HANDI-HAM system to help people with physical disabilities obtain amateur licenses. The system provides materials and instruction to persons with disabilities interested in obtaining ham licenses. The Center also provides information to other hams, "verticals," who wish to help people with disabilities earn a license.

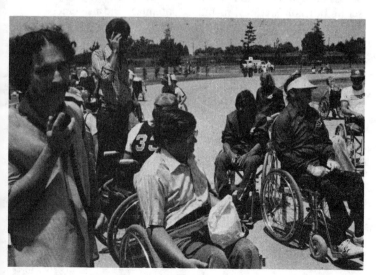

Public service has been a ham tradition since the very beginning. Whether it's a walk-a-thon, the Olympic Torch Run or the aftermath of a tornado, hams are always there to help with communications, which they provide at no cost to the group involved.

Once you've earned your license, you can join the thousands of other hams on the air. Then you'll begin to experience the thrill of Amateur Radio firsthand. As a ham, you can contact other hams in your town and around the world. You can talk into a microphone to use either single sideband (SSB) or frequency modulation (FM) to communicate. If you want, you can experience the thrill of using the international Morse code (called "CW" by hams). You can even communicate by packet radio or radioteletype using a computer. You can do all this on parts of special frequency bands set aside by the FCC for Amateur Radio operators.

For your first contact, you'll probably tune around looking for a station calling "CQ" (calling for any station to make contact). Perhaps you'll even try calling a CQ on your own. Suddenly you'll hear your own call coming back! It's hard to describe the excitement. Someone else is sending your call sign back to let you know that they hear you and want to make contact.

Each time you send a CQ, you'll wonder who will answer. It could be a ham in the next town, the next state or clear across the country. The whole world is full of hams to talk to.

There are many wonderful things you can do as a ham. After you have been on the air for a while, you'll be known as one of the regulars on the band. It's surprising how many people from all over you'll recognize and who will recognize you. Many a fast friendship has developed through repeated on-the-air contacts.

Soon you'll be collecting contacts with different states and exchanging QSL cards (postcards) with other hams you've talked to. These special cards commemorate each contact. They also serve as proof of the contact as you begin working toward some of the awards issued by the American Radio Relay League. [The Worked All States (WAS) award is one popular example.] You'll learn more about the special language and abbreviations that hams use as you study.

Chapter 9 has a list of common "Q signals" used by most hams.

There is a certain intrigue about DX (long-distance communication) that catches many hams. Talking to hams from other lands can be quite an experience. After all, foreign hams are people just like you who enjoy finding out about other people and places! Also, hams in other countries often speak enough English to carry on a limited conversation, so you'll have little problem there. Whether you start as a Novice or a Technician, Amateur Radio offers many opportunities to contact DX stations.

If you enjoy a little competition, perhaps you'll like on-the-air contesting. The object of a contest is to work as many people in as many different areas as possible in a certain time. Each year, the American Radio Relay League sponsors a "Novice/Technician Roundup" contest. In the Roundup, you have the chance to contact old friends and make new ones. You might work some new states or countries, and if you use Morse code you will increase your code speed. You are certain to improve your general operating skills and ability. Most of all, though, you will have fun.

OTHER MODES

Novice- and Technician-class operators may use just about every operating mode available to Amateur Radio operators. You should become familiar with these modes. In addition to voice and Morse code, you may want to investigate some of the less traditional modes.

With slow-scan television (SSTV), hams send still photos to each other, one frame at a time. It takes about 8 seconds for the bright band of light to creep down the screen to make a complete picture. (Your home TV makes 30 complete pictures per second.) SSTV pictures are more like those shots of the moon or Saturn that you may have seen transmitted from space. SSTV pictures may be transmitted around the

world via shortwave ham transmitters. Amateur Radio operators were the first to flash TV snapshots of Mars to foreign countries.

Facsimile (fax) is a means of sending drawings, charts, maps and graphs. You can even play games over the air by transmitting fax pictures of each move.

With radioteletype transmission (RTTY), a ham can type out a message and send it over the air to a friend's station. Even if the friend is away, his or her radioteletype system can receive and hold the message until he or she returns. Early RTTY systems used mechanical machines cast off by news services. Today, many hams use personal computer systems. These display the message silently on a TV screen rather than using roll after roll of paper with noisy, clacking typewriter keys. Packet radio is a modern computer-controlled system capable of relaying messages and storing them for later reception by the intended ham.

HAM SATELLITES

Hams use satellites to communicate in voice, code, radioteletype and packet radio around the world.

Some schools use the OSCARs to instruct students in science and math. No license is needed to listen, so many students across the country have eavesdropped on Amateur Radio transmissions through an OSCAR. A receiver and an antenna are all you need to introduce students to the exciting world of space technology.

Hams from many countries worked in a joint effort to build several OSCARs. Weighing less than your living-room TV and powered by sun-charged batteries, OSCARs retransmit hams' "uplink" signals down to other earthbound stations.

You can operate in any of these exciting modes when you become an Amateur Radio operator. Take the time to explore the adventure of ham radio!

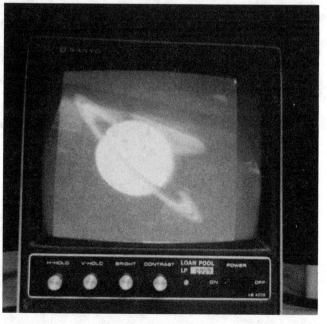

There are many hobbies within the hobby of Amateur Radio. Some hams collect QSL cards and awards. Others love the thrill of talking to rare DX stations in foreign lands, while still others enjoy exchanging pictures by slow-scan television. You'll find one or more of these pastimes enjoyable, and in time you'll probably try most of them.

ELEMENT 2 (NOVICE) SYLLABUS

(Required for all operator licenses)

The complete syllabus contains 30 blocks, with one question to come from each block.

Subelement 2A Commission's Rules (10 Exam Questions)

One question must be from the following:

2A-1 Basis and purpose of the amateur service {97.1}
2A-2 Amateur service, definition {97.3(a)(4)}
2A-3 Amateur communication, definition {97.3(a)(4)}
2A-4 Amateur operator, definition {97.3(a)(1)}

One question must be from the following:

2A-5 Operator license, definition {97.5(d)(1)}
2A-6 Primary station license, definition {97.5(a), (d)(1)}
2A-7 Amateur station, definition {97.3(a)(5)}
2A-8 Control operator, definition {97.3(a)(11)}
2A-9 Amateur operator license classes {97.9(a)}

One question must be from the following:

2A-10 Novice control operator frequency privileges {97.301(e), (f)}

One question must be from the following:

2A-11 Amateur operator license eligibility {97.5(d)(1)}
2A-12 Novice license exam elements {97.501(e); 97.503(a)(1), (b)(1)}
2A-13 Primary station license eligibility {97.5(d)(1)}
2A-14 Mailing address furnished by licensee {97.21}
2A-15 Valid US call sign assignment {97.17(f)}
2A-16 Length of time license is valid {97.23(a)}

One question must be from the following:

2A-17 Novice control operator emission privileges {97.3(c); 97.305(c); 97.307(f)(9), (10)}

One question must be from the following:

2A-18 Transmitter power on 3700-3750 kHz, 7100-7150 kHz, 21100-21200 kHz {97.3(b)(6); 97.313(a), (c)(1)}
2A-19 Novice transmitter power on 28.1-28.5 MHz, 220-225 MHz, 1270-1295 MHz {97.3(b)(6); 97.313(c)(2), (d), (e)}
2A-20 Digital communications (Limited to concepts only) {97.3(c)(2); 97.305(c)}

One question must be from the following:

2A-21 Station licensee responsibility {97.103(a), (b)}
2A-22 When control operator is required {97.7; 97.103}
2A-23 Who may be control operator {97.7}
2A-24 Control operator location {97.109(a), (b)}
2A-25 Amateur operator license availability {97.9(a)}
2A-26 Primary station license availability {97.5(e)}

One question must be from the following:

2A-27 Station identification {97.119(a)}
2A-28 Points of communication {97.111(a)(1), (2), (3), (4)}
2A-29 Operation away from fixed-station location {97.5(e)}
2A-30 Business communication {97.113(a)}

One question must be from the following:

2A-31 International communications {97.111(a)(1)}
2A-32 Messages for hire {97.113(b)}
2A-33 Broadcasting {97.3(a)(10); 97.113(b)}
2A-34 Third-party traffic (Definition) {97.3(a)(38); 97.115(a)}
2A-35 Transmission of music {97.113(d)}
2A-36 Codes and ciphers {97.113(d)}

One question must be from the following:

2A-37 False signals {97.113(d)}
2A-38 Unidentified communications {97.119(a)}
2A-39 Malicious interference {97.101(d)}
2A-40 Notices of violation {This topic is no longer covered in the Part 97 Rules.}

Subelement 2B Operating Procedures (2 Exam Questions)

One question must be from the following:

2B-1 Choosing a frequency
   2B-1-1 Tune-up and operation
   2B-1-2 For emergency operation
2B-2 Morse Radiotelegraphy
   2B-2-1 Establishing a contact
   2B-2-2 Choosing a sending speed
   2B-2-3 Proper use of $\overline{AR}$, $\overline{SK}$, $\overline{BT}$, $\overline{DN}$ and $\overline{KN}$
   2B-2-4 Proper use of CQ, DE and K
   2B-2-5 RST signal reporting system
   2B-2-6 Proper use of QRS, QRT, QTH, QRZ and QSL
2B-3 Radiotelephony
   2B-3-1 Establishing a contact
   2B-3-2 Standard International Telecommunication Union phonetics

One question must be from the following:

2B-4 Radioteleprinting
   2B-4-1 Establishing a contact
   2B-4-2 Sending speed (Limited to the concept that both stations must be using the same speed)
2B-5 Packet radio
   2B-5-1 Connecting to and monitoring other packet radio stations
   2B-5-2 Digipeaters and networking (Limited to concepts only)
2B-6 Repeater use
   2B-6-1 Establishing a contact through a repeater
   2B-6-2 Purpose of repeater operations
   2B-6-3 Input/output frequency separation (Limited to concept only; specific frequency splits not required)
   2B-6-4 Simplex versus repeater operation
   2B-6-5 Special features of repeaters (Autopatch, time-out timers)

Subelement 2C Radio-Wave Propagation
(1 Exam Question)

One question must be from the following:

2C-1 Line of sight
2C-2 Ground wave
2C-3 Sky wave
2C-4 Sunspot cycle
2C-5 Sunspots and their influence on the ionosphere
2C-6 Reflecting VHF/UHF radio waves

Subelement 2D Amateur Radio Practices
(4 Exam Questions)

One question must be from the following:

2D-1 How to prevent use of amateur station by unauthorized persons
2D-2 Station lightning protection
2D-3 Ground system

One question must be from the following:

2D-4 VHF/UHF RF safety precautions
2D-5 Purpose of safety interlocks and other safety devices
2D-6 Antenna installation safety procedures

One question must be from the following:

2D-7 Standing wave ratio
  2D-7-1 SWR Meter
  2D-7-2 Acceptable SWR readings
  2D-7-3 Common causes of high SWR readings

One question must be from the following:

2D-8 Radio frequency interference
  2D-8-1 RF overload of consumer electronic products
  2D-8-2 Harmonic radiation interference to consumer electronic products
  2D-8-3 Handling RFI complaints

Subelement 2E Electrical Principles
(4 Exam Questions)

One question must be from the following:

2E-1 Metric prefixes
  2E-1-1 giga (G)
  2E-1-2 mega (M)
  2E-1-3 kilo (k)
  2E-1-4 centi (c)
  2E-1-5 milli (m)
  2E-1-6 micro (μ)
  2E-1-7 pico (p)

One question must be from the following:

2E-2 Concept of current
  2E-2-1 Electron movement
  2E-2-2 Current units
2E-3 Concept of voltage
  2E-3-1 Electrical pressure
  2E-3-2 Voltage units
2E-4 Concept of conductor
2E-5 Concept of insulator
2E-6 Concept of resistance
  2E-6-1 Opposition to electron movement
  2E-6-2 Resistance units

One question must be from the following:

2E-7 Ohm's Law (Any calculations will be kept to a very low level; integer math only—NO fractions or decimal math will be included)
2E-8 Concept of energy
2E-9 Concept of power
  2E-9-1 Rate of using energy
  2E-9-2 Power units
2E-10 Concept of open circuit
2E-11 Concept of short circuit

One question must be from the following:

2E-12 Concept of frequency
  2E-12-1 Concept of dc
  2E-12-2 Concept of ac
  2E-12-3 Frequency units
  2E-12-4 Concept of AF
  2E-12-5 Concept of RF
2E-13 Concept of wavelength

Subelement 2F Circuit Components
(2 Exam Questions)

One question must be from the following:

2F-1 Schematic representation of a resistor
2F-2 Schematic representation of a switch
2F-3 Schematic representation of a fuse
2F-4 Schematic representation of a battery

One question must be from the following:

2F-5 Schematic representation of a ground
2F-6 Schematic representation of an antenna
2F-7 Schematic representation of a bipolar transistor
2F-8 Schematic representation of a triode vacuum tube

Subelement 2G Practical Circuits
(2 Exam Questions)

One question must be from the following:

2G-1 Functional layout of Novice station equipment
  2G-1-1 Transmitter, receiver, (or transceiver), power supply, antenna switch, antenna feed line, antenna
  2G-1-2 Transceiver, antenna switch, SWR meter, impedance matching device, antenna

One question must be from the following:

2G-2 Morse telegraphy station equipment layout (Block diagram)
2G-3 Radiotelephone station equipment layout (Block diagram)
2G-4 Radioteleprinter station equipment layout (Block diagram)
2G-5 Packet-radio station equipment layout (Block diagram)

Subelement 2H Signals and Emissions
(2 Exam Questions)

One question must be from the following:

2H-1 Emission types (Definition)
 2H-1-1 A1A (CW)
 2H-1-2 F1B (RTTY)
 2H-1-3 F3E (FM Phone)
 2H-1-4 J3E (SSB Phone)
2H-2 Key clicks
2H-3 Chirp
2H-4 Superimposed hum

One question must be from the following:

2H-5 Undesirable harmonic radiation and other spurious emissions

2H-6 Electromagnetic radiation and safety awareness

2H-7 Adjacent channel interference (Proper settings for drive, mic gain, use of speech compression, concept of deviation in FM modulation)

Subelement 2I Antennas and Feed Lines
(3 Exam Questions)

One question must be from the following:

2I-1 1/2-wavelength dipole (Approximate lengths)
2I-2 1/4-wavelength vertical (Approximate lengths)
2I-3 Advantages of 5/8-wavelength vertical antennas

One question must be from the following:

2I-4 Yagi antennas
 2I-4.1 Concept of a directional antenna
 2I-4.2 Names of Yagi elements (driven element, reflector and director)
2I-5 RF safety near antennas

One question must be from the following:

2I-6 Coaxial cable
2I-7 Parallel-conductor feed line
2I-8 Antenna matching device
2I-9 Balun
2I-10 Horizontal antenna polarization (Element orientation)
2I-11 Vertical antenna polarization (Element orientation)

Subelement 3AA Commission's Rules
(5 Exam Questions)

3AA-1 Control point, definition {97.3 (a)(12)}
3AA-2 Frequency privileges for Technician class control operators {97.301(a), (e)}
3AA-3 Renewal or modification of operator and station licenses {97.19; 97.23}
3AA-4 Emission privileges for Technician class control operators {97.305; 97.307}
3AA-5 Selection and use of frequencies {97.303}
3AA-6 Transmitter power
   3AA-6-1 Definition {97.3(b)(6)}
   3AA-6-2 Minimum power necessary {97.313(a)}
   3AA-6-3 Maximum power permitted {97.313(b), (c), (e), (f), (g)}
   3AA-6-4 Power of station in beacon operation {97.203(c)}
3AA-7 Digital communications
   3AA-7-1 Maximum sending speed {97.305(c); 97.307(f)(3), (4), (5), (6)}
   3AA-7-2 Maximum frequency shift {97.305(c); 97.307(f)(3), (4), (5), (6)}
   3AA-7-3 Maximum permitted bandwidth above 50 MHz {97.305(c); 97.307(a), (b), (c), (f)(1), (2), (5), (6)}
3AA-8 Station identification
   3AA-8-1 Operating with a Certificate of Successful Completion of Examination {97.9(b); 97.119(e)}
   3AA-8-2 Telephony (what language to use) {97.119(b)(2)}
   3AA-8-3 Phonetic alphabet {97.119(b)(2)}
3AA-9 Beacon operation
   3AA-9-1 Definition {97.3(a)(9)}
   3AA-9-2 Class of license required {97.203(a)}
3AA-10 Radio control of model craft and vehicles {97.215}
3AA-11 Emergency communications
   3AA-11-1 Definition {97.403}
   3AA-11-2 Declaration of general state of communications emergency {97.401(c)}
3AA-12 Broadcasting {97.113(c)}
3AA-13 Permissible one-way transmissions {97.111(b)}
3AA-14 Domestic and international third-party communications {97.115}
3AA-15 Third-party participation {97.115(b)}
3AA-16 Transmission of indecent or profane language {97.113(d)}
3AA-17 Communication through satellites {97.209}

Subelement 3AB Operating Procedures
(3 Exam Questions)

3AB-1 RST signal reporting system
3AB-2 Repeater operation
   3AB-2-1 Use of a repeater
   3AB-2-2 Repeater versus simplex operation
   3AB-2-3 Input/output frequency separation (Frequency splits used on various repeater subbands)
   3AB-2-4 Frequency coordination
3AB-3 Operating courtesy
3AB-4 Distress calling procedures
3AB-5 Emergency preparedness drills
   3AB-5-1 RACES drills
   3AB-5-2 Messages identified as "drill" or "test"
3AB-6 Providing emergency communications
   3AB-6-1 Tactical communications
   3AB-6-2 Health and welfare traffic
   3AB-6-3 Equipment considerations

Subelement 3AC Radio-Wave Propagation
(3 Exam Questions)

3AC-1 Ionosphere
   3AC-1-1 Definition
   3AC-1-2 D layer
   3AC-1-3 E layer
   3AC-1-4 F layers
3AC-2 Ionospheric absorption
3AC-3 Daily variation in ionization levels of ionosphere
3AC-4 Maximum usable frequency
3AC-5 Scatter propagation
3AC-6 Line-of-sight propagation
3AC-7 Tropospheric bending and ducting

Subelement 3AD Amateur Radio Practices
(4 Exam Questions)

3AD-1 Electrical wiring safety
   3AD-1-1 Wiring polarity
   3AD-1-2 Dangerous voltages and currents
   3AD-1-3 Placement and rating of fuses and switches
3AD-2 Voltmeters
   3AD-2-1 Connection in circuit
   3AD-2-2 Extending range of meters
3AD-3 Ammeters
   3AD-3-1 Connection in circuit
   3AD-3-2 Extending range of meters
3AD-4 Multimeters
3AD-5 Wattmeters
   3AD-5-1 Connection in circuit
   3AD-5-2 Interpreting measurements
3AD-6 Marker generators
3AD-7 Signal generators
3AD-8 Impedance-match indicators
   3AD-8-1 SWR meters
   3AD-8-2 Placement in feed line
3AD-9 Dummy antennas
3AD-10 Use of S meters
3AD-11 RF Safety
   3AD-11-1 Thermal effects of RF on the body
   3AD-11-2 American National Standards Institute (ANSI) RF protection guide (Limited to the concept that a guide exists and that it sets exposure limits under certain circumstances)
   3AD-11-3 Minimizing exposure to RF

Subelement 3AE Electrical Principles
(2 Exam Questions)

3AE-1 Resistance
  3AE-1-1 Definition
  3AE-1-2 Units
  3AE-1-3 Resistors in series
  3AE-1-4 Resistors in parallel
3AE-2 Ohm's Law
3AE-3 Inductance
  3AE-3-1 Definition
  3AE-3-2 Units
  3AE-3-3 Inductors in series
  3AE-3-4 Inductors in parallel
3AE-4 Capacitance
  3AE-4-1 Definition
  3AE-4-2 Units
  3AE-4-3 Capacitors in series
  3AE-4-4 Capacitors in parallel

Subelement 3AF Circuit Components
(2 Exam Questions)

3AF-1 Resistors
  3AF-1-1 Construction types
  3AF-1-2 Variable and fixed resistors
  3AF-1-3 Color code
  3AF-1-4 Power rating
  3AF-1-5 Schematic symbols
3AF-2 Inductors
  3AF-2-1 Construction
  3AF-2-2 Variable and fixed inductors
  3AF-2-3 Factors affecting inductance
  3AF-2-4 Schematic symbols
3AF-3 Capacitors
  3AF-3-1 Construction
  3AF-3-2 Variable and fixed capacitors
  3AF-3-3 Factors affecting capacitance
  3AF-3-4 Schematic symbols

Subelement 3AG Practical Circuits
(1 Exam Question)

3AG-1 Low-pass filters
  3AG-1-1 Frequency characteristics
  3AG-1-2 Applications
3AG-2 High-pass filters
  3AG-2-1 Frequency characteristics
  3AG-2-2 Applications
3AG-3 Band-pass filters
  3AG-3-1 Frequency characteristics
  3AG-3-2 Applications

3AG-4 Transmitter and receiver block diagrams (Know functions of various blocks and how they work together)
  3AG-4-1 A1A transmitters and receivers
  3AG-4-2 F3E transmitters and receivers

Subelement 3AH Signals and Emissions
(2 Exam Questions)

3AH-1 Modulation (definition)
3AH-2 Emission types
  3AH-2-1 NØN (Test)
  3AH-2-2 A1A (CW)
  3AH-2-3 F1B (RTTY)
  3AH-2-4 F2A (MCW)
  3AH-2-5 F2B (RTTY)
  3AH-2-6 F2D (Data)
  3AH-2-7 F3E (FM Phone)
  3AH-2-8 G3E (PM Phone)
3AH-3 RF carrier
3AH-4 Frequency modulation
3AH-5 Phase modulation
3AH-6 Bandwidth (Limited to concept that different emissions occupy different bandwidths)
3AH-7 Deviation
  3AH-7-1 Relation to audio modulating signal
  3AH-7-2 Overdeviation

Subelement 3AI Antennas and Feed Lines
(3 Exam Questions)

3AI-1 Parasitic beam antennas
  3AI-1-1 Yagi antennas
  3AI-1-2 Quad antennas
  3AI-1-3 Delta loop antennas
3AI-2 Polarization of antennas and radio waves
  3AI-2-1 Horizontal polarization
  3AI-2-2 Vertical polarization
3AI-3 Standing wave ratio (SWR)
  3AI-3-1 Definition
  3AI-3-2 Forward and reflected power
  3AI-3-3 Significance of SWR to system
3AI-4 Balanced and unbalanced conditions
  3AI-4-1 Feed lines
  3AI-4-2 Antennas
  3AI-4-3 Balun transformers
3AI-5 Feed-line attenuation
  3AI-5-1 Changes with line type
  3AI-5-2 Changes with line length
  3AI-5-3 Changes with frequency
3AI-6 RF safety
  3AI-6-1 Feed lines
  3AI-6-2 Antennas

━━━━KEY WORDS━━━━

Amateur operator—A person holding a written authorization to be the control operator of an amateur station.

Amateur service—A radiocommunication service for the purpose of self-training, intercommunication and technical investigations carried out by amateurs, that is, duly authorized persons interested in radio technique solely with a personal aim and without pecuniary interest. (*Pecuniary* means payment of any type, whether money or other goods.)

Amateur station—A station licensed in the amateur service, including necessary equipment, used for amateur communication.

Control operator—An amateur operator designated by the licensee of a station to be responsible for the transmissions of an amateur station.

Emission—The transmitted signal from an amateur station.

Emission privilege—Permission to use a particular emission type (such as Morse code or voice).

False or deceptive signals—Transmissions that are intended to mislead or confuse those who may receive the transmissions. For example, distress calls transmitted when there is no actual emergency are false or deceptive signals.

Frequency bands—A group of frequencies where communications of a particular service, such as the amateur service, are authorized.

Frequency privilege—Permission to use a particular group of frequencies.

Malicious interference—Intentional, deliberate obstruction of radio transmissions.

Operator license—The portion of an Amateur Radio license that gives permission to operate an amateur station.

Peak envelope power (PEP)—The average power of a signal at its largest amplitude peak.

Station license—The portion of an Amateur Radio license that authorizes an amateur station at a specific location. The station license also lists the call sign of that station.

Third-party communications—Messages passed from one amateur to another on behalf of a third person.

Third-party participation—The way an unlicensed person can participate in amateur communications. A control operator must ensure compliance with FCC rules.

Ticket—Commonly used name for an Amateur Radio license.

Unidentified communications or signals—Signals or radio communications in which the transmitting station's call sign is not transmitted.

Chapter 2

The Radio Spectrum: A Valuable Resource

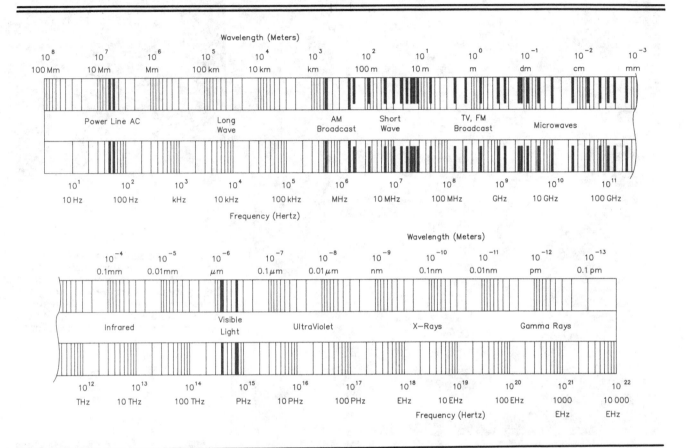

Figure 2-1— The electromagnetic spectrum, showing the range from the 60-hertz ac power line in your home, through the radio frequencies, X-rays and gamma rays. Amateur Radio operations use a small, but significant, portion of these frequency bands. The amateur bands are represented as short bars on the graph.

When you tune an AM or FM broadcast radio to your favorite station, you select a specific spot on the tuning dial. There are many stations spread across that dial. Each radio station occupies a small part of the entire range of "electromagnetic waves." Other parts of this range, or spectrum, include microwaves, X-rays and even infrared, ultraviolet and visible light waves.

Figure 2-1 shows the electromagnetic spectrum from below the radio range all the way through the X-rays. Amateur Radio occupies only a small part of the total available space; countless users must share the electromagnetic spectrum.

You may be thinking: "Who decides where Amateur Radio frequencies will be, and where my favorite FM broadcast station will be?" That's a good question, and the answer has several parts.

Radio signals travel to distant corners of the globe, so there must be a way to prevent total chaos on the bands. The International Telecommunication Union (ITU) has the important role of dividing the entire range of communications frequencies among those who use them. Many radio services have a need for communications frequencies. These services include commercial broadcast, land mobile and private radio (including Amateur Radio). ITU member nations decide which radio services will be given certain bands of frequencies, based on the needs of the different services. This process takes place at ITU-sponsored World Administrative Radio Conferences (WARCs).

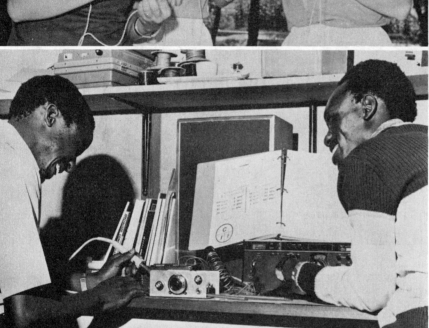

Nearly every country on earth has its share of active Amateur Radio operators. Above left, a direction-finding exercise in China; above a ham in Rome; left, two enthusiastic newcomers to Amateur Radio in Botswana; below, an Amateur Radio station in the Kingdom of Tonga.

WHY IS THERE AMATEUR RADIO?

In the case of Amateur Radio, the ITU has long recognized that hams are invaluable in times of emergency or disaster. At an ITU WARC held in 1979, Amateur Radio gained several new bands of frequencies. Mighty praise indeed!

The ITU makes these allocations on an international basis. The Federal Communications Commission (FCC) decides the best way to allocate **frequency bands** to those services using them in the US. The FCC is the United States governing body when it comes to Amateur Radio. In fact, an entire part of the FCC Rules is devoted to the amateur service—Part 97. As your amateur career develops, you'll become more familiar with Part 97.

To gain the privilege of sending a radio signal over the airwaves in the US, you must pass a license exam. To earn a Novice license, you will need to pass a 30-question exam covering basic radio theory and FCC regulations, as well as a Morse code exam. To earn a Technician license, you will need to pass two written exams—the 30-question Novice written test plus a more comprehensive 25-question written exam. There is no Morse code requirement for the Technician exam. Whether you choose to learn the code and try for the Novice license or work toward the code-free Technician license, this book will prepare you to earn your first Amateur Radio license.

THE FIVE PRINCIPLES

In Section 97.1 of its Rules, the FCC describes the basis and purpose of the amateur service. It consists of five principles:

(a) Recognition and enhancement of the value of the amateur service to the public as a voluntary noncommercial communication service, particularly with respect to providing emergency communications.

Probably the best-known aspect of Amateur Radio is our ability to provide life-saving emergency communications. Normal communications channels often break down during hurricanes, earthquakes, tornadoes, airplane crashes and other disasters. Amateur Radio is frequently the first available means of contact with the outside world from the affected area. Red Cross and other civil-defense agencies rely heavily on the services of volunteer radio amateurs.

One of the more noteworthy aspects of Amateur Radio is its noncommercial nature. In fact, amateurs may not accept any form of payment for operating their radio stations. (There is one limited exception to this rule, which we will explain later.) This means that hams make their services available free of charge. This is true whether they are assisting a search-and-rescue operation in the Sierra Nevada, relaying health-and-welfare messages from a disaster-stricken Caribbean island or providing communications assistance at the New York City Marathon. Talk about value!

Why do hams work so hard if they can't be paid? It gives them an immense feeling of personal satisfaction! It's like the good feeling you get when you lend a hand to an elderly neighbor, only on a much grander scale. Hams operate their

In the days before the giant eruption that demolished vast areas around the Mount St Helens volcano in Washington, volunteer amateurs monitored its behavior. Hams are ready to do whatever they can when someone needs their communications services. Because of the suddenness and extent of that eruption, two hams lost their lives while helping to monitor the volcano.

stations only for personal satisfaction and enjoyment. They don't talk about business matters on the air. (FCC rules don't allow business communications over Amateur Radio.)

(b) Continuation and extension of the amateur's proven ability to contribute to the advancement of the radio art.

In the early days of radio there were no rules, but in 1912 Congress passed a law to regulate the airwaves. Amateurs had to keep to a small range of frequencies (known as "short waves"). There they would remain "out of the way"—everyone knew that radio waves couldn't travel very far at those frequencies. Ha! Amateurs soon overcame the restrictions. They were among the first to experiment with radio propagation, the study of how radio waves travel through the atmosphere. When vacuum tubes became available, amateurs began to develop much-improved radio communication circuits.

Today, the traditions and spirit in Amateur Radio remain. Amateurs continue to experiment with state-of-the-art technologies. Advancement of the radio art takes a major portion of an amateur's energies. The FCC promotes this amateur experimentation and technical development by establishing rules that are consistent with amateur techniques.

Section 97.1 of the amateur rules continues:

(c) Encouragement and improvement of the amateur service through rules which provide for advancing skills in both the communications and technical phases of the art.

Along with some of the technical aspects of the service, amateurs also hold special training exercises in preparation for communications emergencies. Simulated Emergency Tests and Field Days, where amateurs practice communicating under emergency conditions, are just two ways amateurs sharpen their operating skills.

The Commission's rules even specify a "service within a service" called the Radio Amateur Civil Emergency Service, or RACES. RACES provides amateur communications assistance to federal, state and local civil defense in times of need.

(d) Expansion of the existing reservoir within the amateur radio service of trained operators, technicians and electronics experts.

Self-training, intercommunication and technical investigation are all important parts of the amateur service. We need more amateurs who are experienced in communications methods, because they are a national resource to the public

(e) Continuation and extension of the amateur's unique ability to enhance international goodwill.

Hams are unique, even in this time of worldwide jet travel. They journey to the far reaches of the earth and talk with amateurs in other countries every day. They do this simply by walking into their ham shacks. International peace and coexistence are very important today. Amateurs represent their countries as ambassadors of goodwill. Amateur-to-amateur communications often cross the cultural boundaries between societies. Amateur Radio is a teacher in Lincoln, Nebraska, trading stories with the headmaster of a boarding school in a London suburb. It is a tropical-fish hobbyist learning about fish in the Amazon from a missionary stationed in Brazil. Amateur Radio is a way to make friends with other people everywhere.

These five principles provide the basis and purpose for the amateur service, as set down by the FCC. These principles place a large responsibility on the amateur community—a responsibility you will share. It is the Commission's duty to ensure that amateurs are able to operate their stations properly, without interfering with other radio services. *All amateurs must pass an examination before the FCC will issue a license authorizing amateur station operation.* It's a very serious matter.

[At this point you should turn to Chapter 12 and study the questions that cover this material in the Novice question pool. Before you turn to Chapter 12, though, it may be helpful to understand a bit about the numbering system used for these questions. The numbers match the study guide or syllabus printed at the end of Chapter 1. The syllabus forms a type of outline, and the numbering system follows this outline format. There are nine subelements, labeled A through I. This chapter covers subelement A, so all the question references will be to questions with numbers that begin "2A." There are 40 syllabus points in subelement 2A. You will be told to study questions 2A-1, 2A-2 and so on. Finally, each individual question about a particular syllabus point has its own number, so the complete question numbers take the form, "2A-1.1," "2A-1.2" and so on.

You should study questions 2A-1.1 through 2A-1.4 in Chapter 12 now. If you have difficulty with any of these questions, review the material in this section.]

THE AMATEUR SERVICE

The FCC defines some important terms in Section 97.3 of the amateur rules. The **amateur service** is "A radio communication service for the purpose of self-training, intercommunication and technical investigations carried out by amateurs, that is, duly authorized persons interested in radio technique solely with a personal aim and without pecuniary interest." *Pecuniary* means related to money or other payment. In other words, you can't be paid for operating your station or providing a communications service for some individual or group. Amateurs learn various communications skills on their own, and carry out technical experiments in electronics and radio principles.

An **amateur operator** is a person holding a valid license (**ticket**) to operate an amateur station. In the United States, the Federal Communications Commission issues these licenses. An amateur operator performs communications in the amateur service.

How does the FCC define an **amateur station**? "A station licensed in the amateur service, including the apparatus necessary for carrying on radiocommunications." The person operating an amateur station has an interest in self-training, intercommunication and technical investigations or experiments.

An Amateur Radio license is really two licenses in one—

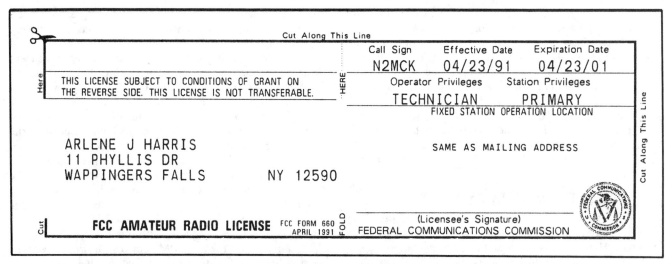

Figure 2-2—The wallet-size Amateur Radio license looks like this. Figure 2-6 shows the certificate-size version of the same license.

an **operator license** and a **station license**. The operator license is one that lets you operate a station within your authorized privileges. The station license authorizes you to have an amateur station. It also lists the call sign that identifies that station. Figure 2-2 shows an actual Amateur Radio license.

One piece of paper includes both licenses. You won't even be able to tell which part is which license. It is important to realize that your license includes both of these parts, however.

The operator license lists your license class and gives you the authority to operate an amateur station. The station license includes the address of your primary, or main, Amateur Radio station. The station license also lists the call sign of your station.

You must have your original operator license, or a photocopy, in your possession any time you are operating an amateur station. You are using the *operator license* portion when you serve as the control operator of a station. It is a good idea to carry a copy of your license in your wallet or purse at all times. That way you are sure to have it if a chance to operate arises.

You must also have your original station license, or a photocopy of it, in your station any time someone operates the station. The station license can be in the control operator's possession or you can have it on display in the station.

In early 1991, the FCC began issuing two-part, laser-printed licenses. One part (Figure 2-2) is small enough to carry with you; the other (Figure 2-6) can be framed and displayed in your shack. This means you can carry your license *and* display it! Laser ink can smear, so it's a good idea to have your wallet copy laminated. It's all right to carry a photocopy of the license, so both originals can be kept safely at home if you prefer. Your original license must be available for inspection by any Government official or representative of the FCC, however. Don't lose the original license!

The FCC issues all licenses for a 10-year term. You should always renew your license for another 10 years before the present one expires. If your license was issued in November 1990, it will expire in November 2000. It's a good idea to form the habit of looking at the expiration date on your license every now and then. You'll be less likely to forget to renew the license in time, then.

If you do forget to renew your license, you have up to two years to apply for a new license. After the two-year grace

period, you will have to take the exam again. Your license is not valid during this two-year grace period, however. You may not operate an amateur station with an expired license. All the grace period means is that the FCC will renew the license if you apply during that time.

If you move or change your name, you will need to modify your license. Notify the FCC of the new information on an FCC Form 610 (available from ARRL).

[Turn to Chapter 12 and study those questions with numbers that begin 2A-2, 2A-3, 2A-4, 2A-5, 2A-6 and 2A-7. Also study those questions with numbers that begin 2A-16, 2A-25 and 2A-26. Review this section if you have difficulty with any of these questions.]

THE CONTROL OPERATOR

A **control operator** is an "amateur operator designated by the licensee of a station to be responsible for the transmissions from that station to assure compliance with the FCC Rules." In effect, the control operator operates the Amateur Radio station. Only a licensed ham may be the control operator of an amateur station. If another licensed radio amateur operates your station with your permission, he or she assumes the role of control operator.

Any amateur operator may designate another licensed operator as the control operator, to share the responsibility of station operation. The FCC holds both the control operator and the station licensee responsible for proper operation of the station. If you are operating your own Amateur Radio station, then you are the control operator at that time.

A control operator must be present at the station control point whenever the transmitter is operating. This means that you may not allow an unlicensed person to operate your radio transmitter while you are not present. There is one time when a transmitter may be operating without a control operator being present, however. Some types of stations, such as repeater stations, may be operated by automatic control. In this case there is no control operator at the transmitter control point.

Your Novice or Technician license authorizes you to be the control operator of an amateur station in the Novice or Technician frequency bands. This means you can be the control operator of your own station or someone else's station. In either case, you are responsible to the FCC for the proper operation of the station.

If you allow another licensed ham to operate your station, you are still responsible for its proper operation. You are always responsible for the proper operation of your station. Your primary responsibility as the station licensee is to ensure the proper operation of your station.

[Before you go on to the next section, you should turn to Chapter 12 and study the questions with numbers that begin 2A-8, 2A-21, 2A-22, 2A-23 and 2A-24. If you have difficulty with any of these questions, review the material in this section.]

AMATEUR LICENSE CLASSES

There are five kinds, or levels, of amateur license. They vary in degree of knowledge required and **frequency privileges** granted. Higher class licenses have more comprehensive examinations. In return for passing a more difficult exam you earn more frequency privileges (frequency space and modes of operation).

The first step is either the Novice or Technician license. The FCC issues these ''beginner's'' licenses to those who demonstrate the ability to operate an Amateur Radio transmitter safely and properly.

An applicant for a Novice license must show a basic proficiency in Morse code by passing a test at 5 words per minute (WPM). The written part of the exam covers some very basic radio fundamentals and knowledge of a few rules and regulations. With a little study and some common sense, you'll soon be ready to pass the Novice exam.

An applicant for a Technician license must pass a more difficult written test, but there is no Morse code requirement.

Anyone (except an agent of a foreign government) is eligible to qualify for an Amateur Radio operator license. There is no age requirement. To hold an Amateur Radio station license, you must have a valid operator license. (Remember, both licenses are printed on the same piece of paper.)

A Novice or Technician license gives you the freedom to develop operating and technical skills through on-the-air experience. These skills will help you upgrade to a higher class of license, with additional privileges.

As a Novice, you will be able to communicate with other amateur stations in the exotic reaches of the world. Novices provide public service through emergency communications and message handling. They enhance international goodwill just like operators with higher license classes.

As a Technician, you will be able to use a wide range of frequency bands—all amateur bands above 50 MHz, in fact. Technicians use *repeaters*, packet radio and orbiting satellites to relay their signals over a wider area. Technician class licensees who pass the 5-WPM Morse code test also gain Novice HF privileges.

Later, you will probably want to earn greater operating privileges. As you gain operating experience, you will prepare for a higher-class license—the gateway to more frequencies and modes.

There is a certain thrill to having more frequencies available to talk with other amateurs on the far side of the globe. That is a powerful incentive to upgrade to the General class license (the next step up from Technician). You will have to pass a 13-WPM Morse code exam and another theory and rules exam to earn the General class license. The General class license gives voice privileges on eight high-frequency (HF)

bands. These bands typically carry signals over great distances. For this reason, the General class license has been a very popular one.

As you progress and mature in Amateur Radio, you will develop specialized interests in such exciting modes as amateur television and satellite communication. You'll also want even more privileges, and that is where the Advanced and Amateur Extra licenses come in. To obtain one of these, you must be prepared to face exams on the more technical aspects of the hobby. For the Amateur Extra license, the top-of-the-line, there is an expert's code test at 20 words per minute.

To qualify for a higher-class license, you must pass the theory exam for each level up to that point. For example, suppose you want to go from Novice directly to Amateur Extra. You will have to take the Technician, General and Advanced theory exams along with the Amateur Extra test. (You can just take the 20-WPM code test, however, without passing the 13-WPM General class code test.)

[You should turn to Chapter 12 now and study the questions with numbers that begin 2A-9, 2A-11 and 2A-13. Review the material in this section if you have difficulty with any of these questions.]

THE NOVICE LICENSE

A Novice license allows you to operate on portions of six Amateur Radio bands. We normally identify these bands by specifying the frequency range they cover or by listing the wavelength in meters. (You will learn more about the relationship between frequency and wavelength later in this book.) Table 2-1 lists the frequency range for each of the Novice bands. This table also serves as a comparison between Novice privileges and those given to higher-class licensees.

Frequency Privileges

When operating, you must stay within your assigned frequency bands. Novice operators may transmit on portions of six bands in the radio spectrum. Amateurs usually refer to these frequency bands by their wavelength. Novices may operate in the 80, 40, 15 and 10-meter bands, and in the 1.25-meter (222-MHz) and 23-centimeter (1270-MHz) bands. These bands are further divided into subbands for the different classes of license. Novice operators have **frequency privileges** (or permission to operate) on these subbands:

3675-3725 kHz in the 80-meter band
(5167.5 kHz—Alaska only, emergency communications, single-sideband voice emissions only)
7100-7150 kHz in the 40-meter band
21,100-21,200 kHz in the 15-meter band
28,100-28,500 kHz in the 10-meter band
222.1-223.91 MHz in the 1.25-meter band
1270-1295 MHz in the 23-centimeter band

We use the metric system of measurement in electronics. Chapter 3 includes a full explanation of the metric system and terms like *kilo, mega* and *centi* that we have used here. For now it is important that you know that *kilohertz* and *megahertz* are measures of the frequency of a radio signal. The *hertz* (Hz) is the basic unit of frequency. Kilo means thousand and mega means million. We can list any of the amateur frequency bands in either kilohertz or megahertz. For example, the 80-meter Novice band can be written either as 3.675 to 3.725 MHz, or 3675 to 3725 kHz.

[You must memorize these Novice frequency privileges. Before you go on to the next section, turn to Chapter 12 and

Table 2-1

Amateur Operator Licenses†

Class	Code Test	Written Examination	Privileges
Novice	5 WPM (Element 1A)	Novice theory and regulations (Element 2)	Telegraphy on 3675-3725, 7100-7150 and 21,100-21,200 kHz with 200 watts PEP output maximum; telegraphy, RTTY and data on 28,100-28,300 kHz and telegraphy and SSB voice on 28,300-28,500 kHz with 200 W PEP max; all amateur modes authorized on 222.1-223.91 MHz, 25 W PEP max; all amateur modes authorized on 1270-1295 MHz, 5 W PEP max.
Technician		Novice theory and regulations; Technician-level theory and regulations. (Elements 2 and 3A)*	All amateur privileges above 50.0 MHz. Technician-class licensees who have passed a 5-WPM code test also have HF Novice privileges.
General	13 WPM (Element 1B)	Novice theory and regulations; Technician and General theory and regulations. (Elements 2, 3A and 3B)	All amateur privileges except those reserved for Advanced and Amateur Extra class; see Table 2-2
Advanced	13 WPM (Element 1B)	All lower exam elements, plus Advanced theory. (Elements 2, 3A, 3B and 4A)	All amateur privileges except those reserved for Amateur Extra class; see Table 2-2.
Amateur Extra	20 WPM (Element 1C)	All lower exam elements, plus Extra-class theory (Elements 2, 3A, 3B, 4A and 4B)	All amateur privileges

†A licensed radio amateur will be required to pass only those elements that are not included in the examination for the amateur license currently held.

*If you hold a valid Technician class license issued before March 21, 1987, you also have credit for Element 3B. You must be able to prove your Technician license was issued before March 21, 1987 to claim this credit.

study the questions that begin with numbers 2A-10. Review these frequencies often as you study the remaining material in this book.]

Emission Privileges

Amateur operators transmit a wide variety of signals. These include Morse code, radioteletype, several types of voice communications and even television pictures. An **emission** is any radio-frequency (RF) signal from a transmitter.

There is a system for describing the various types of signals (or emissions) found on the amateur bands. Different modes are given identifiers, called *emission types.*

You should be familiar with the various emission types. The FCC lists the **emission privileges** for each license class by giving the emission types each may use. An emission privilege is FCC permission to use a particular emission type, such as Morse code or single-sideband phone. As a Novice licensee, you will be permitted to use all of the emission types (except pulse) on at least one frequency band. The emission types defined by the FCC are:

- CW—Morse code telegraphy.
- Data—Computer communications modes, often called *digital communications* because digital computers are used.
- Image—Television and facsimile communications.
- MCW—Morse code telegraphy using a keyed audio tone.
- Phone—Speech (voice) communications.
- Pulse—Communications using a sequence of controlled signal variations.
- RTTY—Direct-printing telegraphy communications (received by automatic techniques). Since digital computers are often used on RTTY, these signals are also often called *digital communications.*
- SS—Spread-spectrum communications in which the signal energy is spread across a wide bandwidth.
- Test—Transmissions containing no information.

On 80, 40 and 15 meters, Novices may transmit only Morse code (CW). The transmitter produces this Morse code signal by *keying* (switching on and off) the signal from a continuous-wave (CW) transmitter. On 10 meters, Novices may use CW from 28.1 to 28.5 MHz. Novice operators may also transmit radioteletype (RTTY) and data from 28.1 to 28.3 MHz, and single-sideband phone from 28.3 to 28.5 MHz. On the frequencies 222.1-223.91 MHz and 1270-1295 MHz, Novices may use all emissions authorized to higher-class licensees on these bands, including FM phone and digital modes, such as packet radio. Table 2-2 summarizes the amateur band limits and operating modes for each license class.

Hams often describe radioteletype (RTTY) and packet radio or other data emissions as *digital communications.* These are signals intended to be received and printed or displayed on a computer screen automatically. Information transferred directly from one computer to another is an example of digital communications.

[You have to memorize these Novice emission privileges. You should turn to Chapter 12 now and study those questions with numbers that begin 2A-17 and 2A-20. Review the material in this section if you have difficulty with any of the questions.]

Novice Transmitter Power

The FCC has issued rules explaining how transmitter power should be measured at the output of the transmitter. Novice licensees may use a maximum of 5 W **peak envelope power (PEP)** output on the 1270-MHz band, 25 W PEP on the 222-MHz band, and 200 W PEP on the 80, 40, 15 and 10-meter bands. The 200 W limitation also applies to any other licensed radio amateur who operates in the 80, 40 and 15-meter Novice bands. Remember that Novices may use up to 200 W PEP on any Novice frequency below 30 MHz.

In addition to these Novice bands, higher-class licensees

Table 2-2

US AMATEUR BANDS

Revised Sept 1, 1991

160 METERS

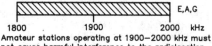

E,A,G

1800   1900   2000   kHz

Amateur stations operating at 1900–2000 kHz must not cause harmful interference to the radiolocation service and are afforded no protection from radiolocation operations.

80 METERS

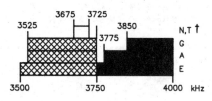

3675   3725
3525   3775   3850

N,T †
G
A
E

3500   3750   4000   kHz

5167.5 kHz (SSB only): Alaska emergency use only.

40 METERS

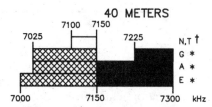

7100   7150
7025   7225

N,T †
G *
A *
E *

7000   7150   7300   kHz

* Phone operation is allowed on 7075–7100 kHz in Puerto Rico, US Virgin Islands and areas of the Caribbean south of 20 degrees north latitude; and in Hawaii and areas near ITU Region 3, including Alaska.

30 METERS

E,A,G

10,100   10,150   kHz

Maximum power on 30 meters is 200 watts PEP output. Amateurs must avoid interference to the fixed service outside the US.

20 METERS

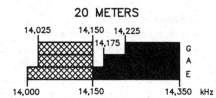

14,025   14,150   14,225
14,175

G
A
E

14,000   14,150   14,350   kHz

17 METERS

E,A,G

18,068   18,110   18,168   kHz

15 METERS

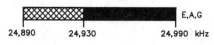

21,100   21,200
21,025   21,300
21,225

N,T
G
A
E

21,000   21,200   21,450   kHz

12 METERS

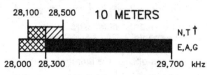

E,A,G

24,890   24,930   24,990   kHz

10 METERS

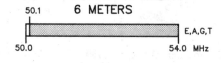

28,100   28,500

N,T †
E,A,G

28,000   28,300   29,700   kHz

Novices and Technicians are limited to 200 watts PEP output on 10 meters.

6 METERS

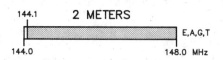

50.1

E,A,G,T

50.0   54.0   MHz

2 METERS

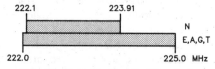

144.1

E,A,G,T

144.0   148.0   MHz

1.25 METERS

222.1   223.91

N
E,A,G,T

222.0   225.0   MHz

Novices are limited to 25 watts PEP output from 222.1 to 223.91 MHz.

70 CENTIMETERS **

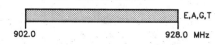

E,A,G,T

420.0   450.0   MHz

33 CENTIMETERS **

E,A,G,T

902.0   928.0   MHz

23 CENTIMETERS **

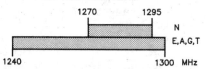

1270   1295

N
E,A,G,T

1240   1300   MHz

Novices are limited to 5 watts PEP output from 1270 to 1295 MHz.

US AMATEUR POWER LIMITS

At all times, transmitter power should be kept down to that necessary to carry out the desired communications. Power is rated in watts PEP output. Unless otherwise stated, the maximum power output is 1500 W. Power for all license classes is limited to 200 W in the 10,100–10,150 kHz band and in all Novice subbands below 28,100 kHz. Novices and Technicians are restricted to 200 W in the 28,100–28,500 kHz subbands. In addition, Novices are restricted to 25 W in the 222.1–223.91 MHz subband and 5 W in the 1270–1295 MHz subband.

Operators with Technician class licenses and above may operate on all bands above 50 MHz. For more detailed information see The FCC Rule Book.

KEY

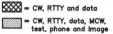

▨ = CW, RTTY and data

▦ = CW, RTTY, data, MCW, test, phone and image

■ = CW, phone and image

▨ = CW and SSB

▨ = CW, RTTY, data, phone, and image

□ = CW only

E = AMATEUR EXTRA
A = ADVANCED
G = GENERAL
T = TECHNICIAN
N = NOVICE

† Only Technician–class licensees who have passed a 5 – WPM code test may use these frequencies.

** Geographical and power restrictions apply to these bands. See The FCC Rule Book for more information about your area.

Above 23 Centimeters:

All licensees except Novices are authorized all modes on the following frequencies:
2300–2310 MHz
2390–2450 MHz
3300–3500 MHz
5650–5925 MHz
10.0–10.5 GHz
24.0–24.25 GHz
47.0–47.2 GHz
75.5–81.0 GHz
119.98–120.2 GHz
142–149 GHz
241–250 GHz
All above 300 GHz

For band plans and sharing arrangements, see *The ARRL Operating Manual.*

may use a maximum of only 200 W PEP on the 30-meter band. On all other bands, the rules limit the maximum transmitter output power in the amateur service to 1500 W PEP output. Higher-class licensees may use 1500 W PEP in the Novice sections of 10 meters, 222 MHz and 1270 MHz. In practice, unless you're attempting something as challenging as "moonbounce"—bouncing a signal off the moon—amateurs rarely use more than a couple of hundred watts on the VHF and UHF bands.

So far, we have been talking about the *maximum* transmitter power that the rules allow. There is another rule to consider, though. According to FCC rules, an amateur station must use the *minimum* transmitter power necessary to maintain reliable communication. What this means is simple—if you don't *need* 200 W to contact your friend across town, don't use it!

[Before proceeding to the next section turn to Chapter 12 and study the questions with numbers that begin 2A-18 and 2A-19. Review this section if you have any difficulties.]

THE NOVICE EXAM

The FCC refers to the various exams for Amateur Radio licenses as exam *Elements*. For example, exam Elements 1A, 1B and 1C are the 5, 13 and 20 word-per-minute (WPM) code exams. Element 2 is the Novice written exam. Table 2-1 summarizes the exams and privileges that go with each license class.

The table shows that you must pass exam Element 1A and Element 2 for the Novice license. The purpose of Element 1A is to prove your ability to send and receive messages using the international Morse code at a speed of 5 words per minute. The Element 2 written exam covers basic FCC Rules and Novice operating procedures, along with basic electronics theory.

[Now turn to Chapter 12 and study questions 2A-12.1 through 2A-12.3. Review this section if you have difficulty with any of these questions.]

What Will My Novice Exam Be Like?

Two amateurs with General class licenses or higher, who are 18 or older, can give the test for a Novice license. The examiners must not be relatives of anyone taking the exam. The exams can be given at the convenience of the candidates and the examiners, at any location they agree to.

There is probably an active Volunteer Examining Team somewhere in your area. These teams conduct tests for the higher classes of Amateur Radio licenses. Chances are that the Volunteer Examiners will give you the Novice exam at one of their regular exam sessions.

If you have any trouble locating examiners, write to:
Educational Activities Department
ARRL Headquarters
225 Main Street
Newington, CT 06111
We will refer you to someone near you who can arrange your test. We will also supply a list of ARRL/VEC Volunteer Exam sessions in your area.

The code test is normally given first. The examiners will usually send five minutes of five-word-per-minute code, and then test your copy. The test usually takes one of two forms. The examiners may ask you 10 questions based on the contents of the transmission, and you must answer 7 of the 10 questions correctly. Or, the examiners may check your answer sheet for one minute of solid (perfect) copy out of the five-minute transmission.

The written test consists of 30 questions on general operating practices, rules and regulations, and basic radio theory. To pass, you must correctly answer 22 of the 30 questions on your exam.

Your exam must include 30 questions taken from the pool of questions printed in Chapter 12 of this book. Your examiners should choose one question from each of the 30 question-pool subsections. Tests are also available from the ARRL Educational Activities Department if the examiners wish to use one of those.

The *questions* must be used exactly as they are printed in Chapter 12. Your examiners are free to decide the format for your answers, though most examiners use the multiple-choice format.

The ARRL Educational Activities Department will supply your examiners with a multiple-choice test, if they want to request it. We appreciate receiving a self-addressed stamped envelope for sending out these exams. The examiners must send a photocopy of their licenses (or other proof) to show that they are eligible to give the exams. (The exams are not available for students to use as practice!) Chapter 12 has the complete pool of questions with multiple-choice answers.

THE TECHNICIAN LICENSE

With Technician license in hand, you'll be able to operate on all the VHF, UHF and microwave bands allocated to the amateur service—and there are a lot of them! Table 2-2 lists the frequency range for each of the popular Technician bands. For a complete list of the amateur bands, including those in the largely experimental microwave region, see *The FCC Rule Book*, published by ARRL.

If you decide to learn the international Morse code and are able to pass a 5 word-per-minute code test, you will have earned an enhanced Technician license. A code certificate (in addition to your regular Technician class license) allows you to operate on the four HF Novice subbands that normally allow for direct worldwide communication.

THE TECHNICIAN EXAM

The Technician class exam consists of two written tests, Elements 2 and 3A. Chapters 12 and 13 of this book contain every question in the question pool from which your exam will be composed. If you study this book carefully, you should be able to pass the Technician class exam. If you wish to qualify for the enhanced Technician license, you'll also need a computer program or cassette tapes that teach international Morse code. The ARRL offers a set of two 90-minute cassettes called *Your Introduction to Morse Code*. The ARRL also offers *Morse University* for Commodore® 64 and 128 computers and *Morse Tutor* for IBM® PC and compatible computers.

What Will the Exam Be Like?

All US exams except the Novice are administered by volunteer examiners who are certified by a Volunteer Examiner Coordinator (VEC). *The FCC Rule Book* contains details on the VE program. Novice exams do not come under the regulations involving VECs.

To qualify for a Technician class license, you must pass FCC Exam Elements 2 and 3A. If you already hold a valid Novice license, then you have credit for passing Elements 1A and 2, and will not have to retake them. In that case when you upgrade to Technician, you will retain your Novice HF privileges.

The Element 3A exam consists of 25 questions taken from a pool of more than 250. The FCC specifies nine subelements, or divisions, for each exam element. These are the Commission's Rules, Operating Procedures, Radio-Wave Propagation, Amateur Radio Practices, Electrical Principles, Circuit Components, Practical Circuits, Signals and Emissions, and Antennas and Feed Lines.

The question pools for all amateur exams are maintained by a Question Pool Committee selected by the Volunteer Examiner Coordinators. The FCC allows VEs to select the questions for an amateur exam, but they must use the questions exactly as they are released by the VEC that coordinates the test session. If you attend a test session coordinated by the ARRL/VEC, your test will be designed by the ARRL/VEC, and the questions and answers will be exactly as they are printed in Chapter 13.

Finding an Exam Opportunity

To determine where and when an exam will be given, contact the ARRL/VEC Office, or watch for announcements in the Hamfest Calendar and Coming Conventions columns in *QST*. Many local clubs sponsor exams, so they are another good source of information on exam opportunities. ARRL officials such as Directors, Vice Directors and Section Managers receive notices about test sessions in their area. See page 8 in the latest issue of *QST* for names and addresses.

To register for an exam, send a completed Form 610 to the VE Team responsible for the exam session if preregistration is required. Otherwise, bring the form to the session. Registration deadlines, and the time and location of the exams, are mentioned prominently in publicity releases about upcoming sessions.

Taking the Exam

By the time examination day rolls around, you should have already prepared yourself. This means getting your schedule, supplies and mental attitude ready. Plan your schedule so you'll get to the examination site with plenty of time to spare. There's no harm in being early. In fact, you might have time to discuss hamming with another applicant, which is a great way to calm pretest nerves. Try not to discuss the material that will be on the examination as this may make you even more nervous. By this time, it's too late to study anyway!

What supplies will you need? First, be sure you bring your current *original* Amateur Radio license, if you have one. Bring along several sharpened number 2 pencils and two pens (blue or black ink). Be sure to have a good eraser. A pocket calculator may also come in handy. You may use a programmable calculator if that is the kind you have, but take it into your exam "empty" (cleared of all programs and constants in memory). Don't program equations ahead of time because you may be asked to demonstrate that there is nothing in the calculator's memory. You will probably *not* be allowed to take math tables, such as trigonometry tables or logarithm tables into the exam with you.

The VE Team is required to check two forms of identification before you enter the test room. This includes your *original* Amateur Radio license (if you have one). A photo ID of some type is best for the second form, but is not required by FCC. Other acceptable forms of ID include a driver's license, a piece of mail addressed to you, a birth certificate or some other such document.

The following description of the testing procedure applies to exams coordinated by the ARRL/VEC, although many other VECs use a similar procedure.

Code Tests

If you are interested in using Morse code and gaining the additional privileges granted to Technicians who have passed a 5-WPM code test, this information will be of interest to you.

The code tests are usually given before the written exams. The 20-WPM exam is usually given first, then the 13-WPM exam and finally the 5-WPM test. There is no harm in trying the 20- or 13-WPM exams even though you are testing for the Technician exams.

Before you take the code test, you'll be handed a piece of paper to copy the code as it's sent. The test will begin with about a minute of practice copy. Then comes the actual test: five minutes of Morse code. You are responsible for knowing the 26 letters of the alphabet, the numerals 0 through 9, the period, comma, question mark, $\overline{AR}$, $\overline{SK}$, $\overline{BT}$ and $\overline{DN}$. You may copy the entire text word for word, or just take notes on the content. At the end of the transmission, the examiner will hand you 10 questions about the text. Simply fill in the blanks with your answers. (You must spell each answer exactly as it was sent.) Some examining teams may choose to use a multiple-choice format for the code-test answers. If you get at least 7 correct, you pass! Alternatively, the exam team has the option to look at your copy sheet if you fail the 10-question exam. If you have one minute of solid copy, they can certify that you passed the test on that basis. The format of the test transmission is similar to one side of a normal on-the-air amateur conversation.

A sending test may not be required. The Commission has decided that if applicants can demonstrate receiving ability, they most likely can also send at that speed. But be prepared for a sending test, just in case! Subpart 97.503(a) of the FCC rules says, "A telegraphy examination must be sufficient to prove that the examinee has the ability to send correctly by hand and to receive correctly by ear texts in the international Morse code at not less than the prescribed speed..."

Written Tests

The examiner will give each applicant a test booklet, an answer sheet and scratch paper. After that, you're on your own. The first thing to do is read the instructions. Be sure to sign your name every place it's called for. Do all of this at the beginning to get it out of the way.

Next, check the examination to see that all pages and questions are there. If not, report this to the examiner immediately. When filling in your answer sheet, make sure your answers are marked next to the numbers that correspond to each question.

Go through the entire exam, and answer the easy questions first. Next, go back to the beginning and try the harder questions. The really tough questions should be left for last. Guessing can only help, as there is no additional penalty for answering incorrectly.

If you have to guess, do it intelligently: At first glance, you may find that you can eliminate one or more "distractors." Of the remaining responses, more than one may seem correct; only one is the best answer, however. To the applicant who is fully prepared, incorrect distractors to each question are obvious. Nothing beats preparation!

After you've finished, check the examination thoroughly. You may have read a question wrong or goofed in your arithmetic. Don't be overconfident. There's no rush, so take your time. Think, and check your answer sheet. When you feel you've done your best and can do no more, return the test booklet, answer sheet and scratch pad to the examiner.

The Volunteer-Examiner team will grade the exam right away. The passing mark is 74%. (That means no more than 6 incorrect answers on the Element 3A exam.) You will receive a Certificate of Successful Completion of Examination (CSCE) showing all exam elements that you pass. If you are already licensed, and you pass the exam elements required to earn a higher class of license, the CSCE authorizes you to operate with your new privileges. When you use these new privileges, you must sign your call sign, followed by the slant mark ("/"; on voice, say "stroke" or "slant") and the letters KT (for Novices upgrading to Technician). There is one exception to this rule: If you previously held a Technician license and later pass the 5-WPM code test, you do not have to use the "KT" indicator when you use your new privileges or when you operate on the bands already allocated to Technicians (50 MHz and above).

If you pass only some of the exam elements required for a higher class license, you will still receive a CSCE. That certificate shows what exam elements you passed, and is valid for one year. Use it as proof that you passed those exam elements so you won't have to take them over again next time you try for the upgrade.

If you hold a CSCE for the 5-WPM code test, make sure you keep it in a safe place. Along with your actual Technician license, it serves as authorization to operate on the HF Novice bands.

FILLING OUT YOUR FCC FORM 610

Congratulations! You have passed the test or tests required for your first Amateur Radio license. What's next? More paperwork! All applications for new amateur licenses, or modifications or renewals, are made on an FCC Form 610. Figure 2-3 shows a Form 610 completed for a successful Novice applicant.

Your examiners will fill out the Administering VE's report as shown at the top of the form in Figure 2-3. Your part begins in Section I, a third of the way down the form. Check box 2C, "EXAMINATION FOR NEW LICENSE." Skip items 3 and 4, and fill out items 5, 6, 7 and 8. Remember that you cannot use a post office box for your station location. You must show the actual location of your station in item 8.

Unless you plan to install an antenna over 200 feet high, or your station will be in a designated wilderness area, wildlife preserve or nationally recognized scenic and recreational area, check "NO" on item 9. Since you are applying for a new license, check "NO" in box 10, and leave boxes 11 and 12 blank. Be sure to sign and date your application in boxes 13 and 14.

If you passed the Novice exam, your examiners should fill out Section II-A on the back of the form. This is where the examiners list their qualifications, and certify that you have passed the exam. Be sure to have *both* examiners fill in Section II-A. When all parts of the form are complete, the examiners will send it to FCC, Box 1020, Gettysburg, PA 17326. After that comes the hard part—waiting for your new license!

If you pass the Technician exam, the Volunteer Examiner will complete the top half of the first side and Section II-B on the back. The examiners then forward the form with the other paperwork from your exam session to the Volunteer Examiner Coordinator responsible for the session. After a final check, the Form 610 will be sent to the FCC in Gettysburg, Pennsylvania, for processing.

The 610 Form serves as the application for your license. You will use the same form to renew your license before it expires. This form also serves another very important purpose. Line 7 provides the FCC with a mailing address where they can contact you. If you move, or your address changes for any reason, use an FCC Form 610 to notify them of your new address. It's important that you receive any mail sent to you by the FCC.

[Turn to Chapter 12 and study exam question 2A-14.1. If you have trouble answering this question reread the last paragraph.]

FEDERAL COMMUNICATIONS COMMISSION
GETTYSBURG, PA 17326

Approved OMB
3060-0003
Expires 12/31/92
See instructions for information
regarding public burden estimate

APPLICATION FOR AMATEUR RADIO
STATION AND/OR OPERATOR LICENSE

ADMINISTERING VEs' REPORT		EXAMINATION ELEMENTS							
Applicant is credited for: ➡		1(A)	1(B)	1(C)	2	3(A)	3(B)	4(A)	4(B)
A. CIRCLE CLASS OF FCC AMATEUR LICENSE HELD: N T G A	Class ➡	(NT)	(GA)	(NTGA)	(NTGA)	(TGA)	(GA)	(A)	
B. CERTIFICATE(S) OF SUCCESSFUL COMPLETION OF AN EXAMINATION HELD: ➡		Date Issued	Date Issued	Date Issued	Date Issued	Date Issued	Date Issued	Date Issued	Date Issued
C. FCC COMMERCIAL RADIOTELEGRAPH OPERATOR LICENSE HELD:	Number: ___ Exp. Date: ___								
D. EXAMINATION ELEMENTS PASSED THAT WERE ADMINISTERED AT THIS SESSION: ➡		X			X				

E. APPLICANT IS QUALIFIED FOR OPERATOR LICENSE CLASS: ☐ NONE:

E1. ☒ NOVICE (Elements 1(A), 1(B), or 1(C) and 2)

E2.
- ☐ TECHNICIAN (Elements 1(A), 1(B), or 1(C), 2 and 3(A))
- ☐ GENERAL (Elements 1(B) or 1(C), 2, 3(A), and 3(B))
- ☐ ADVANCED (Elements 1(B) or 1(C), 2, 3(A), 3(B) and 4(A))
- ☐ AMATEUR EXTRA (Elements 1(C), 2, 3(A), 3(B), 4(A), and 4(B))

H. Date of VEC coordinated examination session:

I. VEC Receipt Date:

F. NAME OF VOLUNTEER-EXAMINER COORDINATOR: (VEC coordinated sessions only)

G. EXAMINATION SESSION LOCATION: (VEC coordinated sessions only)

SECTION I

1. IF YOU HOLD A VALID LICENSE ATTACH THE ORIGINAL LICENSE OR PHOTOCOPY ON BACK OF APPLICATION. IF THE VALID LICENSE OR CERTIFICATE OF SUCCESSFUL COMPLETION OF AN EXAMINATION WAS LOST OR DESTROYED, PLEASE EXPLAIN.

2. CHECK ONE OR MORE ITEMS, NORMALLY ALL LICENSES ARE ISSUED FOR A 10 YEAR TERM.

2A. ☐ RENEW LICENSE—NO OTHER CHANGES ➡   EXPIRATION DATE (Month, Day, Year)

2B. ☐ REINSTATE LICENSE EXPIRED LESS THAN 2 YEARS ➡

2C. ☐ EXAMINATION FOR NEW LICENSE

2D. ☐ EXAMINATION TO UPGRADE OPERATOR CLASS   FORMER LAST NAME   SUFFIX (Jr., Sr., etc.)

2E. ☐ CHANGE CALL SIGN (Be sure you are eligible—See Inst. 2E)

2F. ☐ CHANGE NAME (Give former name) ➡   FORMER FIRST NAME   MIDDLE INITIAL

2G. ☐ CHANGE MAILING ADDRESS

2H. ☐ CHANGE STATION LOCATION

3. CALL SIGN (If you checked 2C above, skip items 3 and 4)

4. OPERATOR CLASS OF THE ATTACHED LICENSE:

5. CURRENT FIRST NAME: Angela   M.I.: M   LAST NAME: Beebe   SUFFIX (Jr., Sr., etc.)

6. DATE OF BIRTH: 01/13/66 (MONTH DAY YEAR)

7. CURRENT MAILING ADDRESS (Number and Street): 41 Washington Street   CITY: Bristol   STATE: CT   ZIP CODE: 06010

8. CURRENT STATION LOCATION (Do not use a P.O. Box No., RFD No., or General Delivery. See Instruction 8): 41 Washington Street   CITY: Bristol   STATE: CT

9. Would a Commission grant of your application be an action which may have a significant environmental effect as defined by Section 1.1307 of the Commission's Rules? See instruction 9. If you answer yes, submit the statement as required by Sections 1.1308 and 1.1311. ☐ YES   ☒ NO

10. Do you have any other amateur radio application on file with the Commission that has not been acted upon? If yes, answer items 11 and 12.   ☐ YES   ☒ NO

11. PURPOSE OF OTHER APPLICATION

12. DATE SUBMITTED (Month, Day, Year)

CERTIFICATION

I CERTIFY THAT all statements herein and attachments herewith are true, complete, and correct to the best of my knowledge and belief and are made in good faith; that I am not a representative of a foreign government; that I waive any claim to the use of any particular frequency regardless of prior use by license or otherwise; and that the station to be licensed will be inaccessible to unauthorized persons.

WILLFUL FALSE STATEMENTS MADE ON THIS FORM OR ATTACHMENTS ARE PUNISHABLE BY FINE AND IMPRISONMENT U.S. CODE TITLE 18, SECTION 1001

13. SIGNATURE OF APPLICANT: (Must match Item 5)   *Angela Beebe*

14. DATE SIGNED: Nov. 17, 1990

(OVER)

FCC Form 610, February 1990

Figure 2-3—A completed FCC Form 610. All applications for new Amateur Radio licenses must be submitted using this form.

ATTACH THE ORIGINAL LICENSE OR PHOTOCOPY HERE

SECTION II — EXAMINATION INFORMATION

SECTION II-A FOR NOVICE OPERATOR EXAMINATION ONLY. To be completed by the Administering VEs after completing the Administering VE's Report on the other side of this form.

CERTIFICATION

I CERTIFY THAT I have complied with the Administering VE requirements stated in Part 97 of the Commission's Rules; THAT I have administered to the applicant and graded an amateur radio operator examination in accordance with Part 97 of the Commission's Rules; THAT I have indicated in the Administering VE's Report the examination element(s) the applicant passed; THAT I have examined documents held by the applicant and I have indicated in the Administering VE's Report the examination element for which the applicant is given examination credit in accordance with Part 97 of the Commission's Rules.

1A. VOLUNTEER EXAMINER'S NAME: (First, MI, Last, Suffix) *(Print or Type)*

Michael B. Kaczynski

1B. VE'S MAILING ADDRESS: (Number, Street, City, State, ZIP Code)

70 Braeburn Rd, Bristol CT 06010

1C. VE'S OPERATOR CLASS: ☐ GENERAL ☐ ADVANCED ☑ AMATEUR EXTRA	1D. VE'S STATION CALL SIGN W1OD

1E. LICENSE EXPIRATION DATE: 4/21/97 | **1F. IF YOU HAVE AN APPLICATION PENDING FOR YOUR LICENSE, GIVE FILING DATE:**

1G. SIGNATURE: (Must match Item 1A) Michael B. Kaczynski	DATE SIGNED Nov. 17, 1990

2A. VOLUNTEER EXAMINER'S NAME: (First, MI, Last, Suffix) *(Print or Type)*

Thomas M. Namnoum

2B. VE'S MAILING ADDRESS: (Number, Street, City, State, ZIP Code)

55 Spruce St, Newington CT 06111

2C. VE'S OPERATOR CLASS: ☐ GENERAL ☐ ADVANCED ☑ AMATEUR EXTRA	2D. VE'S STATION CALL SIGN KM1O

2E. LICENSE EXPIRATION DATE: 6/30/97 | **2F. IF YOU HAVE AN APPLICATION PENDING FOR YOUR LICENSE, GIVE FILING DATE:**

2G. SIGNATURE: (Must match Item 2A) Thomas M. Namnoum	DATE SIGNED Nov. 17 1990

SECTION II-B FOR TECHNICIAN, GENERAL, ADVANCED, OR AMATEUR EXTRA OPERATOR EXAMINATION ONLY. To be completed by the Administering VEs after completing the Administering VE's Report on the other side of this form.

CERTIFICATION

I CERTIFY THAT I have complied with the Administering VE requirements stated in Part 97 of the Commission's Rules; THAT I have administered to the applicant and graded an amateur radio operator examination in accordance with Part 97 of the Commission's Rules; THAT I have indicated in the Administering VE's Report the examination element(s) the applicant passed; THAT I have examined documents held by the applicant and I have indicated in the Administering VE's Report the examination element(s) for which the applicant is given examination credit in accordance with Part 97 of the Commission's Rules.

1A. VOLUNTEER EXAMINER'S NAME: (First, MI, Last, Suffix) *(Print or Type)*	1B. VE'S STATION CALL SIGN:
1C. SIGNATURE: (Must match Item 1A)	DATE SIGNED:
2A. VOLUNTEER EXAMINER'S NAME: (First, MI, Last, Suffix) *(Print or Type)*	2B. VE'S STATION CALL SIGN:
2C. SIGNATURE: (Must match Item 2A)	DATE SIGNED:
3A. VOLUNTEER EXAMINER'S NAME: (First, MI, Last, Suffix) *(Print or Type)*	3B. VE'S STATION CALL SIGN:
3C. SIGNATURE: (Must match Item 3A)	DATE SIGNED:

FCC Form 610
February 1990

Well, the big day has finally arrived—your "ticket" came in the mail from the FCC! You have permission to operate an amateur station. Now you are ready to put your very own amateur station on the air!

As the proud owner of a new Amateur Radio ticket, you'll soon be an "on-the-air" person instead of an "off-the-air" person. You probably can't wait to make your first contact! You'll be putting all the information you had to learn for the exam to good use.

First things first. When you get your new ticket, "hot off the press," make a few photocopies of it. Then put the original license in a safe place. You must have your license (or a photocopy) available whenever you operate, so put one of those copies in your wallet. That magic piece of paper is your **operator license**, which lets you operate a station within your Novice or Technician privileges. It is also your **station license**, and lists the call sign that identifies your station.

CALL SIGNS

The FCC issues call signs on a systematic basis. When they process your application, you get the next call sign to come out of the FCC computer. The FCC issues call signs from four "groups," depending on the class of license.

Novice class licensees are given "Group D" call signs. These have a "two-by-three" format—two letters followed by a number, followed by three letters. The letters before the number make up the call sign *prefix*, and the letters after the number are the *suffix*. An example of a Novice call sign is KA1IFB.

Technician class licensees have "Group C" call signs. These have a "one-by-three" format—a one-letter prefix, a number and a three-letter suffix. An example: N7IAL.

The call-sign formats of other Amateur Radio license classes follow. Group C calls are also given to General class amateurs. Advanced class amateurs get calls from Group B—the "two-by-two" group. KB9NM is an example of a call from this group. Group A calls are for Amateur Extra class operators only. These calls are of the "one-by-two" or "two-by-one" format. (K8CH is a one-by-two call; AA2Z is a two-by-one call.)

Once you have a call sign, you may keep it as long as you want to (unless your license expires or is revoked). In other words, there's no requirement to change your call sign when you upgrade to a higher license class. The FCC gives amateurs their choice in this matter.

The number in the call sign shows the district where the call was first issued. Figure 2-4 shows the 10 US call districts. Amateurs may keep their calls when they move from one district to another. This means the number is not always an indication of where an amateur is. It tells only where he or she was living when the license was first issued. For example, WB3IOS received her license in Pennsylvania, in the third call district, but she now lives in the first district.

The first letter of a US call will always be A, N, K or W. These letters are assigned to the United States as amateur call-sign prefixes. Other countries use other prefixes—LA2UA is a Norwegian call sign, and VU2HO is from India.

[Now it's time to turn to Chapter 12 and study some questions. You should be able to answer all of the questions with numbers that begin 2A-15. If you have any difficulty, review this section.]

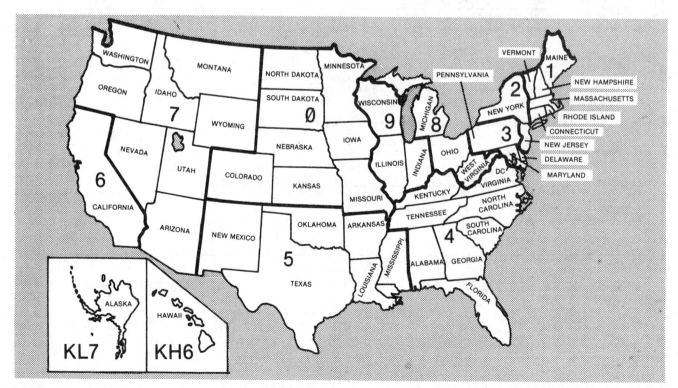

Figure 2-4—The 10 US call districts. An amateur holding the call sign WA1STO lived in the first district when the FCC assigned her that call. Alaska is part of the seventh call district, but has its own set of prefixes: AL7, KL7, NL7 and WL7. Hawaii, part of the sixth district, has the AH6, KH6, NH6 and WH6 prefixes.

Keep your operation "above board"—set an operating example that will make you proud. You should be familiar with the basic operating and technical rules. You should also know the standard operating practices used for the various modes you operate. Chapter 9 includes detailed information about operating your station. In this section we will study the FCC rules of operating and cover some very simple guidelines.

Logbooks are useful for recording dates, calls, names and locations of those stations you contact. When you confirm contacts by sending QSL cards, a logbook is a convenient way to keep track of these exchanges. Your log will provide a useful and interesting history, if you choose to keep one. Figure 2-5 shows an example of the information many amateurs keep in a logbook.

TIME OUT FOR STATION IDENTIFICATION

FCC regulations are very specific about station identification. You must identify your station every 10 minutes or less during a contact and at the end of the contact. You do not have to identify with every transmission, only at the required intervals. Identify your station by transmitting the station call sign listed on your license.

The rules prohibit **unidentified communications or signals** (where the transmitting station's call sign is not transmitted). Be sure you understand the proper station identification procedures, so you don't violate this rule.

You don't have to transmit your call sign at the beginning of a contact. In most cases it will help you establish the communications, though. Unless you give your call sign, the other stations won't know who you are! When you take part in a net or talk with a group of hams regularly, they may learn to recognize your voice. Then you may not have to give your call sign for them to know who you are.

You do not have to transmit both call signs when you are talking with another ham—only your own. The exception is in cases of third-party communications with a station in a foreign country. (You'll learn more about third-party

communications later in this chapter.) Then you do have to transmit both call signs at the end of the contact.

Let's look at an example of how to identify an Amateur Radio station properly. KB4IYK and WB9RRU have been in communication for 45 minutes and are now signing off. Each operator has already transmitted his call four times (once after each 10-minute interval). Each should now transmit his call one more time as they sign off, for a total of five times during the QSO. (QSO means a two-way contact or communication with another ham.)

Suppose the QSO had lasted only 8 minutes. Each station would be required to transmit his call sign only once (at the end of the communication). You may identify more often than this to make it easier to communicate on a crowded band. But the rules specify only that you identify every 10 minutes, and at the end of a contact. On voice, identification is simply "from KB4IYK." In Morse code, use DE KB4IYK ("DE" means *from* in French).

[You should turn to Chapter 12 now, and study those questions with numbers that begin 2A-27 and 2A-38. Review this section if you have any difficulty with those questions.]

POINTS OF COMMUNICATIONS

Who can you talk to with your new license? The FCC defines "points of communication" to specify what kinds of radio stations you may talk with. It's pretty simple, actually: *You may converse with all amateur stations at any time.* This includes amateurs in foreign countries, unless either amateur's government prohibits the communications. (There are a few countries in the world that do not allow Amateur Radio. There are also times when a government will not allow its amateurs to talk with people in other countries.)

The FCC must authorize any communication with any stations not licensed in the amateur service. An example of such authorization is when amateur stations communicate with military communications stations on Armed Forces Day each year.

DATE	FREQ.	MODE	POWER	TIME	STATION WORKED	REPORT SENT	REPORT REC'D	TIME OFF	COMMENTS QTH / NAME / QSL VIA	QSL S	QSL R
16 NOV	3715	A1A	100	1800	KA1EBV	589	479	1835	MANOMET, MA - JOHN WILLIAMS	✓	
"	"	"	"	1840	WB7TPY	599	599	1855	TUFTS UNIVERSITY - DAVE GOES TO DENTAL SCHOOL		
17 NOV	28.125	A1A	100	2000	VP2ML	579	589	2003	CARIBBEAN - CHOD - NICE WX! BIG PILE UP	✓	✓
	28.140	"	"	2010	KA0HJD W0SH	599	599	2015	DESMOINES, IA - KRISTEN AND DAD, W0SH THEY COLLECT OLD TELEGRAPH KEYS!	✓	✓
	3710	A1A	100	2033	KA1GQJ	579	589	2055	LINDA - NURSE IN A HOSPITAL	✓	
20 NOV	3715	A1A	100	1645	NA1L	559	559	1700	DALE IS A LAWYER; GOOD SIGNAL, KA1IXI, XYL - CHERYL	✓	✓
	3722	A1A	100	1702	AA2Z	599	599	1705	EAST HAMPTON, CT - WOW! MARK WORKS AT ARRL HQ!!	✓	✓
	3720	A1A	100	2315	WA1TBY			2325	NENN - QNI QTC 2		
	21.175	A1A	100	2332	N6TR	539	569	2345	OREGON - SAID HIS NAME WAS "TREE"?!		✓

Figure 2-5—Most amateurs keep a station logbook to record information about each contact.

WELL, TELL HIM AGAIN, JEEVES—NO THIRD-PARTY TRAFFIC WORK WITH NEPTUNE

from October 1955 QST

Another example of amateurs communicating with nonamateur stations is during Radio Amateur Civil Emergency Service (RACES) operation. During an emergency, a registered RACES station may conduct civil-defense communications with stations in the Disaster Communications Service. During such emergencies, RACES stations may also communicate with other US Government stations authorized to conduct civil-defense communications.

[Turn to Chapter 12 now and study questions 2A-28.1 and 2A-28.2. Review this section if you have difficulty with any of these questions.]

BROADCASTING

Amateur Radio is a two-way communications service. Amateur Radio stations may not broadcast information intended for reception by the general public. There are also restrictions regulating one-way transmissions of information of general interest to other amateurs. Amateur stations may transmit one-way signals while in beacon operation or radio-control operation. Novice control operators don't have these privileges, however.

[Now turn to Chapter 12 and study question 2A-33.1. If you are uncertain of the answer to this question, review this section.]

THIRD-PARTY COMMUNICATIONS

Communication on behalf of anyone other than the operators of the two stations in contact is **third-party communications**. (Many hams call it *third-party traffic*.) For example, sending a message from your mother-in-law to her relatives in Scarsdale on Valentine's Day is third-party communications. Third-party communications of a personal nature is okay, but passing messages involving business matters is not. The Amateur Service is not the place to conduct business.

You can pass third-party messages to other stations in the United States. Outside the US, FCC rules strictly limit this type of communication to those countries that have *third-party communications agreements* with the US.

In many countries, the government operates the telephone system and other communications lines. You can imagine why these governments are reluctant to allow their amateur operators to pass messages. They would be in direct competition with the government-operated communications system.

The ARRL monthly journal, *QST*, periodically publishes a list of countries with which the US has a third-party communications agreement. The list does change, and sometimes there are temporary agreements to handle special events. Check such a list, or ask someone who knows, before you try to pass a message to another country.

You may allow an unlicensed person to participate in Amateur Radio from your station. This is **third-party participation**. It is another form of third-party communications.

You (as control operator) must always be present to make sure the unlicensed person follows all the rules. You can allow your family members and friends to enjoy some of the excitement of Amateur Radio in this way. They can speak into the microphone or even send Morse code, as long as you are present to control the radio. They can also type messages on your computer keyboard to talk with someone using packet radio or radioteletype.

There is one important rule to keep in mind about third-party participation. If the unlicensed person was an amateur operator whose license was suspended or revoked by the FCC, that person may not participate in any amateur communication. You can't allow that person to talk into the microphone of your transmitter or operate your Morse code key or computer keyboard.

[Now turn to Chapter 12 and study question 2A-31.1 and the questions with numbers that begin 2A-34. Review this section as needed.]

BUSINESS COMMUNICATIONS

Amateur communication is noncommercial radio communication between amateur stations, solely with a personal aim and without pecuniary or business interest. *Pecuniary* refers to payment of any type.

This definition tells us that amateur operators should not conduct any type of business communications. This does not apply just to your business interests. It applies to anyone else's business as well.

Obviously, you would not use Amateur Radio to keep in touch with your company's delivery trucks. But what about using the repeater autopatch to call the local Pizza Palace and order dinner on your way home? Sure, it isn't *your* business, but it is a business call. Don't do it!

Some hams believe it is okay to send a message to ARRL Headquarters asking for some forms or other information. After all, the ARRL is a not-for-profit organization. It is still a business, however, and such requests *are* the business of the League. Messages like that are not allowed over Amateur Radio, because they are business messages.

As with most rules, there is a possible exception to the business communications rule. Your car has just broken down in the middle of a busy expressway. Can you use the autopatch to call a garage for help? Now you have an emergency. Your property (car), and possibly your life, are in immediate

danger. In an emergency, you can use Amateur Radio to call a business for help.

There are many examples of times when personal property or lives are in immediate danger. You may use Amateur Radio to call for help in such a situation, even though you seem to be violating other rules. Just be sure you really have an emergency situation first.

No one can use an amateur station for monetary gain. You must not accept payment in any form for the use of your station at any time. This also means you may not accept payment for transmitting a message for anyone. Payment means more than just money here. It refers to any type of compensation, which would include materials or services of any type.

There is one exception to this rule. A club station intended primarily for transmitting Morse code practice and information bulletins of interest to all amateurs may employ a paid control operator. That person can be paid to serve as the control operator only when the station is actually transmitting code practice or bulletins. This exception allows the ARRL to pay a control operator for W1AW, the station at League Headquarters in Newington, Connecticut. The station is dedicated to Hiram Percy Maxim, the League's first president. The W1AW operator can't make general contacts with other hams after the code-practice sessions, however.

[Before you go on to the next section, turn to Chapter 12 and study those questions with numbers that begin 2A-30 and 2A-32. If you have any difficulty with any of them, review this section.]

OTHER ASSORTED RULES

Under FCC rules, amateurs may not transmit music of any form. They may not use obscene, indecent or profane language. You can't use codes or ciphers to obscure the meaning of transmissions. This means you can't make up a "secret" code to send messages over the air to a friend.

Amateurs may not cause **malicious** (intentional) **interference** to other communications. You may not like the other operator's practices, or you may believe he or she is violating the rules. You have no right to interfere with their communications, however.

Amateurs may not transmit **false or deceptive signals**, such as a distress call when no emergency exists. You must not, for example, start calling MAYDAY (an international distress signal) unless you are in a life-threatening situation.

[Now it's time to turn to Chapter 12 again, and study a few questions. You should be able to answer those questions with numbers that begin 2A-35, 2A-36, 2A-37 and 2A-39.

Review this section if you have difficulty with any of these questions.]

Official Notices of Violation

The FCC is the agency in charge of maintaining law and order in radio operation in the US. The International Telecommunication Union (ITU) sets up international rules that the government agencies of each country must follow. Both sets of rules provide the basic structure for Amateur Radio in the United States.

Suppose you receive an official notice from the FCC informing you that you have violated a regulation. Now what should you do? Simple: Whatever the notice tells you to do.

Operating a station at your summer cottage is considered *portable operation*—operating at a place other than that shown on the station license. When you use a transceiver installed in your car, you're conducting a *mobile operation*—operating a station while in motion or during halts at unspecified locations. Amateurs do *not* have to notify the FCC before placing a station in portable or mobile operation.

The FCC will mail any notices of violation to the permanent mailing address shown on your license. There may be times when you will operate your station away from home for a long period. Arrange to have your mail forwarded from your permanent mailing address to your temporary home in those cases.

There exists a philosophy in Amateur Radio that is deeply rooted in our history. This philosophy is as strong now as it was in the days of the radio pioneers. We are talking about the *self-policing* of our bands. Over the years, amateurs have become known for their ability to maintain high operating standards and technical skills. We do this without excessive regulation by the FCC. The Commission itself has praised the amateur service for its tradition of self-policing. Perhaps the underlying reason for this is the amateur's sense of pride, accomplishment, fellowship, loyalty and concern. Amateur Radio is far more than just a hobby to most amateurs.

As a new or prospective amateur operator, you will begin to discover the wide horizons of your new pastime. You will learn more about the rich heritage we all share. Take this sense of pride with you, and follow the Amateur's Code.

[This completes your study of the first part of the chapter. The remainder covers the rules and regulations you'll need to know to pass the Element 3A exam for the Technician license. Before moving on, turn to Chapter 12 and study the questions that begin 2A-29 and 2A-40. By now you should have no difficulty with the questions in subelement 2A on the question pool.]

The Amateur's Code

The Radio Amateur is:

CONSIDERATE...never knowingly operates in such a way as to lessen the pleasure of others.

LOYAL...offers loyalty, encouragement and support to other amateurs, local clubs, and the American Radio Relay League, through which Amateur Radio in the United States is represented nationally and internationally.

PROGRESSIVE...with knowledge abreast of science, a well-built and efficient station and operation above reproach.

FRIENDLY...slow and patient operating when requested; friendly advice and counsel to the beginner; kindly assistance, cooperation and consideration for the interests of others. These are the hallmarks of the amateur spirit.

BALANCED...radio is an avocation, never interfering with duties owed to family, job, school, or community.

PATRIOTIC...station and skill always ready for service to country and community.

—The original Amateur's Code was written by Paul M. Segal, W9EEA, in 1928.—

NOT FOR TECHNICIANS ONLY

ADDITIONAL RULES INFORMATION FOR THE TECHNICIAN EXAM

KEY WORDS

Bandwidth—The width of a frequency band outside of which the mean power of the total emission is attenuated at least 26 dB below the mean power of the total emission, including allowances for transmitter drift or Doppler shift.

Beacon station—An amateur station transmitting communications for the purposes of observation of propagation and reception or other related experimental activities.

Broadcasting—Transmissions intended to be received by the general public, either direct or relayed.

Control point—The location at which the control operator function is performed.

Earth station—An amateur station located on, or within 50 km of, the Earth's surface intended for communications with space stations or with other Earth stations by means of one or more other objects in space.

Grace period—The time FCC allows following the expiration of an amateur license to renew that license without having to retake an examination. Those who hold an expired license may not operate an amateur station until the license is reinstated.

MAYDAY—From the French "m'aider" (help me), MAYDAY is used when calling for emergency assistance in voice modes.

One-way communications—Transmissions that are not intended to be answered. The FCC strictly limits the types of one-way communications allowed on the amateur bands.

Repeater station—An amateur station that automatically retransmits the signals of other stations.

SOS—A Morse code call for emergency assistance.

Space station—An amateur station located more than 50 km above the Earth's surface.

Temporary state of communications emergency—When a disaster disrupts normal communications in a particular area, the FCC can declare this type of emergency. Certain rules may apply for the duration of the emergency.

This section covers the rules and regulations you will need to know to pass your Technician class exam. Some of the Technician-level material has already been covered in the first part of this chapter. If you have read and understood it, you're well on your way to knowing what you'll need to know to pass the Technician exam.

CONTROL OPERATOR AND CONTROL POINT

Each amateur station must have a person or persons who are responsible for the proper operation of that station. The **control operator** is that person. The control operator ensures compliance with FCC rules. The licensed amateur at the mike or key is the one who is legally in control.

The FCC assumes that you are always the control operator of your station, unless there is some written record to the contrary. (If the control operator is *not* the station licensee, responsibility for proper station operation is shared between them—they are both responsible.) The control operator function takes place at the **control point**. This control point is usually, but not always, at the radio. In the case of a remotely controlled station, the control point may be elsewhere.

[Before going on, you should turn to Chapter 13 and study the questions numbered 3AA-1.1 and 3AA-1.2.]

TECHNICIAN EMISSION PRIVILEGES

As you can see from Tables 2-1 and 2-2, Technician class operators enjoy *all frequency privileges* allocated to the amateur service *above 30 MHz*. Technician class amateurs can operate on all authorized frequencies, using all authorized modes, on the VHF, UHF and microwave amateur bands. In addition, Technicians who pass a 5-WPM code test gain the same emission privileges that Novices have on the four HF Novice bands.

Technician class licensees may operate on the VHF and UHF bands listed below, plus several others that are higher in frequency. For a complete list of amateur frequency privileges, including the microwave bands where frequency is measured in *gigahertz*, see *The FCC Rule Book*, published by ARRL.

On the 50-MHz (6-meter-wavelength) band: all emission types except pulse—CW, RTTY, data, MCW, test, phone and image—are authorized on 50.1 MHz to 54.0 MHz. On 50.0 to 50.1 MHz, only CW is allowed.

On the popular 144-MHz (2-meter-wavelength) band: all

This gent brought his 10-GHz microwave station to the summit of Mount Monadnock in New Hampshire to take part in an ARRL-sponsored contest. Many hams enjoy operating away from the comforts of home.

emission types (except pulse) from 144.1 to 148 MHz, and CW only from 144.0 to 144.1 MHz. Although the 2-meter band is best known for repeater and packet operation, hams also use it for such *weak-signal* activities as meteor scatter, moonbounce and aurora.

On the 222-MHz band (1¼-meter-wavelength) band: all emission types (except pulse) from 222.0 to 225.0 MHz.

On the 420-MHz (70-cm-wavelength) band: all emission types (except pulse) from 420 to 450 MHz.

On the 902-MHz (33-cm-wavelength) band: all emission types from 902 to 928 MHz.

On the 1240-MHz (23-cm-wavelength) band: all emission types (except pulse) from 1240 to 1300 MHz.

On the 2300-MHz (13-cm-wavelength) band: all emission types from 2300 to 2310 and 2390 to 2450 MHz.

EMISSION STANDARDS

FCC Rules stipulate that no amateur station transmission shall occupy more **bandwidth** than necessary for the information rate and emission type being transmitted, in accordance with good amateur practice. Bandwidth is a measure of how much space your signal takes up. A CW signal has a smaller bandwidth than does a single-sideband phone signal, and an SSB signal in turn has a smaller bandwidth than an AM or FM voice signal.

The Rules specify certain characteristics of RTTY and other emissions, and you should be aware of them to ensure that you're not in violation of the Rules.

RTTY Sending Speed

In the 28- to 50-MHz range, the maximum sending speed for a RTTY transmission is 1200 bauds.

Between 50 and 220 MHz, the maximum sending speed for a RTTY transmission is 19.6 kilobauds

Above 220 MHz, the maximum RTTY sending speed is 56 kilobauds.

RTTY Frequency Shift

Below 50 MHz, the maximum frequency shift permitted for RTTY is 1000 Hz.

Above 50 MHz, there is no maximum frequency shift.

Authorized Bandwidth

Between 50 and 220 MHz, the authorized bandwidth of a RTTY, data or multiplexed emission using a specified digital code is 20 kHz.

Between 220 and 450 MHz, the authorized bandwidth of a RTTY, data or multiplexed emission using an unspecified digital code is 100 kHz.

[Before continuing, take a look at the questions in Chapter 13 numbered 3AA-2.2 through 3AA-2.5, 3AA-4.1 and 3AA-4.2, and 3AA-7-1.1 through 3AA-7-3.3.]

LICENSE TERMS

All licenses issued after January 1984 have a 10-year term. Renew you license before it expires by completing an FCC Form 610 and sending it to the FCC at least 90 days before your current license expires. If you forget to renew your license, you still have a two-year **grace period** in which to send in a request for reinstatement on FCC Form 610. If you send it within the grace period, the FCC will reinstate your expired license automatically after the Form 610 is processed. You will be able to keep your old call sign under these circumstances. It is important to remember that you may not operate your station until your reinstated ticket arrives. After the two-year grace period, you must take the exams over again. If you pass, you will be assigned another call sign.

Modifying Your License

If you move or change your name, you will need to modify your Amateur Radio license. To do this, fill out a current Form 610, following the directions carefully, and mail it to the FCC in Gettysburg, Pennsylvania.

[Before proceeding, turn to Chapter 13 and review the questions numbered 3AA-3.1 through 3AA-3.3.]

TRANSMITTER POWER

In general, outside the HF Novice bands, Technician class operators may operate with a *maximum* peak envelope power (PEP) output of 1500 W. We've emphasized the word *maximum* because the FCC Rules also stipulate: "An amateur station must use the minimum power necessary to carry out the desired communications." Transmitter power is measured in watts of PEP output at the antenna terminals of the transmitter or amplifier.

There are some exceptions to the maximum power rules:
- All who are authorized to operate in the 80, 40 and 15-meter Novice subbands may use a maximum of 200 watts PEP.
- Technicians who are authorized to operate on the Novice bands (those who have passed a 5-WPM code test) are also limited to 200 W PEP on the 10-meter Novice subband, 28.1 to 28.5 MHz.
- All amateurs are limited to 200 W PEP on the 30-meter band (10.1-10.15 MHz). You will be able to use this band when you upgrade to General class.
- Stations in beacon operation are limited to 100 W PEP output.
- Stations operating near certain military installations may use a maximum of 50 W PEP on the 450-MHz band.

FREQUENCY SHARING

If we are to make the best use of the limited amount of available spectrum, there must be ways to ensure that harmful interference is kept to a minimum. The FCC encourages efficient, interference-free sharing of the ham bands by limiting transmitter output power, by assigning services either primary or secondary status on a frequency band and by encouraging repeaters to be *coordinated* (recommended). We've just discussed transmitter power; now we'll take a look at primary and secondary allocations, and repeater coordination.

Primary and Secondary Allocations

The basic frequency-sharing principle is straightforward: Where a band of frequencies is allocated to different services of the same category, the basic principle is the *equality of right to operate*. "Category" refers to whether a service operates on a primary or secondary basis. The amateur service is allocated many different frequency bands, but some of them are allocated on a primary basis and some are secondary. A station in a secondary service must not cause harmful interference to, and must accept interference from, stations in a primary service.

By sharing our frequencies with several other services, including the US military, hams can have the use of a greater amount of spectrum than would otherwise be the case. If you are operating on a band on which the amateur service has a secondary allocation, and a station in the primary service causes interference, you must change frequency immediately. You may also be interfering with the other station, and that is prohibited by Part 97 of the FCC Rules. *The FCC Rule Book* shows which amateur bands are primary allocations and which are secondary.

Repeater Frequency Coordination

A **repeater station** is an amateur station that automatically retransmits the signals of other stations. Repeaters in the same area that use the same or similar frequencies can interfere with each other. As more and more repeater stations have been set up, there have been more and more cases of repeater interference. One effective way of dealing with the problem is *frequency coordination*. Volunteer frequency coordinators have been appointed to ensure that new repeaters use frequencies that will tend not to interfere with existing repeaters in the same area. The FCC encourages frequency coordination, but the process is organized and run by hams and groups of hams who use repeaters.

The FCC has ruled in favor of coordinated repeaters if there is harmful interference between two repeaters. In such a case, if a frequency coordinator has coordinated one but not the other, the licensee of the *uncoordinated* repeater is responsible for solving the interference problem. If both repeaters are coordinated, or if neither is, then both licensees are equally responsible for resolving the interference.

[Now turn to Chapter 13 and review questions numbered 3AA-5.1, 3AA-5.2, 3AA-6-1.1 through 3AA-6-4.1, questions 3AA-11-1.1 through 3AA-11-1.3 and question 3AB-2-4.1.]

EARTH STATIONS

Earth stations are stations located on the Earth, or within 50 km of it, intended for communications with **space stations** or with other Earth stations by means of one or more objects in space. Any amateur can be the control operator of an Earth station, subject to the limitations of his license class. Some specific transmitting frequencies are authorized for Earth stations. These are located in the 40, 20, 17, 15, 12, 10 and 2-meter-wavelength bands, in the 23- and 70-cm-wavelength bands, and in all other amateur bands that are higher in

frequency. A complete list appears in *The FCC Rule Book*.

[Before going further, turn to Chapter 13 and review question 3AA-17.1.]

EMERGENCY COMMUNICATIONS

The FCC not only permits, but encourages, licensed hams to assist in emergencies, notwithstanding the FCC Rules that apply at all other times. The Rules state: "When normal communication systems are overloaded, damaged or disrupted because a disaster has occurred, or is likely to occur,...an amateur station may make transmissions necessary to meet essential communication needs and facilitate relief actions."

The FCC recognizes that "amateurs may provide essential communications in connection with the immediate safety of human life and immediate protection of property when normal communication systems are not available." This is the one exception to the prohibition on business communications on the ham bands.

If you're in the middle of a hurricane, forest fire or blizzard, and you offer your communications services to the local authorities, you can do whatever you need to do to help deal with the emergency. This includes allowing a physician to operate your radio or helping the Red Cross to assess damages.

Other cases aren't as clear cut. If you find yourself stuck on a highway, and there's no telephone nearby, can you call a towing service by using a repeater autopatch or by asking a ham who is listening on the repeater to do so? Sure. Stranded motorists have been killed on the highway while waiting for assistance.

In the wake of a major disaster, the FCC may suspend or change its Rules to help deal with the immediate problem. Part 97 stipulates that when a disaster disrupts normal communications systems in a particular area, the FCC may declare a **temporary state of communication emergency.** The declaration will set forth any special conditions or rules to be observed during the emergency. Amateurs who want to request that such a declaration be made should contact the FCC Engineer in Charge in the area concerned.

[Before going on, review these questions from Chapter 13: 3AA-11-2.1 through 3AA-11-2.4.]

Distress Calls

If you should require immediate emergency help, and you're using a voice (telephony) mode, call **MAYDAY**. Use whatever frequency offers the best chance of getting a useful answer. "MAYDAY" is from the French "m'aider" (help me). On CW (telegraphy), use $\overline{SOS}$ to call for help. Repeat this call a few times, and pause for any station to answer. Identify the transmission with your call sign. Stations that hear your call sign will realize the $\overline{SOS}$ is legitimate. Repeat this procedure for as long as possible, or until you receive an answer.

Be ready to supply the following information to the stations responding to an $\overline{SOS}$ or MAYDAY:
• *The location of the emergency*, with enough detail to permit rescuers to locate it without difficulty.
• *The nature of the distress*.
• *The type of assistance required* (medical, evacuation, food, clothing or other aid.)
• *Any other information* to help locate the emergency area.

[Turn to Chapter 13 and study questions 3AB-4.1 and 3AB-4.2. Review this section if you have difficulty with any of the questions.]

RACES

RACES is a part of the amateur service that provides radio communications only for civil defense purposes. It is active *only* during periods of local, regional or national civil emergencies.

You must be registered with the responsible civil defense organization to operate as a RACES station. RACES stations may not communicate with amateurs not operating in a RACES capacity. Restrictions do not apply when stations are operating in a non-RACES amateur capacity, such as the ARES, the Amateur Radio Emergency Service.

Only civil-preparedness communications can be transmitted during RACES operation. These are defined in section 97.407 of the FCC regulations. Rules permit tests and drills for a maximum of one hour per week. All test and drill messages must be clearly identified as such.

[Now study questions 3AB-5-1.1, 3AB-5-1.2 and 3AB-5-2.1 in Chapter 13. Review as needed.]

Tactical Communications

Tactical communications is first-response communications in an emergency involving a few people in a small area. This type of communications is unformatted and seldom written. It may be urgent instructions or requests such as "Send an ambulance," or "Who has the medical supplies?"

Tactical communications usually use 2-meter repeater net frequencies or the 146.52 MHz simplex calling frequency. Compatible mobile, portable and fixed-station equipment is plentiful and popular for these frequencies. Tactical communications is particularly important when working with local government and law-enforcement agencies. Use the 12-hour local-time system for times and dates when working with relief agencies. Most may not understand the 24-hour system or Coordinated Universal Time (UTC).

Another way to make tactical communications efficient is to use tactical call signs, which describe a function, location or agency. Their use promotes coordination with individuals or agencies who are monitoring. When operators change shifts or locations, the set of tactical calls remains the same. Amateurs may use such tactical call signs as *parade headquarters, finish line, Red Cross* or *Net Control.* This procedure promotes efficiency and coordination in public-service communication activities. Tactical call signs do not fulfill the identification requirements of Section 97.119 of the FCC rules, however. Amateurs must also identify their station operation with their FCC-assigned call sign. Identify at the end of operation and at intervals not to exceed 10 minutes during operation.

Health-and-Welfare Traffic

There can be a large amount of radio traffic to handle during a disaster. Phone lines still in working order are often overloaded. They should be reserved for emergency use by those people in peril. Shortly after a major disaster, *Emergency* messages leave the disaster area. These have life-and-death urgency or are for medical help and critical supplies. Handle them first. Next is *Priority* traffic. These are emergency-related messages, but not of the utmost urgency. Then, handle *health-and-welfare* traffic, which pertains to the well being of evacuees or the injured. This results in timely advisories to those waiting outside the disaster area.

Hams inside disaster areas cannot immediately find out about someone's Aunt Irene when their own lives may be threatened—they are busy handling emergency messages. After the immediate emergency subsides, concerned friends and relatives of possible victims can send health-and-welfare inquiries into the disaster area.

Emergency Equipment

When cities, towns, counties, states or the federal government call for emergency communications, amateurs answer. They press their mobile and portable radio equipment into service, using alternatives to commercial power. Generators, car batteries, windmills or solar energy can provide power for equipment during an emergency, when normal ac power is often out of service. A dipole antenna is the best choice in emergencies—it can be installed easily, and wire is light and portable. Carry an ample supply of wire and you'll be ready to go on the air at any time and any place.

[Before going on, turn to Chapter 13 and study questions 3AB-6-1.1 through 3AB-6-3.2. Review this section if you have difficulty with any of these questions.]

ONE-WAY TRANSMISSIONS

Certain types of transmissions are designated as *one-way.* Only certain kinds of one-way transmissions are permitted on the amateur bands.

Emergencies

Since normal restrictions are suspended when life or property is in immediate danger, as discussed above, one-way transmissions are not considered broadcasting (which is not allowed) under emergency conditions.

Beacons

A **beacon station** is simply a transmitter that alerts listeners to its presence. In the amateur service, beacons are used primarily for the study of radio-wave propagation—to allow amateurs to tell when a band is open to different parts of the country or world. The FCC defines a beacon station as an amateur station transmitting communications for the purposes of observation of propagation and reception or other related experimental activities.

The FCC Rules address beacon operation this way:
- automatically controlled beacon stations are limited to certain parts of the 28, 50, 144, 222 and 432-MHz amateur bands, and all amateur bands above 450 MHz.
- the transmitter power of a beacon must not exceed 100 W.
- any license class, except Novice, can operate a beacon station.

Remote Control of Model Craft

Amateurs are permitted to use radio links to control model craft. Most model control activity takes place on the 6-meter-wavelength band. Remote control operation is permitted with these restrictions:
- station identification is not required for transmission directed only to the model craft. The control transmitter must have a label indicating the station's call sign and the licensee's name and address.
- control signals are not considered codes and ciphers.
- transmitter power cannot exceed 1 watt.

[Before moving on, review questions in Chapter 13 numbered 3AA-9-1.1 through 3AA-10.4]

Other Permitted One-Way Transmissions

Aside from the examples listed above (emergency communications, remote control of a device and beacon operation), Part 97 allows the following kinds of **one-way communications**:

- brief transmissions necessary *to make adjustments to a station;*
- brief transmissions necessary *to establishing two-way communications with other stations*;
- transmissions necessary *to assisting persons learning, or improving proficiency in, the international Morse code;* and
- transmissions necessary *to disseminate information bulletins* (these are to be directed only to amateurs and must consist solely of subject matter of direct interest to the amateur service).

[Before continuing, review questions in Chapter 13 numbered 3AA-13.1 through 3AA-13.4.]

THOU SHALT NOT...
PROHIBITED TRANSMISSIONS

There are some specific things you cannot do on the amateur bands—the FCC calls them *prohibited transmissions*. These include:

- accepting direct and indirect payment for operating an amateur station
- broadcasting
- news gathering
- transmitting music
- aiding criminal activities
- transmitting codes and ciphers
- engaging in obscenity, profanity and indecency.

Payment

You must never accept any money, or other type of material compensation, for operating your station. The amateur service is a voluntary, noncommercial communication service under Part 97. Note that this does not prohibit an organization from providing food during your participation in emergency communications, for example.

There is one exception to the prohibition against receiving payment for operating an amateur station. Payment is allowed to the control operators of a club station if that station is used primarily to transmit Morse code practice and information bulletins of interest to Amateur Radio operators. Payment can be made only for the time the station is transmitting code practice and bulletins, and the code-practice sessions must last at least 40 hours per week. In addition, the station must transmit on at least six medium- and high-frequency bands, and the schedule of transmissions must be published 30 days in advance. This exception allows the control operators at the ARRL Headquarters station, W1AW, to be paid employees of the League.

Broadcasting

Broadcasting refers to transmissions intended to be received by the general public. These may be either direct or relayed. As such, broadcasting must be left to those services that are directly authorized to do so by the FCC—commercial television and radio, for example.

Broadcasting is specifically prohibited in the amateur service. Although you must not transmit anything intended to be received by the public, certain types of one-way transmissions are permitted. These were discussed above.

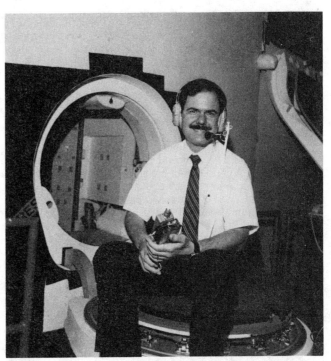

Shuttle astronaut Ron Parise holds the amateur call WA4SIR. He put it to good use when he flew aboard shuttle mission STS-35 in December 1990, making 2-meter voice and packet contacts with hams and schoolchildren across the country. One FCC rule applies specifically to shuttle communications: Amateurs can retransmit US Government shuttle communications to a ham audience—if they get NASA's permission beforehand. (*photo courtesy NASA*)

News Gathering

You must not allow your amateur station to be used for any activity directly related to program production or news gathering for broadcast purposes. There is only one exception: You can transmit news information about an event if the following requirements are met: (1) the news information involves the immediate safety of life of individuals or the immediate protection of property; (2) the news information is directly related to the event; (3) the information can't be transmitted by any other means because normal communications systems have been disrupted or because there are no other communications systems available at the place where the information is originated; and (4) other means of communication could not be reasonably provided before or during the event.

Music

The transmission of music is strictly prohibited in the amateur bands.

Criminal Activity

Amateur Radio may not be used for any purpose, or in connection with any activity, that is contrary to Federal, state or local law.

Codes and Ciphers

You may not hide the meaning of your communications by putting them into codes and ciphers, except for a few specific exceptions cited in Part 97. Codes and ciphers refer to text that has been transformed to conceal its meaning. This restriction is consistent with the FCC's obligations under the international regulations that amateur communications be made in plain language.

Obscenity, Profanity and Indecency

The rules say, quite simply, that you cannot transmit obscene, indecent or profane language or meaning. The FCC has developed standards of obscenity and indecency, but the best rule of thumb is to avoid making any transmissions that could be interpreted as being offensive.

[Before going on, check these questions in Chapter 13: 3AA-12.1, 3AA-14.1, 3AA-14.2, and 3AA-16.1 through 3AA-16.3.]

RETRANSMITTING RADIO SIGNALS

Radio amateurs may retransmit only signals originating in the amateur service, except for emergency communications. Some amateurs like to record W1AW news bulletins and transmit them over a local repeater as a service. No problem, as long as this is done manually (with a control operator present). You must never record an individual's transmissions and play them back over the air without permission. That's poor amateur practice, and transmission of false signals.

You may retransmit US Government space shuttle communications for the exclusive use of other amateurs, provided you get prior approval from the National Aeronautics and Space Administration (NASA).

Automatic retransmission of amateur signals may be done only by repeater, auxiliary, digipeater and space stations.

THIRD-PARTY COMMUNICATIONS

Third-party communications is amateur communication by or under the supervision of the control operator at an amateur station to another amateur station on behalf of any-

one other than the control operator. A *third-party message* is one the control operator (first party) of your station sends to another station (second party) for anyone else (third party). Third-party messages include those that are spoken, written, keystroked, keyed, photographed or otherwise originated by or for a third party, and transmitted by your amateur station live or delayed. A third party may also be a person permitted by the control operator to participate in Amateur Radio communications.

International third-party communications is prohibited, except when
• communicating with a person in a country with which the US shares a third-party agreement, or
• in cases of emergency where there is an immediate threat to lives or property, or
• the third party is eligible to be a control operator of the station.

If a third party is ineligible to be a control operator, he or she may participate in radio communications if the control operator is present at the control point and continuously monitors and supervises the third party's participation. In international third-party communications, your station identification must include the other station's call sign at the end of the communication.

STATION IDENTIFICATION

Under FCC Rules, you must clearly make known the source of your transmissions to anyone receiving them. No station may transmit unidentified communications or signals, or transmit as the station call any call not authorized to the station.

You must identify your station at the end of each contact, and every 10 minutes during the contact. When you identify by phone, you must use English, and the FCC recommends that you use standard phonetics.

If you're a Novice class operator who has passed the Technician exam and holds a Certificate of Successful

Completion of Examination, special rules apply. To identify when operating on a voice mode with your new Technician privileges, give your call sign followed by a word that describes the slant mark and the identifier "KT." An example: KA9GND SLANT KT. Another: KA2FCC STROKE KT. When operating CW or on digital modes, use the fraction bar (/) followed by KT, as in N1GZO/KT.

Technicians who pass the 5-WPM code test and thus qualify for the enhanced Technician license (including HF Novice privileges) need not use the "KT" identifier when using their new privileges or when operating on the Technician bands (50 MHz and above).

You should know one more thing about station identification: There is only one type of emission that can always be used when you identify your station, regardless of frequency or operating mode: Morse code (CW).

[Congratulations! Be sure to review questions in Chapter 13 numbered 3AA-4.3, 3AA-8-1.1 through 3AA-8-3.1, 3AA-12.2 through 3AA-12.5, 3AA-14.3, 3AA-15.1 through 3AA-15.4, 3AB-2-2.2, 3AB-3.1 and 3AB-3.2. Review the material in this chapter until you feel confident, and then move on to Chapter 3.]

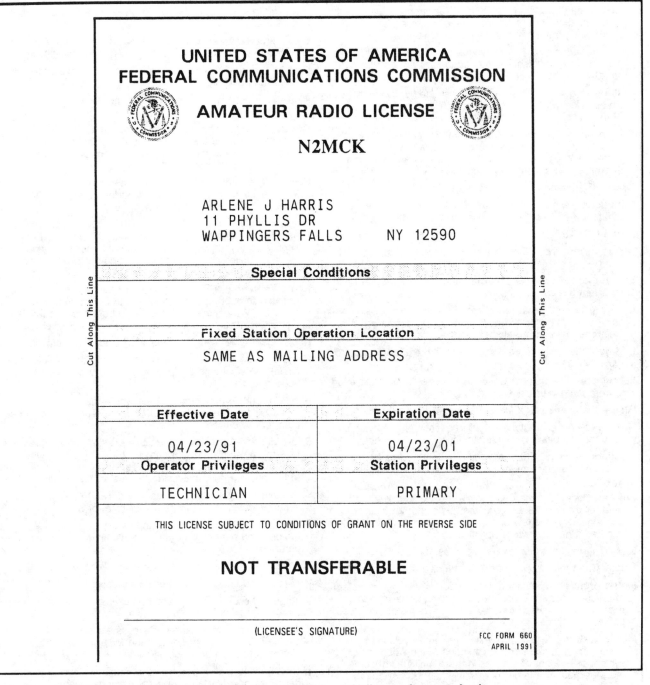

Figure 2-6—You'll want to frame and display this certificate-style license in your shack.

━━━ KEY WORDS ━━━

Alternating current (ac)—Electrical current that flows first in one direction in a wire and then in the other. The applied voltage is also changing polarity. This direction reversal continues at a rate that depends on the frequency of the ac.

Alternator—A machine used to generate alternating-current electricity.

Ampere (A)—The basic unit of electrical current, equal to 6.24×10^{18} electrons moving past a point in one second.[1] We abbreviate amperes as *amps*.

Atom—A basic building block of all matter. Inside an atom, there is a positively charged, dense central core, surrounded by a "cloud" of negatively charged electrons. There are the same number of negative charges as there are positive charges, so the atom is electrically neutral.

Audio frequency (AF)—The range of frequencies that the human ear can detect. Audio frequencies are usually listed as 20 Hz to 20,000 Hz.

Battery—A device that stores electrical energy. It provides excess electrons to produce a current and the voltage or EMF to push those electrons through a circuit.

Breakdown voltage—The voltage that will cause a current in an insulator. Different insulating materials have different breakdown voltages. Breakdown voltage is also related to the thickness of the insulating material.

Centi—The metric prefix for 10^{-2}, or divide by 100.

Conductor—A material that has a loose grip on its electrons, so that an electrical current can pass through it.

Current—A flow of electrons in an electrical circuit.

Direct current (dc)—Electrical current that flows in one direction only.

Electromotive force (EMF)—The force or pressure that pushes a current through a circuit.

Electron—A tiny, negatively charged particle, normally found in an area surrounding the nucleus of an atom. Moving electrons make up an electrical current.

Energy—The ability to do work; the ability to exert a force to move some object.

Frequency—The number of complete cycles of an alternating current that occur per second.

Giga—The metric prefix for 10^9, or times 1,000,000,000.

Hertz (Hz)—An alternating-current frequency of one cycle per second. The basic unit of frequency.

Insulator—A material that maintains a tight grip on its electrons, so that an electrical current cannot pass through it.

Ion—An electrically charged particle. An electron is an ion. Another example of an ion is the nucleus of an atom that is surrounded by too few or too many electrons. An atom like this has a net positive or negative charge.

Kilo—The metric prefix for 10^3, or times 1000.

Mega—The metric prefix for 10^6, or times 1,000,000.

Metric prefixes—A series of terms used in the metric system of measurement. We use metric prefixes to describe a quantity as compared to a basic unit. The metric prefixes indicate multiples of 10.

Metric system—A system of measurement developed by scientists and used in most countries of the world. This system uses a set of prefixes that are multiples of 10 to indicate quantities larger or smaller than the basic unit.

Micro—The metric prefix for 10^{-6}, or divide by 1,000,000.

Milli—The metric prefix for 10^{-3}, or divide by 1000.

Negative Charge—One of two types of electrical charge. The electrical charge of a single electron.

Neutral—Having no electrical charge, or having an equal number of positive and negative charges.

Nucleus—The dense central portion of an atom. The nucleus contains positively charged particles.

Ohm—The basic unit of electrical resistance, used to describe the amount of opposition to current.

Ohm's Law—A basic law of electronics. Ohm's Law gives a relationship between voltage, resistance and current ($E = IR$).

Open circuit—An electrical circuit that does not have a complete path, so current can't flow through the circuit.

Parallel circuit—An electrical circuit where the electrons follow more than one path.

Pico—The metric prefix for 10^{-12}, or divide by 1,000,000,000,000.

Positive charge—One of two types of electrical charge. A positive charge is the opposite of a negative charge. Electrons have a negative charge. The nucleus of an atom has a positive charge.

Power—The rate of energy consumption. We calculate power in an electrical circuit by multiplying the voltage applied to the circuit times the current through the circuit.

Power supply—That part of an electrical circuit that provides excess electrons to flow into a circuit. The power supply also supplies the voltage or EMF to push the electrons along. Power supplies convert a power source (such as the ac mains) to a useful form.

Radio frequency (RF)—The range of frequencies that can be radiated through space in the form of electromagnetic radiation. We usually consider RF to be those frequencies higher than the audio frequencies, or above 20 kilohertz.

Resistance—The ability to oppose an electric current.

Resistor—Any material that opposes a current in an electrical circuit. An electronic component especially designed to oppose current.

Series circuit—An electrical circuit where the electrons must all flow through every part of the circuit. There is only one path for the current to follow.

Short circuit—An electrical circuit where the current does not take the desired path, but finds a shortcut instead. Often the current goes directly from the negative power-supply terminal to the positive one, bypassing the rest of the circuit.

Sine wave—A smooth curve, usually drawn to represent the variation in voltage or current over time for an ac signal.

Subatomic particles—The building blocks of atoms. Electrons, protons and neutrons are the most common subatomic particles.

Transformer—A device that changes ac voltage levels.

Volt (V)—The basic unit of electrical pressure or EMF.

Voltage—The EMF or pressure that causes electrons to move through an electrical circuit.

Voltage source—Any source of excess electrons. A voltage source produces a current and the force to push the electrons through an electrical circuit.

Watt (W)—The unit of power in the metric system. The watt describes how fast a circuit uses electrical energy.

Wavelength—The distance an ac signal will travel during the time it takes the signal to go through one complete cycle.

---

[1]Numbers written as a multiple of some power are expressed in *exponential notation*. This notation is explained in detail on page 3-2.

Chapter 3

Understanding Basic Theory

The purpose of this chapter is to introduce you to basic electronics and radio theory. In this chapter, we first present the theory that you'll need to pass your Novice exam. This basic theory will be a foundation for you to build on. Later in the chapter is a section devoted to the theory needed to pass the Technician exam. Even if you don't plan to try for your Technician license right away, you'll probably want to study this section, too. The theory you learn in this chapter will also help you to assemble and operate your amateur station.

There is much for you to learn, and most of the material presented here will be new to you. To make your study as easy as possible, Chapter 3 is divided into four main sections. We start with basic electrical principles. Once you've learned the basics, we cover resistance, Ohm's Law and power. Then you'll learn about direct and alternating currents. The Technician section of this chapter explains more about alternating current, inductance and capacitance. To get the most from this chapter, you should take it one section at a time. Study the material in each section and really know it before you go on to the next section. The sections build on each other, so you may find yourself referring to sections you've already studied from time to time.

There are many technical terms used in electronics. We have provided definitions that are as simple and to-the-point as possible. You will want to refer often to the **Key Words** at the beginning of this chapter. Don't be afraid to turn back to any section you have already studied. This review is helpful if you come across a term that you are not sure about. You will probably not remember every bit of this theory just by reading the chapter once.

There are many drawings and illustrations presented in this chapter to help you learn the material. Pay attention to these graphics, and you'll find it easier to understand the text. We'll direct you to the Question Pools (Chapters 12 and 13) at appropriate points in the text. Use these directions to help you study the Novice and Technician Question Pools. When you think you've learned the section, you are ready to move on.

If you have trouble understanding parts of this chapter, ask your instructor or another experienced ham for help. Many other books can help, too. The booklet *First Steps in Radio* is a collection of Doug DeMaw's *QST* series. *First Steps* covers a wide range of technical topics written especially for a beginner. To study more advanced theory, you may want to purchase a copy of *The ARRL Handbook*. Both publications are available from your local ham dealer or from ARRL Headquarters.

Remember! Take it slowly, section by section. Before you know it, you'll have learned what you need to know to pass your test and get on the air. Good luck!

In this section, you will learn what electricity is and how it works. We'll introduce you to the atom and the electron, the basic elements of electricity. There are no questions about atoms and electrons on the Novice or Technician exams, but understanding them will help you understand the rest of this chapter.

THE METRIC SYSTEM

We'll be talking about the units used to describe electrical pressure and other electrical units later in this chapter. Before we do that, let's take a few minutes now to become familiar with the **metric system**. This simple system is a standard system of measurement used all over the world. All the units used to describe electrical quantities are part of the metric system.

In the US, we use a measuring system known as the US Customary system. In this system there is no logical progression between the various units of length, weight, volume or other quantities. For example, we have 12 inches in 1 foot, 3 feet in 1 yard and 1760 yards in 1 mile. For measuring the volume of liquids we have 2 cups in 1 pint, 2 pints in 1 quart and 4 quarts in 1 gallon. To make things even more difficult, we use some of these same names for different volumes when we measure dry materials! As you can see, this system of measurements can be very confusing. Even those who are very familiar with the system do not know all the units used for different types of measurements.

It is exactly this confusion that led scientists to develop the orderly system we know as the metric system today. This system uses a basic unit for each different type of measurement. For example, the basic unit of length is the meter (sometimes spelled metre). The basic unit of volume is the liter (or litre). The unit for mass (or quantity of matter) is the gram. The newton is the metric unit of force, or weight, but we often use the gram to indicate how "heavy" something is. We can express larger or smaller quantities by multiplying or dividing the basic unit by factors of 10 (10, 100, 1000, 10,000 and so on). These multiples result in a standard set of prefixes, which can be used with all the basic units. Table 3-1 summarizes the most-used **metric prefixes**. These same prefixes can be applied to any basic unit in the metric system. Even if you come across some terms you are unfamiliar with, you will be able to recognize the prefixes.

We can write these prefixes as powers of 10, as shown in the table. The power of 10 (called the *exponent*) shows how many times you must multiply (or divide) the basic unit by 10. For example, we can see from the table that **kilo** means 10^3. Let's use the meter as an example. If you multiply a meter by 10 three times, you will have a *kilo*meter. (1 meter $\times 10^3 = 1$ m $\times 10 \times 10 \times 10 = 1000$ meters, or 1 kilometer.) If you multiply 1 meter by 10 six times, you have a **mega**meter. (1 meter $\times 10^6 = 1$ m $\times 10 \times 10 \times 10 \times 10 \times 10 \times 10 = 1,000,000$ meters or 1 megameter.)

Notice that the exponent for some of the prefixes is a negative number. This indicates that you must *divide* the basic unit by 10 that number of times. If you divide a meter by 10, you will have a **deci**meter. (1 meter $\times 10^{-1} = 1$ m $\div 10 = 0.1$ meter, or 1 decimeter.) When we write 10^{-6}, it means you must divide by 10 six times. (1 meter $\times 10^{-6} = 1$ m $\div 10 \div 10 \div 10 \div 10 \div 10 \div 10 = 0.000001$ meter, or 1 **micro**meter.)

We can easily write very large or very small numbers with this system. We can use the metric prefixes with the basic units, or we can use powers of 10. Many of the quantities used in basic electronics are either very large or very small numbers, so we use these prefixes quite a bit. You should be sure you are familiar at least with the following prefixes and their associated powers of 10: **giga** (10^9), **mega** (10^6), **kilo** (10^3), **centi** (10^{-2}), **milli** (10^{-3}), **micro** (10^{-6}) and **pico** (10^{-12}).

Let's try an example. We have a receiver dial calibrated in megahertz (MHz), and it shows a signal at a frequency of 3.725 MHz. Where would a dial calibrated in kilohertz show the signal? From Table 3-1 we see that kilo means times 1000, and mega means times 1,000,000. That means that our signal is at 3.725 MHz $\times$ 1,000,000 = 3,725,000 hertz. There are 1000 hertz in a kilohertz, so 3,725,000 divided by 1000 gives us 3725 kHz.

How about another one? If we have a current of 3000 milliamps, how many amps is this? From Table 3-1 we see that milli means multiply by 0.001 or divide by 1000. Dividing 3000 milliamps by 1000 gives us 3 amps. The metric prefixes make it easy to use numbers that are a convenient size simply by changing the units. 3.725 MHz is certainly easier to work with than 3,725,000 hertz!

[Before you go on to the next section, turn to Chapter 12. Be sure you can answer all of the questions in the Novice Question Pool that begin with numbers 2E-1. Review this section if you have any difficulty.]

ELECTRICITY

The word is a spine-tingling mystery. It's the force behind our space-age civilization. It's one of nature's greatest powers. We love it; we fear it. We use it in our work and play. But what is it?

It's a mystery only in our minds. Actually, electricity is the marvelous stuff which, when untamed, we call lightning. One lightning bolt produces enough electricity to supply your needs for a lifetime. In another form, electricity is the power in a battery that cranks the engine to start your car. Electricity also ignites the gasoline in the engine. Yet, with all its power, electricity is the careful messenger carrying information from your brain to your muscles, enabling you to move your arms and legs. You can buy a small container of electricity no bigger than a dime (a battery). Electric utilities generate and transmit

Table 3-1

International System of Units (SI)—Metric Units

Prefix	Symbol	Multiplication Factor	
tera	T	10^{12} =	1,000,000,000,000
giga	G	10^9 =	1,000,000,000
mega	M	10^6 =	1,000,000
kilo	k	10^3 =	1,000
hecto	h	10^2 =	100
deca	da	10^1 =	10
(unit)		10^0 =	1
deci	d	10^{-1} =	0.1
centi	c	10^{-2} =	0.01
milli	m	10^{-3} =	0.001
micro	μ	10^{-6} =	0.000001
nano	n	10^{-9} =	0.000000001
pico	p	10^{-12} =	0.000000000001

Figure 3-1—A phenomenon that has fascinated mankind for ages, lightning is simply a natural source of electricity.

huge amounts of electricity every day. From lightning bolts to brain waves, it's all the same stuff: **electrons**.

INSIDE ATOMS

Everything you can see and touch is made up of **atoms**. Atoms are the building blocks of nature. Atoms are too small to see, but the **subatomic particles** inside atoms are even smaller.

Each atom has a **nucleus** in its center. Other particles orbit around this central core. Think of the familiar maps of our solar system: planets orbit the sun. In an atom, charged particles orbit the central core (the nucleus). Other charged particles make up the nucleus. Figure 3-2 is a simplified illustration of the structure of an atom.

Some particles have **negative charges** while others have **positive charges**. The core of an atom contains positively charged particles. Negative particles, called electrons, orbit around the nucleus. Scientists have identified more than 100 different kinds of atoms. The number of positively and negatively charged particles in an atom determines what type of element that atom is. Different kinds of atoms combine to form various materials. For example, a hydrogen atom has one positively charged particle in its nucleus and one electron around the outside. An oxygen atom has eight positive particles in the nucleus and eight electrons around the outside. When two hydrogen atoms combine with one oxygen atom, we have water.

Have you ever tried to push the north poles of two magnets together? Remember that soft, but firm, pressure holding them apart? Similar poles in magnets repel each other; opposite poles attract each other. You can see this if you experiment with a pair of small magnets.

Charged particles behave in a way similar to the two

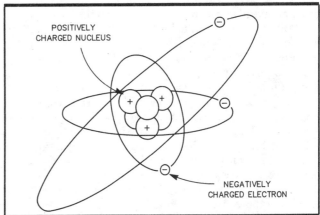

Figure 3-2—Each atom is a microscopic particle composed of a central, dense, positively charged nucleus, surrounded by tiny negatively charged electrons. There are the same number of positive particles in the nucleus and negative electrons outside the nucleus.

DEMONSTRATING ELECTRON FLOW

Here's an easy way to see the power of electrical charges. On a dry day hang some metal foil from dry thread. Rub one end of a plastic comb on wool (or run it through your hair). Then bring the end of the comb near the metal foil.

Rubbing the comb on wool detaches electrons from the wool fibers, depositing them on the surface of the comb. When you bring the charged end of the comb near the foil, free electrons in the foil will be repelled by the negative charge on the comb. The free electrons will move as far from the comb as they can—on the edge farthest from the comb. This leaves the near edge of the foil with a shortage of electrons (in other words, with a positive charge). The near edge of the foil is then attracted to the negatively charged comb.

As soon as the foil touches the comb, some of the excess electrons on the comb flow onto the foil (electricity!). The foil will then have a net negative charge, as the comb does, and the foil will be repelled by the comb. This simple experiment shows the attraction, repulsion and flow of electrons—the heart of electricity.

magnets. A positively charged particle and a negatively charged particle attract each other. Two positive or two negative particles repel each other. Like repels like; opposites attract.

Electrons stay near the central core, or nucleus, of the atom. The positive charge on the nucleus attracts the negative electrons. Meanwhile, since the electrons are all negatively charged, they repel each other. This makes the electrons move apart and fill the space around the nucleus. (Scientists sometimes refer to this area as an electron "cloud.") An atom has an equal balance of negative and positive charges and shows no electrical effect to the outside world. We say the atom is **neutral**.

ELECTRON FLOW

In many materials, especially metals, it's easy to dislodge an electron from an atom. When the atom loses an electron, it upsets the stability and electrical balance of the atom. With one particle of negative charge gone, the atom has an excess of positive charges. The free electron has a negative charge. We call the atom that lost the electron a positive **ion** because of its net positive charge. (An ion is a charged particle.) If there are billions of similar ions in one place, the quantity of charge becomes large enough to cause a noticeable effect.

Positively charged ions can pull negative particles (electrons) from neutral atoms. These electrons can move across the space between the atom and the ion and orbit the positively charged ion. Now the positively charged ion has become a neutral atom again, and another atom has become a positively charged ion! If this process seems confusing, take a look at Figure 3-3. Here we show a series of atoms and positive ions, with electrons moving from one atom to the next. The electrons are moving from right to left in this diagram. We call this flow of electrons *electricity*. Electricity is nothing more than the flow of electrons.

How difficult is it for a positive ion to rip an electron away from an atom? That depends on the individual atoms making up a particular material. Some atoms hold firmly to their electrons and won't let them flow away easily. Other atoms keep only a loose grip on electrons and let them slip away easily. This means that some materials carry electricity better than others. **Conductors** are materials that keep only a loose grip on their electrons. We call those materials that try to hold on to their electrons **insulators**.

Why Do Electrons Flow?

There are many similarities between electricity flowing in a wire and water flowing through a pipe. Most people are familiar with what happens when you open a faucet and water comes out. We can use this to make a useful comparison between water flow and electron flow (electricity). Throughout this chapter we use examples of water flowing in a pipe to help explain electronics.

Do you know how your town's water system works? Chances are, there is a large supply of water stored somewhere. Some towns use a lake or river. Other towns get their water from wells and store it in a tank or reservoir. The system then uses gravity to pull the water down from the tank or reservoir. The water travels through a system of pipes to your house. Because the force of gravity is pulling down on the water in the tank, it exerts a pressure on the water in the pipes. This makes the water flow out of the faucets in your house with some force. If you have a well, you probably have a storage tank. The storage tank uses air pressure to push the water up to the top floor of your house.

In these water systems, a pump takes water from the large supply and puts it into a storage tank. Then the system uses air pressure or the force of gravity to push the water through pipes to the faucets in your home.

We can compare electrons flowing through wire to water flowing through a pipe. We need some force to make water flow through a pipe; what force exerts pressure to make electrons flow through a wire?

VOLTAGE

The amount of pressure that it takes to push water to your house depends on how far you live from the reservoir. If the water has to travel over hills along the way, even more pressure will be required. The pressure required to make electrons flow in an electrical circuit also depends on the opposition that the electrons must overcome. The pressure that forces the electrons through the circuit is known as **electromotive force** or, simply, **EMF**.

EMF is similar to water pressure. More pressure moves more water. Similarly, more EMF moves more electrons. We measure EMF in a unit called the **volt (V)** so we sometimes refer to the EMF as a **voltage**. If more voltage is applied to a circuit, more electrons will flow. We measure voltage with a device called a *voltmeter*.

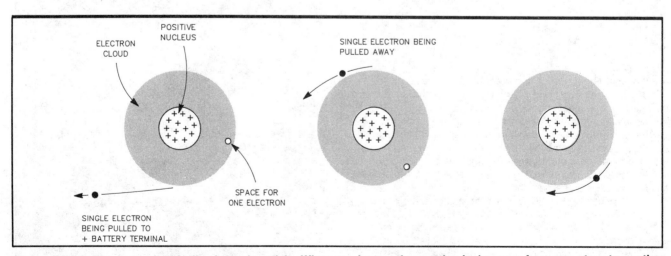

Figure 3-3—An ion is an electrically charged particle. When an electron (a negative ion) moves from one atom to another, the atom losing the electron becomes a positive ion. This electron movement represents an electric current. The electrons are moving from right to left in this drawing.

When you write about volts, use "12 V" if you mean twelve volts or "120 V" if you are saying one-hundred-twenty volts. Using our system of metric prefixes, we can express a thousand volts as "1 kV," or 1 kilovolt.

Another way to think about this electrical voltage pushing electrons through a circuit is to remember that like-charged objects repel. If we have a large group of electrons, the negative charge of these electrons will act to repel, or push, other electrons through the circuit. In a similar way, a large group of positively charged ions attract, or pull, electrons through the circuit.

The basic unit of electromotive force (EMF) is the volt. The volt was named in honor of Allessandro Giuseppe Antonio Anastasio Volta (1745-1827). This Italian physicist invented the electric battery.

Because there are two types of electric charge (positive and negative), there are also two polarities associated with a voltage. A **voltage source** always has two terminals, or poles: the positive terminal and the negative terminal. The negative terminal repels electrons (negatively charged particles) and the positive terminal attracts electrons. If we connect a piece of wire between the two terminals of a voltage source, electrons will flow through the wire. We call this flow an electrical **current**.

Batteries

In our water system, a pump supplies pressure to pull water from the source and force it into the pipes. Similarly, electrical circuits require an electron source and a "pump" to move the electrons along.

A **battery** is one example of a **power supply**. We use a battery as both the source of electrons and the pump that moves them along. The battery is like the storage tank in our water system. A battery provides pressure to keep the electrons moving.

There is an excess of electrons at the negative terminal of a power supply. At the positive terminal there is an excess of positive ions. With a conducting wire connected between the two terminals, the electrical pressure (voltage) generated by the power supply will cause electrons to move through the conductor.

Batteries come in all shapes and sizes. Some batteries are tiny, like those used in hearing aids and cameras. Other batteries are larger than the one in your car. A battery is one kind of voltage source.

[Now turn to Chapter 12 and study the questions with numbers that begin 2E-3. Review this section if you have any difficulty.]

CURRENT

You have probably heard the term "current" used to describe the flow of water in a stream or river. Similarly, we call the flow of electrons an electric current. Each electron is extremely small. It takes quintillions and quintillions of electrons to make your toaster heat bread or your TV draw

pictures. (A quintillion is a one with 18 zeros after it—1,000,000,000,000,000,000. Using powers of 10, as described earlier, we could also write this as 1×10^{18}.)

When water flows from your home faucet, you don't try to count every drop. The numbers would be very large and unmanageable, and the drops are coming out much too fast to count! To measure water flow, you count larger quantities such as gallons and describe the flow in terms of gallons per minute. Similarly, we can't deal easily with large numbers of individual electrons, nor can we count them conveniently. We need a shorthand way to measure the number of electrons. So, as with gallons per minute of water, we have amperes of electric current. We measure current with a device called an *ammeter*.

One **ampere** of current flows in a circuit when 6,240,000,000,000,000,000 or 6.24×10^{18}, electrons move past a point in one second. (Don't worry! You won't have to remember this number.) Rather than write such huge numbers, it's much easier to express the number of electrons flowing in a circuit in amperes. Write "2 A" for two amperes or "100 mA" (milliamps) for 0.1 ampere (sometimes also abbreviated amp or amps). See Table 3-1 to review the list of metric prefixes.

The action of electric current on a magnet was first applied to telegraphy by André Marie Ampère (1775-1836) in 1820. An ampere is the basic unit of electrical current.

[Now study the questions in Chapter 12 that begin with numbers 2E-2. Review this section if you have trouble answering these questions.]

CONDUCTORS

As we pointed out earlier, some atoms have a firm grasp on their electrons and other atoms don't. More current can flow in materials made up of atoms that have only a weak hold on their electrons. Some materials, then, conduct current better than others.

Silver is an excellent conductor. The loosely attached electrons in silver atoms require very little voltage (pressure) to produce an electric current. Copper is much less expensive than silver and conducts almost as well. We can use copper to make wire needed in houses, and in radios and other electronic devices. Steel also conducts, but not as well as copper. In fact, most metals are fairly good conductors, so aluminum, mercury, zinc, tin and gold are all conductors.

INSULATORS

Other materials keep a very firm grip on their electrons. These materials do not conduct electricity very well. Materials such as glass, rubber, plastic, ceramic, mica, wood and even air are poor conductors. Pure distilled water is a fairly good insulator. Most tap water is a good conductor, however, because it has minerals and other impurities dissolved in it. Figure 3-4 lists some common insulators and conductors.

The electric power company supplies 120 V on the wires

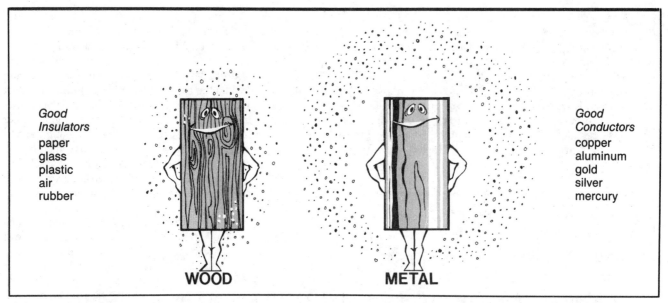

Figure 3-4—Here's one way to show how an insulator differs from a conductor. Wood, on the left, holds onto its electrons pretty tightly, keeping them from flowing between its atoms. Metals, on the other hand, are more generous with their electrons. Electrons are more easily pulled away from the metal atoms, and the metal atoms are then left with a positive charge. If the metal atoms attract extra electrons from neighboring atoms, they become negatively charged.

into your home. That voltage is available for your use at electrical outlets or sockets. Why don't the electrons spill out of the sockets? The insulation between the two sides of the outlet prevents the electrons from flowing from one side to the other. The air around the socket acts as an insulator to stop them from flowing into the room.

Because insulators are *poor* conductors rather than *non*-conductors, every insulator has a **breakdown voltage**. Beyond the breakdown voltage, the insulator will start to conduct electricity. Depending on the material, it may be damaged if you exceed the breakdown voltage. Better insulators have higher breakdown voltages. Breakdown voltage also depends on the thickness of the insulating material. A thin layer of one insulating material (like Teflon® or mica) may be just as good as a much thicker layer of another material (like paper or air).

A good example of an insulator that will conduct at very high voltage is air. Air is a fine insulator at the voltages normally found in homes and industry. When a force of millions of volts builds up, however, there's enough pressure to send a bolt of electrons through the air—lightning.

When you are insulating wires or components, always be sure to use the right insulating material. Make sure you use enough insulation for the voltages you're likely to encounter. Heat-shrinkable tubing or other insulating tubing is often convenient for covering a bare wire or a solder connection. You can also wrap the wire with electrical tape. Several layers of tape, wrapped so it overlaps itself, will provide enough insulation for up to a few hundred volts.

[Before you go on to the next section, turn to Chapter 12 and study questions 2E-4.1 and 2E-5.1. If you have any difficulty, review this section.]

————ELECTRONICS FUNDAMENTALS————

In this section, you'll learn about resistance. You'll see how resistance fits into one of the most fundamental laws of electronics, Ohm's Law. We will also briefly discuss series and parallel circuits. While there are no questions about these circuits on the Novice exam, understanding them will make it much easier for you to understand some of the other concepts you *will* be tested on! If you are preparing for the Technician exam, be sure you understand these circuits.

This section shows you how to do some basic circuit calculations. We have tried to keep the arithmetic simple, and to explain all of the steps in the solution. Associating numbers with a concept often makes it easier to understand. Read these examples and then try the calculations yourself. Be sure you can work the problems in the question pool when you study those questions.

RESISTANCE AND OHM'S LAW

What if you partially blocked a water pipe with a sponge?

Eventually, the water would get through the sponge, but it would have less pressure than before. It takes pressure to overcome the resistance of the sponge.

Similarly, materials that conduct electrical current also present some opposition, or **resistance**, to that flow. **Resistors** are devices that are especially designed to make use of this opposition. Figure 3-5 shows some common resistors.

In a water pipe, increasing the pressure forces more water through the sponge (the resistance). In an electrical circuit, increasing the voltage forces more current through the resistor.

The basic unit of resistance is the ohm, named in honor of Georg Simon Ohm (1787-1854).

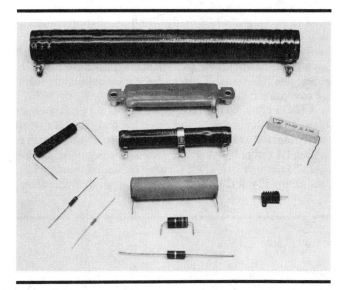

Figure 3-5—This photograph shows some of the many types of resistors. Large power resistors are at the top of the photo. The small resistors are used in low-power transistor circuits.

The relationship between voltage, current and resistance is predictable. We call this relationship **Ohm's Law** and it is a basic electronics principle.

The amount of water flowing through a pipe increases as we increase the pressure and decreases as we increase the resistance. If we replace "pressure" with "voltage," we can write a mathematical relationship for an electric circuit:

$$\text{current} = \frac{\text{voltage}}{\text{resistance}} \qquad \text{(Eq 3-1)}$$

If the voltage stays constant but more current flows in the circuit, we know there must be less resistance. The relationship between current and voltage is a measure of the resistance:

$$\text{resistance} = \frac{\text{voltage}}{\text{current}} \qquad \text{(Eq 3-2)}$$

Finally, we can determine the voltage if we know how much current is flowing and the resistance in the circuit:

$$\text{voltage} = \text{current} \times \text{resistance} \qquad \text{(Eq 3-3)}$$

Scientists are always looking for shorthand ways of writing these relationships. They use symbols to replace the words: E represents voltage (remember EMF?), current is I (from the French word *intensité*) and resistance is R. We measure resistance in units called **ohms**. The abbreviation for ohms is Ω, the Greek capital letter omega. We can now express the above relationship in a couple of letters:

$$E = IR \text{ (volts} = \text{amperes} \times \text{ohms)} \qquad \text{(Eq 3-4)}$$

This is the most common way to express Ohm's Law, but we can also write it as:

$$I = \frac{E}{R} \text{ (amperes} = \text{volts divided by ohms)} \qquad \text{(Eq 3-5)}$$

and

$$R = \frac{E}{I} \text{ (ohms} = \text{volts divided by amperes)} \qquad \text{(Eq 3-6)}$$

E is EMF in volts. I is the number of amperes of current, and R is the number of ohms, the unit we use to measure

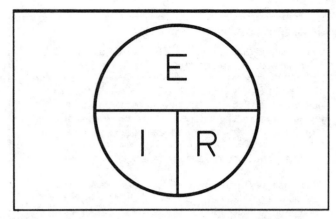

Figure 3-6—A simple diagram to help you remember the Ohm's Law relationships. To find any quantity if you know the other two, simply cover the unknown quantity with your hand or a piece of paper. The positions of the remaining two symbols show if you have to multiply (if they are side by side) or divide (if they appear one over the other as a fraction).

resistance. If you know two of the numbers, you can calculate the third. Figure 3-6 shows a diagram to help you solve Ohm's Law problems. Simply cover the symbol of the quantity that you do not know. If the remaining two are side-by-side, you must multiply them. If one symbol is above the other, then you must divide the quantity on top by the one on the bottom.

If you know current and resistance in a circuit, Ohm's Law will give you the voltage (Eq 3-4). For example, what is the voltage applied to the circuit if 5 amperes of current flows through 20 ohms of resistance? From Eq 3-4 or Figure 3-6, we see that we must multiply 5 amperes times 20 ohms to get the answer, 100 volts. The EMF in this circuit is 100 volts.

$$E = I R \qquad \text{(Eq 3-4)}$$
$$E = 5 \text{ amperes} \times 20 \text{ ohms}$$
$$E = 100 \text{ volts}$$

Suppose you know voltage and resistance—100 volts in the circuit to push electrons against 20 ohms of resistance? Eq 3-5 gives the correct equation, or you can use the diagram

in Figure 3-6. You must divide 100 volts by 20 ohms to find that 5 amperes of current is flowing.

$$I = \frac{E}{R} \qquad \text{(Eq 3-5)}$$
$$I = \frac{100 \text{ volts}}{20 \text{ ohms}}$$
$$I = 5 \text{ amperes}$$

If you know voltage and current in a circuit, you can calculate resistance. Using our example, 100 volts is pushing 5 amperes through the circuit. This time Eq 3-6 is the one to use, and you can also find this from Figure 3-6. 100 divided by 5 equals 20, so the resistance is 20 ohms.

$$R = \frac{E}{I} \qquad \text{(Eq 3-6)}$$
$$R = \frac{100 \text{ volts}}{5 \text{ amperes}}$$
$$R = 20 \text{ ohms}$$

If you know E and I, you can find R. If you know I and R, you can calculate E. If E and R are known, you can find I.

Put another way, if you know volts and amperes, you can calculate ohms. If amperes and ohms are known, volts can be found. Or if volts and ohms are known, amperes can be calculated. Figure 3-7 illustrates some simple circuits and how Ohm's Law can be used to find an unknown quantity in the circuit. Make up a few problems of your own and test how well you understand this basic law of electricity. You'll soon find that this predictable relationship, symbolized by the repeatable equation of Ohm's Law, makes calculating values of components in electrical circuits easy!

[Before you read further, turn to Chapter 12 and study the questions with numbers that begin 2E-6 and 2E-7. **If you are preparing for the Technician exam,** also study questions 3AE-1-1.1 through 3AE-1-2.2, 3AE-2.1 through 3AE-2.3 and 3AE-2.5 through 3AE-2.9 in Chapter 13. Review the material in this section if you have difficulty with any of these questions.]

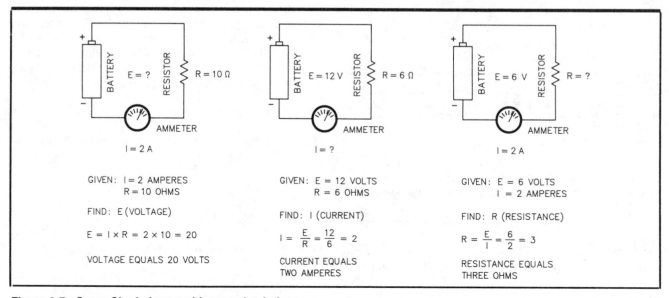

Figure 3-7—Some Ohm's Law problems and solutions.

SERIES AND PARALLEL CIRCUITS

There are two basic ways that you can connect the parts in an electric circuit. If we hook several resistors together in a string, we call it a **series circuit**. If we connect several resistors side-by-side to the same voltage source, we call it a **parallel circuit**.

In our water-pipe example, what would happen to the current through the pipe if we placed another sponge in it? You're right: The second sponge would further reduce the flow. We could do the same thing with a single, larger sponge. The total resistance in a series circuit is the sum of all the resistances in the circuit.

In a series circuit, the same current, I, flows through each resistor, since it has no other path to follow. When a voltage source (like a battery) is hooked to our string of resistors, we can calculate the voltage across each resistor. How? Using Ohm's Law, of course.

Remember E = IR? The voltage across any resistor in the circuit will be its value in ohms multiplied by the current in amperes. We call the voltage across the resistor the *voltage drop*. If we calculate the voltage drop across each resistor in the circuit and add them together, we will get the battery voltage. Figure 3-8 shows that with more resistors in a series circuit, there will be less current.

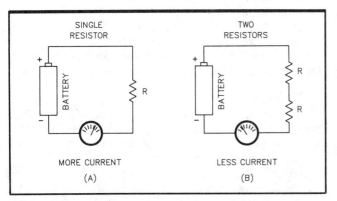

Figure 3-8—Resistance limits the amount of current that can flow in a circuit. Adding a second resistance reduces the current because the total resistance is larger. The total resistance of a string of series-connected resistors is the sum of all the individual resistances.

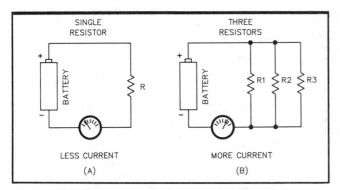

Figure 3-9—Resistors in parallel. In this circuit, the electrical current splits into three separate paths through the resistors. The full battery voltage is applied to each resistor. Current through each individual resistor is independent of the other resistors. For example, if R2 and R3 are changed to a value different than the original value, the current in R1 would remain unchanged. Even if R2 and R3 are removed, the current in R1 remains unchanged.

Now let's look at the case of a parallel circuit. This is similar to having two water pipes running side by side. More water can flow through two parallel pipes of the same size than through a single one. With two pipes, the current is greater for a given pressure.

If these pipes had sponges in them, the flow would be reduced in each pipe. There are still two paths for the water to take. More water will flow than if there was a single pipe with a sponge in it. Now let's go back to electrical resistors and voltage. Adding a resistor in parallel with another one provides two paths for the electrical current to follow. This reduces the total resistance. You can connect more than two resistors in parallel, providing even more paths for the electrons. This will reduce the resistance still more. Figure 3-9 shows that as we add resistors in parallel, we provide more current paths. The result is less total resistance in the circuit and more current.

OPEN AND SHORT CIRCUITS

You've probably heard the term **short circuit** before. A short circuit happens when the current flowing through the components doesn't follow the course we expect it to. Instead, the current finds another path, a shorter one, between the terminals of the power source. This is why we call this path a short circuit. Because there is less opposition to the flow of electrons, there is a larger current. Often the current through the new (short) path is so large that the wires or components can't handle it. When this happens, the wires and components can be damaged. Figure 3-10 shows a bare wire causing a short circuit.

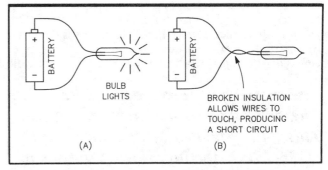

Figure 3-10—Part A shows a light bulb in a working circuit. In B, the insulation covering the wires has broken, and the two wires are touching, so we have a short circuit.

Some people think that a short circuit occurs when there is no resistance in the connection between the positive and negative terminals of the power supply. Actually there will always be *some* resistance but it may be such a small amount that it can be ignored.

In the extreme case, if a short circuit develops in our house wiring, the wire may overheat and can even start a fire. This is why it is important to have a properly rated fuse connected in series with a circuit. We will describe fuses in more detail in Chapter 4.

The opposite of a short circuit is an **open circuit**. In an open circuit the current is interrupted, just as it is when you turn a light switch off. The switch breaks (opens) the circuit, putting a layer of insulating air in the way so no current can flow. This break in the current path presents an extremely high resistance. An open circuit can be good, as when you

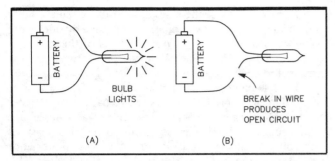

Figure 3-11—Part A shows a light bulb in a working circuit. In B, one wire has broken, preventing the current from flowing through the bulb. This is an example of an open circuit.

throw the on/off switch to off. An open circuit can be bad if it's an unwanted condition caused by a broken wire or a bad component. Figure 3-11 illustrates an open circuit. Sometimes the resistance in the circuit path is so large that it is impractical to measure it. When this is true, we say that there is an *infinite* resistance in the path, creating an open circuit.

[At this time you should turn to Chapter 12 and study the questions with numbers that begin 2E-10 and 2E-11. **If you are preparing for the Technician exam**, also study questions 3AE-1-3.1 through 3AE-1-4.2 in Chapter 13. If you have any difficulty with these questions, review this section.]

ENERGY AND POWER

Energy can be defined as the ability to do work. An object can have energy because of its position (like a rock ready to fall off the edge of a cliff). An object in motion also has energy (like the same rock as it falls to the bottom of the cliff). In electronics, a power supply or battery is the source of electrical energy. We can make use of that energy by connecting the supply to a light bulb, a radio or other circuit.

The basic unit of power is the watt. This unit is named after James Watt (1736-1819), the inventor of the steam engine.

We discussed voltage drops in the last section. As electrons move through a circuit and go through resistances, there is a voltage drop. These voltage drops occur because energy is "used up" or "consumed." Actually, we can't lose the electrical energy; it is just changed to some other form. The resistor heats up because of the current through it; the resistance converts electrical energy to heat energy. More current produces still more heat, and the resistor becomes warmer. If too much current flows, the resistor might even catch fire!

As electrons flow through a light bulb, the resistance of the bulb converts some electrical energy to heat. The filament in the bulb gets so hot that it converts some of the electrical energy to light energy. Again, more current produces more light and heat.

You should get the idea that we can "use up" a certain amount of energy by having a small current go through a

resistance for a long time or by having a larger current go through it for a shorter time. When you buy electricity from a power company, you pay for the electrical energy that you use. You might use all of the power in one day, or use a small amount every day. It doesn't matter to the power company. The electric meter on your house just measures how much energy you use and the power company sends someone around to read the meter each month.

Sometimes it is important to know how fast a circuit can use energy. You might want to compare how bright two different light bulbs will be. If you're buying a new freezer, you might want to know how much electricity it will use in a month. You will have to know how fast the freezer or the light bulbs use electrical energy. We use the term **power** to define the rate of energy consumption. The basic unit for measuring power in the metric system is the **watt**. You have probably seen this term used to rate electrical appliances. You know that a light bulb rated at 75 watts will be brighter than one rated at 40 watts. (Sometimes we abbreviate watts with a capital W.)

In electronics, there is a very simple way to calculate power. Just multiply amperes times volts. The equation is:

$$P = IE \qquad \text{(Eq 3-7)}$$

where

P is power, measured in watts
I is the current in amperes
E is the EMF in volts

For example, suppose a 12-V battery is pushing 3 A of current through a light bulb that is operating normally. Using Eq 3-7, we can find the power rating for this light bulb.

$$P = IE = 3 \text{ A} \times 12 \text{ V} = 36 \text{ W}$$

If you know the power in a system and the voltage applied to the circuit, you can compute the current. Or, if you know power and current, you can find voltage. In other words, if you know any two parts you can find the third. Figure 3-12 shows a diagram to help you with calculations like these, or we can write the equations:

$$I = \frac{P}{E} \qquad \text{(Eq 3-8)}$$

$$E = \frac{P}{I} \qquad \text{(Eq 3-9)}$$

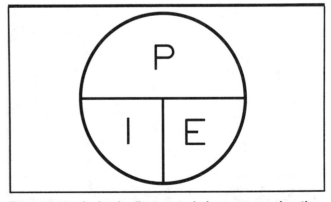

Figure 3-12—A simple diagram to help you remember the power equation relationships. To find any quantity given the other two, simply cover the unknown quantity with your hand or a piece of paper. The remaining two symbols will indicate if you have to multiply (if they are side by side) or divide (if they appear one over the other as a fraction).

If you apply a 10-V EMF to a 20-W circuit, divide 20 by 10 to find that there is a 2-A current.

$$I = \frac{P}{E} = \frac{20\ W}{10\ V} = 2\ A$$

If a 5-A current flows in a 60-W circuit, the EMF is 12 V. To find voltage you simply divide power by current.

$$E = \frac{P}{I} = \frac{60\ W}{5\ A} = 12\ V$$

Suppose you turn on a single light. One-half ampere of current flows through the bulb with 120 volts applied. What's the power rating of the light bulb? Eq 3-7 shows us how to find this power. Multiply 120 volts times ½ (0.5) ampere to calculate that the light is a 60-watt bulb.

$$P = IE = 0.5\ A \times 120\ V = 60\ W$$

By the way, the E and I in the power equation are the same E and I in Ohm's Law. So if we know any two of the four quantities voltage, current, resistance and power, we can calculate the other two.

Remember that a light bulb converts electrical energy into heat and light. The bulb has resistance; it opposes the flow of electrons. Is it possible to find the resistance of the wire inside the light bulb?

Yes. We know the voltage applied to the wire and the amount of current through it. This means that we can use Ohm's Law to calculate the resistance of the wire in the light bulb. Eq 3-6 gives the form of Ohm's Law that we need to find this answer. To find the resistance inside the bulb, divide 120 V by 0.5 A.

$$R = \frac{E}{I} = \frac{120\ V}{0.5\ A} = 240\ \Omega$$

The bulb is the equivalent, then, of a 240-ohm resistor in the circuit.

The resistance of the bulb depends on whether the filament is hot or cold. In this example, the answer of 240 ohms is correct only when the bulb is lit. If you use an ohm-meter (a meter for measuring resistance—only when the bulb is *not* connected to the voltage source!), you will find a different value because the bulb is cold.

[Before you go on to the last section in this chapter, turn to Chapter 12 and study those questions with numbers that begin 2E-8 and 2E-9. **If you are preparing for the Technician exam**, also study question 3AE-2.4 in Chapter 13. Review this section if you have any problems.]

DIRECT AND ALTERNATING CURRENT

In this section, you will learn what we mean by direct current and alternating current. You will also learn the meaning of some important terms that go along with alternating current, such as frequency and wavelength.

WHY USE ALTERNATING CURRENT IN OUR HOMES?

Why do power companies use alternating current in the power lines that run to your home? The main reason is so they can use transformers to change the voltage. This allows the company to use an appropriate voltage for each part of their distribution system. In this way the power company can minimize the power losses in the transmission lines. The generator at the power station produces ac by moving a wire (actually many turns of wire) through a magnetic field in an alternator. The resulting output has a relatively low voltage. Why don't the power companies send this directly through the power lines to your house? At first, this seems like a good idea. It would eliminate the many transformers and power stations that often clutter our landscape.

The answer can be found in Ohm's Law. Even a very good conductor, such as the copper used in the power company's high-voltage lines, has a certain amount of resistance. This factor becomes very important when we consider the very long distances the generated electricity must travel.

Remember that the voltage drop across a resistance is given by the formula E = IR, where I is the value of current and R is the value of resistance. If we can reduce either the resistance of the wire or the value of the current through the wire, we can reduce the voltage drop. The resistance of the wire is relatively constant, although we can reduce it somewhat by using a very large diameter wire. If we increase the voltage, a smaller current will be required for the same power transfer from the generating station to your home.

Using a very high voltage also provides more "overhead." If the power company starts with 750,000 volts, and the voltage has dropped to 740,000 volts by the time it reaches the first substation, they just use a transformer rated for 740,000-V input to give the desired output. If they send 50,000 volts on to the next substation, there is still plenty of overhead. By the time it gets to the power lines outside your house, the voltage has dropped to around 3000 volts. A pole transformer then steps it down to 240 volts to supply power to your house. This voltage is normally split in half to provide two 120-V circuits to your house.

Two Types of Current

Until now, we have been talking about **direct current** electricity, known as **dc** for short. In direct current, the electrons flow in one direction only—from negative to positive. In our water-flow analogy, this is like water that can flow in only one direction. We know that water can flow in more than one direction, however. The tides in the ocean are a good example.

There is a second kind of electricity called **alternating current,** or **ac**. In ac, the terminals of the power supply change from positive to negative to positive and so on. Because the poles change and electrons always flow from negative to positive, ac flows first in one direction, then the other. The current alternates in direction.

The basic unit of frequency is the hertz. This unit is named in honor of Heinrich Rudolf Hertz (1857-1894). This German physicist was the first person to demonstrate the generation and reception of radio waves.

We call one complete round trip a *cycle.* The **frequency** of the ac is the number of complete cycles, or alternations, that occur in one second. We measure frequency in hertz (abbreviated Hz). One cycle per second is 1 Hz. 150 cycles per second is 150 Hz. One thousand cycles per second is one kilohertz (1 kHz). One million cycles per second is one megahertz (1 MHz).

[Now study the questions in Chapter 12 that begin with 2E-12-1, 2E-12-2 and 2E-12-3. Review this section if you have difficulty answering any of these questions.]

More Ac Terminology

Batteries provide direct current. To make an alternating current from this direct-current source, you would have to switch the polarity of the voltage source rapidly. Imagine trying to turn the battery around so the plus and minus terminals changed position very rapidly. This would not be a very practical way to produce ac! You must have a power supply where the polarity is constantly changing. The terminals must be positive and negative one moment, and then negative and positive, constantly switching back and forth.

The power company has a more practical way to create ac: they use a large machine called an **alternator**. The ac supplied to your home goes through 60 complete cycles each second. Thus, the electricity from the power company has a frequency of 60 Hz.

In ac electrical circuits, current builds slowly to a peak flow in one direction, then reverses to build to a peak flow in the opposite direction. If you plot these changes in current on a graph, you get a gentle up-and-down curve. We call this curve a **sine wave**. The ac voltage applied to a simple circuit also varies in this same manner. The voltage gradually builds to a maximum voltage in one direction, then decreases to zero and gradually increases to a peak in the opposite direction (or with the opposite polarity). Figure 3-13 shows several cycles of a sine-wave ac signal.

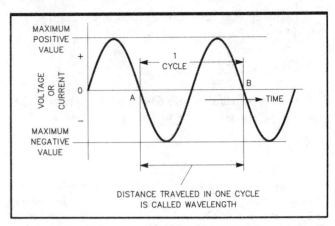

Figure 3-13—The sine wave is one way to show alternating current. Let's follow one cycle starting on line "0" at point A, indicated near the center of the graph. The wave goes in a negative direction to its most negative point, then heads back up to zero. After the wave goes through zero, it becomes more and more positive, reaches the positive peak, then goes back to zero again. This is one full cycle of alternating current.

Alternating current can do things direct current can't. For instance, a 120-V ac source can be increased to a 1000-V source with a **transformer**. Transformers can change the value of an ac voltage, but not a dc voltage. The power company supplies 120-V ac to your house.

Frequency and Wavelength

We discussed the frequency of an ac signal earlier. From this discussion, you must realize that alternating currents and voltages can change direction at almost any rate imaginable. Some signals have low frequencies, like the 60-Hz-ac electricity the power company supplies to your house. Other signals have higher frequencies; for example, radio signals can alternate at more than several million hertz.

When we talk about such a wide range of frequencies, it is common to break the wide range into several smaller ranges. One common breaking point is the difference between **audio-** and **radio-frequency** signals. If you connected an ac signal having a frequency anywhere between 20 Hz and 20,000 Hz (20 kHz) to a loudspeaker, you would hear a sound. Because these signals can produce sounds, they are called audio-frequency (AF) signals. The higher the frequency of the signal, the higher the pitch of the sound you would hear. (Caution— DO NOT connect the 60-Hz power from a household receptacle to a speaker even though 60 Hz is in the audio-frequency range! You may be seriously injured or KILLED by the voltage of this signal!)

Not all people can hear this full range of signals from 20 Hz to 20 kHz. Some people hear the low frequencies better than the high frequencies, and others hear the high frequencies better. This is the general range of frequencies that humans can expect to hear, however. (Dogs can hear signals at a much higher frequency, which is why dog whistles, used for training, don't produce a sound you can hear.)

If a signal has a frequency above the audio-frequency range (20 kHz), we call it a radio-frequency (RF) signal. Signals in the RF range can also be broken into smaller groups, such as very-low frequency (VLF), high frequency (HF), very-high frequency (VHF), ultra-high frequency (UHF) and so on. Don't worry about the names of these ranges for your exam. You will probably hear the terms as you listen in on other hams' discussions, though. The Novice bands are in the HF, VHF and UHF ranges.

If we know the frequency of an ac signal, we can use that frequency to describe the signal. We can talk about 60-Hz power or a 3745-kHz radio signal. **Wavelength** is another quality that can be associated with every ac signal. As its name implies, wavelength refers to the distance that the wave will travel through space in a single cycle. All such signals (sometimes called electromagnetic waves) travel though space at the speed of light, 300,000,000 meters per second (3.00×10^8 m/s). We use the lower-case Greek letter lambda (λ) to represent wavelength.

The faster a signal alternates, the less distance the signal will be able to travel during one cycle. There is an equation that relates the frequency and the wavelength of a signal to the speed of the wave:

$$c = f \lambda \qquad \text{(Eq 3-10)}$$

where

   c is the speed of light, 3.00×10^8 meters per second
   f is the frequency of the wave in hertz
   λ is the wavelength of the wave in meters

We can solve this equation for either frequency or wavelength, depending on which quantity we want to find.

$$f = \frac{c}{\lambda} \qquad \text{(Eq 3-11)}$$

and

$$\lambda = \frac{c}{f} \qquad \text{(Eq 3-12)}$$

From these equations you may realize that as the frequency increases the wavelength gets shorter. As the frequency decreases the wavelength gets longer. Suppose you are transmitting a radio signal on 7.125 MHz. What is the wavelength of this signal? We can use Eq 3-12 to find the answer. First we must change the frequency to hertz:
7.125 MHz = 7,125,000 Hz.

$$\lambda = \frac{c}{f} = \frac{3.00 \times 10^8 \text{ m/s}}{7.125 \times 10^6 \text{ Hz}}$$

$$\lambda = \frac{300,000,000 \text{ m/s}}{7,125,000 \text{ Hz}} = 42 \text{ meters}$$

Of course, you already knew that this frequency was in the 40-meter Novice band, so this answer should not surprise you.

As another example, what is the wavelength of a signal that has a frequency of 3.725 MHz? (3.725 MHz = 3,725,000 Hz.)

$$\lambda = \frac{c}{f} = \frac{3.00 \times 10^8 \text{ m/s}}{3.725 \times 10^6 \text{ Hz}}$$

$$\lambda = \frac{300,000,000 \text{ m/s}}{3,725,000 \text{ Hz}} = 80.5 \text{ meters}$$

Even if you have trouble with this arithmetic, you should be able to learn the frequency and wavelength relationships for the six Novice bands, as shown in Table 3-2.

Table 3-2
Novice-Band Frequencies and Wavelengths

Frequency Range (megahertz)		Approximate Wavelength (meters)
3.675 —	3.725	80
7.1 —	7.15	40
21.1 —	21.2	15
28.1 —	28.5	10
222.1 —	223.91	1.25
1270 —	1295	0.23 (23 centimeters)

[Congratulations! You are now well on your way to knowing all the electronics you will need to pass your Novice exam. Turn to Chapter 12 and study the questions that begin 2E-12-4, 2E-12-5 and 2E-13. Don't hesitate to come back to this chapter to review any sections that you are still a little uncertain about. **If you are preparing for the Technician exam**, you should continue with this chapter.]

—— NOT FOR TECHNICIANS ONLY ——
ELECTRICAL THEORY FOR THE TECHNICIAN EXAM

——KEY WORDS——

Core—The material used in the center of a coil. The material used for the core affects the inductance value of the coil.

Dielectric—The insulating material between the plates in a capacitor.

Farad—The basic unit of capacitance.

Henry—The basic unit of inductance.

Induced EMF—A voltage produced by a change in magnetic lines of force around a conductor. When a magnetic field is formed by current in the conductor, the induced voltage always opposes change in that current.

Inductor—An electrical component usually composed of a coil of wire wound on a central core. An inductor stores energy in a magnetic field.

Parallel circuit—An electrical circuit in which the electrons follow more than one path in going from the negative supply terminal to the positive terminal.

Series circuit—An electrical circuit in which all the electrons must flow through every part of the circuit. There is only one path for the electrons to follow.

CALCULATING SERIES AND PARALLEL RESISTANCE

Sometimes it's necessary to calculate the total resistance of resistors connected in a series circuit. Resistors in series are connected end to end like a string of sausages. At other times you must calculate total resistance in a parallel circuit, In a parallel circuit, resistors are side by side like a picket fence. There will be times when you need a certain amount of resistance somewhere in a circuit. There may be no standard resistor value that will give the necessary resistance. Sometimes you may not have a certain value on hand. By combining resistors in parallel or series you can obtain the desired value.

When you connect resistors in series, as in Figure 3-14, the total resistance is simply the sum of all the resistances. Let's use the analogy of a sponge in a water pipe again. Connecting resistors in series is like putting several sponges in the same pipe. The total resistance to the water would be the sum of all the individual resistances. Resistors in series add.

$$R_{TOTAL} = R_1 + R_2 + R_3 + \ldots + R_n \qquad \text{(Eq 3-13)}$$

where n is the total number of resistors.

The total resistance of a string of resistors in series is always greater than any individual resistance in the string. All the circuit current flows through each resistor in a series circuit. A series circuit with resistor values of 2 ohms, 3 ohms and 5 ohms has a total resistance of 10 ohms.

In a parallel circuit, things are a bit different. When we connect two or more resistors in parallel, more than one path for current exists in the circuit. See Figure 3-15. This is like

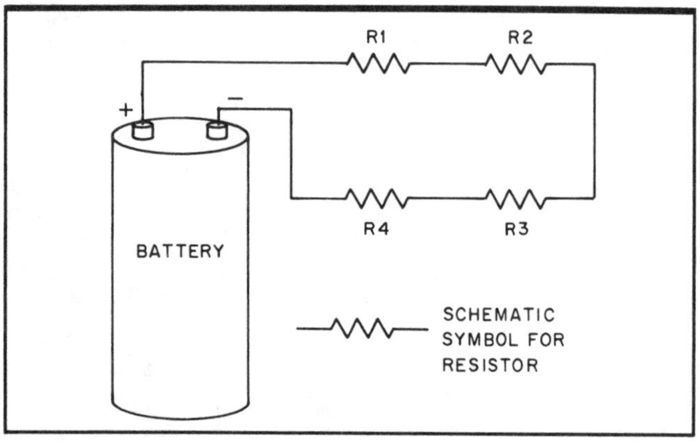

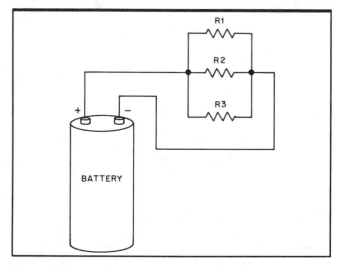

Figure 3-15—In this circuit, the electrical current splits into three separate paths through the resistors. Each resistor is exposed to the full battery voltage. Current through each individual resistor is independent of the other resistors. For example, if R2 and R3 are changed to a value different than the original value, the current in R1 remains unchanged. Even if R2 and R3 are removed, the current in R1 remains unchanged.

Figure 3-14—The total resistance of a string of series-connected resistors is the sum of all the individual resistances.

connecting another water pipe of the same diameter into our water-pipe circuit. When there is more than one path, more water can flow during a given time. With more than one resistor, more electrons can flow. This means there is a greater current.

The formula for calculating the total resistance of resistors connected in parallel is:

$$R_{TOTAL} = \frac{1}{\frac{1}{R_1} + \frac{1}{R_2} + \frac{1}{R_3} + \ldots + \frac{1}{R_n}} \qquad \text{(Eq 3-14)}$$

where n is the total number of resistors. For example, if we connect three 100-ohm resistors in parallel, their total resistance is:

$$R_{TOTAL} = \frac{1}{\frac{1}{100} + \frac{1}{100} + \frac{1}{100}}$$

$$R_{TOTAL} = \frac{1}{\frac{3}{100}} = \frac{1}{0.03} = 33.33 \text{ ohms}$$

If we connect a 25-ohm resistor, a 100-ohm resistor and a 10-ohm resistor in parallel, our equation becomes:

$$R_{TOTAL} = \frac{1}{\frac{1}{25} + \frac{1}{100} + \frac{1}{10}}$$

$$R_{TOTAL} = \frac{1}{0.04 + 0.01 + 0.1} = \frac{1}{0.15} = 6.67 \text{ ohms}$$

To calculate the total resistance of two resistors in parallel, Equation 3-14 reduces to the "product-over-sum" formula. Divide the product of the two resistances by their sum:

$$R_{TOTAL} = \frac{R_1 \times R_2}{R_1 + R_2} \qquad \text{(Eq 3-15)}$$

If we connect two 50-ohm resistors in parallel, the total resistance would be:

$$R_{TOTAL} = \frac{50 \times 50}{50 + 50} = \frac{2500}{100} = 25 \text{ ohms}$$

The total resistance of two equal resistors in parallel is one-half the value of one of the resistors.

Now let's look at any parallel combination of resistors. The total resistance is always less than the smallest value of the parallel combination. You can use this fact to make a quick check of your calculations. The result you calculate should be smaller than the smallest value in the parallel combination. If it isn't, you've made a mistake somewhere!

[Now turn to Chapter 13 and study exam questions 3AE-1-3.1, 3AE-1-3.2, 3AE-1-4.1 and 3AE-1-4.2. Review any equations you have trouble with before going on.]

━━ INDUCTANCE ━━

The motion of electrons produces magnetism. Every electric current creates a magnetic field around the wire in which it flows. Like an invisible tube, the magnetic field is positioned in concentric circles around the conductor. See Figure 3-16A. The field is established when the current flows, and collapses back into the conductor when the current stops. The field increases in strength when the current increases and decreases in strength as the current decreases. The force produced around a straight piece of wire by this magnetic field is usually negligible. When the same wire is formed into a **coil**, the force is much greater. In coils, the magnetic field around each turn also affects the other turns. Together, the combined forces produce one large magnetic field, as shown in Figure 3-16B. Much of the energy in the magnetic field concentrates in the material in the center of the coil (the **core**). Most practical **inductors** consist of a length of wire wound on a core.

An inductor stores energy in a magnetic field. Magnetic fields can also set electrons in motion. When a magnetic field increases in strength, the voltage of a conductor within that field increases. When the field strength decreases, so does the voltage.

Let's apply a dc voltage to an inductor. As there is no current to start with, the current begins to increase when the voltage is applied. This will establish an electrical current in the inductor. The voltage induced by the magnetic field of the inductor opposes the applied voltage. Therefore, the inductor will oppose the increase in current. This is a basic property of inductors. Any changes in current through the inductor, whether increasing or decreasing, are opposed. A voltage is induced in the coil that opposes the applied voltage, and tries to prevent the current from changing. This is

called **induced EMF** (voltage) or back EMF. Gradually a current will be produced by the applied voltage. (The term "gradually" is relative. In radio circuits, the time needed to produce the current in the circuit is often measured in microseconds.)

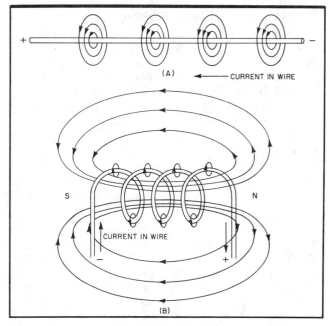

Figure 3-16—A magnetic field surrounds a wire with a current in it. If the wire is formed into a coil, the magnetic field becomes much stronger as the lines of force reinforce each other.

The "final" current that flows through the inductor is limited only by any resistance that might be in the circuit. There is very little resistance in the wire of most coils. The current will be quite large if there is no other resistance.

In the process of getting this current to flow, energy is stored. This energy is in the form of a magnetic field around the coil. When the applied current is shut off, the magnetic field collapses. The collapsing field returns energy to the circuit as a momentary current that continues to flow in the same direction as the original current. This current can be quite large for large values of inductance. The induced voltage can rise to many times the applied voltage. This can cause a spark to jump across switch or relay contacts when the circuit is broken to turn off the current. This effect is called "inductive kickback."

When an ac voltage is applied to an inductor, the current through the inductor will reverse direction every half cycle. This means the current will be constantly changing. The inductor will oppose this change. Energy is stored in the magnetic field while the current is increasing during the first half cycle. This energy will be returned to the circuit as the current starts to decrease. A new magnetic field will be produced during the second half cycle. The north and south poles of the field will be the reverse of the first half cycle. The energy stored in that field will be returned to the circuit as the current again starts to decrease. Then a new magnetic field will be produced on the next half cycle. This process keeps repeating, as long as the ac voltage is applied to the inductor.

FACTORS THAT DETERMINE INDUCTANCE

The inductance of a coil determines several circuit conditions. One is the amount of opposition to changes in current. Another is the amount of energy stored in the magnetic field. The back EMF induced in the coil also depends on the inductance. In turn, the inductance of a coil, usually represented by the symbol L, depends on four things:

1) the type of material used for the core (permeability of the material), and its size and location in the coil;
2) the number of turns used to wind the coil;
3) the length of the coil (spacing of turns);
4) the diameter of the coil (cross-sectional area)

Changing any of these factors changes the inductance. See Figure 3-17.

The basic unit of inductance is the **henry**, named for the American physicist Joseph Henry. The henry is often too large for practical use in measurements. We use the millihenry (10^{-3}) abbreviated mH, or microhenry (10^{-6}) abbreviated μH.

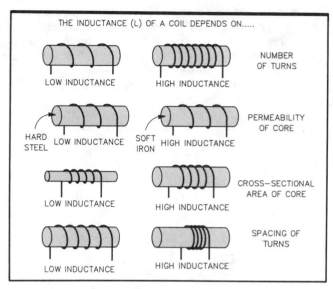

Figure 3-17—The value of an inductor depends on the material used in the core, the number of windings, and the length and diameter of the coil.

INDUCTORS IN SERIES AND PARALLEL

In circuits, inductors combine like resistors. The total inductance of several inductors connected in series is the sum of all the inductances:

$$L_{TOTAL} = L_1 + L_2 + L_3 + \ldots + L_n \qquad \text{(Eq 3-16)}$$

where n is the total number of inductors.

For parallel-connected inductors:

$$L_{TOTAL} = \frac{1}{\dfrac{1}{L_1} + \dfrac{1}{L_2} + \dfrac{1}{L_3} + \ldots + \dfrac{1}{L_n}} \qquad \text{(Eq 3-17)}$$

You should recognize this equation by now, and realize that for two parallel-connected inductors, Equation 3-17 reduces to:

$$L_{TOTAL} = \frac{L_1 \times L_2}{L_1 + L_2} \qquad \text{(Eq 3-18)}$$

For two equal inductors connected in parallel, the total value will be one-half the value of one of the components.

[Turn to Chapter 13 and study questions 3AE-3-1.1, 3AE-3-2.1 through 3AE-3-2.4, 3AE-3-3.1, 3AE-3-3.2, 3AE-3-4.1 and 3AE-3-4.2. Review as needed.]

━━━ CAPACITANCE ━━━

A simple capacitor is formed by separating two conductive plates with an insulating material, or **dielectric**. Connect one plate to the positive terminal of a voltage source. Connect the other plate to the negative terminal. We can build up a surplus of electrons on one plate, as shown in Figure 3-18. At some point, the voltage across the capacitor will equal the applied voltage, and the capacitor is said to be charged. If we then connect a load to the capacitor, it will discharge through the load, releasing stored energy. The basic property of a capacitor is this ability to store a charge in an electric field.

The basic unit of capacitance is the **farad**, named for Michael Faraday. Like the henry, the farad is usually too large a unit for practical measurements. For convenience, we use microfarads (10^{-6}), abbreviated μF, or picofarads (10^{-12}), abbreviated pF.

FACTORS THAT DETERMINE CAPACITANCE

The capacitance value of a capacitor is determined by three factors. Increased plate-surface area will increase capacitance. Increased spacing between plates reduces capacitance. The type of insulating material (dielectric) used

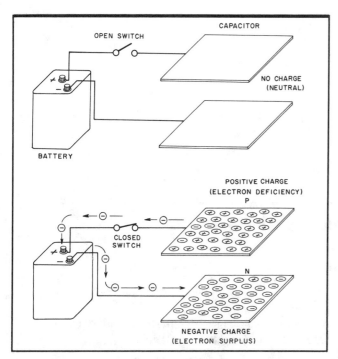

Figure 3-18—When a voltage is applied to a capacitor, an electron surplus (negative charge) builds up on one plate, while an electron deficiency forms on the other plate to produce a positive charge.

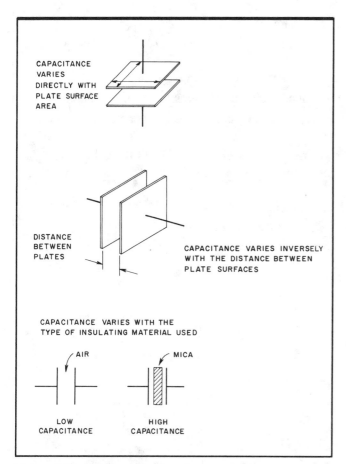

Figure 3-19—The capacitance of a capacitor depends on the area of the plates, the distance between the plates and the type of dielectric material used.

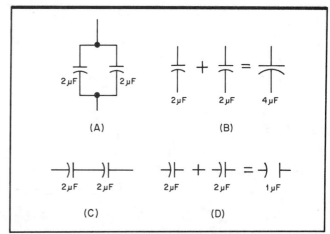

Figure 3-20—Parallel-connected capacitors are shown at A. This connection has the effect of increasing the total plate area, as shown at B. This increases the capacitance. Series connection, shown at C, has the effect of increasing the spacing between the plates, as shown at D. This decreases the capacitance.

between the plates will affect capacitance. See Figure 3-19.

Reducing the spacing between plates or using a material with a higher dielectric constant will increase the capacitance. For a given plate size, using multiple plates in the construction of a capacitor increases capacitance (by giving the effect of increased plate size). The effects of these factors are covered in more detail in Chapter 4.

Capacitors in Series and Parallel

We can increase the value of capacitance by increasing the total plate area. We can effectively increase the total plate area by connecting two capacitors in parallel. The two parallel-connected capacitors act like one larger capacitor, as shown in Figure 3-20A and B. The total capacitance of several parallel-connected capacitors is the sum of all the values.

$$C_{TOTAL} = C_1 + C_2 + C_3 + \ldots + C_n \qquad \text{(Eq 3-19)}$$

where n is the total number of capacitors.

Connecting capacitors in series has the effect of increasing the distance between the plates, thereby reducing the total capacitance, as shown in Figure 3-20C and D. For capacitors in series, we use the familiar reciprocal formula:

$$C_{TOTAL} = \frac{1}{\dfrac{1}{C_1} + \dfrac{1}{C_2} + \dfrac{1}{C_3} + \ldots + \dfrac{1}{C_n}} \qquad \text{(Eq 3-20)}$$

Where there are only two capacitors in series, Equation 3-20 reduces to the product-over-sum formula:

$$C_{TOTAL} = \frac{C_1 \times C_2}{C_1 + C_2} \qquad \text{(Eq 3-21)}$$

As we discovered using this formula for two equal resistors in parallel, two equal capacitors connected in series total half the value of either single capacitor.

[This completes your study of Chapter 3. Now turn to Chapter 13 and study exam questions 3AE-4-1.1, 3AE-4-2.1 through 3AE-4-2.4, 3AE-4-3.1, 3AE-4-3.2, 3AE-4-4.1 and 3AE-4-4.2. Before proceeding to the next chapter, review the material in this section if you have difficulty with any of these questions.]

─── KEY WORDS ───

Battery—A device that converts chemical energy into electrical energy.

Chassis ground—The common connection for all parts of a circuit that connect to the negative side of the power supply.

Double-pole, double-throw (DPDT) switch—A switch that has six contacts. The DPDT switch has two center contacts. The two center contacts can each be connected to one of two other contacts.

Earth ground—A circuit connection to a cold-water pipe or to a ground rod driven into the earth.

Fuse—A thin strip of metal mounted in a holder. When too much current passes through the fuse, the metal strip melts and opens the circuit.

Grid—The control element (or elements) in a vacuum tube.

Potentiometer—Another name for a variable resistor. The value of a potentiometer can be changed without removing it from a circuit.

Resistor—A circuit component that controls current through a circuit.

Rotary switch—A switch that connects one center contact to several individual contacts. An antenna switch is one common use for a rotary switch.

Schematic symbol—A drawing used to represent a circuit component on a wiring diagram.

Semiconductor—Material that has some properties of a conductor and some properties of an insulator.

Single-pole, double-throw (SPDT) switch—A switch that connects one center contact to one of two other contacts.

Single-pole, single-throw (SPST) switch—A switch that only connects one center contact to another contact.

Solid-state devices—Circuit components that use semiconductor materials. Semiconductor diodes, transistors and integrated circuits are all solid-state devices.

Switch—A device used to connect or disconnect electrical contacts.

Triode—A vacuum tube with three active elements: cathode, plate and control grid.

Chapter 4

Circuit Components

Before we look at the operation of electronic circuits, let's discuss some basic information about the parts that make up those circuits. This chapter presents the information about circuit components that you need to know for your Novice or Technician exam. You will find descriptions of several types of fuses, switches, resistors and semiconductor devices. We combine these components with other devices to build practical electronic circuits.

Every circuit component has a **schematic symbol**. A schematic symbol is nothing more than a drawing used to represent a component. We use these symbols when we are making a circuit diagram, or wiring diagram, to show how the components connect for a specific purpose. You will learn the schematic symbols for the circuit components discussed in this chapter. As you discover more about electronics, you will learn how these symbols can be used to illustrate practical circuit connections.

RESISTORS

Resistors are important components in electronic circuits. We talked about the concept of resistance in Chapter 3. A resistor opposes the flow of electrons. We can control the electron flow (the current) by varying the resistance in a circuit.

Most resistors have standard fixed values, so they can be called fixed resistors. Variable resistors, also called **potentiometers**, allow us to change the value of the resistance without removing and changing the component. Potentiometers are used as the volume and tone controls in most stereo amplifiers. Figure 4-1 shows two types of fixed resistors, a potentiometer and their schematic symbols.

[Now turn to Chapter 12 and study those questions with numbers that begin 2F-1. Review this section if you have any problems.]

SWITCHES

How do you control the lights in your house? What turns on your car radio? A **switch**, of course.

The simplest kind of switch just connects or disconnects a single electrical contact. Two wires connect to the switch; when you turn the switch on, the two wires are connected. When you turn the switch off, the wires are disconnected. This is called a **single-pole, single-throw switch**. It connects a single pair of wires (single pole) and has only two positions, on or off (single throw). Sometimes we abbreviate single pole, single throw as **SPST**.

If we want to control more devices with a single switch, we need more contacts. If we add a second contact to a single-pole, single-throw switch we can control a second device or select between two devices. This kind of switch is called a

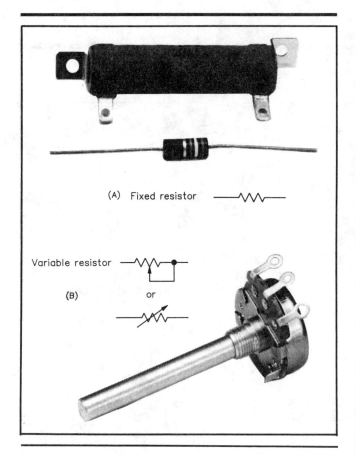

Figure 4-1—Fixed resistors come in many standard values. Most of them look something like the ones shown at A. Variable resistors (also called potentiometers) are used wherever the value of resistance must be adjusted after the circuit is complete. Part B shows a potentiometer.

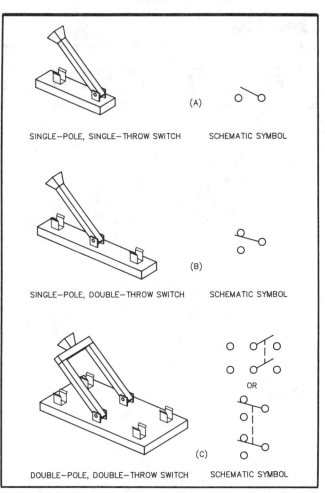

Figure 4-2—A single-pole, single-throw (SPST) switch can connect or disconnect one circuit. A single-pole, double-throw (SPDT) switch can connect one center contact to one of two other contacts. A double-pole, double-throw (DPDT) switch is like two SPDT switches in one package. Each half of the DPDT switch can connect one contact to two other contacts.

single-pole, double-throw switch. Sometimes we abbreviate single pole, double throw as **SPDT**. An SPDT switch connects a single wire (single pole) to one of two other contacts (double throw). The switch connects a center wire to one contact when the switch is in one position. When you flip the switch to the other position, the switch connects the center wire to the other contact.

We can add even more contacts to the switch. A **double-pole, double-throw switch** has two sets of three contacts. We use the abbreviation **DPDT** for double pole, double throw. You can think of a DPDT switch as two SPDT switches in the same box with their handles connected together. A DPDT switch has two center contacts. The switch connects each of these two center contacts (double pole) to one of two other contacts (double throw). Figure 4-2 shows SPST, SPDT and DPDT switches and their schematic symbols.

All these switches are very useful, but they only connect a center contact to one or two other contacts. What if we want to connect a single contact to *several* other contacts? We might want to use one switch to connect our transmitter to several different antennas. We can do this with a **rotary switch.** As its name implies, a rotary switch turns around a central shaft to connect one center contact to several outer contacts.

Switches like this can have many contacts. They can also have more than one center contact, or pole. We specify the particular kind of switch by the number of contacts (positions) it has around the outside, and by the number of center contacts and switch arms (poles) it has. Figure 4-3 shows a

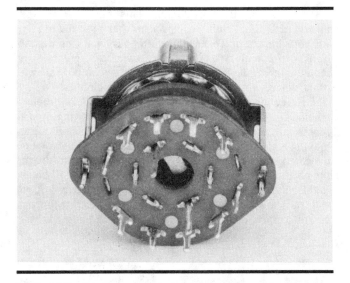

Figure 4-3—A rotary switch can connect one wire to several contacts. Most antenna switches use a rotary switch to connect a transceiver to several antennas. This photograph shows a two-pole, five-position switch; it can connect each center contact to five outside contacts.

Figure 4-4—The schematic symbol for a single-pole, six-position rotary switch.

photograph of a two-pole, five-position rotary switch; it has five separate contacts and two rotary arms. The schematic symbol in Figure 4-4 is a single-pole, six-position rotary switch.

[You should now turn to Chapter 12. Study those questions that have numbers that begin 2F-2. **If you are preparing for the Technician exam,** also study questions 3AF-1-5.1 and 3AF-1-5.2 in Chapter 13. Review this section if you have any problems.]

FUSES

What would happen if your receiver suddenly developed a short circuit? The current, flowing without opposition through the circuit, could easily damage components not built to withstand such high current.

To protect against unexpected short circuits and other problems, most electronic equipment includes one or more fuses. A **fuse** is simply a device made of metal that will heat up and melt when a certain amount of current flows through it. The amount of current that causes each fuse to melt (or "blow") is determined by the manufacturer. When the fuse (usually placed in the main power line to the equipment) blows, it creates an open circuit, stopping the current.

Fuses come in many shapes and sizes. Figure 4-5 shows some of the more common fuse types and the schematic

symbol for a fuse. A fuse in a transistor radio using little power may be designed to blow at 500 mA. The fuses for your home's 120-V circuits may be designed to blow at 15 or 20 A. The principle is the same: When excessive current flows through the fuse it melts, creating an open circuit to protect your equipment. Remember that fuses are designed to protect against too much current, not too much voltage.

[To check your understanding of this section, study exam question 2F-3.1. Review this section if you have any problems.]

BATTERIES

We talked about batteries in Chapter 3. Simply put, a **battery** changes chemical energy into electrical energy. When we connect a wire between the terminals of a battery, a chemical reaction takes place inside the battery. This reaction produces free electrons, and these electrons flow through the wire from the negative terminal to the positive terminal. Batteries may be small or large, round or square. Hearing aid and calculator batteries are tiny. The battery that starts your car is very large. Figure 4-6 shows some different batteries.

Batteries are made up of *cells*. Each cell has a positive electrode and a negative electrode. The cells produce a small voltage. The voltage a cell produces depends on the chemical process taking place inside the cell. Rechargeable nickel-cadmium cells produce about 1.2 volts per cell. Common zinc-acid and alkaline flashlight cells produce about 1.5 volts per cell. The lead-acid cells in a car battery each produce about 2 volts.

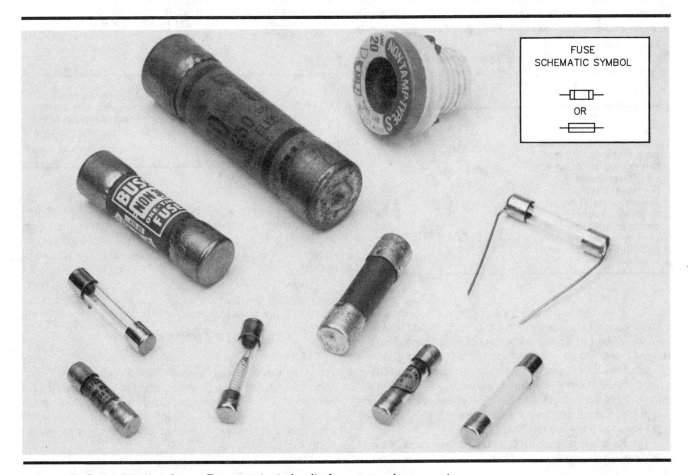

Figure 4-5—Some common fuses. Fuses protect circuits from excessive current.

Figure 4-6—Batteries come in all shapes and sizes. A battery changes chemical energy into electrical energy.

The number of cells in a battery depends on the voltage we want to get out of the battery. If we only need a low voltage the battery may contain only one cell. Small hearing-aid batteries usually contain only one cell. Part A of Figure 4-7 shows the schematic symbol for a single-cell battery. The two vertical lines in the schematic symbol represent the two electrodes in the cell. The long line represents the positive terminal and the short line represents the negative terminal.

Figure 4-7—Some small batteries contain only one cell. We use the symbol at A for a single-cell battery. Manufacturers add several cells in series to produce more voltage. At B, the schematic symbol for a multiple-cell battery.

SINGLE CELL (A)

MULTIPLE—CELL BATTERY (B)

To produce a battery with a higher voltage, several cells must be connected in series so that their outputs add together. Each cell produces a small voltage. The battery manufacturer connects several cells in series to produce the desired battery voltage. Part B of Figure 4-7 shows the schematic symbol for a multiple-cell battery. We use several lines to show the many cells in the battery. Again, the long line at one end represents the positive terminal, and the short line at the other end represents the negative terminal.

[Make a quick trip to Chapter 12 now and look at questions 2F-4.1 and 2F-4.2. Review this section if those questions confuse you.]

ANTENNAS AND GROUNDS

When you use your receiver or transmitter, you must connect it to an antenna. You should also connect all the equipment in your station to a good earth ground. We'll go over these connections later, in Chapter 8. There are really two kinds of ground connections: **chassis ground** and **earth ground**. The metal box that your radio is built on is called a *chassis*. Most manufacturers use the chassis as a common connection for all the places in the circuit that connect to the negative side of the power supply. This common connection is called the chassis ground. The chassis ground has a special schematic symbol.

To keep your station safe, you should also connect the chassis ground to a ground rod driven into the ground or to a cold-water pipe. This connection is called an earth ground because it goes into the earth. An earth ground has a different schematic symbol. Figure 4-8 shows the symbols for a chassis ground and an earth ground.

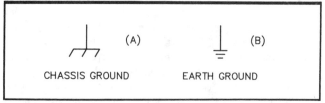

CHASSIS GROUND (A)   EARTH GROUND (B)

Figure 4-8—The metal chassis of a radio is sometimes used to make a common ground connection for all the circuit points that connect to the negative side of the power supply. We use the symbol at A to show those connections on a schematic diagram. Your radio equipment should be connected to a ground rod or a cold-water pipe for safety. We use the symbol at B to show an earth-ground connection.

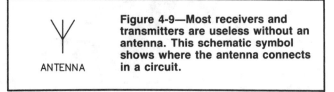

ANTENNA

Figure 4-9—Most receivers and transmitters are useless without an antenna. This schematic symbol shows where the antenna connects in a circuit.

Your receiver won't hear signals and no one will hear your transmitter without an antenna. The antenna is a very important part of any radio installation. We use the symbol shown in Figure 4-9 to represent the antenna on a schematic diagram.

[Now turn to Chapter 12 and study those questions with numbers that begin 2F-5 and 2F-6. If you have any trouble answering the questions, review this section.]

TRANSISTORS

Many of the great technological advances of recent times—men and women in space, computers in homes, ham radio stations tiny enough to be carried in a pocket—all have been made possible by **semiconductor** electronics. Not simply a partial conductor as the name implies, a semiconductor has some of the properties of a conductor and some properties of an insulator.

Diodes and transistors are two types of semiconductors, the **solid-state devices** that have replaced vacuum tubes in most

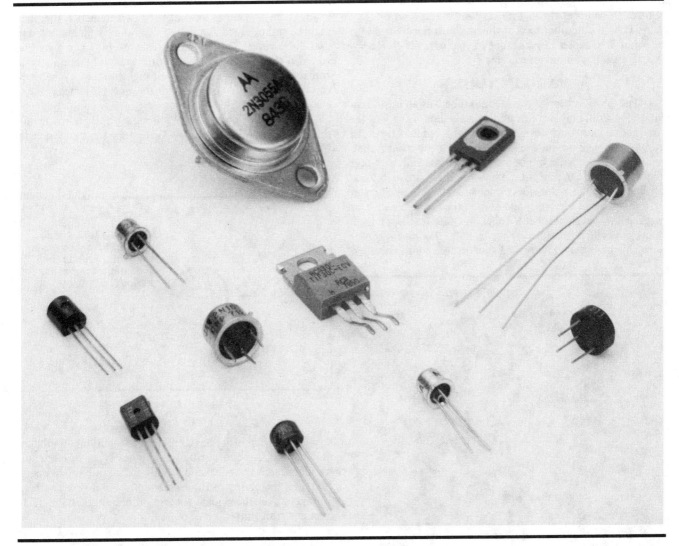

Figure 4-10—Transistors are packaged in many different cases.

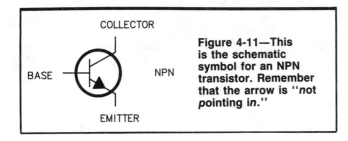

Figure 4-11—This is the schematic symbol for an NPN transistor. Remember that the arrow is "*not pointing in.*"

uses. Most semiconductor devices are much smaller than comparable tubes, and they produce less heat. Semiconductors are also usually less expensive than tubes.

Portable broadcast-band radios, which weighed several pounds and were an armful shortly after World War II, weigh ounces and can be carried in your pocket today. A complete ham radio station, which would have filled a room 50 years ago, now can be built into a container the size of a shoebox, or smaller. Solid-state technology has made all this possible.

Transistors come in many shapes and sizes. Figure 4-10 shows some of the more common case styles for transistors. The most common type of transistor is the **bipolar transistor**. Bipolar transistors are made of two different kinds of material

(*bi* means two, as in *bi*cycle). There are also two kinds of bipolar transistors. Each kind of bipolar transistor has a separate schematic symbol. Figure 4-11 shows the schematic symbol for an *NPN transistor*. You can remember this symbol by remembering that the arrow is "*n*ot *p*ointing i*n*." Figure 4-12 shows the symbol for the other kind of bipolar transistor, the *PNP transistor*. Remember this symbol by saying that the arrow "*points in proudly.*"

You can see from the schematic symbols that transistors have three leads, or electrodes. Each of the electrodes connects to a different part of the transistor. Transistors can amplify small signals; this is what makes them so useful. Usually, we

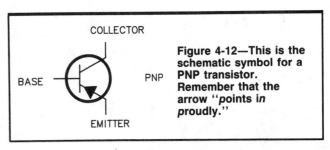

Figure 4-12—This is the schematic symbol for a PNP transistor. Remember that the arrow "*points in proudly.*"

use a low-level signal applied to the *base* of the transistor to control the current through the *collector* and *emitter*.

[Time for another look at the question pool. Study the questions in Chapter 12 with numbers that begin 2F-7. Review this section if you have problems.]

VACUUM TUBES

The development of the vacuum tube was an important milestone in the history of radio. The vacuum tube was the first active electronic device—that is, the vacuum tube can amplify, or produce an enlarged version of the input signal.

From the outside, a tube looks like a glass bulb with pins sticking out of the bottom. Sometimes there are also leads coming out of the top or sides. Some tubes have a metal collar or band around the base, and some tubes have ceramic or metal envelopes (outer shell). Tubes are quite fragile, and will break easily if mishandled. They usually plug into a socket wired into a circuit. Figure 4-13 shows some common tubes.

Figure 4-13—Here are some common vacuum tubes. This figure shows tiny receiving tubes and large transmitting tubes.

Tubes are named for the number of elements they have inside them. All tubes have at least two elements, the plate and the cathode. A tube with only two elements is not very useful, however. Tubes became really useful when inventors added a third element, the *control grid*. The control grid controls the flow of electrons through the tube. When you can control the flow of electrons through the tube, you can use it as an amplifier.

A tube with three elements is called a **triode** (*tri* means three, as in *tri*cycle). Figure 4-14 shows the schematic symbol for a triode vacuum tube.

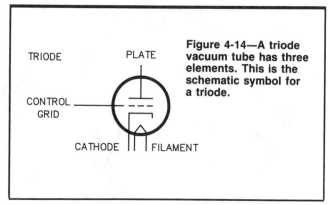

Figure 4-14—A triode vacuum tube has three elements. This is the schematic symbol for a triode.

While transistors have replaced tubes in many modern applications, tubes are still used in many types of electronic circuits. Radio and television sets using tubes are still in operation, and the ability of tubes to handle high power and high voltage makes them ideal for use in the output stage of an amateur transmitter.

[Turn to Chapter 12 and study question 2F-8.1. If you're only preparing for the Novice exam now, that's it for this chapter! By now, you should have a basic understanding of how all of the circuit components included on the Novice exam work. If you had trouble with any of the related questions in the question pool, review those sections before you proceed to the next chapter. **If you're preparing for the Technician exam**, continue with this chapter after you review what you've learned so far.]

──NOT FOR TECHNICIANS ONLY──
ADDITIONAL COMPONENT INFORMATION FOR THE TECHNICIAN EXAM

─────── KEY WORDS ───────

Breakdown voltage—The voltage at which an insulating material will conduct current.

Capacitor—An electronic component composed of two or more conductive plates separated by an insulating material.

Carbon-composition resistor—An electronic component designed to limit current in a circuit; made from ground carbon mixed with clay.

Carbon-film resistor—A resistor made by depositing a gaseous carbon deposit on a round ceramic form.

Ceramic capacitor—An electronic component composed of two or more conductive plates separated by a ceramic insulating material.

Color code—A system in which numerical values are assigned to various colors. Colored stripes are painted on the body of resistors and sometimes other components to show their value.

Core—The material used in the center of an inductor coil.

Dielectric—The insulating material used between the plates in a capacitor.

Dielectric constant—A number used to indicate the relative "merit" of an insulating material. Air is given a value of 1, and all other materials are related to air.

Electrolytic capacitor—A polarized capacitor formed by using thin foil electrodes and chemical-soaked paper.

Electric field—An invisible force of nature. An electric field exists in a region of space if an electrically charged object placed in the region is subjected to an electrical force.

Fixed resistor—A resistor with a fixed nonadjustable value of resistance.

Metal-film resistor—A resistor formed by depositing a thin layer of resistive-metal alloy on a cylindrical ceramic form.

Mica capacitor—A capacitor formed by alternating layers of metal foil with thin sheets of insulating mica.

Mutual coupling—When coils display mutual coupling, a current flowing in one coil will induce a voltage in the other. The magnetic flux of one coil passes through the windings of the other.

Paper capacitor—A capacitor formed by sandwiching paper between thin foil plates, and rolling the entire unit into a cylinder.

Plastic-film capacitor—A capacitor formed by sandwiching thin sheets of Mylar™ or polystyrene between thin foil plates, and rolling the entire unit into a cylinder.

Potentiometer—A resistor whose resistance can be varied continuously over a range of values.

Reactance—The property of an inductor or capacitor (measured in ohms) that impedes current in an ac circuit without converting power to heat.

Resistor—Any material that opposes a current in an electrical circuit. An electronic component specifically designed to oppose current.

Rotor—The movable plates in a variable capacitor.

Stator—The stationary plates in a variable capacitor.

Toroidal inductor—A coil wound on a donut-shaped ferrite or powdered-iron form.

Variable capacitor—A capacitor that can have its value changed within a certain range.

Variable resistor—A resistor whose value can be adjusted over a certain range.

Wire-wound resistor—A resistor made by winding a length of wire on an insulating form.

This section presents the additional information about circuit components that you will need to know to pass your Technician class written exam. You will find descriptions of resistors, capacitors and inductors. You can combine these components with other devices to build practical electronic circuits. We describe some of these circuits in Chapter 5.

Turn to the Element 3A questions in Chapter 13 when directed to do so. How well you understand the questions will show you where you need to do some extra studying. You should thoroughly understand how these components work. When you do, you will have no problem learning to connect them to make a circuit perform a specific task.

RESISTORS

We have seen that current in a circuit is the flow of electrons from one point to another. A perfect insulator would allow no electron flow (zero current), while a perfect conductor would allow infinite electron flow (infinite current). In practice, however, there is no such thing as a perfect conductor or a perfect insulator. Partial opposition to electron flow occurs when the electrons collide with other electrons or atoms in the conductor. The result is a reduction in current, and the conductor produces heat.

Resistors allow us to control the current in a circuit by controlling the opposition to electron flow. As they oppose the flow of electrons they dissipate electrical energy in the form of heat. The more energy a resistor dissipates, the hotter it will become. Figure 4-15A shows the schematic symbol for all nonadjustable resistors. Part B shows a common resistor. You will learn how to interpret the colored stripes on a resistor later in this chapter.

All conductors exhibit some resistance. Table 4-1 shows

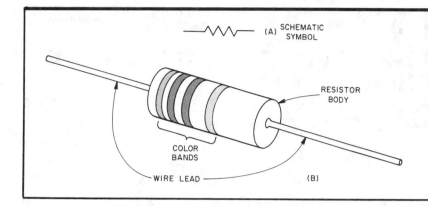

Figure 4-15—Part A shows the schematic symbol for a resistor. Part B shows a typical resistor, including the colored stripes that identify the resistor value. Resistors made in this way range in power rating from 1/8 watt to 2 watts.

the resistance in ohms per 1000 feet of some common copper and nickel American wire gauge (AWG) wire sizes. We can see that the smaller the conductor, the greater the resistance. This is just what we would expect. Think of electron flow in a conductor as being like water flow in a pipe. If we reduce the size of the pipe, not as much water can flow through it.

One simple way of producing a resistor is to use a length of wire. For example, we can see from Table 4-1 that the resistance of 1000 feet of number 28 nickel wire is 337 ohms. Therefore, if we need a resistor of 3.4 ohms, we can use 10 feet of this size nickel wire. We can wind it over a form of some sort. Then we have a unit of a much more convenient size. This is precisely how **wire-wound resistors** are constructed. See Figure 4-16. There is a problem with this type

Table 4-1

Wire Resistance Per 1000 Feet

AWG Wire Size	Diam (inches)	Material	Ohms per 100 ft at 25°C
20	0.032	Copper	10.35
22	0.025	Copper	16.46
24	0.020	Copper	26.17
26	0.016	Copper	41.62
28	0.013	Copper	66.17
30	0.010	Copper	105.2
20	0.032	Nickel	52.78
22	0.025	Nickel	83.95
24	0.020	Nickel	133.47
26	0.016	Nickel	212.26
28	0.013	Nickel	337.47
30	0.010	Nickel	536.52

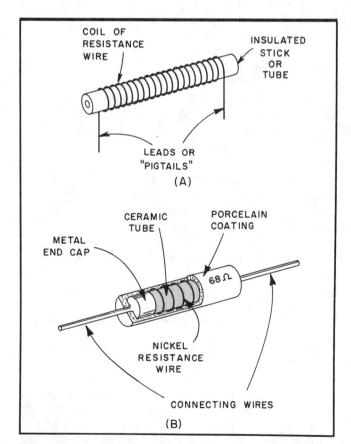

Figure 4-16—A simple wire-wound resistor is shown at A. At B is a commercially produced wire-wound resistor. These resistors are produced by winding resistive wire around a nonconductive form. Most wire-wound resistors are then covered with a protective coating.

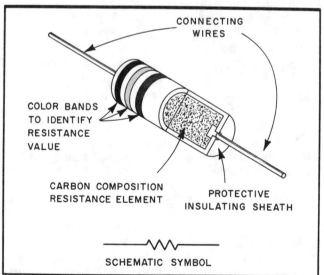

Figure 4-17—Composition resistors are composed of a mixture of carbon and clay. The resistance is controlled by varying the amount of carbon in the material when the resistor is manufactured.

of construction. At radio frequencies, the wire-wound construction causes the resistor to act as an inductor. It does not behave as a pure resistance. For RF circuits, we must have resistors that are noninductive.

There is another way to form a resistor. This is to connect leads to both ends of a block or cylinder of material that has a high resistance. Figure 4-17 shows a resistor made in this way. It uses a mixture of carbon and clay as the resistive element. This type of resistor is a **carbon-composition resistor**. The proportions of carbon and clay determine the value of the resistor.

An advantage of carbon-composition resistors is the wide range of available values. Other advantages are low inductance and capacitance plus good surge-handling capability. The ability to withstand small power overloads without being completely destroyed is another advantage. The main disadvantage is that the resistance of the composition resistor will vary widely. Variations are caused by operating temperature changes and resistor aging.

Another type of carbon resistor is the **carbon-film resistor**. These are manufactured by using high temperatures to break down certain gaseous hydrocarbons. The resulting carbon is then deposited in a thin layer or film on a round ceramic form. The resistor is sealed with a plastic or other insulating material. The thickness of the deposited film provides a means to control the final resistance.

The major advantages of carbon-film resistors are low cost and improved stability with age and temperature changes. These resistors cannot withstand electrical overloads or surges. They can be used as fuses for some applications.

The **metal-film resistor** has replaced the carbon-composition type in many low-power applications today. Metal-film resistors are formed by depositing a thin layer of resistive alloy on a cylindrical ceramic form. Nichrome (an alloy made of nickel and chromium) or other materials are used. See Figure 4-18. This film is then trimmed away in a spiral fashion to form the resistance path. The trimming can be done on a mechanical lathe or by using a laser. The resistor is then covered with an insulating material to protect it.

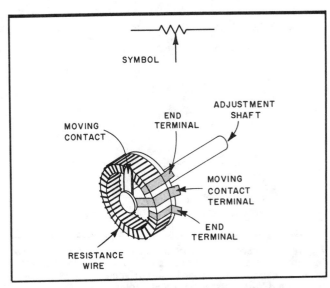

Figure 4-19—The typical construction of a wire-wound variable resistor. As the shaft is rotated, the moving contact is electrically connected to different parts of the wire winding. This effectively changes the length of wire between the end terminal and moving-contact terminal. Increasing or decreasing wire length between terminals thus increases or decreases resistance.

Because of the spiral shape of the resistance path, metal-film resistors will exhibit some inductance. The effects of this inductance increase at higher frequencies. The higher the resistance of the unit, the greater the inductance will be. This is caused by the increased path length. Metal-film resistors provide much better temperature stability than other types.

You can easily recognize the "dog bone" shape of a carbon-film or metal-film resistor. They are thinner in the middle than at the ends. This is because of the metal end caps used to connect the leads to the resistive element.

Most resistors have standard fixed values. They are called **fixed resistors**. Variable resistors are sometimes called **potentiometers**. They can be used to adjust the voltage, or potential, in a circuit. Potentiometers are also used a great deal in electronics. The construction of a wire-wound variable resistor and the schematic symbol for all variable resistors is shown in Figure 4-19. Variable resistors are also made with a ring of carbon compound in place of the wire windings. There, a connection is made to each end of the resistance ring. A third contact is attached to a movable arm, or wiper. The wiper can be moved across the ring. As the wiper moves from one end of the ring to the other, the resistance varies from minimum to maximum.

[Now turn to Chapter 13 and study questions 3AF-1-1.1, 3AF-1-2.1 and 3AF-1-2.2. Review as needed.]

Color Codes

Standard fixed resistors are usually found in values ranging from 2.7 Ω to 22 MΩ (22 megohms, or 22,000,000 ohms). Resistance tolerances on these standard values can be ±20%, ±10%, ±5%, and ±1%. A tolerance of 10% on a 200-ohm resistor means that the actual resistance of a particular unit may be anywhere from 180 Ω to 220 Ω. (Ten percent of 200 is 20, so the resistance can be 200 + 20 or 200 − 20 ohms.)

It is not always practical to print the resistance values on the side of a small resistor. A **color code** shows the value

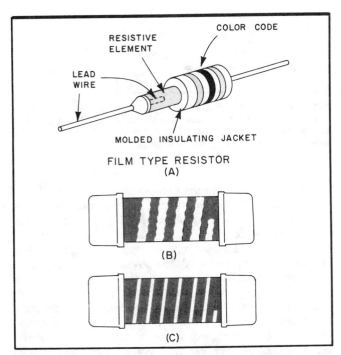

Figure 4-18—The construction of a typical metal-film resistor is shown at A. Film resistors are formed by depositing a thin film of material on a ceramic form. Material is then trimmed off in a spiral to produce the specified resistance for that particular resistor. The excess material may either be trimmed with a mechanical lathe or a laser. A lathe produces a rather rough spiral, like that shown in part B. The laser produces a finer cut, shown at C.

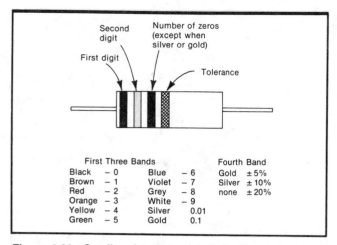

Figure 4-20—Small resistors are labeled with a color code to show their value. For example, proceeding from left to right, a resistor with color bands of yellow/violet/brown/ gold is a 470-Ω resistor with a 5% tolerance.

First Three Bands				Fourth Band	
Black	– 0	Blue	– 6	Gold	±5%
Brown	– 1	Violet	– 7	Silver	±10%
Red	– 2	Grey	– 8	none	±20%
Orange	– 3	White	– 9		
Yellow	– 4	Silver	0.01		
Green	– 5	Gold	0.1		

of the resistor. As shown in Figure 4-20, the color of the first three bands shows the resistor value. The color of the fourth band indicates the resistor tolerance.

Power Ratings

Resistors are also rated according to the amount of power they can safely handle. Power ratings for wire-wound resistors typically start at 1 watt and range to 10 W or larger. Resistors with higher power ratings are also physically large. Greater surface area is required to dissipate the increased heat generated by large currents. Carbon-composition and film resistors are low-power components. You will find these resistors in 1/8-watt, 1/4-W, 1/2-W, 1-W and 2-W power ratings. A resistor that is being pushed to the limit of its power rating will feel very hot to the touch. Sometimes a resistor gets very hot during normal operation. You should probably replace it with a unit having a higher power-dissipation rating.

[Turn to Chapter 13 and study questions 3AF-1-3.1 through 3AF-1-3.4, 3AF-1-4.1 and 3AF-1-4.2. Review this section as needed.]

INDUCTORS

In Chapter 3 we learned that an inductor stores energy in a magnetic field. When a voltage is first applied to an inductor, with no current flowing through the circuit, the inductor will oppose the current. Remember from Chapter 3 that inductors oppose any change in current. A voltage that opposes the applied voltage is induced in the coil, and this voltage tries to prevent a current. Gradually, though, the current will build up. Only the resistance in the circuit will limit the final current value. The resistance in the wire of the coil will be very small.

In the process of getting this current to flow, the coil stores energy. The energy is in the form of a magnetic field around the wire. As the field strength is increasing, the voltage that opposes the current is formed. When you shut off the applied current, the magnetic field collapses. The collapsing field returns the stored energy to the circuit. The energy will have the form of a momentary current in the same direction as the original current. This current is produced by the EMF generated by the collapsing magnetic field. Again, this voltage opposes any change in the current already flowing in the coil.

The amount of opposition to changes in current is called **reactance**. The reactance of the inductor, the amount of energy stored in the magnetic field and the back EMF induced in the coil all depend on the amount of inductance.

The amount of inductance that a coil exhibits, represented by the symbol L, depends on four things:
1) the type of material used in the **core**, and its size and location in the coil
2) the number of turns used to wind the coil
3) the length of the coil and
4) the diameter of the coil

Changing any of these factors changes the inductance.

If we add an iron or ferrite core to the coil, the inductance increases. We can also use brass as a core material in radio-frequency variable inductors. It has the opposite effect of iron or ferrite: The inductance decreases as the brass core enters the coil. A movable core can be placed in a coil, as shown in Figure 4-21. The amount of inductance can be varied as the core moves in and out of the coil. The common schematic symbols for various inductors are shown in Figure 4-22.

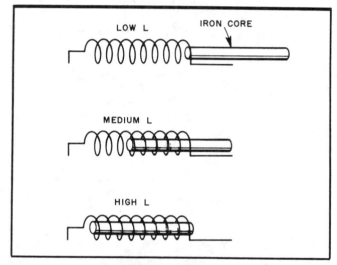

Figure 4-21—The inductance of a coil increases as an iron core is inserted. Many practical inductors of this type use screw threads to allow moving the core in precise amounts when making small changes in inductance.

Ferrite comes from the Latin word for iron. So what is the difference between an iron and a ferrite core? Well, iron cores can be made from iron sheet metal. The layers of material that make up an ac power transformer core are made that way. Cores can also be made from powdered iron mixed with a bonding material. This holds the powdered iron together so it can be molded into the desired shape. Manufacturers mix other metal alloys with the iron "ferrous" material when they make some cores. We call these ferrite cores. They can select the proper alloy to provide the desired characteristics, producing cores designed to operate best over a specific frequency range. We use iron cores most often at low frequencies. The audio-frequency range and ac-power circuits are good applications for these cores. Ferrite cores are manufactured in a wide range of compositions. This optimizes their operation for specific radio-frequency ranges.

It takes some amount of energy to magnetize the core material for any inductor. This energy represents a loss in the coil. Winding the coil on an iron material increases the

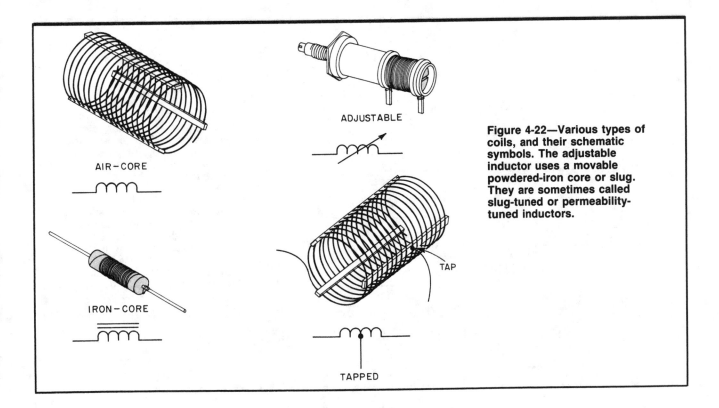

Figure 4-22—Various types of coils, and their schematic symbols. The adjustable inductor uses a movable powdered-iron core or slug. They are sometimes called slug-tuned or permeability-tuned inductors.

AIR-CORE

IRON-CORE

ADJUSTABLE

TAP

TAPPED

inductance of the coil. The energy needed to magnetize the core also increases. Some coils are wound on thin plastic forms, or made self supporting. Then the only material inside the coil is air. These are air-wound coils. They are among the lowest loss types of inductors. Air-wound coils are normally used in high-power RF circuits where energy loss must be kept to a minimum.

Toroid Cores

A **toroidal inductor** is made by winding a coil of wire on a doughnut-shaped core called a toroid. Toroidal core materials are usually powdered-iron or ferrite compounds. The toroidal inductor is highly efficient. This is because there is no break in the circular core. All the magnetic lines of force

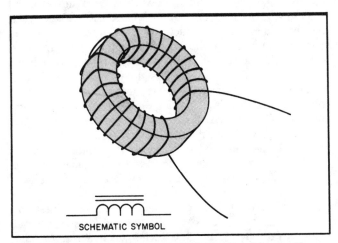

SCHEMATIC SYMBOL

Figure 4-23—A toroidal coil. This type of coil has self-shielding properties. Some inductors in some circuits will interact with the magnetic fields of other inductors. To prevent this a metal shield is used to enclose them. Toroidal inductors confine magnetic fields so well that shields are usually not necessary.

remain inside the core. This means there is very little mutual coupling between two toroids mounted close to each other in a circuit. See Figure 4-23. Mutual coupling can be a problem, especially in an RF circuit. There, signals from one stage could be coupled into another stage without following the proper signal path. Toroid cores can often help eliminate the mutual coupling that would occur between other types of coils.

In theory, a toroidal inductor requires no shield to prevent its magnetic field from spreading out and interfering with outside circuits. This self-shielding property also helps keep outside forces from interfering with the toroidal coil. Toroids can be mounted so close to each other that they can almost touch, but because of the way they are made, there will be almost no inductive coupling between them. Toroidal coils wound with only a small amount of wire on ferrite or iron cores can have a very high inductance value.

[Turn to Chapter 13 and study exam questions 3AF-2-1.1 through 3AF-2-1.4, 3AF-2-2.1, 3AF-2-2.2, 3AF-2-3.1 through 3AF-2-3.4 and 3AF-2-4.1 through 3AF-2-4.3. Review any material you have difficulty with before going on.]

CAPACITORS

In Chapter 3 we learned that the basic property of a **capacitor** is the ability to store an electric charge. In an uncharged capacitor, the potential difference between the two plates is zero. As we charge the capacitor, this potential difference increases until it reaches the full applied voltage. The difference in potential creates an **electric field** between the two plates. See Figure 4-24. A field is an invisible force of nature. We put energy into the capacitor by charging it. Until we discharge it, or the charge leaks away somehow, the energy is stored in the electric field. When the field is not moving, we sometimes call it an electrostatic field.

When we apply a dc voltage to a capacitor, current will flow in the circuit until the capacitor is fully charged to the applied voltage. After the capacitor has charged to the full

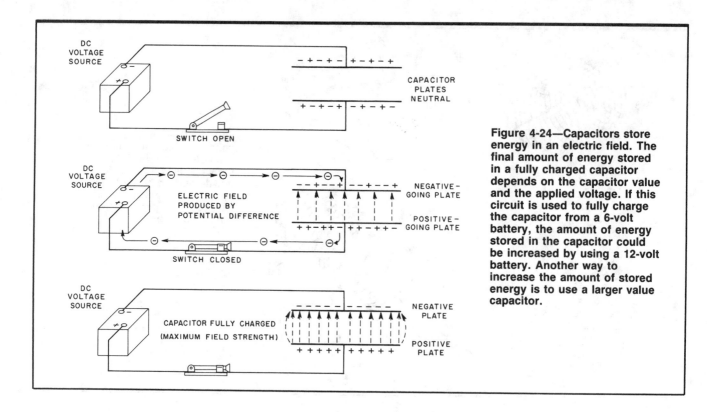

Figure 4-24—Capacitors store energy in an electric field. The final amount of energy stored in a fully charged capacitor depends on the capacitor value and the applied voltage. If this circuit is used to fully charge the capacitor from a 6-volt battery, the amount of energy stored in the capacitor could be increased by using a 12-volt battery. Another way to increase the amount of stored energy is to use a larger value capacitor.

applied voltage, no more current will flow in the circuit. For this reason, capacitors can be used to block dc in a circuit. Because ac voltages are constantly reversing polarity, we can block dc with a capacitor while permitting ac to pass.

Factors That Determine Capacitance

Remember from Chapter 3 that the value of a capacitor is determined by three factors: the area of the plate surfaces, the distance between the plates and the type of insulating material used between the plates. As the surface area increases, the capacitance increases. For a given plate area, as the spacing between the plates decreases, the capacitance increases.

For a given value of plate spacing and area, the type of **dielectric** material used in the capacitor determines the capacitance. A capacitor using air as the dielectric is used for comparison purposes. Other dielectric materials are related to the standard air-dielectric capacitor by the **dielectric constant** of the material used. See Table 4-2. From the chart we can see that if polystyrene is used as the dielectric in a capacitor, it will have 2.6 times the capacitance of an air-dielectric capacitor with the same plate spacing and area.

Voltage Ratings

We cannot increase the voltage applied to a capacitor indefinitely. Eventually we will reach a voltage at which the dielectric material will break down. The breakdown of an insulating material means that the applied voltage is so great that the material will conduct. In a capacitor, this means a spark will jump from one plate to the other. The capacitor will probably be ruined. Different dielectric materials have different **breakdown voltages**, as shown in Table 4-2. The voltage rating of a capacitor is very important. Failure of a capacitor from too much voltage may also damage other components in the circuit. For this reason, capacitors are usually labeled with both their capacitance in microfarads or picofarads and their voltage rating. The voltage rating is specified in working-volts dc (WVDC). Sometimes the tolerance and temperature coefficient are also printed on them.

[Now turn to Chapter 13 and study exam questions 3AF-3-1.1, 3AF-3-1.2, 3AF-3-2.1 through 3AF-3-2.4 and 3AF-3-3.1 through 3AF-3-3.3. Review any material you have difficulty with.]

PRACTICAL CAPACITORS

Practical capacitors are described by the material used for their dielectric. Mica, ceramic, plastic-film, polystyrene,

Table 4-2

Dielectric Constants and Breakdown Voltages

Material	Dielectric Constant*	Breakdown Voltage**
Air	1.0	21
Alsimag 196	5.7	240
Bakelite™	4.4-5.4	300
Bakelite™, mica filled	4.7	325-375
Cellulose acetate	3.3-3.9	250-600
Fiber	5-7.5	150-180
Formica™	4.6-4.9	450
Glass, window	7.6-8	200-250
Glass, Pyrex™	4.8	335
Mica, ruby	5.4	3800-5600
Mycalex	7.4	250
Paper, Royalgrey	3.0	200
Plexiglas®	2.8	990
Polyethylene	2.3	1200
Polystyrene	2.6	500-700
Porcelain	5.1-5.9	40-100
Quartz, fused	3.8	1000
Steatite, low loss	5.8	150-315
Teflon®	2.1	1000-2000

*At 1 MHz   **In volts per mil (0.001 inch)

paper and electrolytic capacitors are in common use today. They each have properties that make them more or less suitable for a particular application.

Mica Capacitors

Mica capacitors consist of many strips of metal foil separated by thin strips of mica. See Figure 4-25. Alternate plates are connected and each set of plates is connected to an electrode. The entire unit is then encased in plastic or ceramic insulating material. An alternative to this form of construction is the "silvered-mica" capacitor. In the silvered-mica type, a thin layer of silver is deposited directly onto one side of the mica. The plates are stacked so that alternate layers of mica are separated by layers of silver.

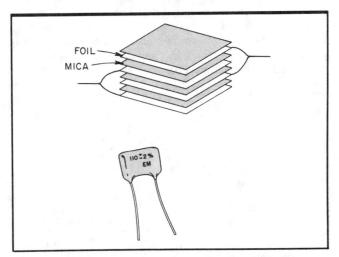

Figure 4-25—Mica capacitors are formed by interleaving metal foil with thin sheets of mica. These capacitors have a relatively stable capacitance value when subjected to temperature changes.

From Table 4-2 we can see that mica has a very high voltage breakdown rating. For this reason, mica capacitors are frequently used in transmitters and high-power amplifiers. In these applications the ability to withstand high voltages is important. Mica capacitors also have good temperature stability—their capacitance does not change greatly as the temperature changes. Typical capacitance values for mica capacitors range from 1 picofarad to 0.1 microfarad, and voltage ratings as high as 35,000 are possible. Figure 4-26 shows the schematic symbol for all fixed capacitors.

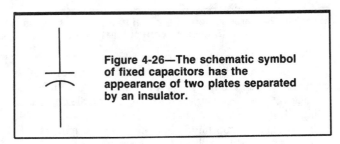

Figure 4-26—The schematic symbol of fixed capacitors has the appearance of two plates separated by an insulator.

Ceramic Capacitors

Ceramic capacitors are constructed by depositing a thin metal film on each side of a ceramic disc, as shown in Figure 4-27. Wire leads are then attached to the metal films. Then

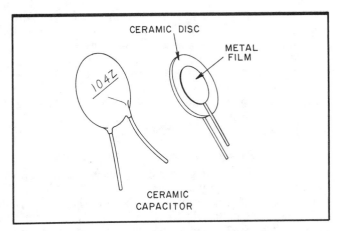

Figure 4-27—In the ceramic capacitor, electrodes are deposited on both sides of a ceramic disc.

the entire unit is covered with a protective plastic or ceramic coating. Ceramic capacitors are inexpensive and easy to construct, and they are in wide use today.

Ordinary ceramic capacitors cannot be used where temperature stability is important—their capacitance will change with a change in temperature. Special ceramic capacitors (called NPØ for negative-positive zero) are used for these applications. The capacitance of an NPØ unit will remain substantially the same over a wide temperature range. The range of capacitance values available with ceramic capacitors is typically 1 picofarad to 0.1 microfarad, with working voltages up to 1000.

Ceramic capacitors are often connected across the transformer primary or secondary winding in a power supply. These capacitors, called suppressor capacitors, suppress transient voltage spikes, preventing them from getting through the power supply.

Paper Capacitors

In its simplest form, the **paper capacitor** consists of a layer of paper between two layers of metal foil. The foil and paper are rolled up, as shown in Figure 4-28. Wires are connected to the foil layers, and the capacitor is encased in plastic or dipped in wax to protect it. One end of the capacitor some-

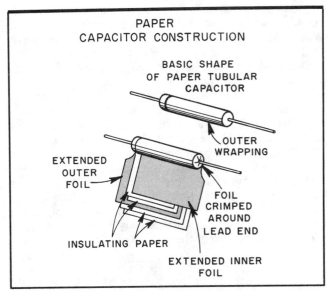

Figure 4-28—Paper tubular capacitors are formed of rolled foil with insulating paper layers.

times has a band around it. This does not mean that the capacitor is polarized. It means only that the outside layer of foil is connected to the marked lead. This way, the outside of the capacitor can be grounded where necessary for RF shielding.

Paper capacitors can be obtained in capacitance values from about 500 picofarads to around 50 microfarads. Their voltage ratings go up to about 600 WVDC. Paper capacitors are generally inexpensive, but their large size for a given value makes them impractical for some uses.

Plastic-Film Capacitors

Construction techniques similar to those used for paper capacitors are used for **plastic-film capacitors**. Thin sheets of Mylar™ or polystyrene are sandwiched between sheets of metal foil, and rolled into a cylinder. Typical values range from 5 picofarads to 0.47 microfarad. The plastic material gives capacitors with a high voltage rating in a physically small package. Plastic-film capacitors also have good temperature stability.

Electrolytic Capacitors

In **electrolytic capacitors**, the dielectric is formed after the capacitor is manufactured. The construction of aluminum-electrolytic capacitors is very similar to that of paper capacitors. Two sheets of aluminum foil separated by paper are soaked in a chemical solution. Then they are rolled up and placed in a protective casing. After assembly, a voltage is applied to the capacitor. This causes a thin layer of aluminum oxide to form on the surface of the positive plate next to the chemical. The aluminum oxide acts as the dielectric, and the foil plates act as the electrodes.

The layer of oxide dielectric is extremely thin. Electrolytic capacitors can be made with a very high capacitance value in a small package. Electrolytic capacitors are polarized—dc voltages must be connected to the positive and negative capacitor terminals with the correct polarity. The positive and negative electrodes in an electrolytic capacitor are clearly marked. Connecting an electrolytic capacitor incorrectly causes gas to form inside the capacitor and the capacitor may actually explode. This can be very dangerous. At the very least the capacitor will be destroyed by connecting it incorrectly.

Another type of electrolytic capacitor is the tantalum-dielectric type. Tantalum capacitors have several advantages over aluminum-electrolytic capacitors. Tantalum capacitors can be made even smaller than aluminum-electrolytic capacitors for a given capacitance value. They are manufactured in several forms, including small, water-droplet-shaped solid-electrolyte capacitors. These are formed on a small tantalum pellet that serves as the anode, or positive capacitor plate. An oxide layer on the outside of the tantalum pellet serves as the dielectric. A layer of manganese dioxide is the solid electrolyte. Layers of carbon and silver form the cathode, or negative capacitor plate. The entire unit is dipped in epoxy to form a protective coating on the capacitor. Their characteristic shape explains why these tantalum capacitors are often called "tear drop" capacitors.

Electrolytic capacitors are available in voltage ratings of greater than 400 V, and capacitance values from 1 microfarad to 100,000 microfarads (0.1 farad). Electrolytic capacitors with high capacitance values and/or high voltage ratings are physically very large. They are used mostly in power-supply filters. Large values of capacitance are necessary in these filters to provide good smoothing of the pulsating dc from the rectifier.

Variable Capacitors

In some circuits it is necessary or desirable to vary the capacitance at some point. An example is in the tuning circuit of a receiver or transmitter VFO. We could use a rotary switch

to select one of several different fixed-value capacitors. It is much more convenient to use a **variable capacitor**, however. A basic air-dielectric variable capacitor is shown in Figure 4-29. This figure also shows the schematic symbol for a variable capacitor. One set of plates (called the **stator**) is fixed. The other set of plates (called the **rotor**) can be rotated. The rotation controls the amount of plate area shared by the two sets of plates. When the capacitor is fully meshed, all the rotor plates are down in between the stator plates. In this position, the capacitor will have its largest value of capacitance. When the rotor is unmeshed, the value of capacitance is at a minimum. The capacitance can be varied smoothly between the maximum and minimum values.

Another type of variable capacitor is the compression variable. In this type of variable capacitor, the spacing between the two plates is varied. When the spacing is at its minimum, the capacitance is at a maximum value. When the spacing is adjusted to its maximum, the value of capacitance is at a minimum. This type of variable capacitor is usually used as a trimmer capacitor. A trimmer capacitor is a control used to peak or fine tune a part of a circuit. It is usually left

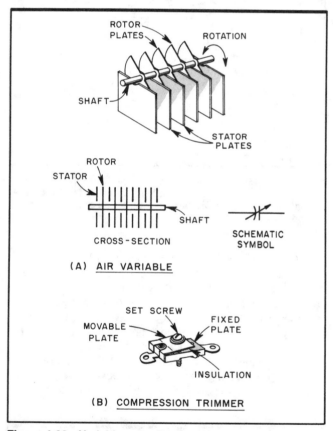

Figure 4-29—Variable capacitors can be made with air as the dielectric, or with mica or ceramic dielectrics.

alone once adjusted to the correct value.

Variable capacitors are subject to the same rules as other capacitors. If a variable capacitor is to be used with a high voltage on its plates, a large plate spacing or a dielectric with a high breakdown voltage will be required. Air-variable capacitors used in transmitters and high-power amplifiers have their plates spaced much farther apart than those used in receivers.

[This completes your study of Chapter 4. Now turn to Chapter 13 and study questions 3AF-3-1.3, 3AF-3-1.4, 3AF-3-4.1 and 3AF-3-4.2. Review any material you have difficulty with before going on.]

———— KEY WORDS ————

Antenna switch—A switch used to connect one transmitter, receiver or transceiver to several different antennas.

Block diagram—A drawing using boxes to represent sections of a complicated device or process. The block diagram shows the connections between sections.

Electronic keyer—A device that generates Morse code dots and dashes electronically.

Hand key—A simple switch used to send Morse code.

Impedance-matching network—A device that matches the impedance of an antenna system to the impedance of a transmitter or receiver. Also called an antenna-matching network or Transmatch.

Modem—Short for modulator/demodulator. A modem modulates a radio signal to transmit data and demodulates a received signal to recover transmitted data.

Microphone—A device that converts sound waves into electrical energy.

Packet radio—A communications system in which information is broken into short bursts. The bursts (packets) also contain addressing and error-detection information.

Power supply—A circuit that provides a direct-current output at some desired voltage from an ac input voltage.

Radioteletype (RTTY)—Radio signals sent from one teleprinter machine to another machine. Anything that one operator types on his teleprinter will be printed on the other machine.

Receiver—A device that converts radio signals into audio signals.

SWR meter—A measuring instrument that can indicate when an antenna system is working well.

Teleprinter—A machine that can convert keystrokes (typing) into electrical impulses. The teleprinter can also convert the proper electrical impulses back into text. Computers have largely replaced teleprinters for amateur radioteletype work.

Terminal node controller—A TNC accepts information from a computer and converts the information into packets. The TNC also receives packets and extracts information to be displayed by a computer.

Transceiver—A radio transmitter and receiver combined in one unit.

Transmit-receive (TR) switch—A device that allows you to connect one antenna to a receiver and a transmitter. The switch connects the antenna to the receiver or transmitter as you operate the switch.

Transmitter—A device that produces radio-frequency signals.

Chapter 5
Practical Circuits

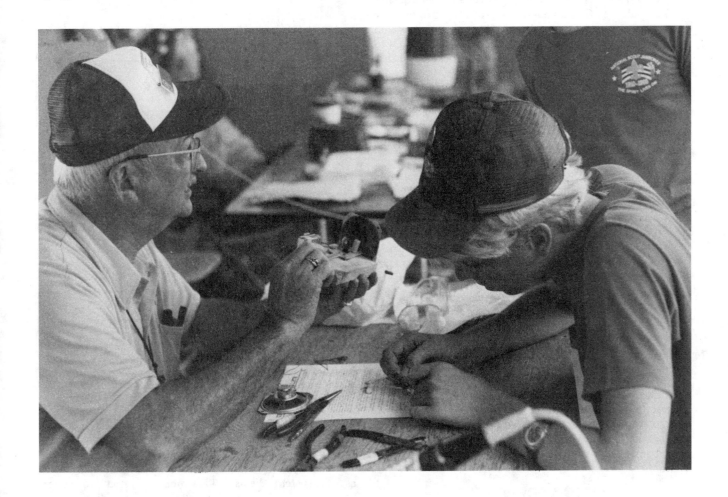

I n the last chapter, you learned about some of the components that make up electronic circuits. In this chapter, we'll introduce some of the basic equipment that goes into an Amateur Radio station. We will briefly cover receivers, transmitters, transceivers, antenna switches and other equipment. We'll show you how to connect the equipment to make a fully functional ham radio station.

Some of the terms may be confusing at first. Don't worry if you don't understand everything. Most of the ideas presented in this chapter are reinforced later in the book. We'll talk more about connecting your station equipment in Chapters 8 and 9.

Throughout this chapter we use **block diagrams**. In a block diagram, each part of a station is shown as a box. The diagram shows how all the boxes connect to each other. Study the block diagrams carefully and remember to turn to Chapters 12 and 13 when instructed to study exam questions.

Figure 5-1 shows a block diagram of a very simple Amateur Radio station. Let's discuss the blocks one by one.

TRANSMITTERS

A **transmitter** is a device that produces a radio-frequency (RF) signal. Television and radio broadcast stations use powerful transmitters to put their signals into the air. Radio amateurs use lower-powered transmitters to send signals to each other. A transmitter produces an electrical signal that can be sent to a distant receiver.

We call the signal from a transmitter the *radio-frequency carrier*. To transmit Morse code, you could use a telegraph key as a switch to turn the carrier on and off in the proper code pattern. If you want to transmit voice signals, you need extra circuitry in the transmitter to add voice content to the carrier. We call this extra circuitry a *modulator*.

Many modern amateur transmitters have a separate **power supply**. The power supply converts the 120 V ac from your wall sockets into 12 V dc (usually) to power the transmitter.

RECEIVERS

The transmitter is a sending device. It sends a radio-frequency (RF) signal to a transmitting antenna, and the antenna radiates the signal into the air. Some distance away, the signal produces a voltage in a receiving antenna. That ac voltage goes from the receiving antenna into a **receiver**. The receiver converts the RF energy into an audio-frequency (AF) signal. You hear this AF signal in headphones or from a loudspeaker.

Just about everyone is familiar with receivers. Receivers take electronic signals out of the air and convert them into signals that we can see or hear. Your clock radio is a receiver and so is your television set. If you look around the room you're in right now, you'll probably see at least one receiver. The receiver is a very important part of an Amateur Radio station.

TRANSCEIVERS

In many modern Amateur Radio stations, the transmitter and receiver are combined into one box. We call this combination a **transceiver**. It's really more than just a transmitter and receiver in one box, though. Some of the circuits in a transceiver are used for both transmitting and receiving. Transceivers generally take up less space than a separate transmitter and receiver.

SWITCHES

Now we have the basic parts of our amateur station. The folks at the radio club gave you an old receiver, transmitter and power supply. You bring them home and set them on your desk. Now what?

Well, you know that you need to connect an antenna to the receiver if you want to hear signals. You also have to connect an antenna to the transmitter when you send out a signal. But you only have one antenna. What should you do?

You could disconnect the antenna from the receiver and connect it to the transmitter. You'd have to do this every time you switch over from receive to transmit and again to switch from transmit to receive. Most radios have their antenna connectors on the rear panel, however. Besides, these connectors

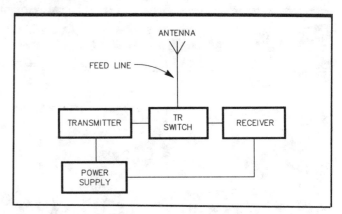

Figure 5-1—A TR switch connects between the transmitter, receiver and antenna.

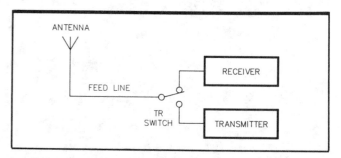

Figure 5-2—The simplest TR switch is an SPDT switch with the center arm connected to the antenna. One position connects the antenna to the receiver; the other position connects the antenna to the transmitter.

aren't designed to make it easy to remove and reconnect cables rapidly.

What you need is a **transmit-receive switch** (also known as a **TR switch**). We use a TR switch to connect one antenna to a receiver and a transmitter. Remember our discussion of switches from Chapter 4? The simplest TR switch is a single-pole, double-throw (SPDT) switch, like the one in Figure 5-2. The antenna connects to the center arm, and the receiver and transmitter connect to the outside contacts. If you throw the switch one way, the transmitter connects to the antenna. The other switch position connects the receiver to the antenna.

Many TR switches use relays to switch the antenna. A relay uses a magnetic coil to make or break contacts. You can think of a relay as a remotely operated switch. When you throw a switch at your operating position, current passes through the relay coil and the relay arm switches from one set of contacts to another. A transmit-receive relay may have several contacts. Extra contacts can be used to quiet the receiver in the transmit mode or to switch accessory devices.

THE SIMPLEST STATION

The block diagram in Figure 5-1 shows how we connect all this equipment together. The power supply connects to the transmitter. The receiver and transmitter both connect to the TR switch. The TR switch connects the transmitter and receiver to the antenna, one at a time. This is just about all you need for the most basic Amateur Radio station.

CONNECTING MANY ANTENNAS

What if you have more than one antenna? Again, you could disconnect the antenna from your transmitter or receiver and reconnect another feed line. This can be very inconvenient. A simpler technique is to use an **antenna switch**. We mentioned antenna switches in Chapter 4. An antenna switch connects one transmitter, receiver or transceiver to several antennas. You can switch from one antenna to another with a simple flick of the switch.

The antenna switch connects at the point where the feed lines from all the antennas come into the station. See Figure 5-3. An antenna switch connects one receiver, transmitter or transceiver to one of several antennas.

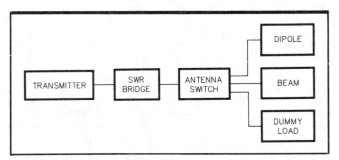

Figure 5-3—An antenna switch can connect a transmitter to one of several antennas.

IMPEDANCE-MATCHING NETWORKS

Another useful accessory that you will see in many ham shacks is an **impedance-matching network**. (Impedance is similar to resistance.) This device may let you use one antenna on several bands. The matching network may also allow you to use your antenna on a band it is not designed for. Sometimes we call the impedance-matching network an *antenna tuner* or *Transmatch*. These names indicate the main function of the impedance-matching network. The network matches (tunes) the impedance of the load (the antenna and feed line) to the impedance of your transmitter. We usually connect the impedance-matching network right where the antenna comes into the station. See Figure 5-4.

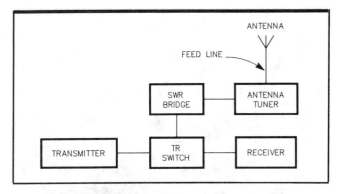

Figure 5-4—An antenna tuner (or impedance-matching network) connects directly to the antenna feed line. Placing an SWR meter between the tuner and the transmitter lets you see when the tuner is adjusted properly.

MONITORING THE SYSTEM

Another thing you may want to add to your station is an **SWR meter**. This device is also called an SWR bridge. The SWR meter measures something called the *standing-wave ratio*. You don't need to know too much about SWR right now. We will go over it in more detail later in the book.

Standing-wave ratio is a good indicator of how well your antenna system is working. If you install an SWR meter in your station, you can keep an eye out for problems with your antenna. If you spot the problems early you can head them off before they damage your equipment.

The SWR meter can be connected at several points in your station. One good place to connect the meter is between the antenna switch and transceiver. See Figure 5-4. If you use a separate receiver and transmitter, you can connect the SWR meter between the TR switch and the rest of the antenna system. An SWR meter can also be used between an impedance-matching network and the transmitter. The SWR meter then indicates when the matching network is adjusted properly.

[Now turn to Chapter 12. Study those questions with numbers that begin 2G-1-1 and 2G-1-2. Review this section if you have any problems.]

STATION ACCESSORIES

So far, we have been talking about very basic station layout. We showed you how to connect a transmitter, receiver and antenna switch together to make a simple station. To communicate effectively, you will need a few simple accessories. Let's look at what you need.

MORSE CODE KEYING

Morse code is transmitted by switching the output of a transmitter on and off. Inventive radio operators have developed many devices over the years to make this switching easier.

The simplest kind of code-sending device is one you're probably already familiar with: the **hand key**, or straight key. See Figure 5-5. A hand key is a simple switch. When you press

down on the key, the contacts meet and the transmitter produces a signal.

The code you make with a hand key is only as good as your "fist" or your ability to send well-timed code. An **electronic keyer**, like the one in Figure 5-6, makes it easier to send well-timed code. You must connect a *paddle* to the keyer. The paddle has two switches, one on each side. When you press one side of the paddle, one of the switches closes and the keyer sends a continuous string of dots. When you press the other side of the paddle, the keyer sends dashes. With a little practice and some rhythm, you can send perfectly timed code with a keyer. You may want to start out with a hand key, however. Using a hand key can help you develop the rhythm you need to send good code. When you can send good code with a hand

Figure 5-5—A hand key (or straight key) is the simplest type of code-sending device.

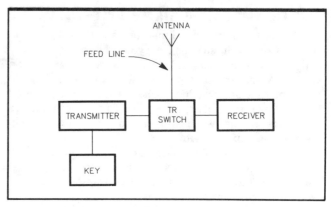

Figure 5-7—The keying device connects directly to the transmitter.

Figure 5-6—You can produce perfect code characters with an electronic keyer and a little practice.

key, you're ready to try a keyer.

Both the hand key and the electronic keyer connect directly to the transmitter. The key in the block diagram in Figure 5-7 is connected to the transmit section of the transceiver.

MICROPHONES

If you want to transmit voice, you'll need a **microphone**. A microphone converts sound waves into electrical signals that can be used by a transmitter. All voice transmitters require a microphone of some kind. Like a code key, the microphone connects directly to the transmitter. The microphone in Figure 5-8 is connected to the transmit section of the transceiver.

[Time for a trip to Chapter 12. Study those questions with numbers that begin 2G-2 and 2G-3. Review this section if you have problems.]

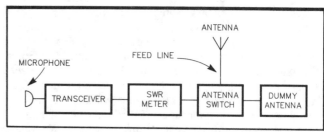

Figure 5-8—A microphone also connects directly to the transmitter. You will need a microphone to transmit voice.

RADIOTELETYPE AND DATA COMMUNICATIONS

Radioteletype (RTTY) and data communications are Amateur Radio transmissions that are designed to be received and printed automatically. Sometimes called *digital communications*, they often involve direct transfer of information (data) between computers. When you type information into your computer, the computer (with the help of some accessory equipment) processes the information. The computer then sends the information to your transmitter and the transmitter sends it out over the air. The station on the other end receives the signal, processes it and prints it out on a computer screen or printer. RTTY and data communications have become a popular form of ham-radio communication. Here we will talk about setting up a station for **radioteletype** and **packet radio** communications.

RADIOTELETYPE

Radioteletype (RTTY) communications have been around for a long time. You may have seen big noisy **teleprinter** machines in old movies. A teleprinter is something like an electric typewriter. When you type on the teleprinter keys, however, the teleprinter sends out electrical codes that represent the letters you are typing. If we send these codes to another teleprinter machine, the second machine reproduces everything you type. Hams have been converting this equipment and using it on the air for years. You can also send and receive radioteletype with a computer. These days computers are so cheap and readily available that they have just about replaced the old noisy teleprinters.

We use a **modem** for Amateur Radio digital communications. Modem is short for *mo*dulator-*dem*odulator. The modem accepts information from your computer and uses the information to modulate a transmitter. The modulated transmitter produces a signal that we send out over the air. When another station receives the signal, the other station uses a similar modem to demodulate the signal. The modem then passes the demodulated signal to a computer. The computer processes and displays the signal.

Sometimes hams use an older teleprinter instead of a computer. The teleprinter converts and displays information from the modem. A complete radioteletype station must have a computer or teleprinter, a modem and a transmitter. The modem connects between the computer and the transmitter, as shown in Figure 5-9.

received packets contain any errors. If the received packet contains errors, the receiving station asks for a retransmission. The retransmission and error checking continue until the receiving station gets the packet with no errors.

Breaking up the data into small parts allows several users to share a channel. Packets from one user are transmitted in the spaces between packets from other users. The addressing information allows each user's TNC to separate packets for that station from packets intended for other stations. The addresses also allow packets to be relayed through several stations before they reach their final destination. The error-checking information in each packet assures perfect copy.

A TNC connects to your station the same way a modem does. The TNC goes between the radio and the computer, as shown in Figure 5-10.

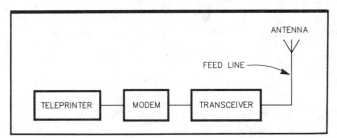

Figure 5-9—A typical radioteletype station. The modem connects between the transceiver and the teleprinter.

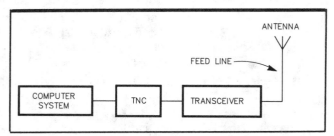

Figure 5-10—In a packet radio station, the terminal node controller (TNC) connects between the transceiver and a computer.

PACKET RADIO

Packet radio uses a **terminal node controller (TNC)** as an interface between your computer and transceiver. We might call a TNC an "intelligent" modem. The TNC accepts information from your computer and breaks the data into small pieces called *packets*. Along with the information from your computer, each packet contains addressing, error-checking and control information.

The addressing information includes the call signs of the station sending the packet and the station the packet is being sent to. The address may also include call signs of stations that are being used to relay the packet. The receiving station uses the error-checking information to determine whether the

[Turn to Chapter 12 and study the questions with numbers that begin 2G-4 and 2G-5. If you have any problems, review this last section.]

If you're preparing for the Novice exam, that's all for this chapter. Don't worry if you're a bit confused by some of the terms. We covered a lot of information fairly quickly. We'll go over a lot of the operating information later in the book. For now, become familiar with the terms, and study the block diagrams carefully. If you are preparing only for the Novice exam, you don't have to continue with this chapter.

If you are preparing for the Technician exam, continue with this chapter *after* you review Chapter 12.

——— NOT FOR TECHNICIANS ONLY ———

ADDITIONAL PRACTICAL CIRCUIT INFORMATION FOR THE TECHNICIAN EXAM

———— **KEY WORDS** ————

Amplifier—A device usually employing electron tubes or transistors to increase the voltage, current or power of a signal. The amplifying device may use a small signal to control voltage and/or current from an external supply. A larger replica of the small input signal appears at the device output.

Amplitude modulation (AM)—A method of combining an information signal and an RF (radio-frequency) carrier. In double-sideband voice AM transmission, we use the voice information to vary (modulate) the amplitude of an RF carrier. Shortwave broadcast stations use this type of AM, as do stations in the Standard Broadcast Band (540-1600 kHz). Few amateurs use double-sideband voice AM, but a variation, known as *single sideband*, is very popular.

Attenuate—To reduce in amplitude.

Band-pass filter—A circuit that allows signals to go through it only if they are within a certain range of frequencies. It attenuates signals above and below this range.

Beat-frequency oscillator (BFO)—An oscillator that provides a signal to the product detector. In the product detector, the BFO signal and the IF signal are mixed to produce an audio signal.

Cutoff frequency—In a high-pass, low-pass or band-pass filter, the cutoff frequency is the frequency at which the filter output is reduced to ½ of the power available at the filter input.

Detector—The stage in a receiver in which the modulation (voice or other information) is recovered from the RF signal.

Direct-conversion receiver—A receiver that converts an RF signal directly to an audio signal with one mixing stage.

Filter—A circuit that will allow some signals to pass through it but will greatly reduce the strength of others.

Frequency modulation—The process of varying the frequency of an RF carrier in response to the instantaneous changes in the modulating signal.

High-pass filter—A filter that allows signals above the cutoff frequency to pass through. It attenuates signals below the cutoff frequency.

Intermediate frequency (IF)—The output frequency of a mixing stage in a superheterodyne receiver. The subsequent stages in the receiver are tuned for maximum efficiency at the IF.

Low-pass filter—A filter that allows signals below the cutoff frequency to pass through and attenuates signals above the cutoff frequency.

Mixer—A circuit used to combine two or more audio- or radio-frequency signals to produce a different output frequency.

Modulate—To vary the amplitude, frequency, or phase of a radio-frequency signal.

Oscillator—A circuit built by adding positive feedback to an amplifier. It produces an alternating current signal with no input except the dc operating voltages.

Phase modulation—Varying the phase of an RF carrier in response to the instantaneous changes in the modulating signal.

Reactance modulator—A device capable of modulating an ac signal by varying the reactance of a circuit in response to the modulating signal. (The modulating signal may be voice, data, video, or some other kind depending on what type of information is being transmitted.)

Selectivity—A measure of how well a receiver can separate a desired signal from other signals on nearby frequencies.

Sensitivity—The ability of a receiver to detect weak signals.

Stability—A measure of how well a receiver or transmitter will remain on frequency without drifting.

Superheterodyne receiver—A receiver that converts RF signals to an intermediate frequency before detection.

Variable-frequency oscillator (VFO)—An oscillator used in receivers and transmitters. The frequency is set by a tuned circuit using capacitors and inductors. The frequency can be changed by adjusting the components in the tuned circuit.

In this section we will discuss low-pass, high-pass and band-pass filter circuits. We'll show you block diagrams of complete transmitters and receivers, and investigate how the stages connect to make them work.

Keep in mind that entire books have been written on each topic covered in this section. You may not understand some of the circuits from our brief discussion. It would be a good idea to consult some other reference books. *The ARRL Handbook for Radio Amateurs* is a good starting point. Even that book won't tell you everything about a topic. The discussion in this chapter will help you understand the circuits well enough to pass your Technician class license exam, however.

FILTERS

A problem for hams is harmonic interference to entertainment equipment. Harmonics are multiples of a given frequency. Your transmitter radiates undesired harmonics along with your signal. In the high-frequency amateur bands (3.5 to 29.7 MHz), the frequency you're transmitting on is much lower than the TV or FM channels. Some of your harmonics may fall within the home entertainment bands. The entertainment receiver cannot distinguish between the TV or FM signals that are supposed to be there and your harmonics, which are not. If your harmonics are strong enough, they can interfere with the broadcast signal.

Harmonic interference must be cured at your transmitter. It is your responsibility as a licensed amateur. You must see that harmonics from your transmitter are not strong enough to interfere with other services. As mentioned before, all harmonics generated by your transmitter must be attenuated well below the strength of the fundamental frequency. If harmonics from your transmitting equipment exceed these limits, you are at fault.

You can usually tell harmonic interference when you see it on a TV set. This type of interference shows up as crosshatch or a herringbone pattern on the TV screen. See Figure 5-11. Unlike overload, interference from radiated harmonics seldom affects all channels. Rather, it may bother the one channel that is frequency-related to the band you're on. Generally, the low TV channels (channels 2-6) are most affected by harmonics from amateur transmitters operating below 30 MHz. Channels 2 and 6 are especially affected by 10-meter transmitters, and channels 3 and 6 experience trouble from 15-meter transmitters.

There are several possible cures for harmonic interference. We will discuss a few of them here. Try each step in the order we introduce them. Chances are good that your problem will be quickly solved. You should be familiar with three **filters**: the low-pass filter, the high-pass filter and the band-pass filter.

Filters pass certain frequencies and block others. All modern radio communication devices use filter circuits. These filter circuits allow various kinds of equipment to operate on different frequencies without interfering with each other. Under certain conditions, some equipment may need a little extra help. A transmitter may need extra filtering of the output signal to reduce interference to television receivers. In other cases, the transmitter may already be well filtered (clean), but a TV receiver may need extra filtering of its input signals. A basic understanding of filters and their applications will often allow you to solve interference problems.

LOW-PASS FILTERS

The first step you should take is installation of a **low-pass filter** in the transmission line between your transmitter and antenna. A low-pass filter is one that passes all frequencies

Figure 5-11—Harmonic interference may be visible as cross-hatching of the TV screen. More severe interference can completely destroy the picture. The width of the cross-hatch lines will vary, depending on the transmitter frequency.

below a certain frequency, called the **cutoff frequency**. We measure the filter cutoff frequency by putting a variable-frequency signal into the filter. The input signal power is kept constant while the frequency is increased. At the same time we measure the filter output power. At some frequency the output begins to decrease. When the output power has decreased to ½ the input power, we have found the cutoff frequency. Frequencies above the cutoff frequency are **attenu-**

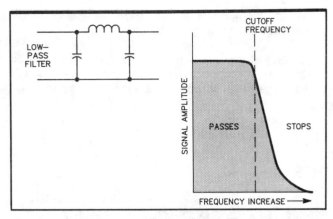

Figure 5-12—A low-pass filter schematic diagram and its output-versus-frequency curve. The low-pass filter passes signals below the cutoff frequency and attenuates signals above the cutoff frequency.

ated, or significantly reduced in amplitude. See Figure 5-12.

The cutoff frequency depends on the design of the low-pass filter. The capacitors are chosen to provide a path to ground for the desired high frequencies. The inductor has a value that passes the low frequencies you want, but blocks the higher frequencies. One other important trait that must be considered in the design of a low-pass filter is the characteristic impedance. Most external low-pass filters intended for amateur use will have a characteristic impedance of 50 ohms.

The low-pass filter is always connected between the transmitter and the antenna, as close to the transmitter as possible. The filter should have the same impedance as the feed line connecting the transmitter to the antenna. Filters should be used only in a feed line with a low standing-wave ratio. The cutoff frequency has to be higher than the highest frequency used for transmitting. A filter with a 45-MHz cutoff frequency would be fine for the high-frequency bands. The filter would significantly attenuate 6-meter (50-MHz) signals. Most modern transmitters have a low-pass filter built into their output circuitry to prevent excess harmonic radiation.

[Now turn to Chapter 13 and study exam questions 3AG-1-1.1, 3AG-1-1.2, 3AG-1-2.1 and 3AG-1-2.2. Review this section if you have trouble with any of these questions.]

HIGH-PASS FILTERS

Sometimes entertainment devices experience interference from amateur transmissions even though the transmitting device is operating properly. The harmonics can be well below levels necessary to prevent interference. This happens because the design of the entertainment device is inadequate when it is operating in the presence of strong signals. In this situation, it may be necessary to reduce the level of the amateur signal reaching the entertainment device (TV or FM stereo receiver, or VCR). The desired higher frequency signals must be allowed to pass unaffected. **High-pass filters** can do this.

A high-pass filter passes all frequencies above the cutoff frequency, and attenuates those below it. See Figure 5-13. A high-pass filter should be connected to a television set, stereo receiver or other home-entertainment device that is being interfered with. It will attenuate the signal from an amateur station. The inductors have a value that allows them to conduct the lower frequencies to ground. The capacitor tends to block these low-frequency signals. At the same time it allows the higher-frequency television or FM broadcast signals to pass through to the receiver. This is useful in reducing the amount of lower-frequency signal (at the ham's operating frequency). The lower-frequency signal might overload a television set, causing disruption of reception. For best effect, the filter should be connected as close to the television-set tuner as possible. Put it inside the TV if it is your own set and you don't mind opening the cabinet. You can also attach it directly to the antenna terminals on the back of the television. If the set belongs to your neighbors, have them contact a qualified service technician to install the filter. That way you are not held responsible if something goes wrong with the set later on.

[Turn to Chapter 13 and study questions 3AG-2-1.1, 3AG-2-2.1 and 3AG-2-2.2. Review this section as needed.]

BAND-PASS FILTERS

A **band-pass filter** is a combination of a high-pass and low-pass filter. It passes a desired range of frequencies while rejecting signals above and below the pass band. This is shown in Figure 5-14. Band-pass filters are commonly used in

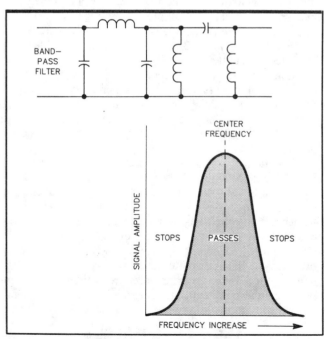

Figure 5-14—A band-pass filter schematic diagram and its output-versus-frequency curve are shown. The band-pass filter passes only those signals within the passband.

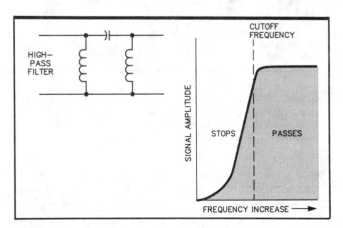

Figure 5-13—A high-pass filter schematic diagram and its output-versus-frequency curve are shown. The high-pass filter attenuates only those signals below the cutoff frequency.

receivers to provide different degrees of rejection. Very narrow filters are used for CW reception. Wider filters are switched in for SSB and AM double-sideband reception. (SSB and AM are explained later.)

[Now turn to Chapter 13 and study questions 3AG-3-1.1, 3AG-3-1.2 and 3AG-3-2.1. Review this section as needed.]

TRANSMITTERS

Amateur transmitters range from the simple to the elaborate. They generally have two basic stages, an **oscillator** and a power **amplifier** (PA). This chapter introduces the CW transmitter and the FM transmitter.

Separate receivers and transmitters have been replaced by transceivers in most amateur stations. A transceiver combines circuits necessary for receiving and transmitting in one package. Some circuit sections may perform both transmitting and receiving functions. Other sections are dedicated to transmit-only or receive-only functions. To simplify some of the following information, we will speak of transmitter or receiver circuits. The principles of operation are the same in transceivers. The transmitter topics apply to transceivers in the transmit mode. Receiver topics apply to transceivers in the receive mode.

Remember that an oscillator produces an ac waveform with no input except the dc operating voltages. You may be familiar with audio oscillators, like a code-practice oscillator. An RF oscillator can be used by itself as a simple low-power transmitter, but the power output is very low. See Figure 5-15. In a practical transmitter the signal from the oscillator is usually fed to one or more amplifier stages.

CW TRANSMITTERS

A block diagram of a simple amateur transmitter is shown in Figure 5-16A. It produces CW (continuous-wave unmodulated) radio signals when the key is closed. The simple transmitter consists of a crystal oscillator followed by a driver stage and a power amplifier. A crystal oscillator uses a quartz crystal to keep the frequency of the radio signal constant.

Crystal oscillators are not practical in many cases. A different crystal is needed for each operating frequency. After a while, this becomes quite expensive, as well as impractical. If we use a variable-frequency oscillator (VFO) in place of the crystal oscillator, as shown in Figure 5-16B, we can change the transmitter frequency at will.

Great care in design and construction is required if the stability of a VFO is to compare with that of a crystal oscillator. Stability means the ability of a transmitter to remain on one frequency without drifting. The frequency-determining components of a VFO are very susceptible to changes in temperature, supply voltage, vibration and changes in the amplifiers following the VFO. These factors have far less effect on the frequency of a vibrating quartz crystal.

FM TRANSMITTERS

When a radio signal or carrier is modulated, some characteristic of the radio signal is changed in order to convey information. We transmit information by modulating any property of a carrier. For example, we can modulate the frequency or phase of a carrier. **Frequency modulation** and **phase modulation** are closely related. The phase of a signal cannot be varied without also varying the frequency, and vice versa. Phase modulation and frequency modulation are especially

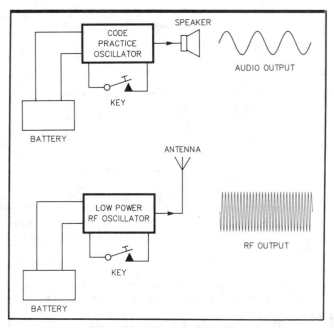

Figure 5-15—Audio- and radio-frequency oscillators are shown. Even a low-power RF oscillator connected to a good antenna can send signals hundreds of miles.

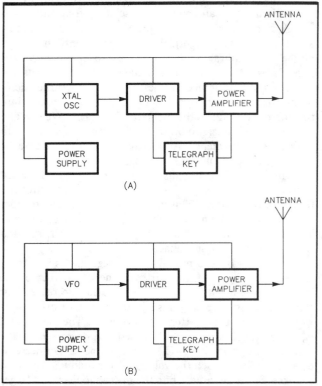

Figure 5-16—Part A shows a block diagram of a basic crystal-controlled CW transmitter. B shows a simple VFO-controlled CW transmitter.

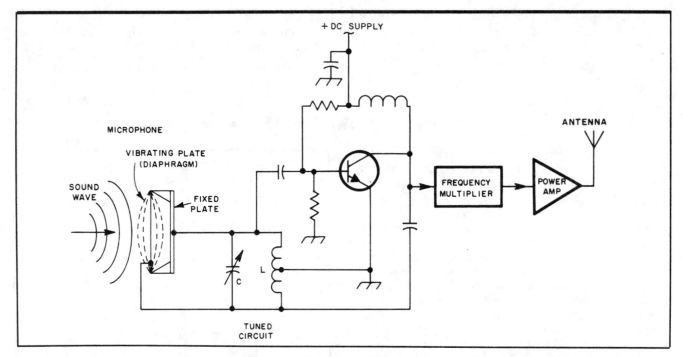

Figure 5-17—This diagram shows a simple FM transmitter. The frequency of the oscillator is changed by changing the capacitance in the resonant circuit. The vibrating plate in the microphone is part of the total capacitance in the resonant circuit.

suited for channelized local UHF and VHF communication. They feature good audio fidelity and high signal-to-noise ratio.

The simplest type of FM transmitter is shown in Figure 5-17. Remember that a circuit containing capacitance and inductance is resonant at some frequency. A resonant circuit in the feedback path of an oscillator can control the oscillator frequency. By changing the resonant frequency of the tuned circuit, we can change the oscillator frequency.

A capacitor microphone is just a capacitor with one movable plate (the diaphragm). When you speak into the microphone, the diaphragm vibrates and the spacing between the two plates of the capacitor changes. When the spacing changes, the capacitance changes. We can connect the microphone to the resonant circuit in our oscillator. Speaking into the microphone varies the oscillator frequency. We can add frequency multipliers to bring the oscillator frequency up to our operating frequency. Adding an amplifier to increase the power provides a simple FM transmitter.

In practical FM systems, the carrier frequency is varied or modulated by changes in voltage that represent information to be transmitted. This information may originate from a microphone, a computer modem or even a video camera. The carrier frequency changes in proportion to the rise and fall of the modulating voltage.

In other words, a modulating voltage that is becoming more positive increases the carrier frequency. As the voltage becomes more negative, the carrier frequency decreases. For some purposes, reversing this relationship will work just as well (FM voice transmitters, for instance). The main point is, the carrier frequency is increased and decreased by the modulating signal voltage. The amount of increase or decrease depends on how much the voltage of the modulating signal changes. Speaking loudly into the microphone causes larger variations in carrier frequency than speaking in a normal voice. Speaking *too* loudly, though, may cause distortion.

One way to shift the frequency of the oscillator is to use a **reactance modulator**. A reactance modulator uses a vacuum tube or transistor. It is connected so that it changes either the capacitance or inductance of the oscillator resonant circuit. The changes occur in response to an input signal.

Modern FM transmitters may use a *varactor diode* to modulate the oscillator. A varactor diode changes capacitance when its bias voltage changes. You can connect a varactor diode to a crystal oscillator as shown in Figure 5-18. The varactor diode will "pull" the oscillator frequency slightly when the audio input changes.

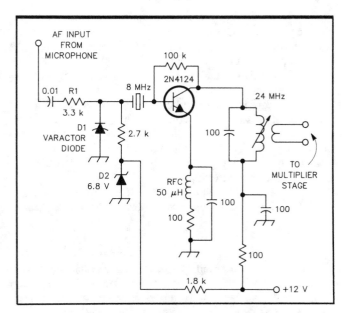

Figure 5-18—A varactor diode (D1) can be used to frequency modulate an oscillator. The capacitance of the varactor diode changes when the bias voltage varies.

Phase Modulation

One problem with direct-modulated FM transmitters is frequency stability. Designs that allow the oscillator frequency to be easily modulated may have an unfortunate side effect. It becomes more difficult to minimize unwanted frequency shifts arising from changes in temperature, supply voltage, vibration and so on. The frequency multiplying stages also multiply any drift or other instability problems in the oscillator. With phase modulation, the modulation takes place after the oscillator stage. Phase modulation produces what is called *indirect FM*.

The most common method of generating a phase-modulated telephony signal is to use a reactance modulator. A vacuum tube or a transistor is connected so that it changes either the capacitance or inductance of a resonant circuit in response to an input signal. The RF carrier is passed through this resonant circuit. Changes in the resonant circuit caused by the reactance modulator cause phase shifts in the RF carrier. Figure 5-19 shows the connection of a reactance modulator.

[Now turn to Chapter 13 and study questions 3AG-4-1.2, 3AG-4-1.3, 3AG-4-1.5, 3AG-4-2.2, 3AH-1.1 through 3AH-2-2.2, 3AH-5.1 and 3AH-5.2. Review this section as needed.]

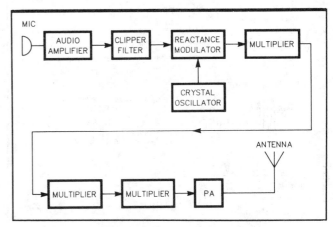

Figure 5-19—This is a block diagram of a phase-modulated transmitter, showing the reactance modulator.

RECEIVERS

The main purpose of any radio receiver is to change radio-frequency signals (which we can't hear or see) to signals that we can hear or see. A good receiver can *detect* weak radio signals. It separates them from other signals and interference. Also, it stays tuned to one frequency without drifting.

The ability of a receiver to detect weak signals is called **sensitivity**. **Selectivity** is the ability to separate (select) a desired signal from undesired signals. **Stability** is a measure of the ability of a receiver to stay tuned to a particular frequency. In general, then, a good receiver is very sensitive, selective and stable.

Amateur receivers can be simple or complex. You can build a simple solid state receiver that will work surprisingly well. *The ARRL Handbook for Radio Amateurs* has receiver plans, including sources for parts and circuit boards.

DETECTION

The detector is the heart of a receiver. It is where we collect the information we want from the signal. "Crystal sets" using galena crystals and "cat's whiskers" were an early form of **amplitude modulation (AM)** detector. AM is generated by varying the amplitude of an RF signal in response to a microphone or other signal source. The cat's whisker is just a thin, stiff piece of wire. With the galena crystal it forms a point-contact diode. See Figure 5-20.

Today, however, more sensitive and selective receivers are required. In addition, crystal sets cannot receive single sideband (SSB) and CW signals properly. The crystal set shows how simple a receiver can be. It is an excellent example of how detection works. Every receiver has some type of detector. Figure 5-21A shows another simple receiver. Diode D1 does the same job as the cat's-whisker detector.

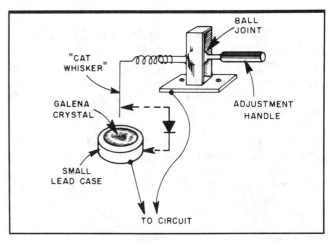

Figure 5-20—Here is an example of a galena crystal and a cat's whisker, the detector in a crystal set.

Some later AM receivers had circuits similar to Figure 5-21B. This is a tuned-radio-frequency (TRF) receiver. An incoming signal causes current to flow from the antenna, through the resonant tuned circuit, to ground. The current induces a voltage with the same waveform in L2. The L1-C1 circuit resonates at the frequency of the incoming signal and tends to reject signals at other frequencies. The diode rectifies the RF signal, allowing only half the waveform to pass through. Capacitor C2 fills in and smoothes out the gaps between the cycles of the RF signal. Only the audio signal passes on to the headphones. Amplification can improve the sensitivity of this receiver, but other receiver types have much better selectivity.

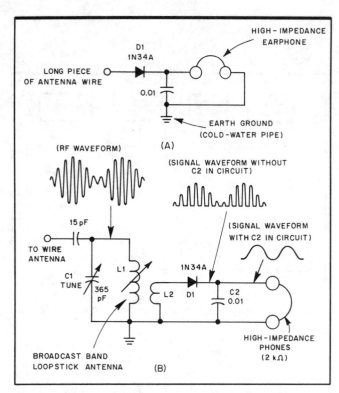

Figure 5-21—Illustration A shows a simple AM receiver using a crystal detector. It consists only of a wire antenna, detector diode, capacitor, earphone and earth ground. The circuit at B has a tuned circuit that helps separate the broadcast-band signals, but otherwise operates the same as the circuit at A.

DIRECT-CONVERSION RECEIVERS

The next step up in receiver complexity is shown in Figure 5-22. Direct-conversion means the RF signal is converted directly to audio, in one step. The incoming signal is combined with one from a **variable-frequency oscillator** (VFO) in the **mixer** stage. We mix an incoming signal at 7040 kHz with a signal from the VFO at 7041 kHz. The output of the mixer contains signals at 7040 kHz, 7041 kHz, 14,081 kHz and 1 kHz (the original signals and their sum and difference frequencies). One of these signals (1 kHz) is within the range of human hearing. We use an audio amplifier and hear it in the headphones.

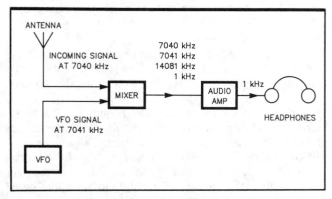

Figure 5-22—A block diagram of a direct-conversion receiver. This receiver converts RF signals directly to audio, using only one mixer.

By changing the VFO frequency, other signals in the range of the receiver can be converted to audio signals. Direct-conversion receivers are capable of providing good usable reception with relatively simple, inexpensive circuits. Their main disadvantages are microphonics and ac hum.

Microphonics are caused by vibrating circuit components when the receiver is tuned or adjusted. A receiver must amplify microvolt signals to several volts, so they can be heard on a speaker or in headphones. Direct-conversion receivers do most of their amplification at AF (audio frequencies). A large amount of audio amplification is needed to build up the mixer (detector) output signal. Unfortunately, the movement of components generates signals (like a microphone) that are also amplified. Better receiver designs avoid microphonics by sharing the amplification among RF, IF (intermediate frequency) and AF stages.

Hum is induced from the 60-Hz ac power lines in buildings and houses. The 60-Hz ac can sometimes modulate the VFO signal. You will then hear a hum or buzz in the headphones.

SUPERHETERODYNE RECEIVERS

A block diagram of a simple **superheterodyne receiver** for CW and SSB is shown in Figure 5-23. The first mixer produces a signal at the **intermediate frequency** or IF, typically 9 MHz in a modern receiver. All the amplifiers after the first mixer are designed for peak efficiency at the IF. The superhet receiver solves the selectivity/bandwidth problem by converting all signals to the same IF before filtering and amplification. To receive SSB and CW signals, a second mixer, called a product detector, is used. The product detector mixes the IF signal with a signal from the **beat-frequency oscillator (BFO)**. The output from the product detector contains audio that can be amplified and sent to a speaker or headphones.

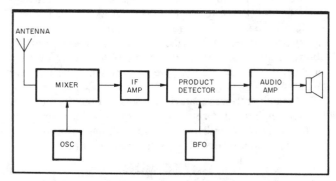

Figure 5-23—A block diagram of a superheterodyne SSB/CW receiver. One mixer converts the incoming signal to the intermediate frequency (IF) and another mixer, called a product detector, recovers the audio or Morse code.

FM RECEIVERS

An FM superheterodyne receiver is similar, but with a few different stages. It has a wider bandwidth filter and a different type of detector. One common FM detector is the frequency **discriminator**. The discriminator output varies in amplitude as the frequency of the incoming signal changes. You can see that it performs the opposite job of the frequency or phase modulator we studied earlier in this chapter.

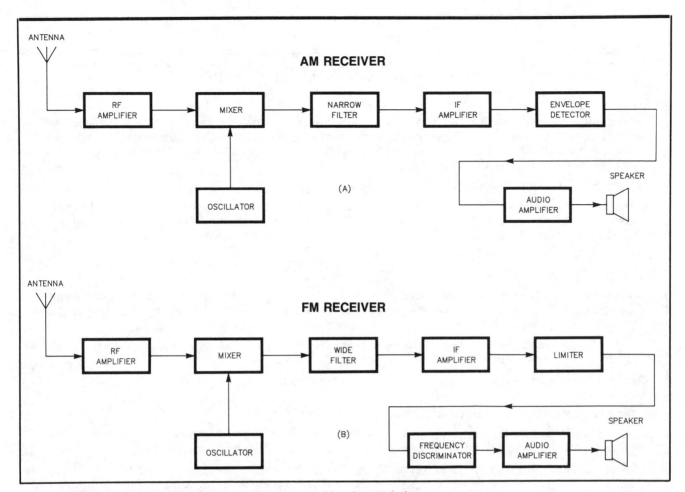

Figure 5-24—AM and FM receivers use similar stages, with a few variations.

Most FM receivers also have a **limiter** stage between the IF amplifier and the detector. The limiter makes the receiver less sensitive to amplitude variations and pulse noise than AM or SSB/CW receivers. As its name suggests, the limiter output remains almost constant when the signal level fluctuates. Noise pulses are also amplitude-modulated signals. The limiter does not pass them on to the detector. This feature makes FM popular for mobile and portable communications. A comparison between an AM receiver and an FM receiver is shown in Figure 5-24.

[This completes your study of this chapter. Now turn to Chapter 13 and study questions 3AG-4-1.1, 3AG-4-1.4 and 3AG-4-2.1. Review any material you're unsure of before you go on.]

──── KEY WORDS ────

Band spread—A receiver quality used to describe how far apart stations on different nearby frequencies will seem to be. We usually express band spread as the number of kilohertz that the frequency changes per tuning-knob rotation. Band spread and frequency resolution are related. The amount of band spread determines how easily signals can be tuned.

Bandwidth—The range of frequencies that will pass through a given filter.

Beat-frequency oscillator (BFO)—A receiver circuit that provides a signal to the detector. The BFO signal mixes with the incoming signal to produce an audio tone for CW reception. A BFO is needed to copy CW and SSB signals.

Continuous wave (CW)—Morse code telegraphy.

DX—Distance; foreign countries.

General-coverage receiver—A receiver used to listen to a wide range of frequencies. Most general-coverage receivers tune from frequencies below the standard-broadcast band to at least 30 MHz. These frequencies include the shortwave-broadcast bands and the amateur bands from 160 to 10 meters.

Ham-bands-only receiver—A receiver designed to cover only the bands used by amateurs. Usually refers to the bands from 80 to 10 meters, sometimes including 160 meters.

Lower sideband (LSB)—The common single-sideband operating mode on the 40, 80 and 160-meter amateur bands.

Multimode transceiver—Transceiver capable of SSB, CW and FM operation.

Offset—The 300- to 1000-Hz difference in CW transmitting and receiving frequencies in a transceiver. For a repeater, offset refers to the difference between its transmitting and receiving frequencies.

Receiver—A device that converts radio waves into signals we can hear or see.

Receiver incremental tuning (RIT)—A transceiver control that allows for a slight change in the receiver frequency without changing the transmitter frequency. Some manufacturers call this a clarifier (CLAR) control.

Resolution—The space between markings on a receiver dial. The greater the frequency resolution, the easier it is to separate signals that are close together. Frequency resolution and band spread are related.

Rig—The radio amateur's term for a transmitter, receiver or transceiver.

Selectivity—The ability of a receiver to separate two closely spaced signals.

Sensitivity—The ability of a receiver to detect weak signals.

Shack—The room where an Amateur Radio operator keeps his or her station equipment.

Single sideband (SSB)—A common mode of voice operation on the amateur bands. SSB is a form of amplitude modulation.

Transceiver—A radio transmitter and receiver combined in one unit.

Transmitter—A device that produces radio-frequency signals.

Transmit-receive (TR) switch—A device used for switching between transmit and receive operation. The TR switch allows you to share one antenna between a receiver and a transmitter.

Upper sideband (USB)—The common single-sideband operating mode on the 20, 17, 15, 12 and 10-meter HF amateur bands, and all the VHF and UHF bands.

Variable-frequency oscillator (VFO)—A circuit used to control the frequency of an amateur transmitter.

Chapter 6

Selecting Your Equipment

Having an amateur license and no station is a little like having a driver's license but no car. Without a station, your license is just another piece of paper. You can probably arrange to use a friend's equipment or operate from a club station when your license first arrives. Very soon, you'll want to have your own station.

Most hams look with pride at their operating position. When hams meet, conversation always turns to the station. Whenever hams visit each other, the "shack" is usually the first stop on the tour. Many amateurs who develop friendships on the air eventually swap pictures of their stations. It's no wonder, really. Hams devote many hours to their hobby, and they spend most of these hours in their shacks. The shack is where a ham operates on the air, repairs equipment, makes improvements and experiments with new projects.

As a newcomer to Amateur Radio, you may find the wide assortment of equipment, antennas and available accessories confusing at first. You'll wonder, "Why is this antenna better than that one?" or "What features does this receiver offer? Do I really need them all?"

You have to decide what your goals are. Take a look at your available resources (how much money you have to spend). Do a little research and then choose the equipment that best suits your needs. Actually, selecting your station equipment can be very easy, if you know what you want it to do. The information in this chapter will help you select a radio that will provide you with many hours of enjoyable operating.

Before you go out and purchase a room full of equipment, find out how big the room is! Try to get some idea of how much space you will have for your shack. Chapter 8 has more detailed information about where to locate your station. Some hams use a corner of a bedroom or den, and some use a fold-out shelf in a closet. Available space may be an important consideration in what equipment you purchase.

When you know how much space you have, you're ready to select your equipment. There are many factors to consider. "Specs" (specifications) are very important, but don't choose your equipment on that basis alone. Some rigs are technical marvels but very difficult and frustrating for a new ham to operate. Other gear may look great but have a lot of technical problems. The most important consideration is what works for you. Choose equipment that will be enjoyable and comfortable to operate.

There are many different places to look for equipment. Check with local hams to see what they use. Find out what they like about certain pieces of gear and what problems they have had. Learn from their experience. They are as proud of their shacks as you will be of yours. When you are deciding what you want, there is no substitute for sitting down and listening to a rig. (For the name of a local radio club, contact ARRL Headquarters.)

Another place to look is your local radio store. Check the telephone book for ham radio retailers in your area. Most large metropolitan areas have at least one. If you visit the store, you will be able to see and compare several of the newest pieces of equipment. In addition, most ham stores have antennas set up so you can listen to receivers you might buy.

The popular ham magazines carry many ads in each issue. When you look through any issue of *QST*, you can find ads from many manufacturers. Local dealers and large mail-order companies also advertise in *QST*. This book includes ads from most manufacturers and many dealers. Many of the ads list features and specifications, and will give you a rough idea of what the equipment costs.

QST has an advertising acceptance policy that can help protect you. If a piece of equipment doesn't live up to its manufacturer's claims, you won't see it advertised in *QST*. It's a good idea to study the ads and have some equipment in mind when you visit the local ham store.

BUYING USED EQUIPMENT

Many newcomers to Amateur Radio simply cannot afford to purchase new equipment. Even if you don't have to worry about money, you might not want to spend a lot at first. Buying used equipment is a good alternative to purchasing new equipment for your station: You can still get good-quality gear, and pay quite a bit less than if you purchased it new. Even if you decide to buy a new transceiver, think about buying used accessories.

SHOULD YOU BUILD YOUR OWN EQUIPMENT?

There was a time when almost all hams built their own rigs. The cost was small, and the operators took great pride in their work. Many hams still build their own equipment, either from used parts or as kits. Commercially made equipment is more affordable now than it used to be, but some hams still build their own equipment. We hope you will try building at least some part of your station as well. The satisfaction of being able to say, "I built it myself!" is a joy you will never forget.

Most beginners won't want to build a modern transmitter, receiver or transceiver. The electronics have gotten much more complicated over the years, and this complexity can frustrate an inexperienced builder. If you have a limited ham radio budget, buy used equipment.

WHAT SHOULD I BUY?

The answer to that question depends largely on available resources and personal preferences. Older issues of amateur magazines can provide a lot of information on equipment you may see on the used market. The New Products and Product Review columns in *QST* are a good start. Many local libraries carry back issues of *QST*. Local hams may also have some *QST*s. If you can't find the issues you need, you can purchase many of them from ARRL HQ. In addition, several product guides and product-review anthologies are available. They summarize features and performance of recently manufactured equipment.

Don't just rush out and buy the first piece of equipment you can find. Buying used radio equipment is much like buying a used car: You really should "kick the tires" a bit. Examine the equipment closely (as well as you can). Don't get snowed by salesmanship. A couple of old adages apply: "You (generally) get what you pay for" and "caveat emptor" —buyer beware. Perhaps we should add a third: "All things come to those who wait..." Have patience!

Surplus Equipment

There's still some WW II government surplus equipment on the market, and you may also see some newer surplus gear. Generally speaking, a beginner who doesn't have an Elmer should stay away from this equipment.

Much of the military equipment is big and heavy. You might also have to find some special connectors or build a power supply to use it. Some units produce large amounts of television interference (TVI), and that's one thing we can all do without!

Many units that appear to be bargains will require quite a bit of work to get them on the air. Many hams enjoy using surplus gear, but it's not cost-effective for the beginner. You might try a surplus rig later, when you have gained some experience and want to do some tinkering.

Tube Availability

You might wonder about the practicality of buying tube-type equipment. After all, modern equipment uses transistors and integrated circuits, and many companies have stopped making tubes. Tubes are still available, but they are becoming expensive. A few electronic supply houses still stock tubes. Many amateurs have plenty of tubes (often free for the asking) in their "junk boxes." Some excellent transceivers made in the 1970s used tubes in the power-amplifier stages. These tubes usually are readily available.

Sidebands

There are two kinds of single sideband: **upper sideband (USB)** and **lower sideband (LSB)**. Hams usually use LSB on 160, 80 and 40 meters, and USB on 20, 17, 15, 12 and 10 meters. Upper sideband is also used on VHF and UHF. Some radios automatically switch to the correct sideband for the operating frequency. Others have separate USB and LSB positions on the mode switch. You will always use the USB position for 10-meter and VHF/UHF SSB operation.

WHERE CAN I FIND USED GEAR?

There are many different sources of used ham gear. You can buy gear from equipment retailers and local hams. You may see what you want listed in the pages of ham magazines (see the *QST* Ham Ads) or used-equipment flyers. Other sources are auctions, flea markets, hamfests and even garage sales.

If you belong to an Amateur Radio club, ask your instructor and other club members. They can often provide you with some leads and other useful information about buying used gear. The club members can help you select a particular unit or a complete station. They can also help you test it to ensure it works properly. They will certainly provide some helpful hints on connecting all the pieces.

One of the safest ways to purchase used equipment is to buy it from a local retailer. Often the dealer sets aside a section of the ham shop for used equipment. When you buy from such a source, there's usually some sort of warranty (30 days is typical) on the equipment. If a problem comes up within that time, you can bring it back to the retailer for repairs. Ask about the warranty *before* you buy.

Many dealers route the used equipment they've received through their service shop. This ensures that the gear is working properly before they place it on the used-equipment shelf. Some dealers will even allow you to operate the equipment before you buy it. This is the best way to determine the rig's capabilities and condition.

When you buy used gear from an individual, you generally have no guarantees. Ask to see the unit in operation. You might even wish to take along a more knowledgeable ham who can help you make the decision. A local ham can be your best source of information on used equipment.

You may already know what you want or what you need. The hard part is deciding which of those used rigs provides the best value for your hard-earned dollars. An "old-timer" can be an invaluable source of information. Chances are, he or she may have at one time owned a similar piece of equipment. With the seller's permission, your ham friend could

operate the equipment and note any potential problems— your future headaches!

Local hamfests, flea markets and auctions are some of the better opportunities to see a quantity of used equipment. For the careful buyer, they may also be the source of some excellent equipment. But you have to know what you're looking for. What are the capabilities of the equipment, its current market value, cost of repairs and availability of repair parts?

At a hamfest or flea market, you may not be able to test equipment before you buy it. A thorough visual inspection by an experienced eye will generally suffice if the price is right, however. Again, help from an experienced amateur is a wise choice. You can usually tell a lot from the external appearance of equipment. If it looks physically abused, chances are it has been treated badly on the air as well.

There are some simple precautions you should take if you're buying gear from another ham through the mail. Try to be sure you'll have the right to return the equipment if you don't like what you receive. Shipment by truck freight with the right of inspection permits you to examine the package contents before you accept delivery. If you don't like what you receive, simply refuse delivery. You may be asked to pay by bank check or money order, rather than personal check.

There is one other very important point to keep in mind when you buy used equipment from any source. Be sure you get an owner's manual with the radio! Some hams may even have the service or shop manual. A shop manual can be a valuable addition, because it generally has more complete service procedures and troubleshooting guidelines.

If you are not getting at least an owner's manual with the radio, be cautious about making the purchase. Manuals for some pieces of equipment are available from the manufacturer. Several companies sell manuals for used or surplus equipment; see Table 6-1.

Table 6-1

Sources of Equipment Manuals

Brock Publications (Swan,
    Cubic, Siltronix)
PO Box 5004
Oceanside, CA 92054
619-757-0372

Collins S-Line: See VISTA
    Technology, Inc

Cubic Communications: See
    Brock Publications

R. L. Drake Co
540 Richard St
Miamisburg, OH 45342
513-886-3211

Hallicrafter Manuals
Ardco Electronics††
PO Box 95, Dept Q
Berwyn, IL 60402

Hammarlund Manuals
Pax Manufacturing Co
100 East Montauk Hwy
Lindenhurst, NY 11757
516-957-7200

HI Manuals, Inc†
PO Box 802
Council Bluffs, IA 51502

Howard W. Sams Co
Photofact Division
2647 Waterfront Pkwy
East Drive
Indianapolis, IN 46214
317-298-5566

ICOM America, Inc
2380 116th Ave NE
Bellevue, WA 98004
206-454-7619

Kenwood USA Corporation
PO Box 22745
2201 E Dominguez St
Long Beach, CA 90801-5745
213-639-9000

Siltronix manuals: See
    Brock Publications

Swan manuals: See
    Brock Publications

Ten-Tec, Inc
Hwy 411 East
Sevierville, TN 37862
615-453-7172

US Government Surplus
General Services Administration
National Archives and Record
    Services
Washington, DC 20408

US Government Surplus
Slep Electronics Co††
PO Box 100
Otto, NC 28763

VISTA Technology, Inc
    (Collins Radio manuals)
3041 Rising Springs
Bellbrook, OH 45305
513-426-6700

Yaesu USA
17210 Edwards Rd
Cerritos, CA 90701
213-404-2700

†HI Manuals will not answer requests for information unless
    you include a $5 research fee. Order their catalog ($2)
    to see if they have the manual you need.

††Write for manual prices (specify model).

GOING SHOPPING

Once you've faced the decision of whether to buy new gear or used gear, you must think about a few more details. Don't worry: After you finish this chapter you'll know just what to look for when you go out to buy that first rig.

HF EQUIPMENT

Transceiver or Separates?

Although this section refers to HF equipment, much of the information applies to VHF/UHF transceivers, too. One of the first decisions you'll face is whether to use a **transceiver** or a separate **receiver** and **transmitter**. When you make this decision, keep your space limitations in mind. A transceiver, as the name implies, combines both a transmitter and receiver in one package. That means you can fit a transceiver in a smaller space than that required by most separates. In fact, some newer transceivers require less than one foot of desk space. See Figure 6-1. Transceivers are easier to set up. Usually, you just connect a microphone and CW key, attach an antenna, plug in the ac-power cord and you're ready to go.

With separates, you may have to do a little wiring between the transmitter and receiver. You'll also need a **transmit-receive (TR) switch** to switch the antenna between the two units.

Figure 6-1—The Yaesu FT-747 is a good example of a trend toward less complicated transceivers. You can work the world with this rig and a good antenna.

Transceivers are easier to operate than a separate receiver and transmitter. A single control sets both the transmit and receive frequency. With one frequency control to set, you're sure to be transmitting and receiving on the same frequency.

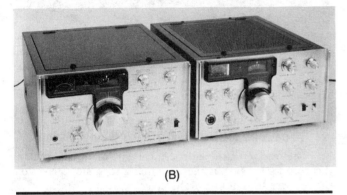

(A)

(B)

Figure 6-3—The Radio Shack HTX-100 is a small, inexpensive 10-meter transceiver.

Figure 6-2—(A) The Heath HR-1680 and HX-1681 "twins." The transmitter is a CW-only rig designed to cover portions of the 80, 40, 20, 15 and 10-meter bands. At B, a pair of Kenwood "twins" produced in the 1970s. The receiver is all solid-state. The transmitter uses solid-state devices except for the driver and final-amplifier stages, which use tubes.

Until recently, some manufacturers offered "twins"—separates interconnected so they can act as a transceiver. See Figure 6-2.

Separate transmitter-receiver combinations were popular because they offered better performance and flexibility than transceivers of the time. Modern transceivers have all the features once offered only in separates.

A primary advantage of a transceiver is that it automatically transmits and receives on the same frequency, which takes some care and practice with a separate receiver and transmitter. A simple transceiver suitable for Novice operation is shown in Figure 6-3. Although it operates only on 10 meters, it can be a good value for a new Novice.

Modern transceivers are at least equal to, and sometimes better than, a separate receiver and transmitter. Most offer split-frequency capability. Another feature offered in most new transceivers is a bank of frequency memories that allow you to switch quickly from one frequency to another. Figure 6-4 shows two modern, full-featured transceivers.

If you do decide to buy an older rig, try to avoid "boat anchors." This is what hams call radios that require two people simply to get them in the trunk of your car! While many of the older radios were excellent performers in their time, the saying "They don't build 'em like they used to" is true. Modern, solid-state radios offer far better reliability and performance. Right now, you want a rig you can *use*, not one you have to nurse back to health after every contact! After a little looking, you'll probably decide that either a transceiver or separate "twins" will work well for you.

(A)

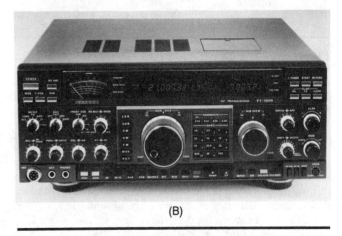

(B)

Figure 6-4—Two modern transceivers with lots of "bells and whistles." (A) The ICOM IC-781 uses a computer-monitor type display in place of a digital readout. (B) The Yaesu FT-1000D allows you to listen on two frequencies at the same time. All the knobs and switches on these rigs can be intimidating to a Novice. If you read the instruction manual carefully you should have no trouble understanding everything, however.

Price

An important consideration for most of us is price. Don't be dismayed if you can't afford a new transceiver right away. Plenty of good, used transceivers are available at reasonable prices.

When you decide what kind of gear you want, you'll have to examine specific features. The next few sections describe some of the things to look for. Remember that many of the features explained here apply to separate transmitters and receivers as well as transceivers.

Frequency Display

Of all the controls on a rig, you use the frequency control most often. The frequency display includes the knobs, dials, gears and readout. Make certain the mechanism works freely, the dial markings are understandable, and you feel comfortable operating it.

Two different types of tuning-dial mechanisms are available on recently manufactured transceivers and separates: Digital and analog.

Most manufacturers now use digital displays (Figure 6-5). They are generally quite accurate, and are easier to use than analog dials.

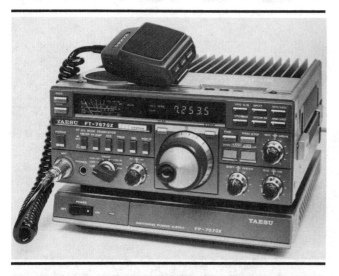

Figure 6-5—The Yaesu FT-757GX is a marvel of modern miniaturization. The transceiver is all solid state and has a digital frequency display. The rig also includes a general-coverage receiver and 100-watt transmitter with a built-in electronic keyer. All this fits in a box the size of a portable typewriter.

The analog circular dial (Figure 6-6) was very common before digital dials became popular. The dial is usually calibrated in kilohertz. A fixed pointer indicates where the dial is tuned. Circular dials vary in **resolution**. The farther apart the markings on the dial, the better the resolution. The better the resolution, the easier it is to tell what frequency you're on. A dial with markings every 1 kHz or less is best, although some may be marked only every 5 kHz. The megahertz part of the display is marked on the panel at the band switch.

Choose the dial mechanism you are most comfortable reading and tuning. Make sure the knob operates smoothly. Avoid radios that feel sloppy and slip or skip—that's part of your comfort and accuracy.

Figure 6-6—An example of a transceiver with an analog circular dial.

Receiver Selectivity and Sensitivity

The receiver is the most critical part of the station. In this section, *receiver* applies to either a separate receiver or the receiver section of a transceiver.

Whether you buy separates or a transceiver, there are two important specifications you should know about: selectivity and sensitivity. **Selectivity** is the ability of a receiver to separate two closely spaced signals. This determines how well you can receive one signal that is very close to another. **Sensitivity** is the ability of a receiver to detect weak signals. Selectivity is more important than sensitivity. The ability to isolate the signal you are receiving from all the others nearby directly affects how much you will enjoy your time on the air.

We use **bandwidth** to measure selectivity. Bandwidth is nothing more than how wide a range of frequencies you hear with the receiver tuned to one frequency. With a 6-kHz bandwidth, you can hear signals as far as 3 kHz above and below where you are tuned.

If you can't hear signals more than 200 Hz above or below where your receiver is tuned, your receiver has a bandwidth of 400 Hz. Narrower bandwidth means better selectivity. Narrow bandwidth makes it easier to copy one signal when another is close in frequency.

Special filters built into modern equipment determine the selectivity. Generally, these filters contain quartz crystals arranged to provide a specific selectivity. Some receivers come with several filters. You can choose the filter that gives the best reception.

Look for a selectivity of 500 Hz or less for CW operation. Receivers designed for single-sideband voice operation come with a standard filter selectivity of 2.4 to 2.8 kHz. This filter is usable on CW, but a 500-Hz filter is much better. If the receiver has provision for adding narrow-bandwidth accessory filters, you can buy them later. While selectivity is very important, it comes with a price! The more filters a receiver has and the better their quality, the more the receiver or transceiver will cost.

An *audio filter* (Figure 6-7) is an inexpensive way to add selectivity to a receiver that has only an SSB filter. An audio filter doesn't work against interference as well as a crystal filter, but it may mean the difference between maintaining a QSO or losing one.

Audio filters are simple to construct (see *The ARRL Handbook for Radio Amateurs*). If you don't want to build a filter, you can purchase one of the many available com-

Figure 6-7—Audio filters. At left is an Autek QF1-A. The large filter at right is a JPS Communications NIR-10. The smaller filter at right is the j-Com Magic Notch, a switched-capacitor notch filter.

mercial units. Audio filters are easy to use. They plug into the receiver headphone or speaker jack, and you plug your headphones or a speaker into the filter.

Another selectivity feature available on some receivers is a *notch filter*. This filter can be used to cut out, or notch, a specific frequency from within the received bandwidth. A notch filter is handy when you're trying to receive a signal that is very close in frequency to another signal. By adjusting the notch control, you can effectively eliminate the unwanted signal.

The BFO

If you are buying a separate receiver, make sure it has a built-in **beat-frequency oscillator (BFO)**. Some receivers intended strictly for listening to AM shortwave broadcast stations do not contain a BFO. These receivers are unusable for CW or SSB.

You should have no trouble determining that a receiver has a BFO. Some older receivers, usually the general-coverage units, actually have a front-panel control labeled BFO. Other receivers have a built-in crystal oscillator that serves as a BFO. These receivers usually have a switch labeled LSB, USB, CW, RTTY or some combination of these labels. If your receiver has such a switch, you're in business.

Other Receiver Features

You may find other features on receivers that improve their performance or make them easier to use. Most have a meter that shows the strength of the received signal. Most of the time, the first thing the operator you are working wants to know is his or her signal strength. These meters, called *S meters*, will tell you. They are also useful when you are comparing two antennas. Or, you can use the S meter when you are trying to rotate a directional antenna for maximum signal strength.

Some receivers have a *crystal calibrator*. They produce a signal every 25 or 100 kHz. You can use the calibrator to make sure the dial or display is accurate.

Besides the filters already mentioned, some receivers have *noise blankers*. They are mostly useful for filtering ignition noise from cars and trucks. Some blankers can help reduce power-line noise as well. Some receivers have filters between the intermediate stages. These may be called variable IF filters, or the receiver may have a control labeled PASSBAND TUNING or VARIABLE BANDWIDTH TUNING. An *RF gain* control is sometimes helpful when interference is heavy.

Receiver incremental tuning (RIT) allows you to shift the receiver frequency over a limited range without affecting the transmitter frequency. Although transceivers theoretically transmit and receive on exactly the same frequency, there may actually be a slight frequency difference, or **offset.** This offset can vary from transceiver to transceiver. RIT lets you retune the receiver slightly. This enables you to compensate if the station you are working has a different offset.

All these features can add to your operating enjoyment. They may not be necessities if you are on a tight budget, however. Frequency coverage, tuning mechanism, frequency resolution, selectivity and sensitivity are the most important things to look for.

THE TRANSMITTER

If you are following our advice and considering a transceiver, you'll find many common transmitter features among them. Almost all transceivers offer voice operation.

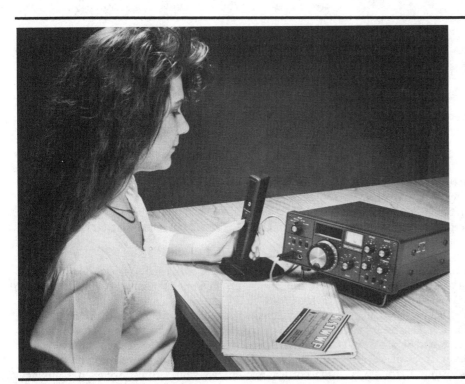

Figure 6-8—The Ten-Tec Argosy II is a transceiver available on the used market. This solid-state, CW/SSB transceiver makes operation as uncomplicated as possible.

Voice capability is important if you want to operate voice or data on the 10-meter Novice band (most data modes use the voice part of the radio).

Power output varies somewhat from rig to rig. Most transceivers produce about 100 watts output, which is less than the 200 watts output that Novices are allowed to use. This may sound bad, but it isn't. Most of the time, if 100 watts won't make the contact, neither will 200. One-hundred watts will even drive a high-power linear amplifier, if you decide to get one when you upgrade to General or a higher class license. Figure 6-8 shows a simple operating position, with an inexpensive transceiver as the station rig. This transceiver produces *less than* 100 watts, but it has been used to contact over 100 countries!

A shortcoming of most rigs made before 1980 is their inability to operate on the 17, 12, and 30-meter bands. When you upgrade to the General or higher class license, you may want to use those bands. You'll also be able to use much larger portions of the 80, 40, 15 and 10-meter bands, plus the 160- and 20-meter bands. The rig you buy may cover bands you can't use right now, but they'll be there, waiting for you when you upgrade.

A typical separate ham transmitter runs between 75 and 200 W PEP output from the final amplifier. It operates upper and lower sideband and CW, and has VFO control. The transmitter will cover the 80, 40, 20, 15 and 10-meter amateur bands. Some also include the 160-meter band.

Newer transceivers also cover the 30, 17 and 12-meter bands. Either will be more than adequate for all the operating you're likely to do as a Novice. It will also serve you well after you earn a higher-class license. Figure 6-9 shows a compact 160-10 meter transceiver suitable for mobile or home station use.

Figure 6-9—The ICOM IC-735 has many desirable features for a home-station rig, but is small enough for mobile and portable use.

As with the receiver, you should choose a transmitter that is easy to operate. Look for the same features in the transmitter tuning dial as you would in a receiver dial.

Modern transceivers or transmitters with vacuum-tube final amplifiers develop more than 100 watts PEP output. The workhorse of the final-amplifier-tube family is the 6146. It's tough and can take a beating—such as prolonged key-down periods or antenna mismatches. Given a little time to cool down, the 6146 will bounce right back as good as new. The Kenwood TS-830S is a popular transceiver that uses 6146 tubes in its final amplifier. It should be available at reasonable prices on the used market. This transceiver is shown in Figure 6-10.

Tube-type transmitters use two basic types of keying circuits: cathode keying and grid-block keying. If you use a

Figure 6-10—The Kenwood TS-830S transceiver uses 6146 tubes in the final-amplifier section.

hand key, the voltage polarity at the key jack is of little consequence. If you use an electronic keyer with a transistor switch in the output circuit, polarity must be considered.

Keyers that use relays with floating (ungrounded) contacts in the output circuit are more flexible since key-jack voltage polarity is unimportant. But relay contacts can stick and the trend is to use transistorized output stages in modern keyers.

Cathode keying presents a positive voltage to the transmitter key jack. In cathode keying, the key line opens and closes the cathode circuit of one or more tubes in the transmitter. When the key is up, there is an open circuit in the tube cathode. This effectively shuts off the tube so it draws no plate or screen current; thus, no RF output.

Grid-block keying uses a negative voltage applied to the grid(s) of the keyed tube(s). This voltage, usually at a reduced amplitude, is also present at the transmitter key jack. With the key open, the bias voltage cuts off the tube. Closing the key removes or reduces the bias and the tube conducts.

As a rule, older transmitters used cathode keying while more modern tube equipment uses grid-block keying. Fully transistorized rigs may use either positive or negative polarity at the key jack.

Before you connect a keyer to any rig, you should check the key-jack voltage and polarity. Make sure your keyer works with the rig. Check your equipment manual. It should tell you the type of keying circuit used in your transmitter, and the key-jack voltage. If you built the keyer, the construction article should tell you the appropriate keying voltage.

There are ways to change the keyer output circuit. You can use a transistor or optoisolator, but these techniques are beyond the scope of this book. A more-experienced amateur may be able to help you if you face this problem. Also, *The ARRL Handbook for Radio Amateurs* contains more information.

Other Transmitter Features

MICROPHONE

To talk on SSB, you will need to add a microphone to your transceiver. The microphone connects to the microphone jack on your radio.

Individual voices and microphones have different characteristics. Your rig should have a microphone gain control you can adjust for a clean signal. Most SSB transmitters have an automatic level control (ALC) meter to help you determine the correct microphone-gain setting. See your equipment manual for instructions on adjusting everything to the right levels.

SPEECH PROCESSOR

Speech processing increases the average power of a single-sideband signal. Used properly, a speech processor can greatly improve the readability of a signal. Misused, however, it can severely degrade the audio quality and make the signal more difficult to understand.

Almost all SSB transmitters and transceivers built since 1980 have speech processors as standard equipment. There is also a variety of accessory speech processing equipment for transmitters without built-in processing.

On some rigs, there is no adjustment for the speech processor; there is just an on/off control. Other gear has one or more variable controls to set the speech processing level. Always check your equipment instruction manual for information on setup and operation. When you think you've got everything adjusted properly, ask other amateurs for on-the-air checks.

VOICE-OPERATED SWITCH (VOX)

Most SSB transceivers and transmitters have a voice-operated switch (VOX). The VOX switches the rig into transmit automatically when you speak into the microphone, then back to receive when you stop talking. VOX is handy because it allows you to listen during pauses and lets you keep both hands free.

There are usually three VOX controls: gain, delay and anti-VOX. *VOX gain* sets the sensitivity. Adjust this control so the VOX keys the transmitter when you speak in a normal voice.

VOX delay sets the interval between when you stop talking and when the transceiver switches back to receive. Most hams set this control so the rig switches after a short pause in speech.

Anti-VOX works with VOX gain to keep receiver audio from keying the VOX. If improperly set, speaker audio can key the transmitter. You could set the VOX gain so speaker audio wouldn't key the transmitter, but if you did, you'd have to shout to activate the VOX. Anti-VOX circuitry allows the VOX to ignore audio from the speaker, yet respond when you speak into the microphone.

VHF AND UHF EQUIPMENT

Whether you are working toward the Novice or the Technician license, you have a wide variety of VHF and UHF equipment to choose from. Many transceivers for these bands operate only in the FM mode. Other gear can be used only for SSB and CW work. For both FM and SSB/CW operation, you need a third type, the **multimode transceiver**, like the one in Figure 6-11. You have to know what modes you'd like to try before you can choose a rig. Unlike five- or six-band HF transceivers, most VHF and UHF equipment operates on only one band. Two- and three-band rigs are becoming more popular, however.

Also consider where you'll use the equipment. Some VHF/UHF equipment is best for home station operation. Other, more compact, units work well for mobile operation. Portable, hand-held transceivers can be used anywhere.

Although manufacturers sometimes design equipment for a certain application, you can use it wherever you want. If you like, you can use a hand-held transceiver in a car, or a mobile rig at your home station. There are, however, some

Figure 6-11—The ICOM IC-375A 222-MHz transceiver. This rig can be used on FM, SSB and CW.

trade-offs to consider when you want to use a rig at home and in your car or portable.

Base-Station and Mobile Equipment

FM base stations often consist of a multimode transceiver or a mobile transceiver. Multimode base-station transceivers often have built-in ac power supplies and are larger than FM-only rigs.

Mobile rigs are often smaller than base-station transceivers, and they operate from a 13.8-V automobile electrical system. See Figure 6-12. You'll need an external, accessory power supply to use one at home.

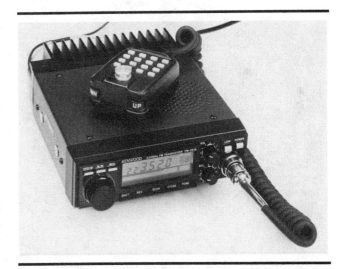

Figure 6-12—Modern VHF FM rigs are usually very small, like the Kenwood TM321A shown here.

FM mobile transceivers usually have all the features found in base-station equipment. Power output for mobile and base-station equipment is typically in the 10- to 25-watt range. The rig's physical size and the power supply are the most important things to consider. Other than size and power requirements, there is no particular advantage to either a base-station unit or a mobile unit for FM work. Many amateurs buy a mobile transceiver and external power supply, and use the same radio at home and in the car.

Transverters

There are fewer radios available for VHF/UHF SSB and CW work than for FM. Much SSB and CW operation is done with a *linear transverter* used with a regular 10-meter HF transceiver. A transverter converts signals from one band to another. For example, a 222- to 28-MHz transverter receives a signal at 222.1 MHz and converts it to 28.1 MHz for reception on an HF receiver. Likewise, the transverter accepts a 28.1-MHz signal from your HF transmitter and converts it for transmission on 222.1 MHz.

The transverter has no external controls. The transceiver operates exactly like it does on HF; the only difference is that you're transceiving on 222 MHz instead of 28. Most transverters have 10 to 25 watts RF output. Transverters are available for all VHF/UHF bands, as well as several microwave (above 1000 MHz) bands.

Multiband and Multimode Transceivers

Multiband transceivers combine more than one VHF/UHF band in one box. Optional modules for other bands may be available. For example, the unit shown in Figure 6-13 comes supplied with modules for 144 to 148 and 420 to 450 MHz. A separate 1270- to 1300-MHz module is available at extra cost. This rig has the additional ability to transmit on one band and receive on another, at the same time. Amateur Radio repeater satellites require users to transmit and receive on separate bands, which is easy if you have two rigs. With transceivers like this one, you need only one rig.

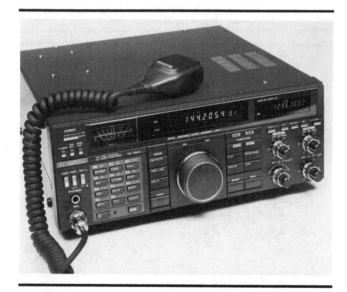

Figure 6-13—The Kenwood TS-790A is a multiband, multimode transceiver. It operates on the 144- to 148-MHz and 420- to 450-MHz bands. Operation on 1240 to 1300 MHz is possible with an optional module.

The transceiver shown earlier in Figure 6-11 is also a multimode rig. It can be used on FM and SSB voice, and also on CW. Not all multiband rigs are multimode, and some multimode rigs operate on only one band.

Hand-held Transceivers

Hand-held VHF or UHF FM transceivers (often called HTs) are very popular. Such equipment is the most compact of the lot. See Figure 6-14. HTs are self-contained stations.

Figure 6-14—The Kenwood TH31BT and the Yaesu FT-109H 222-MHz FM hand-held transceivers. This type of rig is a complete portable station, with an autopatch tone pad and a flexible vertical antenna.

They use battery power and have a built-in antenna, speaker and microphone.

Most hand-held units can be used with an external 12-V supply and an external antenna. Some offer accessory external speakers and microphones, which are handy for mobile or home-station use.

To reduce size and conserve battery power, HTs usually have lower power output than mobile or base-station rigs. A typical HT has 1 or 2 watts output; a high-power HT may produce 5-7 watts.

FM TRANSCEIVER FEATURES

VHF and UHF FM transceivers have many features not always found on HF rigs. While many of these features are not essential, they are useful. All FM transceivers have a *squelch* control that quiets the receiver when no signal is present. Squelch lets you leave your transceiver on without having to listen to noise when the frequency is not in use.

All newer transceivers use a *synthesizer* to control the operating frequency, while many older ones use VFOs or crystals. Synthesized and most VFO-type transceivers can operate on any frequency in the band. Crystal-controlled radios have a front-panel control to allow you to switch between two or more repeater or simplex channels.

If you live in an area with many repeaters, you'll want a synthesized transceiver. You should also consider this type if you plan to use repeaters in other areas, perhaps on business or vacation trips. If you add the cost of crystals (about $15 per channel) to the cost of a second-hand crystal-controlled transceiver, the total cost may be more than that of a synthesized transceiver.

Most crystal-controlled transceivers require two crystals for each repeater or simplex channel. One crystal is for the transmitter (repeater input frequency) and one is for the receiver (repeater output frequency). For simplex operation, you need two crystals for the same frequency.

Synthesized transceivers offer almost unlimited frequency flexibility. Going from simplex to repeater operation is as easy as flipping a switch. The transceiver comes factory programmed for the proper repeater frequency **offset** for the band. You dial up the repeater output frequency and the transceiver automatically switches to the repeater input frequency when you transmit.

It may be inconvenient to tune a synthesized radio all over the band to change frequency. This is true if you normally operate on only a few repeater or simplex frequencies, perhaps separated by hundreds of kilohertz. For added convenience, synthesized transceivers often have *memories* to store your favorite frequencies. You store them in the memory and recall them as needed. For example, memory 1 may be for the local repeater input on 222.32 MHz, memory 2 for the 223.5 MHz simplex frequency, and so on.

Synthesized transceivers sometimes offer automatic *scanning* up and down the band, or among repeater channels. This feature is handy if you're traveling and want to find an active repeater.

There are other FM transceiver features, sometimes standard and sometimes available as options. These include *tone pads* for autopatch use and *tone-burst* or *subaudible-tone generators* for repeaters that require such tones for access. An autopatch provides a connection between the amateur station and the telephone line. A tone pad is a 12- or 16-button keypad used to generate audio tones similar to those used on some telephone systems.

FOR MORE INFORMATION

We've tried to give you a few guidelines in this chapter. There are lots of rigs out there, both new and used. Take your time and try to get as much information as you can. Talk to other hams and read the Product Reviews in *QST*. Advertisements in *QST* and this book will tell you what's available. Remember that everyone has an opinion, though. What they like might not be what you like.

Most of all, don't worry! If you buy a used rig and you don't like it, you can probably sell it for almost as much as you paid for it. Start small and simple. Ham radio is fun; part of the fun is dreaming about new equipment and upgrading your station as you upgrade your license.

——— KEY WORDS ———

Antenna—A device that picks up or sends out radio waves.

Balun—Contraction for *bal*anced to *un*balanced. A device to couple a balanced load to an unbalanced source, or vice versa.

Beam antenna—A directional antenna. A beam antenna must be rotated to provide coverage in different directions.

Characteristic impedance—The opposition to electric current that an antenna feed line presents. Impedance includes factors other than resistance, and applies to alternating currents. Ideally, the characteristic impedance of a feed line is the same as the transmitter output impedance and the antenna input impedance.

Coaxial cable—coax (pronounced kó-aks). A type of feed line with one conductor inside the other.

Dipole antenna—See **Half-wave dipole**. A dipole need not be ½ wavelength long.

Directivity—The ability of an antenna to focus transmitter power into certain directions. Also its ability to enhance received signals from specific directions.

Director—An element in front of the **driven element** in a Yagi and some other directional antennas.

Driven element—The part of an antenna that connects directly to the feed line.

Feed line (feeder)—See **Transmission line**.

Gain—A measure of the directivity of an antenna.

Half-wave dipole—A basic antenna used by radio amateurs. It consists of a length of wire or tubing, opened and fed at the center. The entire antenna is ½ wavelength long at the desired operating frequency.

Inverted-V dipole—A half-wave dipole antenna with its center elevated and the ends drooping toward the ground. Often called an inverted V.

Ladder line—Parallel-conductor feeder with insulating spacer rods every few inches.

Matching network—A device that matches one impedance level to another. For example, it may match the impedance of an antenna system to the impedance of a transmitter or receiver. Amateurs also call such devices a Transmatch, impedance-matching network or match box.

Multiband antenna—An antenna that will operate well on more than one frequency band.

Omnidirectional—Antenna characteristic meaning it radiates equal power in all compass directions.

Open-wire feed line—Parallel-conductor feeder with air as its primary insulation material.

Parallel-conductor feed line—Feed line with two conductors held a constant distance apart.

Polarization—Describes the electrical-field characteristic of a radio wave. An antenna that is parallel to the surface of the earth, such as a dipole, produces horizontally polarized waves. One that is perpendicular to the earth's surface, such as a quarter-wave vertical, produces vertically polarized waves.

Quarter-wavelength vertical antenna—An antenna constructed of a quarter-wavelength long radiating element placed perpendicular to the earth.

Radiate—To convert electric energy into electromagnetic (radio) waves. An antenna radiates radio waves.

Random-length wire antenna—An antenna having a length that is not necessarily related to a wavelength for which it is used.

Reflector—An element behind the driven element in a Yagi and some other directional antennas.

Resonant frequency—The desired operating frequency of a tuned circuit. In an antenna, the resonant frequency is one where the feed-point impedance contains only resistance.

RF burn—A flesh burn caused by exposure to a strong field of RF energy.

Sloper—A ½-wave dipole or ¼-wave end-fed antenna that has one end elevated and one end nearer the ground.

Standing-wave ratio (SWR)—Sometimes called VSWR. A measure of the impedance match between the feed line and the antenna. Also, with a Transmatch in use, a measure of the match between the feed line from the transmitter and the antenna *system*. The system includes the Transmatch and the line to the antenna. VSWR is the ratio of maximum voltage to minimum voltage along the feed line. It is also the ratio of antenna impedance to feed-line impedance when the antenna is a purely resistive load.

SWR meter—A device used to measure SWR.

Transmatch—See **Matching network**.

Transmission line—The wires or cable used to connect a transmitter or receiver to an antenna.

Twin lead—Parallel-conductor feed line with wires encased in insulation.

Vertical antenna—A common amateur antenna, usually made of metal tubing. The radiating element is vertical. There are usually four or more radial elements parallel to or on the ground.

Wavelength—Often abbreviated λ. The distance a radio wave travels in one RF cycle. The wavelength relates to frequency. Higher frequencies have shorter wavelengths.

Yagi antenna—The most popular type of amateur directional (beam) antenna. It has one driven element and one or more additional elements.

Chapter 7

Choosing an Antenna

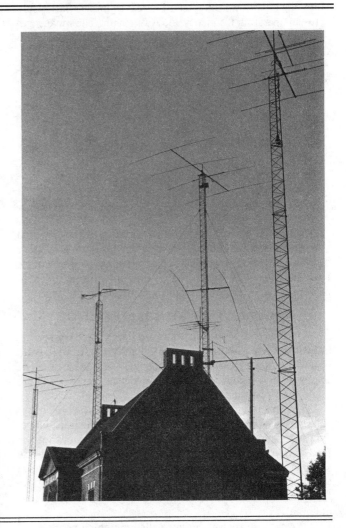

The "antenna farm" at W1AW (ARRL Headquarters) is a bit bigger than you'll need as a Novice or Technician. Large beam antennas on tall towers almost always ensure the best communications, however.

We know that a transmitter generates radio-frequency energy. We convert this electrical energy into radio waves with an **antenna**. An antenna may be just a piece of wire or other conductor designed to **radiate** the energy. An antenna converts current into an electromagnetic field (radio waves). The radio waves spread out or *propagate* from the antenna. You might relate their travel to the ever-expanding waves you get when you drop a pebble in water. Waves from an antenna radiate in all directions, though, not just in a flat plane.

It also works the other way. When a radio wave crosses an antenna, it generates a voltage in the antenna. That voltage isn't very strong, but it's enough to create a small current. That current travels through the **transmission line** to the receiver. The receiver detects the radio signal. In short, the antenna converts electrical energy to radio waves and radio waves to electrical energy. This process makes two-way radio communication possible with just one antenna.

Your success in making contacts depends heavily on your antenna. A good antenna can make a fair receiver seem like

a champ. It can also make a few watts sound like a whole lot more. Remember, you'll normally use the same antenna to transmit *and* receive. Any improvements to your antenna make your transmitted signal stronger, and increase the strength of the signals you receive.

Assembling an antenna system gives you a chance to be creative. You may discover, for example, that property size or landlord restrictions rule out a traditional antenna. If so, you can innovate. *The ARRL Antenna Book*, *The ARRL Antenna Compendiums*, and similar publications offer suggestions. This chapter contains a few suggestions, too.

Some antennas work better than others. Antenna design and construction have kept radio amateurs busy since the days of Marconi. You'll probably experiment with different antenna types over the years. Putting up a better antenna is an inexpensive but rewarding way to improve your station.

WAVELENGTHS

We sometimes talk about antenna lengths in wavelengths. A **wavelength** relates to the operating frequency. When you construct an antenna for one particular amateur band, you cut it to the proper wavelength. Often you'll see the Greek letter lambda (λ) used as an abbreviation for wavelength. For example, ½ λ means "one-half wavelength."

Most popular ham antennas are less than 1 λ long. (A very popular antenna is a ½-λ dipole. You'll learn how to build one later in this chapter.) There is a simple relationship between operating frequency and wavelength. The wavelength is shorter at the higher frequencies. Wavelength is longer at the lower frequencies.

If numbers interest you, use this equation to find the wavelength for a specific frequency.

$$\lambda \text{ (in feet)} = \frac{984}{\text{f (in MHz)}} \qquad \text{(Eq 7-1)}$$

This equation gives the wavelength in feet. The frequency is given in megahertz (MHz). Let's say we wanted to know the wavelength for 7.15 MHz. We divide 984 by 7.15, and the answer is about 137.6 feet.

Whenever we talk about an antenna, we specify its design frequency or the amateur band it covers. We could talk about an "80-meter dipole," for example, one intended for operation in the 80-meter band. Antennas are tuned circuits. A simple antenna such as a dipole or a ¼-λ vertical has a **resonant frequency**. Such antennas do best at their resonant frequency, as do most other tuned circuits.

To change the resonant frequency of a tuned circuit, you vary the capacitor value or the inductor value. You can change the resonant frequency of an antenna by changing its length, which affects its capacitance *and* inductance.

FEED LINES

To get RF energy from your transmitter to an antenna you use **transmission line**. A transmission line is a special cable or arrangement of wires. Such lines commonly go by the name **feed line**, or **feeders** for short. They feed power to the antenna, or feed a received signal from the antenna to the receiver.

CHARACTERISTIC IMPEDANCE

One electrical property of a feed line is its **characteristic impedance**. In Chapter 3 you learned that resistance is an opposition to electric current. Impedance is another form of opposition to electric current. Impedance includes factors other than resistance, however.

The spacing between line conductors and the type of insulating material determine the characteristic impedance. Characteristic impedance is important because we want the feed line to take all the transmitter power and feed it to the antenna. For this to occur, the transmitter (source) must have the same impedance as its load (the feed line). In turn, the feed line must have the same impedance as its load (the antenna).

We can use special circuits called **matching networks** if any of these impedances are different. Still, careful selection of a feed line can minimize such matching problems.

COAXIAL CABLE

Several different feeder types are available for amateur use. The most common is **coaxial cable**. Called "coax" (pronounced kó-aks) for short, this feed line has one conductor inside the other. It's like a wire inside a flexible tube. The center conductor is surrounded by insulation, and the insulation is surrounded by a wire braid called the shield. The whole cable is then encased in a tough vinyl outer coating, which makes the cable weatherproof. See Figure 7-1. Coax comes in different sizes, with different electrical properties. Figure 7-1 also shows other types of coaxial cables used by amateurs.

The most common types of coax have either a 50-ohm or 72-ohm impedance. Coax designated RG-58 and RG-8 are 50-ohm cables. Some coax designations may also include a suffix such as /U, A/U or B/U, or bear the label "polyfoam." Feed line of this type may be used with most antennas. Cables labeled RG-59 or RG-11 are 72-ohm lines. Many hams use these types to feed dipole antennas.

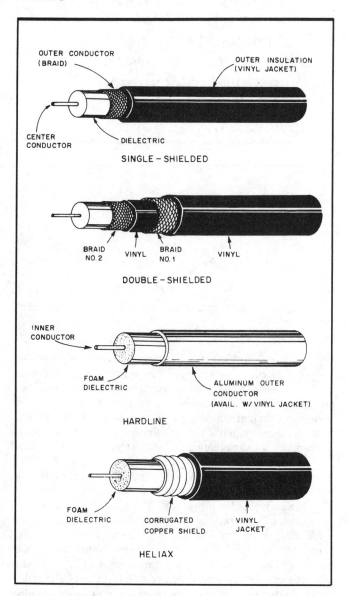

Figure 7-1—Types of coaxial cable used by amateurs. Abbreviated *coax*, it has a center conductor surrounded by insulation. The second conductor, called the shield, goes around that. Plastic insulation covers the entire cable.

The impedance of a ½-λ dipole far from other objects is about 73 ohms. Practical dipoles placed close to the earth, trees, buildings, etc, have an input impedance closer to 50 ohms. In any case, the small impedance mismatch caused by using 50- or 72-ohm cable as an antenna feeder is unimportant.

In choosing the feed line for your installation, you'll have a trade-off between electrical characteristics and physical properties. The RG-58 and RG-59 types of cable are about ¼ inch in diameter, comparatively lightweight, and reasonably flexible. RG-8 and RG-11 are about ½ inch in diameter, nearly three times heavier, and considerably less flexible. As far as operation goes, RG-8 and RG-11 will handle much more power than RG-58 and RG-59.

Any line that feeds an antenna absorbs a small amount of transmitter power. That power is lost, because it serves no useful purpose. (The lost power warms the feed line slightly.) The loss occurs because the wires are not perfect conductors, and the insulating material is not a perfect insulator. Signal loss also increases when the SWR is greater than 1:1, so we try to keep the SWR below 2:1 if possible.

The larger coax types, RG-8 and RG-11, have less signal loss than the smaller types. If your feed line is less than 100 feet long, you probably won't notice the small additional signal loss, at least on the HF bands. This, combined with light weight and flexibility, is why most HF operators find the smaller coax better suited to their needs. Also, the smaller feed line costs about half as much per foot as the larger types.

On the VHF/UHF bands, however, Novices and Technicians will find the losses in RG-58 and RG-59 more noticeable. On these bands, most amateurs use RG-8 coax or even lower-loss special coaxial cables.

Coaxial cable has several advantages as a feed line. It is readily available, and is resistant to weather. Most common amateur antennas have characteristic impedances of about 50 ohms. Coax can be buried in the ground if necessary. It can be bent, coiled and run next to metal with little effect. Its major drawback is its cost.

PARALLEL-CONDUCTOR FEED LINE

Parallel-conductor feed line is another popular line type for use below 30 MHz. The most familiar example of this feeder is the 300-ohm ribbon used for TV antennas. It has two parallel conductors encased along the edges of a strip of plastic insulation. We often call this kind of line **twin lead**. See Figure 7-2A.

Open-wire feed line is another type of parallel-conductor line. It contains two wires separated by plastic spacer rods. There is a rod every few inches along the feeder to maintain a uniform wire separation. The primary insulation is air. See Figure 7-2C. Often called **ladder line**, this type usually has a characteristic impedance between 450 and 600 ohms. The conductors can be bare wire, or they might be insulated with plastic. Ladder line can handle much higher power than twin lead.

You can make ladder line yourself. It is also available commercially, but may be difficult to find. A near equivalent is a cross between twin lead and ladder line. The wires are encased along the edges of a plastic ribbon, but the ribbon is not solid. Instead, it has punched rectangular holes along its length, leaving air as the primary insulation material. The common variety of this line has a 450-ohm impedance. For the same conductor spacing, this line has slightly more loss than ladder line. For most amateur work, the difference is negligible, however.

Parallel-conductor lines have some disadvantages. For example, they cannot be coiled, or run next to metal drain pipes and gutters without adverse effects. Another drawback to these lines is their characteristic impedance of 300 ohms or higher. They cannot be connected directly to most transmitters. Thus, you need an impedance **matching network** if you use any type of parallel-conductor feed line. Connect such a network between your transmitter and your feed line. If you use a matching network, even inexpensive TV twin lead can be used as your feed line. The need for a matching network is the main reason parallel-conductor lines are not used on VHF/UHF. Matching networks are more difficult to build for these frequencies, so most amateurs use coax instead.

The major advantage of ladder line is its very low loss. This means that for the same feeder length, more of your transmitter power will get to your antenna.

It is even possible to use a single wire from your rig to the antenna. We call this a *single-wire feed line*. With this feed arrangement, the feeder often becomes a part of the antenna. It can radiate outdoors, of course, but it can also radiate right in the shack. The impedance of this type of

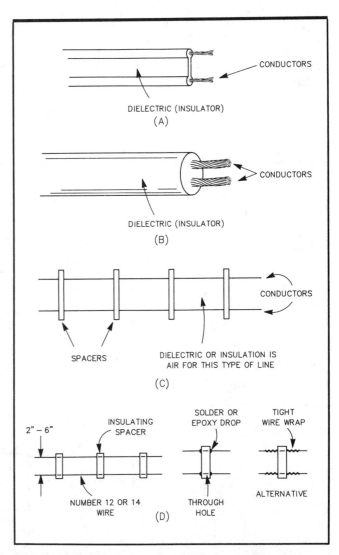

Figure 7-2—Parallel-conductor feed lines. At A, common 300-ohm TV twin lead. B shows 72-ohm transmitting twin lead, designed to carry higher power levels. C shows twin lead that uses air as the dielectric, with insulating spacers every few inches. *Ladder line* is its common name. D shows the construction of home-built ladder line.

antenna system is seldom within the tuning range of most transmitters. You will need an impedance-matching network to connect between the rig and the feed line.

Many new amateurs worry needlessly about feed-line length. If you use coaxial cable between a rig and a dipole or vertical antenna, the cable can be any reasonable length.

A good length to start with is simply the distance between the rig and the antenna! The feed line cannot be any shorter, and any extra length is probably unnecessary.

[Now study the questions in Chapter 12 with numbers that begin 2I-6 and 2I-7. Review this section if you have difficulty with any of the questions.]

IMPEDANCE-MATCHING NETWORKS

Your transmitter won't operate very well if connected to a mismatched feed line. Let's say you want to use parallel-conductor feed lines on your dipoles. Your transmitter probably has an output circuit designed for a 50-ohm load. But that's not what the load will be with this antenna system. An impedance-matching device will provide the proper impedance correction. For some mismatches, a suitable network might contain only an inductor and a capacitor.

A **Transmatch** is a special type of matching network. Transmatches contain variable matching components (inductors and capacitors), and often a band switch. They offer the flexibility of matching a wide range of impedances over a wide frequency range. With a Transmatch, it is possible to use one antenna on several bands. For example, you might use a center-fed wire antenna with inexpensive 300-ohm twin lead.

Each band will use its own Transmatch settings: one combination for 80, one for 40, one for 15, and one for 10 meters.

Connect the Transmatch between the antenna and the **SWR meter**, as Figure 7-3 shows. (An SWR meter measures the mismatch on the feed line between the two pieces of equipment it is connected to.) Adjust the controls on your Transmatch for minimum SWR. Don't worry if you can't achieve a perfect match (1:1). Anything lower than 2:1 will work just fine.

Figure 7-4A shows the schematic diagram for a versatile Transmatch circuit. Part B shows a homemade Transmatch built from this circuit.

[Now study the questions in Chapter 12 numbered 2I-8.1 and 2I-8.2. Review this section if you have difficulty with the questions.]

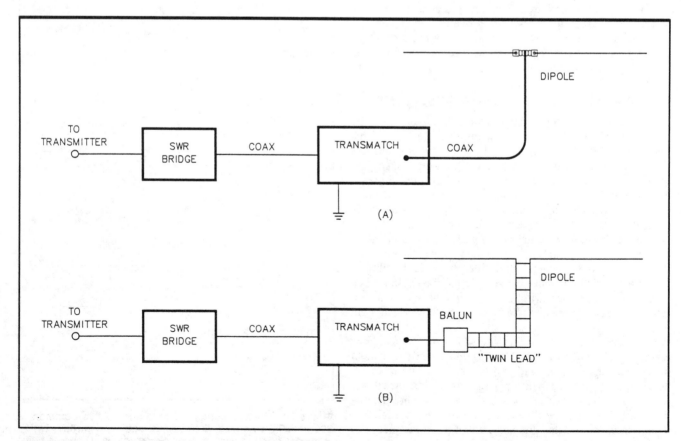

Figure 7-3—With a Transmatch you have flexibility in designing your antenna system. You can use the antenna on several bands, and the length isn't critical. You can use a dipole fed by coax (A) or twin lead (B). With a Transmatch, the dipole legs can be any length, although they should be as long as possible.

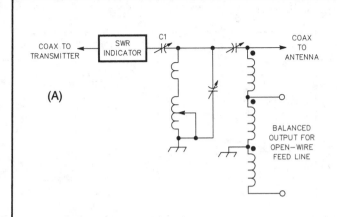

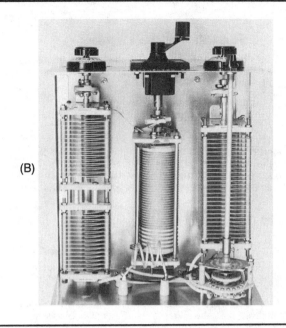

Figure 7-4—At A, the schematic diagram for a versatile Transmatch circuit. B shows a homemade Transmatch constructed from the circuit of A.

BALUNS

A center-fed wire with open ends, such as a dipole, is a **balanced** antenna. In a balanced center-fed antenna, the current flowing into one half of the antenna is equal to the current in the other half. The two currents are also opposite in phase. You can think of a **balanced** antenna as one where neither side connects to ground. A balanced antenna is balanced with respect to ground.

If we feed the antenna with a parallel-conductor line, we keep balance throughout the system. Parallel-conductor feed line is balanced: Neither side connects to ground. You can connect this feed line directly to a dipole antenna.

If we feed a dipole at the center with coax, we upset the system balance. One side of the antenna connects to the coax inner, or center, conductor. The other side connects to the coax shield. The shield connects to ground, so coax is an unbalanced line.

You don't have to go searching for 72-ohm twin lead to have a balanced dipole, however. You can feed it with ordinary 300-ohm twin lead. (To do this, you'll also need a Transmatch at the transmitter end of the line.) Another way is to feed your antenna with coaxial line and use a device called a **balun**. Balun is a contraction for *bal*anced to *un*balanced. You install the balun at the antenna feed point.

Different types of baluns are commercially available, or you can make your own. A common type is a balun trans-former, one with wires wound on a toroidal core. Besides providing a balance, these baluns can transform an impedance, such as from 50 to 75 ohms. Another type is a bead balun. Several ferrite beads go over the outside of the coax, one after the other. The beads tend to choke off any RF current that might otherwise flow on the outside of the shield.

You can easily make another type of choke balun from the coax itself. At the antenna feed point, coil up 10 turns of coax into a roll about 6 inches in diameter. Tape the coax turns together. The inductance of the coiled turns tends to choke off RF currents on the shield.

Feeding a dipole with parallel-conductor line doesn't assure a balanced antenna. You must also consider how the line connects to the transmitter. Most transmitters have a coaxial style connector. Suppose you are using 450-ohm parallel-conductor feed line. To feed such a balanced antenna system, you would need to install a balun at the transmitter end of the line (or use a special balanced matching network). Unless you use a balanced matching network, you need a balun at the transmitter end of the line if you are using any type of parallel-conductor feed line.

[Study questions in Chapter 12 that begin with 2I-9. **If you are preparing for the Technician exam,** also study questions 3AI-4-1.1 through 3AI-4-3.2 in Chapter 13. Review this section if you have difficulty answering these questions.]

STANDING-WAVE RATIO (SWR)

If an antenna system does not match the characteristic impedance of the transmitter, some of the transmitter energy is reflected from the antenna. This reflected energy causes voltage standing waves on the line. When this happens, the RF voltage and current are not uniform along the line. An **SWR meter** measures the voltage **standing-wave ratio**. This is the ratio of the maximum voltage on the line to the minimum voltage. (These two points will always be ¼ λ apart.) Lower SWR values mean a better match exists between the transmitter and the antenna system. If a perfect match

NOT FOR TECHNICIANS ONLY

SWR: What Does It Mean?

You already know that SWR is defined as the ratio of the maximum voltage to the minimum voltage in the standing wave:

$$SWR = \frac{E_{max}}{E_{min}}$$

An SWR of 1:1 means you have no reflected power. The transmission line is said to be "flat." If the load is completely resistive (no reactance), then the SWR can be calculated. Divide the line characteristic impedance by the load resistance, or vice versa. Use whichever gives a value greater than one:

$$SWR = \frac{Z_0}{R} \quad or \quad SWR = \frac{R}{Z_0}$$

where

Z_0 = characteristic impedance of the transmission line
R = load resistance (not reactance)

For example, if you feed a 100-ohm antenna with 50-ohm transmission line, the SWR is 100/50 or 2:1. Similarly, if the impedance of the antenna is 25 ohms the SWR is 50/25 or 2:1.

When a high SWR exists, losses in the feed line are increased. This is because of the multiple reflections from the antenna and transmitter. Each time the transmitted power has to travel up and down the feed line, a little more energy is lost as heat.

This effect is not so great as some people believe, however. Some line losses are less than 2 dB (such as for 100 feet of RG-8 or RG-58 cables up to about 30 MHz). The SWR would have to be greater than 3:1 to add an

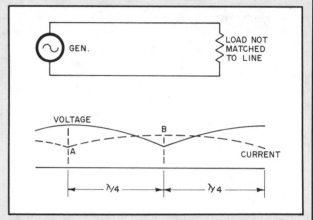

The standing-wave ratio is the ratio of the voltage amplitude at point A to the voltage amplitude at point B, or the ratio of the current amplitude at point B to the current amplitude of point A.

extra decibel of loss because of the SWR. (A high SWR will cause the output power to drop drastically with many solid-state transceivers. The drop in power is caused by internal circuits that sense the high SWR and automatically reduce output power to protect the transceiver.)

A **transmission line** should be terminated in a resistance equal to its characteristic impedance. Then maximum power is delivered to the antenna, and transmission line losses are minimized. This would be an ideal condition. Such a perfect match is seldom realized in a practical antenna system.

---

exists, the SWR is 1:1. Your SWR meter thus gives a relative measure of how well the antenna system impedance matches that of the transmitter.

Modern transmitters are designed to match 52-ohm coaxial lines and antennas. Most commercial antennas are designed to have the same characteristic impedance *when properly adjusted*. So, if your SWR is not 1:1, it means your antenna is not properly adjusted for the frequency you are using. We adjust the antenna for minimum SWR (not always 1:1) somewhere in the middle of the band of interest. On other frequencies the SWR may be higher. If the antenna is properly assembled, an SWR of 2:1 or less is probably all right.

If you are using a matching network, you can probably adjust it so the SWR meter reads 1:1. The SWR on the transmission line between the tuner and the antenna will, however, be different. A matching network can cover up the mismatch, but it does not eliminate it.

SWR METERS

The most common **SWR meter** application is tuning an antenna to resonate on the frequency you want to use. (This discussion applies if you connect the feeder directly to the transmitter output, with no Transmatch.)

An SWR reading of 2:1 or less is quite acceptable. A reading of 4:1 or more is unacceptable. This means there is a serious mismatch between your antenna and your feeder.

To use the SWR meter, you transmit through it. (You *must* have a license to operate a transmitter! What if your license has not arrived by the time you are ready to test your

antenna? Just invite a licensed ham over to operate the transmitter).

How you measure the SWR depends on your type of meter. Some SWR meters have a SENSITIVITY control and a FORWARD-REFLECTED switch. If so, the meter scale usually gives you a direct SWR reading. To use the meter, first put the switch in the FORWARD position. Then adjust the SENSITIVITY control and the transmitter power output until the meter reads full scale. Some meters have a mark on the meter face labeled SET or CAL. The meter pointer should rest on this mark. Next, set the selector switch to the REFLECTED position. Do this *without* readjusting the transmitter power or the meter SENSITIVITY control. Now the meter pointer shows you the SWR value. See Figure 7-5.

You can also measure SWR with a wattmeter, one showing RF power in watts. Your wattmeter may have meters to read both forward and reflected power. If not, it should have a switch or another way to change from forward to reflected power readings. To compute the SWR with a wattmeter, first note both the forward and reflected power for a given transmitter setting. Then consult a graph provided with the meter to find the corresponding SWR.

Find the **resonant frequency** of an antenna by connecting the meter between your transmitter and the feed line going to the antenna. Then measure the SWR at different frequencies across the band. Ideally, you will measure the lowest SWR at the center of the band, with higher readings at each end.

Sometimes your antenna may resonate far off frequency.

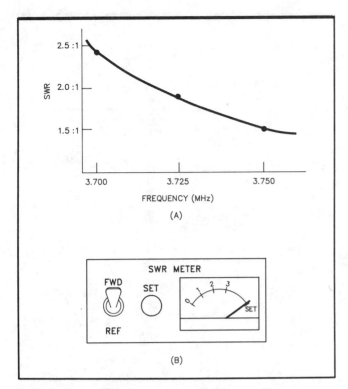

Figure 7-5—To determine if your antenna is cut to the right length, measure the SWR at different points in the band. Plot these values and draw a curve. Use the curve to see if the antenna is too long or too short. Adjusting the length will bring the lowest SWR to the desired frequency. Here the SWR is higher at the low end of the band. This antenna needs to be longer.

See Figure 7-5. In this situation you will not get a "dip" in SWR readings with frequency. Instead, your readings will increase as you change frequency from one end of the band to the other. For example, you might read 2.5:1 at the low-frequency band edge, and 5:1 at the high-frequency end. This means antenna resonance is closer to the low-frequency end of the band than the high. It also means that resonance is below the low-frequency band edge. For a dipole or vertical antenna, this condition exists when the antenna is too long. Trimming the length will correct the problem.

Suppose the readings were 5:1 at the low-frequency end of the band and 2.5:1 at the high end. Here, the antenna is too short. Adding to the antenna length will correct this

problem. Adjusting the antenna length for resonance in this way is what we call *tuning the antenna.*

This method works for dipoles or vertical antennas. It does not show antenna resonance if you have a matching network between the SWR meter and the antenna. Nor does it show resonance for antenna systems that include a matching network at the antenna. An SWR meter *will* show when you have adjusted the matching network properly, however. Use the settings that give you the lowest SWR at your preferred operating frequency.

Finding Antenna Problems with an SWR Meter

Sometimes problems occur when you first install an antenna, or only after the weather batters your antenna for weeks, months or years.

It's handy to have an SWR meter or power meter to help diagnose antenna problems. This section tells how to interpret SWR meter readings to solve specific problems. This information applies to any type of antenna. We assume the antenna you're using normally provides a good match to your feed line at the measurement frequency.

One common problem is a loose connection where the feed line from your station attaches to the antenna wire. Splices or joints are another possible failure point. Your SWR meter will tell if the problem you're experiencing is a poor connection somewhere in the antenna. Observe the SWR reading. It should remain constant. If it is erratic, fluctuating markedly, chances are you have a loose connection. This problem is very easy to see on windy days.

If your SWR reading is unusually high, greater than 10:1 or so, you probably have a worse problem. *Caution:* Do not operate your transmitter with a very high SWR any longer than it takes to read the SWR! The problem could be an open connection or a short circuit. The most likely failure point is at the antenna feed point. The problem might be at the connector attaching your feed line to your transmitter. Carefully check your connections and your feed line for damage. You can also get unusually high SWR readings if the antenna is far from the correct length. This would happen if you try to operate your antenna on the wrong amateur band!

Most hams leave an SWR meter in the line all the time. Any sudden changes in the SWR mean you have a problem, such as a broken wire or bad connection.

[Now study the questions in Chapter 12 with numbers that begin 2D-7-1, 2D-7-2 and 2D-7-3. Review this section if you have difficulty with any of these questions.]

━━━ PRACTICAL ANTENNAS ━━━

Hams use many different kinds of antennas. There is no one best kind. Beginners usually prefer simpler, less expensive types. Some hams with more experience have antenna systems that cost thousands of dollars. Others have antennas that use several acres of property!

THE HALF-WAVE DIPOLE ANTENNA

Probably the most common amateur antenna is a wire cut to ½-λ at the operating frequency. The feed line attaches across an insulator at the center of the wire. This is the **half-wave dipole**. We often refer to an antenna like this as a **dipole**

antenna. (*Di* means two, so a dipole has two equal parts. A dipole could be a length other than ½ λ.) The total length of a half-wavelength dipole is ½ λ. The feed line connects to the center. This means that each side of this dipole is ¼ λ long.

Use Equation 7-2 to find the total length of a ½-λ dipole for a specific frequency. Notice that the frequency is given in megahertz and the antenna length is in feet for this equation.

$$\text{Length (in feet)} = \frac{468}{\text{f(MHz)}} \qquad \text{(Eq 7-2)}$$

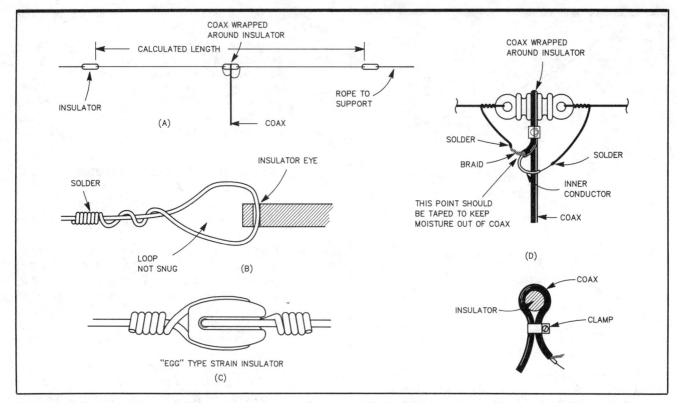

Figure 7-6—Simple half-wave dipole antenna construction. B and C show how to connect the wire ends to various insulator types. D shows the feed line connection at the center.

Equation 7-2 gives us the following approximate lengths for ½-λ dipoles.

Wavelength	Frequency	Length
80 meters	3.700 MHz	126.5 feet
40 meters	7.125 MHz	66 feet
15 meters	21.125 MHz	22 feet
10 meters	28.125 MHz	17 feet
10 meters	28.4 MHz	16.5 feet
2 meters	146.0 MHz	3.25 feet

Figure 7-6A shows the construction of a basic ½-λ dipole antenna. Parts B through D show enlarged views of how to attach the insulators. You can use just about any kind of wire for your dipole. It can range from regular electrical "zip cord" to strong copper-clad steel wire. If possible, use copper wire instead of steel or iron. Copper conducts electricity better. Most hardware or electrical supply stores carry suitable wire. Ordinary house wire, stripped of its insulation, works well. You can sometimes find copper-clad steel wire at a radio store. This wire is used for electric fences to keep farm animals in

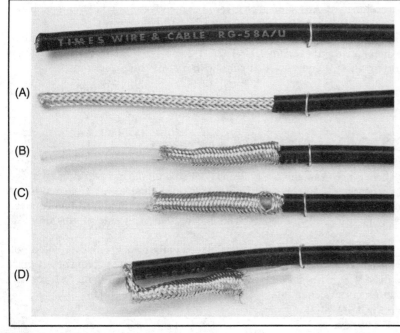

Figure 7-7—Preparing coaxial cable for connection to antenna wire. A—Remove the outer insulation with a sharp knife or wire stripper. If you nick the braid, start over. B—Push the braid in accordion fashion against the outer jacket. C—Spread the shield strands at the point where the outer insulation ends. D—Fish the center conductor through the opening in the braid. Now strip the center conductor insulation back far enough to make the connection and tin (flow solder onto) both center conductor and shield. Be careful not to use too much solder, which will make the conductors inflexible. Also be careful not to apply too much heat, or you will melt the insulation. A pair of pliers used as a heat sink will help. The outer jacket removed in step A can be slipped over the braid as an insulator, if necessary. Be sure to slide it onto the braid before soldering the leads to the antenna wires.

their place, so another place to try is a farm supply store. House wire and stranded wire will stretch with time, so a heavy gauge copper-clad steel wire is best. This wire consists of a copper jacket over a steel core. Such construction provides the strength of steel combined with the excellent conducting properties of copper.

Remember, you want a good conductor for the antenna, but the wire must also be strong. The wire must support itself *and* the weight of the feed line connected at the center.

We use wire gauge to rate wire size. Larger gauge numbers represent smaller wire diameters. Conversely, smaller gauge numbers represent larger wire diameters. Although you can use almost any size wire for your dipole antenna, 12 or 14 gauge is usually best.

Cut your dipole according to the dimension found by Equation 7-2, but leave a little extra length to wrap the ends around the insulators. You'll need a feed line to connect it to your transmitter. For the reasons mentioned earlier, the most popular feed line for use with dipole antennas is coaxial cable. When you shop for coax, look for some with a heavy braided shield. If possible, get good quality cable that has at least 95 percent shielding. If you stick with name brand cable, you'll get a good quality feed line. Figure 7-7 shows the steps required to prepare the cable end for attachment to the antenna wires at the center insulator.

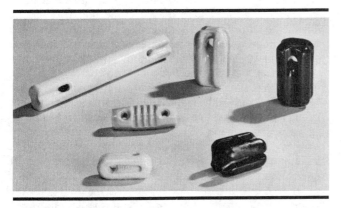

Figure 7-8—Various commercially made antenna insulators.

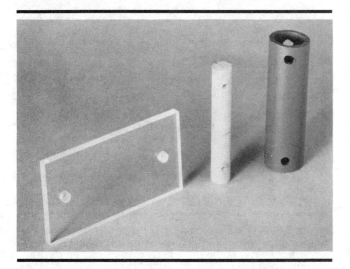

Figure 7-9—Some ideas for homemade antenna insulators.

The final items you'll need for your dipole are three insulators. You can purchase them from your local radio or hardware store (Figure 7-8). You can also make your own insulators from plastic or Teflon blocks. See Figure 7-9. One insulator goes on each end and another holds the two wires together in the center. Figure 7-10 shows some examples of how the feed line can attach to the antenna wires at a center insulator.

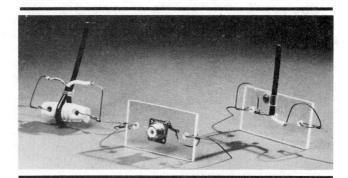

Figure 7-10—Some dipole center insulators have connectors for easy feeder removal. Others have a direct solder connection to the feed line.

[Now turn to the questions in Chapter 12 with numbers that begin 2I-1 and study them. Review this section if you need to.]

ANTENNA LOCATION

Once you have assembled your dipole, find a good place to put it. *Never* put your antenna under, or over the top of electrical power lines. If they ever come into contact with your antenna, you could be electrocuted. Avoid running your antenna parallel to power lines that come close to your station. Otherwise you may receive unwanted electrical noise. Sometimes power-line noise can cover up all but the strongest signals your receiver hears. You'll also want to avoid running your antenna too close to metal objects. These could be rain gutters, metal beams, metal siding, or even electrical wiring in the attic of your house. Metal objects tend to shield your antenna, reducing its capability.

The key to good dipole operation is height. How high? One wavelength above ground is good, and this ranges from about 35 feet on 10 meters to about 240 feet on 80 meters. On the 2-meter band, one wavelength is only about 7 feet. You should still try to install the antenna higher, to get it clear of buildings and trees. Of course very few people can get their antennas 240 feet in the air, so 40 to 60 feet is a good average height for an 80-meter dipole. Don't despair if you can get your antenna up only 20 feet or so, though. Low antennas can work well. Generally, though, the higher above ground and surrounding objects you can get your antenna, the greater the success you'll have. You'll find this to be true even if you can get only part of your antenna up high.

Normally you will support the dipole at both ends. The supports can be trees, buildings, poles or anything else high enough. Sometimes, however, there is just no way you can put your dipole high in the air at both ends. If you're faced with this problem, you have two reasonably good alternatives. You can support your dipole in the middle or at one end.

If you choose to support the antenna in the middle, both ends will droop toward the ground. This antenna, known as

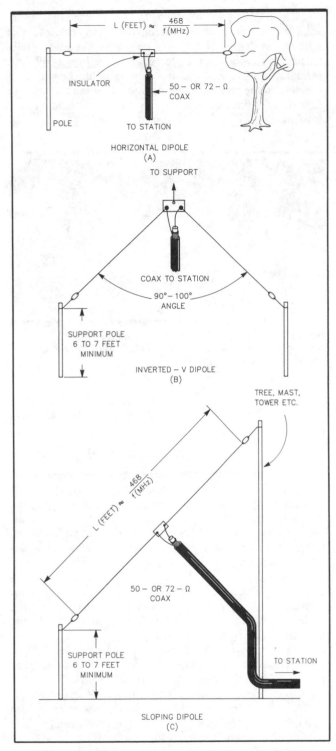

$$L \text{ (FEET)} \approx \frac{468}{f \text{ (MHz)}}$$

INSULATOR

50 – OR 72 – Ω
COAX

TO STATION

POLE

HORIZONTAL DIPOLE
(A)

TO SUPPORT

COAX TO STATION

90° – 100°
ANGLE

SUPPORT POLE
6 TO 7 FEET
MINIMUM

INVERTED – V DIPOLE
(B)

TREE, MAST,
TOWER ETC.

$$L \text{ (FEET)} \approx \frac{468}{f \text{ (MHz)}}$$

50 – OR 72 – Ω
COAX

SUPPORT POLE
6 TO 7 FEET
MINIMUM

TO STATION

SLOPING DIPOLE
(C)

Figure 7-11—These are simple but effective wire antennas. A shows a horizontal dipole. The legs can be drooped to form an inverted-V dipole, as at B. C illustrates a sloping dipole (sloper). The feed line should come away from the sloper at a 90° angle for best results. If the supporting mast is metal, the antenna will have some directivity in the direction of the slope.

an **inverted-V dipole**, works best when the angle between the wires is no less than 90°. See Figure 7-11. If you use an inverted-V dipole, make sure the ends are high enough that no one can touch them. When you transmit, the high voltages present at the ends of a dipole can cause an **RF burn**.

If you support your antenna at only one end, you'll have

what is known as a **sloper**. This antenna also works well. As with the inverted-V dipole, be sure the low end is high enough to prevent anyone from touching it.

If you don't have the room to install a dipole in the standard form, don't be afraid to experiment a little. You can get away with bending the ends to fit your property, or even making a horizontal V-shaped antenna. Many hams have enjoyed countless hours of successful operating with antennas bent in a variety of shapes and angles.

On the 6- and 2-meter bands, dipoles for FM or packet operation work much better if they are installed vertically. Now you need only one support. The coax should come away from the antenna at a right angle for as far as possible, so it doesn't interfere with the radiation from the antenna. Dipoles are not often used on frequencies above the 2-meter band, as other, simpler, antennas work better. We describe one such antenna later in this chapter.

ANTENNA INSTALLATION

After you've built your antenna and chosen its location, how do you get it up? There are many schools of thought on putting up antennas. Can you support at least one end of your antenna on a mast, tower, building or in an easily climbed tree? If so, you have solved some of your problems. Unfortunately, this is not always the case. Hams use several methods to get antenna support ropes into trees. Most methods involve a weight attached to a rope or line. You might be able to tie a rope around a rock and throw it over the intended support. This method works for low antennas. Even a major league pitcher, however, would have trouble getting an antenna much higher than 40 feet with this method.

A better method is to use a bow and arrow, a fishing rod or even a slingshot to launch the weight and rope. See Figures 7-12 and 7-13. You'll find that strong, lightweight fishing line is the best line to attach to the weight. (Lead fishing weights are a good choice.) Regular rope is too heavy to shoot any great distance. When you have successfully cleared the supporting tree, remove the weight. Then tie the support rope to the fishing line and reel it in.

If your first attempt doesn't go over the limb you were hoping for, try again. Don't just reel in the line, however.

Figure 7-12—There are many ways to get an antenna support rope into a tree. These hams use a bow and arrow to shoot a lightweight fishing line over the desired branch. Then they attach the support rope to the fishing line and pull it up into the tree.

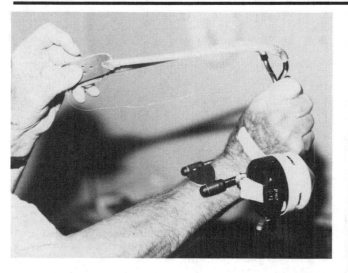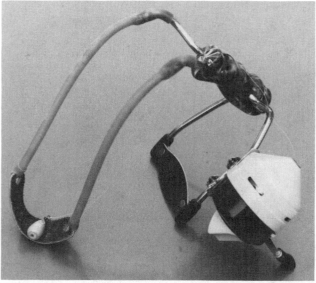

Figure 7-13—Another method for getting an antenna support into a tree. Small hose clamps attach a casting reel to the wrist bracket of a slingshot. Monofilament fishing line attached to a 1-ounce sinker is easily shot over almost any tree. Remove the sinker and rewind the line for repeated shots. When you find a suitable path through the tree, use the fishing line to pull a heavier line over the tree.

Let the weight down to the ground first and take it off the line. Then you can reel the line in without getting the weight tangled in the branches.

You can put antenna supports in trees 120 feet and higher with this method. As with any type of marksmanship, make sure all is clear downrange before shooting. Your neighbors will not appreciate stray arrows, sinkers or rocks falling in their yards!

When your support ropes are in place, attach them to the ends of the dipole and haul it up. Pull the dipole reasonably tight, but not so tight that it is under a lot of strain. Tie the ends off so they are out of reach of passersby. Be sure

to leave enough rope so you can let the dipole down temporarily if necessary.

Just one more step and your antenna installation is complete. After routing the coaxial cable to your station, cut it to length and install the proper connector for your rig. Usually this connector will be a PL-259, sometimes called a UHF connector. Figure 7-14 shows how to attach one of these fittings to RG-8 or RG-11 cable. Follow the step-by-step instructions exactly as illustrated and you should have no trouble. Be sure to place the coupling ring on the cable *before* you install the connector body! If you are using RG-58 or RG-59 cable, use an adapter to fit the cable to the connector. Figure 7-15 illus-

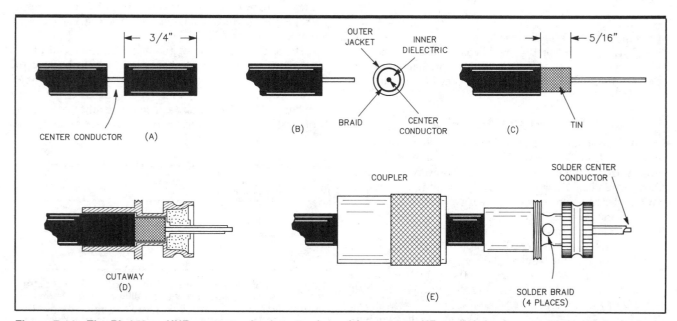

Figure 7-14—The PL-259 or UHF connector is almost universal for amateur HF work. It is also popular for equipment operating in the VHF range. Steps A through E illustrate how to install the connector properly. Despite its name, the UHF connector is rarely used on frequencies above 225 MHz.

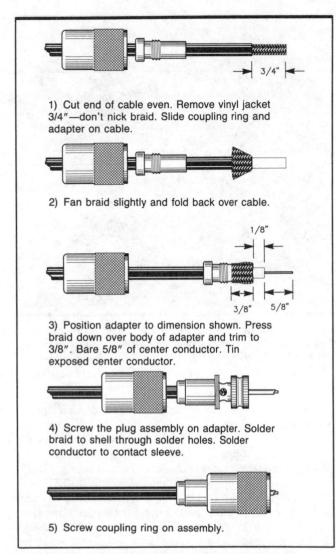

1) Cut end of cable even. Remove vinyl jacket 3/4"—don't nick braid. Slide coupling ring and adapter on cable.

2) Fan braid slightly and fold back over cable.

3) Position adapter to dimension shown. Press braid down over body of adapter and trim to 3/8". Bare 5/8" of center conductor. Tin exposed center conductor.

4) Screw the plug assembly on adapter. Solder braid to shell through solder holes. Solder conductor to contact sleeve.

5) Screw coupling ring on assembly.

Figure 7-15—If you use RG-58 or RG-59 with a PL-259 connector, you should use an adapter, as shown here. Thanks to Amphenol Electronic Components, RF Division, Bunker Ramo Corp, for this information.

trates the steps for installing the connector with adapter. The PL-259 is standard on most rigs. If you require another kind of connector, consult your radio instruction manual or *The ARRL Handbook for Radio Amateurs* for installation information.

Tuning the Antenna

When you build an antenna, you cut it to the length given by an equation. This length is just a first approximation. Nearby trees, buildings or large metal objects and height above ground all affect the antenna resonant frequency. An SWR meter can help you determine if you should shorten or lengthen the antenna. The correct length provides the best impedance match for your transmitter.

The first step is to measure the SWR at the bottom, middle and top of the band. On 80 meters, for example, you would check the SWR at 3.626, 3.700 and 3.724 MHz. (A friend with a higher license class can help you check the SWR over a wider frequency range.) Graph the readings, as shown in Figure 7-16. You could be lucky—no further antenna adjustments may be necessary, depending on your transmitter.

Many tube-type transmitters include an output tuning

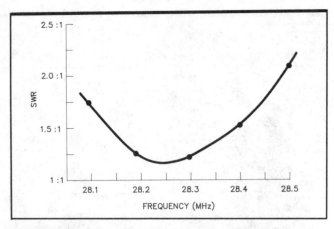

Figure 7-16—This graph shows how the SWR might vary across an amateur frequency band. The point of lowest SWR here is near the center of the band, so no further antenna-length adjustments are necessary.

network. They will usually operate fine with an SWR of 3:1 or less. Most solid-state transmitters (using all transistors and integrated circuits) do not include such an output tuning network. These *no-tune* radios begin to shut down—the power output drops off—as SWR increases.

In any event, most hams like to prune their antennas for the lowest SWR they can get at the center of the band. With a full-size dipole 30 or 40 feet high, your SWR should be less than 2:1. If you can get the SWR down to 1.5:1, great! It's not worth the time and effort to do any better than that.

If the SWR is lower at the low-frequency end of the band, your antenna is probably too long. Disconnect the transmitter and try shortening your antenna at each end. The amount to trim off depends on two things. First is which band the antenna is operating on, and, second, how much you want to change the resonant frequency. Let's say the antenna is cut for the 80-meter band. You'll probably need to cut 8 or 10 inches off each end to move the resonant frequency 50 kHz. You may have to trim only an inch or less for small frequency changes on the 10-meter band. Measure the SWR again (remember to recheck the calibration). If the SWR went down, keep shortening the antenna until the SWR at the center of the band is less than 2:1.

If the SWR is lower at the high-frequency end of the band, your antenna was probably too short to begin with. If so, you must add more wire until the SWR is acceptable. Before you solder more wire on the antenna ends, try attaching a 12-inch wire on each end. Use alligator clips, as Figure 7-17 shows. You don't need to move the insulators yet.

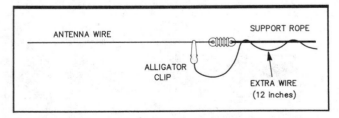

Figure 7-17—If your antenna is too short, attach an extra length of wire to each end with an alligator clip. Then shorten the extra length a little at a time until you get the correct length for the antenna. Finally, extend the length inside the insulators with a soldered connection. (See Figure 7-18.)

Clip a wire on each end and again measure the SWR. Chances are the antenna will now be too long. You will need to shorten it a little at a time until the SWR is below 2:1.

Once you know how much wire you need to add, cut two pieces and solder them to the ends of the antenna. When you add wire, be sure to make a sound mechanical connection before soldering. Figure 7-18 shows how. Remember that these joints must bear the weight of the antenna and the feed line. After you solder the wire, reinstall the insulators at the antenna ends, past the solder connections.

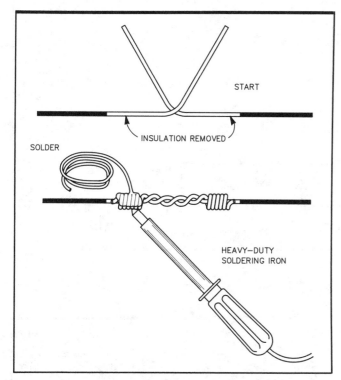

Figure 7-18—When splicing antenna wire, remember that the connection must be strong mechanically and good electrically.

If the SWR is very high, you may have a problem that can't be cured by simple tuning. A very high SWR may mean that your feed line is open or shorted. Perhaps a connection isn't making good electrical contact. It could also be that your antenna is touching metal. A metal mast, the rain gutter on your house or some other conductor would add considerable length to the antenna. If the SWR is very high, check all connections and feed lines, and be sure the antenna clears surrounding objects.

Now you have enough information to construct, install and adjust your dipole antenna. You'll need a separate dipole antenna for each band you expect to operate on. Sometimes a 40-meter dipole will also work on 15 meters, though. Check the SWR on 15 meters—you may have a two-for-one dipole!

MULTIBAND DIPOLE OPERATION

The single-band dipole is fine if you operate on only one band. If you want to operate on more than one band, however, you could build and install a dipole for each band. What if you don't have supports for all these dipoles? Or what if you don't want to spend the money for extra coaxial cable? The popular and inexpensive multiband dipole described here will solve your problems nicely.

A single-band dipole can be converted into a **multiband antenna** without too much difficulty. All you need to do is connect two additional ¼-λ wires for each additional band you want to use. Each added wire connects to the same feed line as the original dipole. The result is a single antenna system, fed with a single coaxial cable, that works on several different bands without adjustment. There is one potential problem with this antenna, though. The antenna will radiate signals on two or more bands simultaneously, so make sure your transmitter is adjusted properly. A poorly adjusted transmitter may produce harmonics of the desired output. If so, energy from your transmitter may show up on more than one band. The FCC takes a dim view of such operation!

Three-Band Dipole

You can build a three-band dipole for 80, 40 and 15 meters from ladder line. To build this antenna, you'll need a 100-foot roll of this line, three insulators and a coax feed line.

This antenna construction is similar to that for a regular dipole. Carefully remove the line from the spool and lay it on the ground. Take care to avoid twists and kinks in the wire. See Figure 7-19. At 33 feet, 6 inches from one end (X), cut *one* of the two wires. At 63 feet, 8 inches from the same end, cut the *other* wire. Remove the plastic spacers between these cuts, separating the open-wire line into two pieces. Measuring from the other end (Y), cut the shorter wire at 33 feet, 6 inches and the longer one at 63 feet, 8 inches. Figure 7-19A shows how the two antenna halves should look at this point.

Reverse the position of the two halves, as Figure 7-19B shows. Now prepare the wire ends for connection to the feed line. Sandpaper the protective coating off both wires at the ends. (X and Y identify these ends in the drawing.) Connect the wire and a piece of coaxial cable in the same manner as described for a single-band dipole. Waterproof the connec-

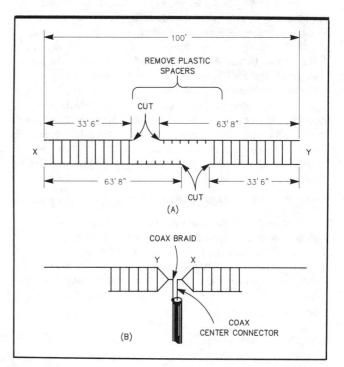

Figure 7-19—At A, cut the two lengths of ladder line as shown. Reverse the two sections to make the three-band dipole antenna, as shown at B.

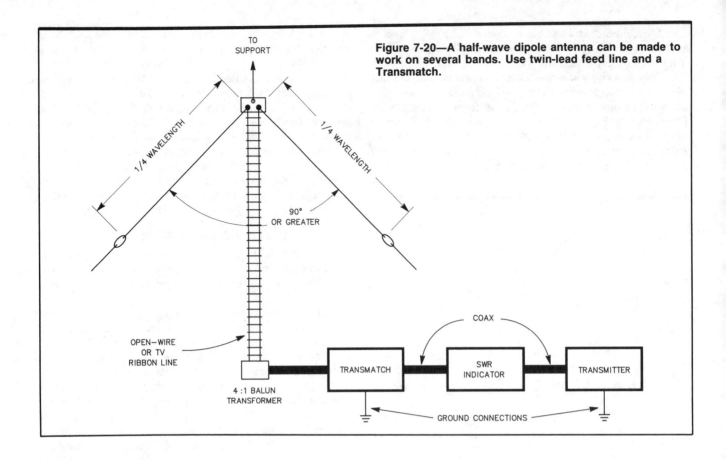

Figure 7-20—A half-wave dipole antenna can be made to work on several bands. Use twin-lead feed line and a Transmatch.

tion with tape. Spray the taped connection with clear lacquer or coat it with liquid rubber or silicone sealant for added protection against weather. Attach insulators to the ends, and your antenna is complete.

All information on antenna location and installation for a single-band dipole also applies to this multiband antenna. Use the same procedure described earlier to tune the antenna for the lowest SWR. Just remember that you must adjust the SWR on two bands. Adjust both the 80-meter part (the longer wire) and the 40/15-meter part (the shorter wire).

Another multiband antenna is shown in Figure 7-20. The legs for this antenna should each be ¼ λ at the lowest frequency you want to use. In other words, if you want to operate on all bands, 80 through 10 meters, each leg should be about 63 feet long. Feed this antenna with open-wire feed line (either 300- or 450-ohm), or TV twin lead. It requires a Transmatch at the station end.

THE QUARTER-WAVE VERTICAL ANTENNA

The ¼-λ **vertical antenna** is simple and popular. It requires only one support and can be very effective. On the HF bands (80-10 meters) it is often used for DX work. See Figure 7-21. This antenna has a vertical radiator that is ¼-λ long. Use Equation 7-3 to find ¼ λ for the radiator. The frequency is given in megahertz and the length is in feet in this equation.

$$\text{Length (in feet)} = \frac{234}{\text{f (in MHz)}} \qquad \text{(Eq 7-3)}$$

Equation 7-3 gives us the following approximate lengths for the radiator and each ground radial of a ¼-λ vertical.

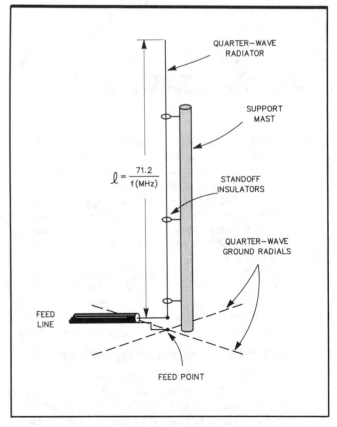

Figure 7-21—The quarter-wave vertical antenna has a center radiator and four or more radials spread out from the base. These radials form a ground plane.

Wavelength	Frequency	Length
80 meters	3.700 MHz	63.25 feet
40 meters	7.125 MHz	33 feet
15 meters	21.125 MHz	11 feet
10 meters	28.150 MHz	8.3 feet
10 meters	28.4 MHz	8.2 feet
6 meters	52.5 MHz	4.5 feet
2 meters	146.0 MHz	1.6 feet (19.25 inches)
1.25 meters	223.0 MHz	1.05 feet (12.6 inches)
70 cm	440.0 MHz	0.53 feet (6.4 inches)
23 cm	1282.5 MHz	0.18 feet (2.2 inches)

As with ½-λ dipoles, the resonant frequency of a ¼-λ vertical decreases as the length increases. Shorter antennas have higher resonant frequencies.

The ¼-λ vertical also has radials. For operation on 80 through 10 meters, the vertical may be at ground level, and the radials placed on the ground. The key to successful operation with a ground-mounted vertical antenna is a good radial system. The best radial system uses *many* ground radials. Lay them out like the spokes of a wheel, with the vertical at the center. Some hams have buried ground radial systems containing over 100 individual wires.

Ideally, these wires would be ¼ λ long or more at the lowest operating frequency. With such a system, earth or ground losses will be negligible. When the antenna is mounted at ground level, radial length is not very critical, however. Studies show that with fewer radials you can use shorter lengths, but with a corresponding loss in antenna efficiency.[1,2] Some of your transmitter power does no more than warm the earth beneath your antenna. With 24 radials, there is no point in making them longer than about 1/8 λ. With 16 radials, a length greater than 0.1 λ is unwarranted. Four radials should be considered an absolute minimum. Don't put the radials more than about an inch below the ground surface.

Compared with 120 radials of 0.4 λ, antenna efficiency with 24 radials is roughly 63%. For 16 radials, the efficiency is roughly 50%. So it pays to put in as many radials as you can.

If you place the vertical above ground, you reduce earth losses drastically. Here, the wires should be cut to ¼ λ for the band you plan to use. Above ground, you need only a few radials—two to five. If you install a multiband vertical antenna above ground, use separate ground radials for each band you plan to use. These lengths are more critical than for a ground-mounted vertical. For elevated verticals, you should have two radials for each band, minimum. You can mount a vertical on a pipe driven into the ground, on the chimney or on a tower.

Once a vertical antenna is several feet above ground, there is little advantage in more height. (This assumes your antenna is above nearby obstructions.) For sky-wave signals, a height of 15 feet for the base is almost as good as 50. This is contrary to the case for a horizontal antenna, where height is important for working DX. Only if you can get the vertical up 2 or 3 wavelengths does the low-angle radiation begin to improve. Even then the improvement is only slight. At VHF and UHF, however, it pays to get the antenna up high. At these frequencies you want the antenna higher than even distant obstructions.

Vertical antennas can also be lengths other than a ¼-λ long. Verticals that are 5/8-λ long are popular on some

[1]J. O. Stanley, "Optimum Ground Systems for Vertical Antennas," *QST*, December 1976, pp 14-15.

[2]B. Edward, "Radial Systems for Ground-Mounted Vertical Antennas," *QST*, June 1985, pp 28-30.

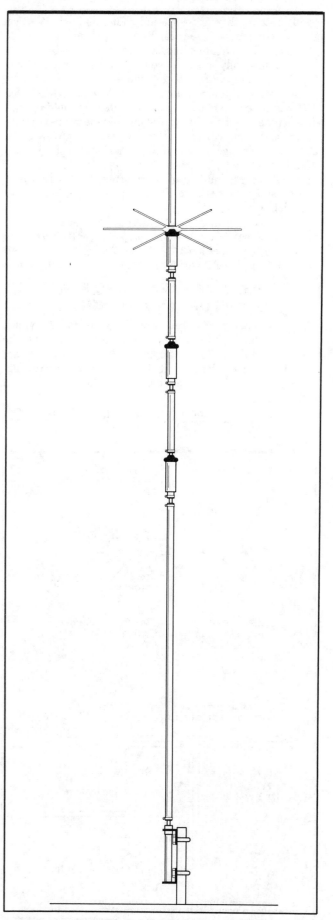

Figure 7-22—Commercial "trap vertical" antennas generally look something like this. These antennas operate on several bands.

bands because they provide a low radiation angle. Vertical antennas that are ½-λ long can be used without ground radials, and this may sometimes be a definite advantage.

Commercially available vertical antennas need a coax feed line, usually with a PL-259 connector. Just as with the dipole antenna, you can use RG-8, RG-11 or RG-58 coax. The instructions that accompany the antenna should provide details for attaching both the feed line and the ground radials.

Some manufacturers offer *trap verticals*. Traps are tuned circuits that change the antenna electrical length. They allow the antenna to work on several bands, making it a *multiband antenna*. Some manufacturers even offer 20- to 30-foot-high vertical antennas that cover all HF bands. Figure 7-22 shows one such antenna.

[Now turn to Chapter 12 and study those questions with numbers that begin 2I-2. **If you are preparing for the Technician exam,** also study question 3AI-6-1.1 in Chapter 13. Review this section if you have difficulty with any of these questions.]

VERTICAL ANTENNAS FOR 146, 222 AND 440 MHz

For FM and packet radio operation with nearby stations, the ease of construction and low cost of a ¼-λ vertical make it an ideal choice. Three different types of construction are shown in Figures 7-23 through 7-26; the choice of construction method depends on the materials available and the desired style of antenna mounting.

The 146-MHz model shown in Figure 7-23 uses a flat

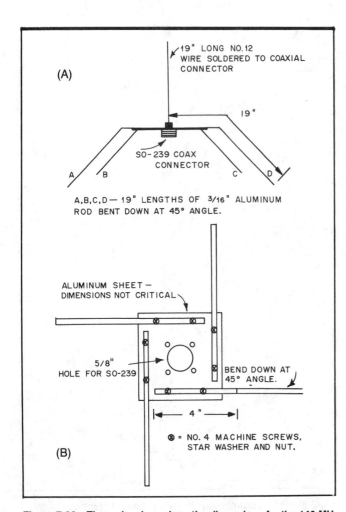

Figure 7-23—These drawings show the dimensions for the 146-MHz groundplane antenna. The radials are bent down at a 45° angle.

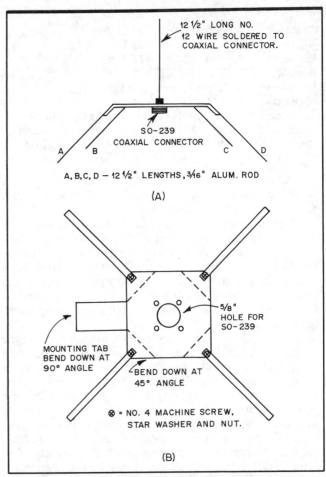

Figure 7-24—Dimensional information for the 222-MHz groundplane antenna. Lengths for A, B, C and D are the total distances measured from the center of the SO-239 connector. The corners of the aluminum plate are bent down at a 45° angle rather than bending the aluminum rod as in the 146-MHz model. Either method is suitable for these antennas.

piece of sheet aluminum, to which radials are connected with machine screws. A 45° bend is made in each of the radials. This bend can be made with an ordinary bench vise. An SO-239 chassis connector is mounted at the center of the aluminum plate with the threaded part of the connector facing down. The vertical portion of the antenna is made of no. 12 copper wire soldered directly to the center pin of the SO-239 connector.

The 222-MHz version, Figure 7-24, uses a slightly different technique for mounting and sloping the radials. In this case the corners of the aluminum plate are bent down at a 45° angle with respect to the remainder of the plate. The four radials are held to the plate with machine screws, lock washers and nuts. A mounting tab is included in the design of this antenna as part of the aluminum base. A compression type of hose clamp could be used to secure the antenna to a mast. As with the 146-MHz version, the vertical portion of the antenna is soldered directly to the SO-239 connector.

A very simple method of construction, shown in Figures 7-25 and 7-26, requires nothing more than an SO-239 connector and some 4-40 hardware. A small loop formed at the inside end of each radial is used to attach the radial directly to the mounting holes of the coaxial connector. After the radial is fastened to the SO-239 with no. 4-40 hardware, a large soldering iron or propane torch is used to solder the radial and the mounting hardware to the coaxial connector.

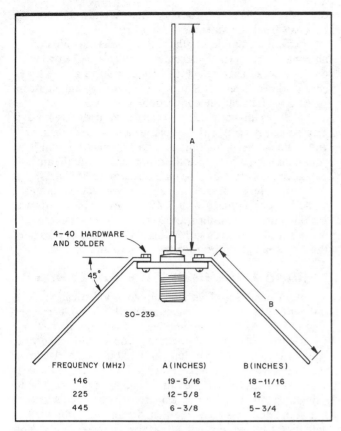

Figure 7-25—Simple groundplane antenna for the 146, 222 and 440-MHz bands. The vertical element and radials are 3/32- or 1/16-in. brass welding rod. Although 3/32-in. rod is preferred for the 146-MHz antenna, no. 10 or 12 copper wire can also be used.

FREQUENCY (MHz)	A (INCHES)	B (INCHES)
146	19 - 5/16	18 - 11/16
225	12 - 5/8	12
445	6 - 3/8	5 - 3/4

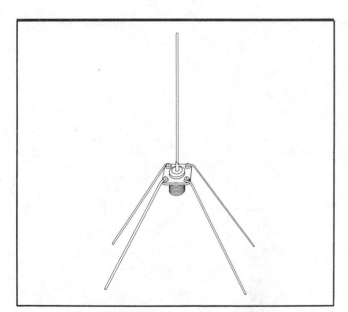

Figure 7-26—A 440-MHz groundplane antenna constructed using only an SO-239 connector, no. 4-40 hardware and 1/16-in. brass welding rod.

The radials are bent to a 45° angle and the vertical portion is soldered to the center pin to complete the antenna. The antenna can be mounted by passing the feed line through a mast of ¾-inch ID plastic or aluminum tubing. A compression hose clamp can be used to secure the PL-259 connector, attached to the feed line, in the end of the mast. Dimensions

for the 146, 222, and 440-MHz bands are given in Figure 7-25.

If these antennas are to be mounted outside it is wise to apply a small amount of RTV sealant or similar material around the areas of the center pin of the connector to prevent the entry of water into the connector and coax line.

A SIMPLE NOVICE VERTICAL

Figure 7-27 shows a simple, inexpensive vertical antenna for 10 and 15 meters. The antenna requires very little space and it's great for working DX. A few materials make up the entire antenna.

12-foot piece of clean 2 × 2 pine from the local lumberyard
20 feet of flat four-wire rotator control cable
20 feet of regular TV twin lead
Several TV standoff insulators

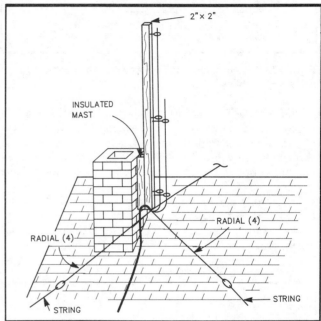

Figure 7-27—A simple Novice vertical antenna for use on 10 and 15 meters.

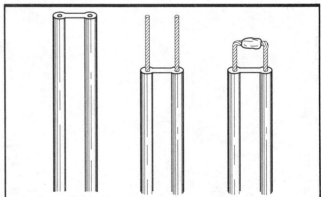

Figure 7-28—For each length of twin lead, strip back the insulation from both ends, connect the two wires, and solder them.

Cut the twin lead into lengths of 11 feet 3 inches, and 8 feet 6 inches. Remove 1 inch of insulation from both wires at both ends on each twin-lead length. Wrap the two wires together securely at each end, as Figure 7-28 shows, and solder. Cover one end of each length of twin lead with electrical tape.

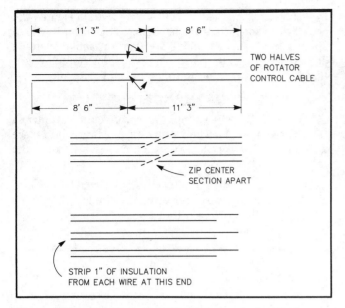

Figure 7-29—Cut some flat TV rotator-control cable to make the radials.

Mount the TV standoff insulators at regular intervals on opposite sides of the 2 × 2. These will support the two pieces of twin lead. Separate the control cable into two pieces of two-conductor cable. Do this by slitting the cable a small amount at one end, then pulling the two pieces apart like a zipper.

Carefully cut the rotator cable as Figure 7-29 shows. Separate the pieces between the center cuts to make four identical sets of two-conductor cable. These make up the radials for the antenna system. Strip about 1 inch of insulation from

each wire on the evenly cut end. The unevenly cut ends will be away from the antenna.

Attach a suitable length of RG-58 coaxial cable to the antenna. Connect the coax center conductor to the two wires on the 2 × 2. Then attach the cable braid to all the radial ends soldered together. Figure 7-30 shows the antenna construction. Make all the connections waterproof.

Now install the 2 × 2. You can do this in different ways. You could clamp it with U bolts to a TV mast, or hang it with a hook over a high branch. Or you might mount it on your house, at the side, near the roof peak. Mount the antenna as high as possible. Hang the radials at about a 45° angle away from the antenna base. For example, you could clamp the wood to your chimney with TV chimney-mount hardware. Let the radials follow the roof slope. Tie them off at the four corners. Unless you are surrounded by buildings or high hills, this antenna should perform well on 10 and 15 meters.

RANDOM-LENGTH WIRE ANTENNAS

If you can't install either a dipole or a vertical, you can still get on the air. Try a **random-length wire antenna**. See Figure 7-31. As the name implies, the antenna requires no specific length. As a rule of thumb, you should make your random-length antenna as long as possible. If you live in an apartment, you might use an antenna running along the ceiling in a few rooms. On the other hand, you may be able to string up a long length of wire outdoors. Use small wire (no. 22 to no. 28) if you want an antenna with low visibility. The only disadvantage of small wire is that it breaks easily. You may have to replace it often.

Random-length antennas are versatile: They can be used almost anywhere. But they do have one major disadvantage. Unlike the dipole and vertical, which can be fed directly from

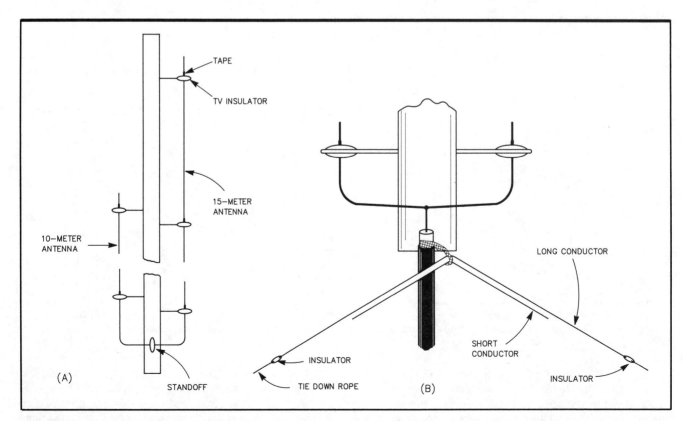

Figure 7-30—Attach the twin lead to the sides of the 2 × 2 with TV standoff insulators, as illustrated at A. At B, connect the feed line to both twin-lead lengths at the base.

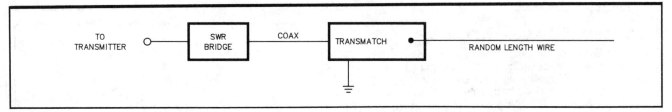

Figure 7-31—With a Transmatch, you can use a wire cut to a convenient random length as an antenna.

the transmitter through coaxial cable, a random-length antenna requires a matching network. The matching network is required because the antenna impedance is not likely to be 50 ohms.

BEAM ANTENNAS

Although generally impractical on 80 meters, and very large and expensive even on 40 meters, directional antennas often see use on 15 and 10 meters. The most common directional antenna that amateurs use is the **Yagi antenna**, but there are other types, too.

Generally called **beam antennas**, these directional antennas have two important advantages over dipole and vertical systems. First, the **directivity** of the antenna suppresses signals coming from directions other than where you point the antenna. This reduces the interference from stations in other directions, and increases your operating enjoyment. Second, a beam antenna concentrates the transmitted signal more in one direction than in others. The antenna provides **gain** in its pointed direction. Gain makes your signal sound stronger to other operators, and their signals sound stronger to you. A graph of an antenna's gain and directivity shows its *radiation pattern*. Figure 7-32 shows some of the Yagi beams at W1AW, the station located at ARRL Headquarters in Newington, Connecticut. Figure 7-33 shows the typical radiation pattern of a Yagi beam.

A Yagi beam antenna has several elements attached to a central *boom*, as Figure 7-34 shows. The feed line connects

Figure 7-32—Yagi beams at W1AW. A single beam sits atop the tower at left. Three stacked beams adorn the taller tower at the right.

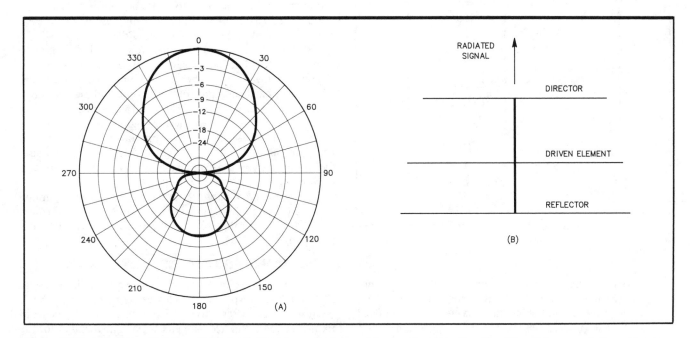

Figure 7-33—Typical radiation pattern for a Yagi beam antenna. The inset shows the direction of beam pointing. The transmitted signal is stronger in the forward direction than in others.

ANTENNA RADIATION PATTERNS

Often one desirable antenna feature is **directivity**. Directivity means the ability to pick up signals from one direction, while suppressing signals from other unwanted directions. Going hand in hand with directivity is **gain**. Gain tells how much signal a given antenna will pick up as compared with that from another antenna, usually a dipole.

An antenna that has directivity should also have gain. These two antenna properties are useful not only for picking up or receiving radio signals, but also for transmitting them. An antenna that has gain will boost your transmitted energy in the favored direction while suppressing it in other directions.

When you mention gain and directivity, most amateurs envision large antenna arrays, made from aluminum tubing, with many elements. Simple wire antennas can also be very effective, however, as illustrated in this antenna radiation pattern. Such patterns reveal both the gain and the directivity of a specific antenna.

Let's say we connect the antenna to a transmitter and send. The pattern shows the relative power received at a fixed distance from the antenna, in various compass directions. If you connect the antenna to a receiver, the pattern shows how the antenna responds to signals from various directions. In the direction where the antenna has gain, the incoming signals will be enhanced. The incoming signals will be suppressed in other directions.

Here is an important point to remember. You can never have antenna gain in one direction without a loss (signal suppression) in one or more other directions. Never! Another way to think of this is that an antenna cannot create power. It can only focus or beam the power supplied by the transmitter.

We call the long, thin lobes in a pattern the **major lobes**. The smaller lobes in a pattern are **minor lobes**. One or more major lobes mean directivity. An antenna with less directivity than this one would have fatter lobes. An antenna with no directivity at all would have a pattern that

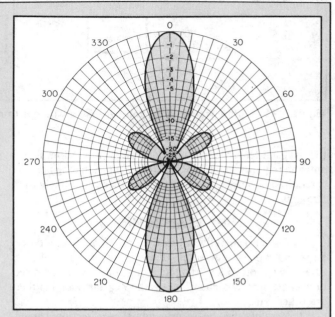

The calculated or theoretical radiation pattern for an extended double Zepp antenna. In its favored directions, this antenna exhibits roughly 2 decibels gain over a half-wave dipole. This would make a 200-watt signal as strong as 317 watts into a dipole. An extended double Zepp antenna may be made with a horizontal wire hanging between two supports. (The wire is 1.28-λ long at the operating frequency and should be fed at the center with open-wire line.) The wire axis is along the 90/270-degree line shown in the chart.

is a perfect circle. A theoretical antenna called an *isotropic radiator* has such a pattern. Radiation patterns are a very useful tool in measuring antenna capability.

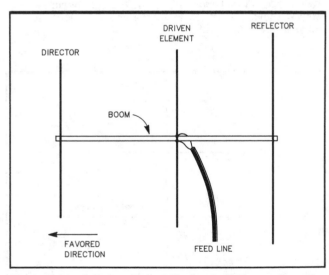

Figure 7-34—A three-element Yagi antenna has a director, a driven element and a reflector. A boom supports the elements.

to only one element. We call this element the **driven element**. On a three-element Yagi like the one shown in Figure 7-34, the driven element is in the middle. The element at the front of the antenna (toward the favored direction) is a **director**. Behind the driven element is the **reflector** element. The driven element is about ½-λ long at the antenna design frequency.

The director is a bit shorter than ½ λ, and the reflector a bit longer.

Yagi beams can have more than three elements. Seldom is there more than one reflector. Instead, the added elements are directors. A standard four-element Yagi would have a reflector, a driven element and two directors.

Because beams are directional, you'll need something to turn them. A single-band beam for 10 or 15 meters can be mounted in the same manner as a TV antenna. You can use a TV mast, hardware and rotator. You could plan to buy a large *triband* beam for use on 10 and 15 meters as a Novice. It will cover 20 meters when you upgrade to a General or higher license class. For such a big antenna you'll need a heavy-duty mount and rotator. You can get good advice about the equipment you'll need from your instructor or from local hams.

[Now turn to Chapter 12 and study questions beginning 2I-4-1.1 through 2I-4-1.3 and questions 2I-4-2.1 through 2I-4-2.4. Review this section if you have any difficulty answering these questions.]

CONVERTING CB ANTENNAS

It is usually a simple matter to convert a Citizen's Band (CB) antenna to work on the Novice 10-meter band. This is because the 11-meter Citizens Band at 27 MHz is close in frequency to the Novice 10-meter band. The formula for the correct length is quite simple—468 divided by the frequency in megahertz (Equation 7-2). The antenna length is given in feet. For example, 468 divided by 27 MHz equals 17.3 feet or 17 feet, 4 inches. The most common antenna type used by CBers, however, is a ¼-λ vertical. It would be half as long, or 8 feet, 8 inches long (Equation 7-3).

To resonate (or tune) such an antenna on 10 meters, you shorten it to the required length. Using Equation 7-2, ½ λ for 28.1 MHz works out to be 16 feet, 8 inches. The length for a ¼-λ vertical, using Equation 7-3, is 8 feet 4 inches. This means removing 8 inches from a dipole, or 4 inches from a full-sized vertical (not loaded with a coil). Before shortening any CB antenna, try the antenna on 10 meters. If your transmitter loads and tunes up, it may be a waste of time to prune the antenna. It may work well just as it is!

ANTENNA POLARIZATION

For VHF and UHF base station operation, most amateurs use a vertical or a beam. For VHF and UHF FM and repeater operation, almost everyone uses vertical **polarization**. For SSB and CW VHF/UHF work, almost everyone uses a beam with horizontal polarization. If you plan to do both VHF weak-signal and FM repeater work, you'll probably need separate antennas for each. This is because signal strength suffers greatly if your antenna has different polarization than the station you're trying to work.

A beam antenna is impractical for VHF and UHF FM mobile operation. Most hams use a vertical of some kind. Mobile antennas are available in several varieties. Most mount on the automobile roof or trunk lid, but some even mount on a glass window.

Most vertical antennas used at lower frequencies are 1/4-λ long. For VHF and UHF, antennas are physically short enough that longer verticals may be used. A popular mobile antenna is a **5/8-λ vertical**, often called a "five-eighths whip." This antenna is popular because it offers more gain than a regular 1/4-λ vertical. Simply stated, "gain" means a con-

centration of transmitter power. A 5/8-λ vertical concentrates the power toward the horizon. Naturally, this is the most useful direction, unless you want to talk to airplanes or satellites. At 220 MHz, a 5/8-λ whip is only 28-1/2 inches long.

Don't use any of the equations in this chapter to calculate how long a 5/8-λ whip is at 220 MHz. The equations won't give the correct answer because of a variety of antenna factors. In addition, there is an impedance-matching network at the antenna feed point. See *The ARRL Handbook* for complete construction details.

A 5/8-λ vertical is great for mobile operation because it is **omnidirectional**. That means it radiates a signal equally well in all compass directions. This is especially useful for mobile operation because you change direction often. One minute you may be driving toward the repeater, and the next minute you may be driving away from it.

[Study the following questions in Chapter 12: 2I-3.1, 2I-3.2, 2I-10-1.1 and 2I-11-1.1. Review this section and adjacent information if you have any difficulty answering the questions.]

INSTALLATION SAFETY

No matter what antenna type you choose to build, you should remember a few key points about safety. If possible, ask someone with experience to help you plan and carry out your installation, especially if climbing is involved. If you use a slingshot or bow and arrow to get a line over a tree, use caution. Make sure you keep everyone away from the "down-range" area. Hitting a helper with a rock or a fishing sinker is not a good idea!

If you build a wire antenna, be sure the antenna ends are out of reach of passersby. The ends should be high enough that a person on the ground cannot touch them. Even at Novice power levels, enough voltage exists at the antenna ends when you transmit to cause RF burns. If you have a vertical antenna with its base at ground level, you might consider building a wooden safety fence around it. The fence should be at least 4 feet away from the antenna. Do not use a metal fence, as this will interfere with the proper antenna operation. If you have a tower, you should either fence it or put shields directly on the tower to prevent unauthorized climbing.

Antenna work sometimes requires that someone climb up on a tower, into a tree, or onto the roof. Never work alone! Work slowly, thinking out each move before you make it. The person on the ladder, tower, tree or roof top should *always* wear a safety belt, and keep it securely anchored. Before each use, inspect the belt carefully for damage such as cuts or worn areas. The belt will make it much easier to work

on the antenna and will also prevent an accidental fall.

Never try to climb a tower carrying tools or antenna components in your hands. Carry what you can with a tool belt, including a long rope leading back to the ground. Then use the rope to pull other needed objects up to your workplace after securing your safety belt! It is helpful (and safe) to tie strings or lightweight ropes to all tools. You can save much time in retrieving dropped tools if you tie them to the tower. This also reduces the chances of injuring a helper on the ground.

Helpers on the ground should never stand directly under the work being done. All ground helpers should wear hard hats for protection. Even a small tool can make quite a dent if it falls from 50 or 60 feet. A ground helper should always observe the tower work carefully. Have you ever wondered why electric utility crews seem to have someone on the ground "doing nothing"? Now you know that for safety's sake, a ground observer with no other duties is free to notice potential hazards. That person could save a life by shouting a warning.

As mentioned earlier, be especially certain that your antenna is not close to any power lines. That is the only way you can be sure it won't come in contact with them!

When using a hand-held transceiver that runs more than a few watts, be careful! Always keep the antenna away from your head and away from others standing nearby. Some

HOW TO LIVE LONG ENOUGH TO UPGRADE

Keep antenna safety in mind when you're setting up your station. Antennas for the ham bands are often large, requiring care and attention to detail when installed. Here are two points to keep in mind when putting up your antenna.

1) Be sure your antenna materials and supports are strong—strong enough to withstand heavy winds without breaking.

2) Keep away from power lines!

If your antenna falls, it could damage your house, garage or property. If it falls into a power line, your house might end up like the unlucky CBer's shown in the photo. A windstorm knocked over his groundplane antenna, sending it into a 34,500-V power line. The resulting fire damaged his house extensively.

Safety pays! Accidents *are* avoidable, if you use good sense.

Photo by Charles Stokes, WB4PVT

antennas are safer than others. A short, helically wound flexible antenna (called a "rubber duck") is not the safest kind. It concentrates its radiation in a small area near your head. A longer antenna, such as a ½-λ whip, would be safer for a hand-held. A ½-λ antenna concentrates its radiation at its center, which will be farther from your head.

[Now study the questions in Chapter 12 with numbers that begin 2D-6 and 2I-5. **If you are preparing for the Technician exam,** also study question 3AI-6-2.1 in Chapter 13. Review this section if you have any problems.]

KEY WORDS

Cubical quad antenna—An antenna built with its elements in the shape of four-sided loops.

Delta loop antenna—A variation of the cubical quad with triangular elements.

Gamma match—A method of matching coaxial feed line to the driven element of a multielement array.

Horizontally polarized wave—An electromagnetic wave with its electric lines of force parallel to the ground.

Major lobe—The shape or pattern of field strength that points in the direction of maximum radiated power from an antenna.

Parasitic element—Part of a directive antenna that derives energy from mutual coupling with the driven element. Parasitic elements are not connected directly to the feed line.

Unbalanced line—Feed line with one conductor at ground potential, such a coaxial cable.

Vertically polarized wave—A radio wave that has its electric lines of force perpendicular to the surface of the earth.

FEED-LINE ATTENUATION

As we have seen, transmission lines can be constructed in a variety of forms. Both parallel-conductor feed line and coaxial cable can be divided into two classes: those in which the majority of the space between the conductors is air, and those in which the conductors are embedded in and separated by a solid plastic or foam insulation (dielectric). Over time, feed line exposed to the weather may become "lossy," meaning its attenuation gradually increases.

Air-Insulated Feed Lines

Air-insulated feed lines have the lowest loss per unit length (usually expressed in dB/100 ft). Adding a solid dielectric between the conductors increases the losses in the feed line. The power loss causes heating of the dielectric. As frequency increases, conductor and dielectric losses become greater for coaxial and parallel-conductor feed lines.

A typical type of construction used for parallel-conductor or "ladder line" air-insulated transmission lines is shown in Figure 7-2. The two wires are supported a fixed distance apart by means of insulating rods called spacers. Spacers are commonly made from phenolic, polystyrene, isolantite or Lucite™. The spacers generally vary in length from 1 to 6 inches. The shorter lengths are desirable at the higher frequencies so the conductors are held a small fraction of a wavelength apart and radiation from the transmission line is minimized. Spacers are placed along the line at intervals that are small enough to prevent the two lines from moving appreciably with respect to each other. This type of line is sometimes referred to as **open-wire** feed line. An advantage of this type of transmission line is that it can be operated at a high SWR and still retain its low-loss properties.

The characteristic impedance of an air-insulated parallel-conductor line depends on the diameter of the wires used in the feed line and the spacing between them. The greater the spacing between the conductors, the higher the characteristic impedance of the feed line. The impedance decreases, however, as the size of the conductors increases. The characteristic impedance of a feed line is not affected by the length of the line.

Solid-Dielectric Feed Lines

Transmission lines in which the conductors are separated by a flexible dielectric have several advantages over air-dielectric line: They are less bulky, maintain more uniform spacing between conductors, are generally easier to install and are neater in appearance. Both parallel-conductor and coaxial lines are available with this type of insulation.

One disadvantage of these types of lines is that the power loss per unit length is greater than air-insulated lines because of the dielectric. As the frequency increases, the dielectric losses become greater. The power loss causes heating of the dielectric. Under conditions of high power or high SWR, the dielectric may actually melt and cause short circuits or arcing inside the line.

We mentioned TV-type parallel-conductor line, commonly called twin lead. Twin lead consists of two no. 20 wires that are molded into the edges of a polyethylene ribbon about a half-inch wide. The presence of the solid dielectric lowers the characteristic impedance of the line as compared to the same conductors in air.

The fact that part of the field between the conductors exists outside the solid dielectric leads to operating disadvantages. Dirt or moisture on the surface of the ribbon tends to change the characteristic impedance. Weather effects can be minimized, however, by coating the feed line with silicone grease or car wax. In any case, the changes in the impedance will not be very serious if the line is terminated in its characteristic impedance (Z_0). If there is a considerable standing-wave ratio, however, then small changes in Z_0 may cause wide fluctuations of the input impedance.

Coaxial Cable

The characteristic impedance of a coaxial line depends on the diameter of the center conductor, the dielectric constant of the insulation between conductors, the inside diameter of the shield braid and the distance between conductors. The characteristic impedance of coaxial cables increases for larger-diameter shield braids, but it decreases for larger-diameter center conductors.

The larger the diameter, the higher the power capability of the line because of the increased dielectric thickness and conductor size. In general, losses decrease as the cable diameter increases, because there is less power lost in the conductor.

Amateurs commonly use RG-8, RG-58 and RG-174 coaxial cable. RG-8 has the least loss and RG-174 has the highest loss. As the frequency increases, the conductor and dielectric losses become greater, causing more attenuation of the signal in the cable. Although the cost, size and weight are larger for RG-8, it is usually the best choice (of the cables mentioned) for a run of over 150 feet for frequencies up to 54 MHz (the amateur 6-meter band). Open-wire transmission line has the least loss of any feed line type commonly used by amateurs.

Of the common coaxial cables discussed here, RG-8 has the least loss. RG-58 has a bit more loss than RG-8, and RG-174 has the most loss of these cables. RG-174 is normally used for cables that connect sections of a transmitter or receiver, or for short interconnecting cables in a low-power system.

Extra cable length increases attenuation. When using coaxial cable, you should try to use a matched antenna and feed line. You should then be able to change feed line lengths without significantly affecting the antenna system. Then your feed line has to be only long enough to reach your antenna. A low SWR on the line means that the impedance "seen" by the transmitter will be about the same regardless of line length.

You can cut off or shorten excess cable length to reduce attenuation of the signal caused by feed-line loss. (This does not apply to multiple antennas in phased arrays or line sections used for impedance-matching purposes.)

Attenuation is not affected by the characteristic impedance of a matched line if the spacing between the conductors in the coaxial cable is a small fraction of a wavelength at the operating frequency.

[Turn to Chapter 13 and study questions 3AI-3-1.1 through 3AI-3-3.3, and 3AI-5-1.1 through 3AI-5-3.3 before continuing with this chapter.]

POLARIZATION OF ANTENNAS AND RADIO WAVES

An electromagnetic wave consists of moving electric and magnetic fields. Remember that a field is an invisible force of nature. We can't see radio waves, but we can show a representation of where the energy is in the electric and magnetic fields. We did this in Chapter 3 to show the magnetic flux around a coil, and the electric field in a capacitor. We can visualize a traveling radio wave as looking something like Figure 7-35. The lines of electric and magnetic force are at

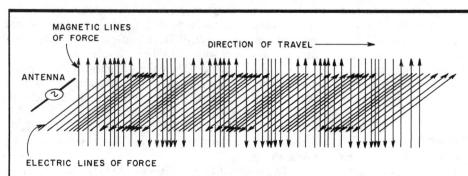

Figure 7-35—A horizontally polarized electromagnetic wave. The electrical lines of force are parallel to the ground. The fields are stronger where the arrows are closer together. The points of maximum field strength correspond to the points of maximum amplitude for the voltage producing the RF signal.

ANTENNA POLARIZATION

The signal sent from an amateur station depends on the antenna type and how it is oriented. A horizontal antenna, parallel to the earth's surface (like a dipole), will produce a *horizontally polarized* signal. A Yagi antenna with horizontal elements will also produce a horizontally polarized signal. See Part A in the drawing.

A vertical antenna (perpendicular to the earth's surface) will produce a *vertically polarized* signal. A Yagi with vertical elements also produces vertical polarization. See Part B in the drawing.

Most communications on the HF bands (80 through 10 meters) use horizontal polarization. Polarization on the HF bands is not critical, however. As a signal travels through the ionosphere, its polarization can change.

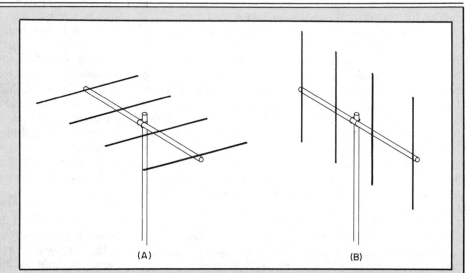

The plane of the elements in a Yagi antenna determines the transmitted signal polarization. If the elements are horizontal, as shown at A, the signal will have horizontal polarization. Vertical mounting, shown at B, produces a vertically polarized wave.

On the VHF/UHF bands, most FM communications use vertical polarization. Here, the polarization *is* important. The signals retain their polarization from transmitter to receiver. If you use a horizontal antenna, you will have difficulty working through most repeaters.

right angles to each other. They are also perpendicular to the direction of travel. These fields can have any position with respect to the earth.

Horizontal Polarization

Polarization is defined by the direction of the electric lines of force in a radio wave. A wave with electric lines of force that are parallel to the surface of the earth is a horizontally polarized wave.

Vertical Polarization

The electric lines of force can also be perpendicular to the earth. This wave is said to be vertically polarized. The polarization of a radio wave as it leaves the antenna is determined by the orientation of the antenna. For example, a half-wavelength dipole parallel to the surface of the earth transmits a wave that is horizontally polarized. A half-wavelength dipole perpendicular to the surface of the earth transmits a vertically polarized wave. An amateur mobile whip antenna is mounted vertically on a car. It transmits a wave that is vertically polarized.

The quarter-wavelength vertical antenna is a popular HF antenna because it provides low-angle radiation when a beam or dipole cannot be placed far enough above ground. Low-angle radiation refers to signals that travel closer to the horizon, rather than signals that are high above the horizon. Low-angle radiation is usually better when you are trying to contact distant stations. Vertical antennas of any length radiate vertically polarized waves.

Polarization is most important when installing antennas for VHF or UHF. Propagation at these frequencies is mostly line of sight. The polarization of a VHF or UHF signal does not change from transmitting antenna to receiving antenna. Best signal reception occurs when both transmitting and receiving stations use the same polarization. The polarization of an HF signal may change many times as it passes through the ionosphere. Antenna polarization at HF is not as important.

Most VHF/UHF FM and data communications is done with vertically polarized antennas. Vertically polarized antennas are more popular for VHF/UHF FM operation, because the antennas used on cars are almost always verticals. Vertical antennas are more useful for repeaters and home-station use on these bands as well, because they are not directional. For long-distance FM work, a vertically polarized beam is the best antenna. Data communication on the VHF/UHF bands is also mostly done with vertically polarized antennas. VHF/UHF CW and SSB operation, however, is done mostly with horizontally polarized antennas.

Most man-made noise tends to be vertically polarized. Thus, a horizontally polarized antenna will receive less noise of this type than a vertical antenna will.

[Turn to Chapter 13 and study questions 3AI-2-1.1, 3AI-2-2.1, 3AI-2-2.2 and 3AI-2-2.3. Review the material in this section as needed.]

MORE ABOUT BEAM ANTENNAS

In most multiple-element antennas, the additional elements are not directly connected to the feed line. They receive power by mutual coupling from the *driven element*. The driven element is the element connected to the feed line. The additional elements then reradiate the power in the proper phase relationship. Proper phasing achieves gain or directivity

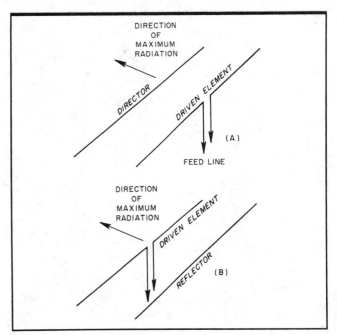

Figure 7-36—In a directional antenna, the reflector element is placed behind the driven element. The director goes in front of the driven element.

over a simple half-wavelength dipole. These elements are called **parasitic elements**.

There are two types of parasitic elements. A director is generally shorter than the driven element. A director is located at the front of the antenna. A reflector is generally longer than the driven element. A reflector is located at the back of the antenna. See Figure 7-36. The direction of maximum radiation from a parasitic beam antenna is from the reflector through the driven element to the director. The term **major lobe** refers to the region of maximum radiation from a directional antenna. The major lobe is also sometimes referred to as the main lobe. Communication in different directions may be achieved by rotating the array in the azimuthal, or horizontal, plane.

Yagi Arrays

The Yagi arrays in Figure 7-37 are examples of antennas that make use of parasitic elements to produce a unidirectional radiation pattern. A Yagi antenna has at least two elements. One element is a driven element. The other elements are directors and/or reflectors. These elements are usually parallel to each other and made of straight metal tubing. Though typical HF antennas of this type have three elements, some may have six or more. Multiband Yagi antennas have many elements. Some elements work on some frequencies and others are used for different frequencies. The radiation pattern of the Yagi antenna is shown in Figure 7-33. This pattern indicates that the antenna will reject signals coming from the sides and back. It selects mainly those signals from a desired direction. There are several types of Yagi antennas.

There are many different methods of connecting the feed line to the driven element of a Yagi antenna. The most common feed system, shown in Figure 7-38, is called the **gamma match**.

The length of the driven element in the most common type of Yagi antenna is approximately an electrical half-wavelength. This means that Yagi antennas are most often used

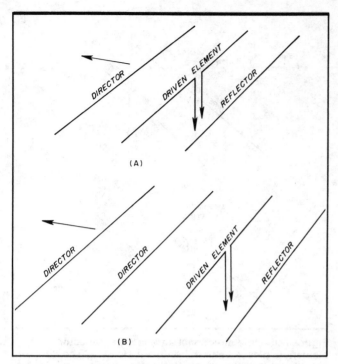

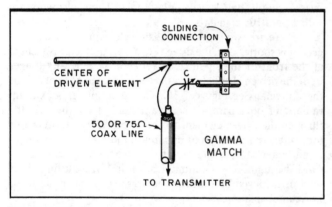

Figure 7-37—At A, a three-element Yagi. At B, a four-element Yagi with two directors.

Figure 7-38—The gamma match—the matching system best suited to matching Yagi antennas to unbalanced (coaxial) feed lines.

for the 20-meter band (14.0 to 14.35 MHz) and higher frequencies. Yagis for frequencies below 14 MHz are very large. They require special construction techniques, heavy-duty supporting towers and large rotators. Yagis for 40 meters are fairly common. Rotatable Yagis for 80 meters are few and far between. You can overcome the mechanical difficulties of large Yagis. Some amateurs build nonrotatable Yagi antennas for 40 and 80 meters, with wire elements supported on both ends.

In a three-element beam, the director is approximately 5% shorter than the driven element. The reflector is approximately 5% longer than the driven element. We can derive a set of equations to calculate these element lengths.

Equation 7-2 can be used to find the length of the driven element for a Yagi with a 146-MHz center frequency.

$$L(ft) = \frac{468}{f(MHz)} = \frac{468}{146} = 3.21 \text{ ft}$$

To find the length of a director or reflector element, we can use Equations 7-4 and 7-5:

$$L_{director} = L_{driven} \times 0.95 \qquad \text{(Eq 7-4)}$$
$$L_{director} = 3.21 \times 0.95$$
$$L_{director} = 3.05 \text{ ft}$$

$$L_{reflector} = L_{driven} \times 1.05 \qquad \text{(Eq 7-5)}$$
$$L_{reflector} = 3.21 \times 1.05$$
$$L_{reflector} = 3.37 \text{ ft}$$

These lengths can vary considerably, however. The actual lengths depend on the spacing between elements and the diameter of the elements. Whether the elements are made from tapered or cylindrical tubing also makes a difference.

The polarization of the signal from a Yagi antenna is determined by antenna placement relative to the surface of the earth. Yagi elements are usually parallel to the surface of the earth, as shown in Figure 7-39A. This way the transmitted wave is horizontally polarized. If the elements are perpendicular to the surface of the earth, as in Figure 7-39B, the wave is vertically polarized.

[Turn to Chapter 13 and study questions 3AI-1-1.1 through 3AI-1-1.7. Review the material in this section as needed.]

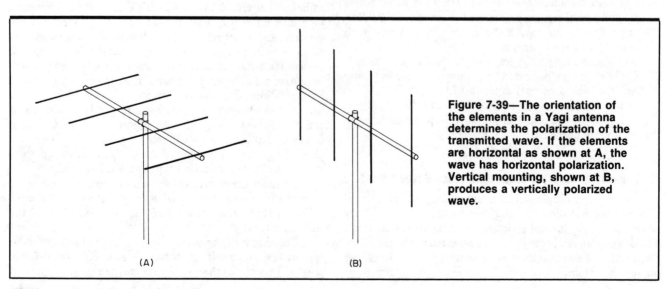

Figure 7-39—The orientation of the elements in a Yagi antenna determines the polarization of the transmitted wave. If the elements are horizontal as shown at A, the wave has horizontal polarization. Vertical mounting, shown at B, produces a vertically polarized wave.

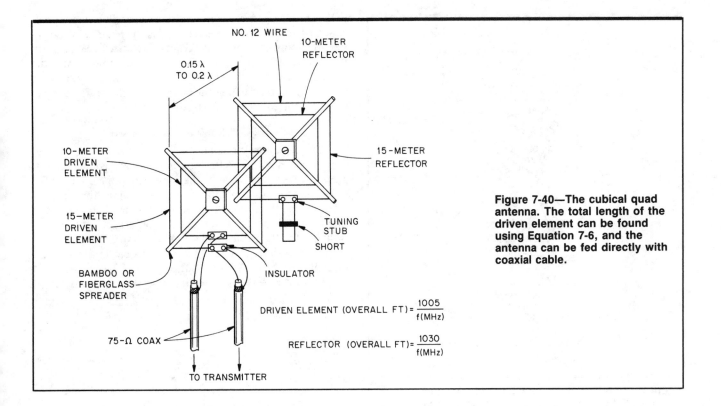

DRIVEN ELEMENT (OVERALL FT) = $\frac{1005}{f(MHz)}$

REFLECTOR (OVERALL FT) = $\frac{1030}{f(MHz)}$

Figure 7-40—The cubical quad antenna. The total length of the driven element can be found using Equation 7-6, and the antenna can be fed directly with coaxial cable.

Cubical Quad Antennas

The **cubical quad antenna** also uses parasitic elements. This antenna is sometimes simply called a *quad*. The two elements of the quad antenna are usually wire loops. The total length of the wire in the driven element is approximately one electrical wavelength. A typical quad, shown in Figure 7-40, has two elements—a driven element and a reflector. A two-element quad could also use a driven element with a director. You can add more elements, such as a reflector and one or more directors. The radiation pattern of a typical quad is similar to that of the Yagi shown in Figure 7-33.

Additional elements can be added to increase the directivity of the antenna. By installing additional loops of the proper dimensions, we can work different frequency bands with the same antenna. This is commonly done as a

modification to a 20-meter quad to provide 15- and 10-meter coverage. The elements of the quad are usually square. Each side is about an electrical quarter wavelength long. The total lengths of the elements are calculated as follows:

Circumference of driven element:

$$C_{driven\ element}\ (ft) = \frac{1005}{f(MHz)} \qquad (Eq\ 7\text{-}6)$$

Circumference of director element:

$$C_{director}\ (ft) = \frac{975}{f(MHz)} \qquad (Eq\ 7\text{-}7)$$

Circumference of reflector element:

$$C_{reflector}\ (ft) = \frac{1030}{f(MHz)} \qquad (Eq\ 7\text{-}8)$$

So for a 52-MHz cubical quad, the element circumference would be:

$$C_{driven\ element}\ (ft) = \frac{1005}{52} = 19.33\ ft$$

$$C_{director}\ (ft) = \frac{975}{52} = 18.75\ ft$$

$$C_{reflector}\ (ft) = \frac{1030}{52} = 19.91\ ft$$

Remember that these equations give the total length of the elements. To find the length of each side of the antenna, we must divide the total length by 4.

The polarization of the signal from a quad antenna can be changed. Polarization is determined by where the feed point is located on the driven element. See Figure 7-41. If the feed point is located in the center of a *horizontal* side, parallel

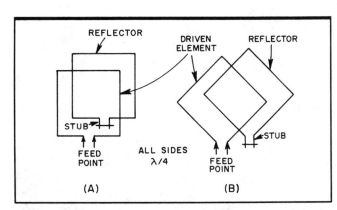

Figure 7-41—The feed point of a quad antenna determines the polarization. Fed in the middle of the bottom side (as shown at A) or at the bottom corner (as shown at B), the antenna produces a horizontally polarized wave. Vertical polarization is produced by feeding the antenna at the side in either case.

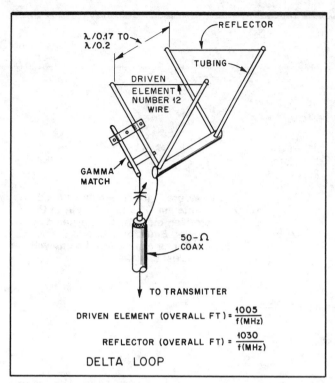

DRIVEN ELEMENT (OVERALL FT) = $\frac{1005}{f(MHz)}$

REFLECTOR (OVERALL FT) = $\frac{1030}{f(MHz)}$

DELTA LOOP

Figure 7-42—A delta loop antenna. The total length of each element can be found using the same equations as used for a quad antenna. The antenna is fed with a gamma match.

to the earth's surface, the transmitted wave will be **horizontally polarized**. When the antenna is fed in the center of a *vertical* side, the transmitted wave is **vertically polarized**. We can turn the antenna 45 degrees, so it looks like a diamond. When the antenna is fed at the bottom corner, the transmitted wave is horizontally polarized. If the antenna is fed at a side corner, the transmitted wave is vertically polarized.

Delta Loop Antennas

The **delta loop antenna**, shown in Figure 7-42, is a variation on the quad. A delta loop antenna has triangular elements, rather than square. The same equations used for the quad will work to calculate the element lengths for the delta loop. Divide the total length by 3 to find the length of each side of the elements. The radiation pattern of a delta loop is similar to that of the quad and Yagi, shown in Figure 7-33.

[Now turn to Chapter 13 and study questions 3AI-1-2.1 through 3AI-1-3.1, 3AI-2-1.2 through 3AI-2-1.3, 3AI-2-2.4 and 3AI-2-2.5. Review this section if you have any problems.]

——— KEY WORDS ———

Antenna switch—A device that allows you to connect more than one antenna (or a dummy antenna) to a station.

Coordinated Universal Time (UTC)—A system of time referenced to time at the prime meridian, which passes through Greenwich, England.

Dummy load (dummy antenna)—A device used when you want to test or tune a transceiver without sending a signal out over the air. Instead of sending the signal to an antenna, you send it to the dummy load, which dissipates (gets rid of) the output power.

Electronic keyer—A device used to produce Morse code dots and dashes electronically. One input generates dots, the other, dashes. Character speed can be adjusted from 5 or 10 words per minute up to 60 or more.

Feed line—The wires or cable used to connect your transceiver to an antenna.

Field-effect transistor volt-ohm-milliammeter (FET VOM)—A type of multimeter. The meter circuit uses an FET amplifier to provide more accurate readings than can be obtained with a VOM. The FET VOM is the solid-state equivalent of a VTVM.

Ground connection—A connection made to the earth for electrical safety.

Multimeter—An electronic test instrument used to measure current, voltage and resistance in a circuit. Describes all meters capable of making these measurements, such as the **VOM**, **VTVM** and **FET VOM**.

QSL card—A postcard sent to another radio amateur to confirm a contact.

Safety interlock—A switch that turns off ac power to a piece of equipment when someone removes the top cover.

Standing-wave-ratio (SWR) meter—A device used for measuring SWR. SWR is a relative measure of the impedance match between an antenna, feed line and transmitter.

Transmit-receive (TR) switch—A device used for switching between transmit and receive operation. This includes changing the antenna between the transmitter and receiver, and making any other changes necessary to go between transmitting and receiving.

Vacuum-tube voltmeter (VTVM)—A type of multimeter that includes a vacuum-tube amplifier to provide more accurate readings than can be obtained with a VOM.

Volt-ohm-milliammeter (VOM)—A type of multimeter, a device used to measure voltage, current and resistance. The VOM is the least expensive (and least accurate) type of multimeter. (See also **field-effect transistor VOM** and **vacuum-tube voltmeter**.)

Chapter 8

Putting It All Together

Y ou have selected your equipment and put up an antenna. Now it's time to turn this collection into a radio station. Once you've connected the various pieces of gear, you'll be ready to begin making on-the-air contacts with your new license.

With some careful thought and planning, you'll have a station that's both efficient and eye-pleasing. Simply think about what you want ahead of time.

STATION LOCATION

First, give some thought to station location. Hams put their equipment in many places. Some use the basement or attic, while others choose the den, kitchen, closet or a spare bedroom. Some hams with limited space build their station into a small closet. A fold-out shelf and folding chair form the operating position!

Where you put your station depends on the room you have available and on your personal tastes. There are, however, several things to keep in mind while searching for the best place. Figure 8-1 shows several amateur stations, with a variety of equipment arrangements and locations.

One often-overlooked requirement for a good station location is adequate electrical service. Eventually you will have several pieces of station equipment, as well as accessories. All

of them will require power to operate. Be sure that at least one, and preferably several, electrical outlets are located near your future operating position. Be sure the outlets provide the proper voltage and current for your rig. Most modern radios require only a few amperes. You may run into problems, however, if your shack is on the same circuit as the air conditioner or washing machine. The total current drawn at any one time must not exceed rated limits. Someday you'll probably upgrade and may want to purchase a linear amplifier. If so, you should have a 240-volt line in the shack, or the capability to get one.

Another must for your station is a good **ground connection**. A good ground not only reduces the possibility of electrical shock but also improves the performance of your station. By connecting *all* of your equipment to ground, you will help to avoid stray RF current in the shack. Stray RF can cause equipment to malfunction. A good ground can also help reduce the possibility of interference. The wire connecting your station to an earth ground should be as short as possible.

Basement and first-floor locations generally make it easier to provide a good ground connection for your station. You can also find a way to put your ham shack on the second or third floor—or even on the top floor of a high-rise apartment, for that matter.

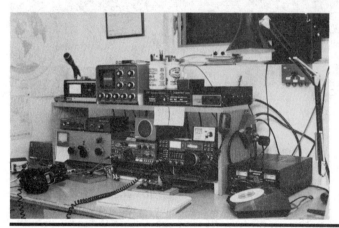

Figure 8-1—There are many ways to arrange your station equipment. The most important considerations are safe operation and a layout that pleases you.

Your radio station will require a **feed line** of some sort to connect the antenna to the radio. So you will need a convenient means of getting the feed line into the shack. There are many ways of doing this, but one of the easiest and most effective requires only a window. Many hams simply replace the glass pane in a nearby window with a clear acrylic panel. The panel can be drilled to accept as many feed lines as needed. Special threaded "feedthrough" connectors make the job easy. If you decide to relocate your station, the glass pane can be replaced. This will restore the window to its original condition.

A simpler, more temporary approach is to pass the feed lines through the open window and close it gently. Do this carefully, because crushed coaxial cable will give you nothing but trouble. Be sure to secure the window with a block of wood or some other "locking" device. Your new equipment,

seen through an open window, may tempt an unwanted visitor!

Another important requirement for your station is comfort. The space should be large enough so you can spread out as needed. Operating from a telephone booth isn't much fun! Because you will probably be spending some time in your shack (an understatement!), be sure it will be warm in the winter and cool in the summer. It should also be as dry as possible. High humidity can cause such equipment problems as high-voltage arcing and switch-contact failure.

If your station is in an area often used by other family members, be sure they know what they shouldn't touch. You should have some means of ensuring that no "unauthorized" person can use your equipment. One way to do this is to install a key-operated on-off switch in the equipment power line. When the switch is turned off and you have the key in your pocket, you will be sure that no one can misuse your station.

You will eventually want to operate late at night to snag the "rare ones" on 80 and 40 meters. Although a Morse code or voice contact is music to your ears, it may not endear you to a sleeping family. Putting your station in a bedroom shared with others may not be the best idea. You can keep the "music" to yourself, however, by using a good pair of headphones when operating your station.

WHAT IS A GOOD GROUND?

Most amateurs connect their equipment to a ground rod driven into the ground as close to the shack as possible. For a few dollars you can purchase a 1/2- or 5/8-inch-diameter, 8-foot-long ground rod at any electrical supply store. (Eight feet is the shortest practical length for your station ground rod.) Drive this copper-clad steel rod into the ground outside of your house, as close to your station location as possible. (Don't settle for the short, thin "ground rods" sold by some discount electronics stores. The copper cladding on the outside of most of these steel rods is very thin. They begin to rust almost immediately when they are put in the ground.)

Run a heavy copper wire (number 10 or larger) from your shack and attach it to the rod with a clamp. You can purchase the clamp when you buy the ground rod. Heavy copper strap or flashing (sold at hardware or roofing-supply stores) is even better. The braid from a piece of RG-8 coaxial cable also makes a good ground cable. Figure 8-2 shows one method of grounding each piece of equipment in your station. It's important to keep the cable between your station and the earth ground as short as possible.

Many hams ground their station equipment by connecting the ground wire to a cold-water pipe. Caution is in order here. If you live in an apartment or have your shack in an attic, be careful. The cold-water pipe near your transmitter may follow such a long and winding path to the earth that it may not act as a ground at all! It may, in fact, act as an antenna, radiating RF energy—exactly what you don't want it to do.

Beware too, of the nonmetallic cold-water pipes being used more and more. PVC and other plastic pipes are effective insulators. There may be a piece of copper water pipe running close by your station. If there is a piece of PVC pipe connected between that spot and where the water line enters your house, however, you will not have a ground connection!

It is also important to ground all antennas and feed lines to protect against damage from lightning. This is discussed later in the chapter.

[Study the questions in Chapter 12 that begin with 2D-3. If you have questions after studying these questions, review the material in this section.]

ARRANGING YOUR EQUIPMENT

Before you set everything up and hook up the cables, think about where you want each piece of equipment. While there is no one best layout for a ham station, some general rules do apply. Of course, the location you've chosen for your station may limit your choices a bit. For example, if you're going to put the station in the basement, you'll probably have a lot of space. If you'll be using a corner of the bedroom or den, however, you'll want to keep the equipment in a small area.

Generally, the piece of gear that requires the most adjustment is the transceiver (or receiver if you have one). Make sure you can conveniently reach its controls, and keep in mind which hand you're going to use to make the adjustments. It doesn't make much sense to put the transceiver on the left side of the desk or table if you're going to adjust it with your right hand. Once you've found the best location for the transceiver, you can position the rest of your equipment around it.

If you'll be using Morse code, placement of the telegraph key is also very important. It must be easy to reach with the hand you send with, and placed so your arm will be supported when you're using it. Try to position it away from anything dangerous, such as sharp corners and edges, rough surfaces and electrical wires.

If you have room for a desk or table long enough to hold all your gear, you'll probably like this arrangement. If you're pressed for space, however, a shelf built above the desk top is a good solution. Make certain the shelf is high enough to permit free air circulation above your transceiver. Leave at least 3 inches of space between the top of the tallest unit on the desktop and the bottom of your shelf. In building the

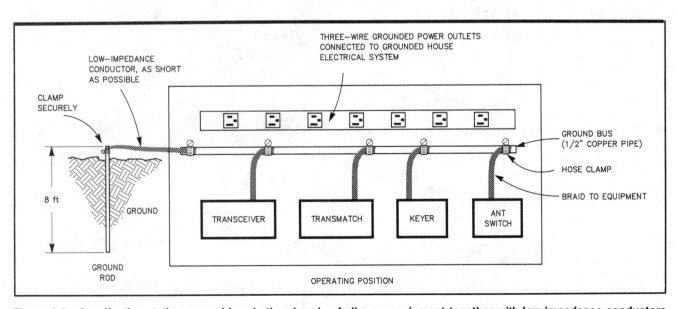

Figure 8-2—An effective station ground bonds the chassis of all your equipment together with low-impedance conductors and ties into a good earth ground.

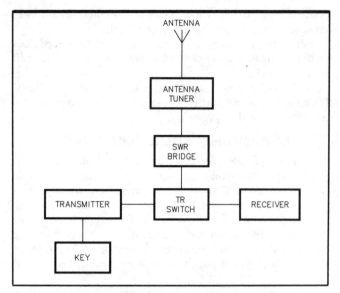

Figure 8-3—This block diagram shows the equipment connections in a typical amateur station.

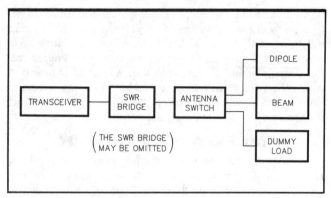

Figure 8-4—A block diagram of an amateur station showing the placement of an antenna switch.

shelf, keep in mind the weight of the equipment you're going to place on it. Try to restrict the shelf space to units you don't have to adjust very often. The station clock, SWR meter and antenna rotator control box are examples of this kind of equipment.

After you have a good idea of where you want everything, you can start connecting the cables. Figure 8-3 shows a block diagram of a typical amateur station.

A **transmit-receive (TR) switch** is used to switch the antenna from the receiver to the transmitter. A **standing-wave-ratio (SWR) meter** is used to help you tune the antenna when it is first erected. An SWR meter is also used to monitor the power going out to the antenna when the station is in use. Often a **dummy load** or **dummy antenna** is also connected. Many hams use an **antenna switch** to select the dummy load or one of several antennas, as shown in Figure 8-4. The next section covers these accessories in more detail.

If you're using a separate transmitter and receiver, you'll need a TR switch. You can purchase a TR switch or relay, or you can build one from a relay or knife switch. You'll also have to make up two short coaxial cables to connect your transceiver or transmitter to the switch.

ACCESSORIES

Until now, we have talked about the bare necessities—what you need to set up a basic Amateur Radio station. Few hams are content with the bare necessities, however. Part of the fun in Amateur Radio is adding accessories that make operating more convenient and enjoyable.

DUMMY LOAD

A **dummy load**, sometimes called a **dummy antenna**, is nothing more than a large resistor. It replaces your antenna when you want to operate your transmitter without radiating a signal. The dummy load safely converts the RF energy coming out of your transmitter into heat. The heat goes into the air or into the coolant, depending on the type of dummy load. It does all this while presenting your transmitter with a constant 50-ohm load. Dummy loads are used to test transmitters, or to make tuning adjustments after changing bands. When looking at dummy loads, be sure the one you choose is rated for the power level you'll be using.

Relatively inexpensive, a dummy load is one of the most useful accessories you can own. Every conscientious amateur should own one. You can build your own (see Figure 8-5), buy a kit or buy one that's ready to use. The container, often a gallon paint can, acts as a shield to keep RF energy from being radiated. The container can be filled with transformer oil, which allows the dummy load to dissipate greater RF power.

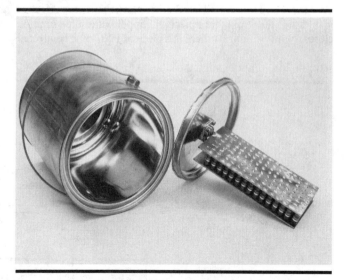

Figure 8-5—A dummy load is really just a resistance that provides your transmitter with a proper load when you are tuning up.

ANTENNA SWITCH

An **antenna switch** enables you to choose between several antennas without disconnecting and reconnecting any cables.

EARLY RADIO GEAR

Today's compact and efficient radio gear bears little resemblance to the crude apparatus used at the turn of the century. Early radios often had a range of only a few miles. Today's amateur who "home-brews" only assembles components. Early ham experimenters often had to create their own parts from scratch.

There were no transistors, not even tubes, to generate a signal. Little printed material existed to explain how. Communication was by a form of man-made static. The simplest transmitter started with a spark coil (usually a Model T Ford ignition coil). A key in series with a battery energized the coil, electrifying a spark gap across the high-voltage winding. You connected an antenna wire to one side of the gap and a good ground to the other side, as shown in the diagram. Without the ground, you wouldn't be heard at the end of your block. Even with it, you would be fortunate to be heard five miles away. And because there was no real tuning, the output was as broad as the proverbial barn door. It probably occupied a space as large as that between 1500 and 4000 kHz.

More advanced sets used a large coil or "helix" of copper strap or tubing in the antenna lead. This inductor "peaked" the energy at one particular wavelength (measured in meters, not kilocycles or kilohertz). The aerial was often a series of parallel wires shaped like a hammock. These were as high in the air as feasible, and sized to fit the selected wave. Yet the output was still gross, perhaps wider than any present medium-frequency band.

More progressive (and wealthier) amateurs used a spiked, motor-driven metal (but insulated) wheel or "chopper" inserted between spark gap terminals. The speed of rotation determined the interruption rate and imparted a distinctive tone to the output energy. This assisted the receiving operator in discerning the desired signal from other, interfering ones. There was no law, and no licensing. Amateurs had as much right to any part of the spectrum as anyone else, including the US Navy. Each operator had to do the best he could to work through heavy interference.

The transmitter used by Hiram Percy Maxim, 1AW, at his home in Hartford, Connecticut, was fairly advanced for its day. The photo shows a coil or "oscillation transformer" on the left. The large box housed a four-spiked wheel to form a rotary spark gap. The meter, a luxury, measured antenna current. Yet his range, too, was limited. When Maxim wanted to get some information by wireless to a colleague in Springfield, Massachusetts, about 20 miles away, he had to ask another amateur halfway between to relay the message. This was the seed of the idea that led to the founding of the American Radio Relay League in 1914.

Many of the useful advances in two-way wireless and radio (as distinguished from broadcasting) over the years have been in the form of narrowing the emitted signal bandwidth. That way, the finite spectrum can accommodate an ever greater number of communication channels. With today's equipment and techniques, thousands of interference-free contacts can occur in the space once occupied by a single spark transmitter.

Figure 8-4 shows a block diagram of an amateur station with an antenna switch connected. Antenna switches come in many different configurations and sizes. They range from those that switch between only two antennas to those that switch between six or more. Most antenna switches use a circular or rotary switch. Some have the coaxial-cable connectors arranged around the switch element. This circular arrangement is designed to fit behind a panel. Others have the connectors lined up in a row. This arrangement forms a rectangular box made to mount on a table top or wall.

The antenna switch is especially useful for switching between your antenna and dummy load, or between the antennas you have for different bands. When choosing an antenna switch, be sure the one you buy is rated for the power level you are using. The connectors on the switch should match the ones on your antenna feed lines and equipment.

If they don't, your interconnecting cables will have to have different connector types on each end.

KEYERS

As you operate on the air and gain experience, your code speed will increase. A straight hand key works well at speeds up to about 15 words per minute. After that, you'll probably want to buy (or build) an **electronic keyer** to improve your high-speed sending.

An electronic keyer automatically produces dots and dashes of exactly the right length and spacing for the speed selected. Most are capable of sending at speeds ranging from 5 to 60 words per minute. The keyer uses a paddle that is moved to the left or right. Left produces dashes; right produces dots. Some paddles provide a switch or other means to accommodate left-handed sending.

Figure 8-6—Electronic keyers produce perfectly timed dots and dashes.

Some keyers are called iambic, or squeeze, keyers. If both paddles are squeezed at the same time, the keyer will produce a string of alternating dots and dashes. Iambic keyers make it easier to send code at higher speeds because less hand movement is required. The iambic technique can be tricky to learn, however. Figure 8-6 shows a modern electronic keyer. Some modern transceivers have built-in keyers.

Whether you use a straight key or an electronic keyer, you should always place a great emphasis on your "fist"—the way your CW sounds on the air. Practice until you are proficient in sending. Take care to space your words and letters properly. People you meet on the air won't think much of you if your timing is off and they have a difficult time copying your signal.

QSL CARDS

Postcards with call signs and other information on them are called **QSL cards**. Hams send them to stations they have contacted to provide written confirmation of the contact. Each card should contain information about the contact—date, time, frequency, mode, signal report and the call sign of the station contacted. QSL cards are said to be the final courtesy of a QSO. You will be asked for your card quite often.

There are many sources of QSL cards—many QSL printers advertise in the ham magazines, or you might want to try a local printer. Be sure of one thing when you design your QSL card: All the information should be on one side of the card only.

Your QSL card can be an expression of your personality. It can be a way of informing other hams about your part of the country. For example, a ham living in Philadelphia may use the Liberty Bell in some way. A Wyoming ham could use Old Faithful. One ham who is interested in soaring has a picture of his sailplane on the front of his QSL. Hams who belong to ARRL can order special "ARRL member" QSL cards from printers that advertise in *QST*. Some radio clubs offer QSLs for club members, with the club logo worked into the design.

LOGBOOK AND STATION CLOCK

Many hams keep a complete logbook to keep track of the stations they've contacted; you'll probably want to do so, too. A log is particularly handy for exchanging QSL cards.

If you keep a log, you'll need a clock to keep track of the time. Although you can use any clock that's handy, a 24-hour clock is most convenient. It eliminates the question of whether a contact was made in the AM or in the PM. In 24-hour time, 0300 is 3 AM, while 2200 is 10 PM. There can be only one time we call 16:15. But what about 4:15? Does it mean AM or PM? Another reason is that most hams interested in communicating with other hams outside of the US keep track of the hour in terms of **Coordinated Universal Time**, or **UTC**. UTC is a 24-hour system, and requires a 24-hour clock. So you might as well invest in a good one. A conversion table that shows the UTC equivalent to your local time is easy to make. You can put together a dial-type device;

BEGIN A COLLECTION OF COLORFUL QSLs AND AWARDS

Once hams discover how equipment and operator work best, they begin to look around for something to do with those skills and with all the incoming QSL cards they begin to collect. Each time one ham makes contact with another, they exchange cards confirming that QSO, as it's called.

Hams use these QSL cards as proof of contact, and to earn specific certificates and awards. There are hundreds of awards to work toward. These include the popular Worked All States award and the Worked All Continents certificate. One of the most prestigious awards is the Five-Band DX Century Club, or Five-Band DXCC. Many hams display these colorful cards and awards like wallpaper on the walls of their shack.

Ever hear of Coordinated Universal Time? Do you know if it is light or dark at 0400 hours? Do you know how to use the 24-hour time system? If you answered no to any of these questions, you'd better read on!

Keeping track of time can be pretty confusing when you are talking to other hams around the world. Europe, for example, is anywhere from 4 to 11 hours ahead of us here in North America. Over the years, the time at Greenwich, England, has been universally recognized as *the* standard time in all international affairs, including ham radio. (We measure longitude on the surface of the earth in degrees east or west of the Prime Meridian. This imaginary line runs approximately through Greenwich, and is halfway around the world from the International Date Line.)

If you use UTC, you and the station you contact will be able to reference a common date and time, wherever you happen to be located. Mass confusion would occur if everyone used their own local time. Coordinated Universal Time (abbreviated UTC) is the name for what used to be called Greenwich Mean Time.

Twenty-four hour time lets you avoid the equally confusing question about AM and PM. If you hear someone say he made a contact at 0400 hours UTC, you will know immediately that this was 4 hours past midnight, UTC, since the new day always starts just after midnight. Likewise, a contact made at 1500 hours UTC was 15 hours past midnight, or 3 PM.

Maybe you have begun to figure it out: Each day starts at midnight, 0000 hours. Noon is 1200 hours, and the afternoon hours merely go on from there. You can think of it as adding 12 hours to the normal PM time—3 PM is 1500 hours, 9:30 PM is 2130 hours, and so on. However you learn it, be sure to use the time everyone else does—UTC.

The photo shows a specially made clock, with an hour hand that goes around only once every day, instead of twice a day like a normal clock. Clocks with a digital readout that show time in a 24-hour format are quite popular as a station accessory.

see the accompanying sidebar about the N7BH World Time Finder.

TEST EQUIPMENT

One of the most useful of all ham accessories is the multimeter. Multimeters are used to measure voltage, current and resistance. The most common multimeter is the **volt-ohm-milliammeter**, or **VOM**. These handy meters come in all sizes and price ranges. The biggest advantage of a VOM is its portability. You can take a VOM just about anywhere, even to the top of a 100-foot tower.

In selecting a VOM, consider the number of ranges it has, the ease with which you can change ranges, the readability of the meter and the ohms-per-volt rating. Most VOMs provide at least 20,000 ohms/volt of sensitivity. This means the internal resistance of the meter is equal to the range setting in volts multiplied by 20,000. The greater the ohms/volt rating, the more accurate and, therefore, useful the VOM. A meter rated at less than 20,000 ohms/volt will not be very accurate. Whatever VOM you purchase, make certain it's designed to operate in an RF field. Some give wildly inaccurate readings in the presence of an RF field.

Another multimeter hams use is the **vacuum-tube voltmeter**, or **VTVM**. This type of meter uses a vacuum-tube amplifier in its circuitry to provide a much higher input impedance than an ordinary VOM. A VTVM usually requires an ac power source to operate the vacuum tubes. Because of this, it isn't very portable. It does provide a sensitivity in the order of 11,000,000 ohms/volt, however. As a result, it is much more accurate than the standard VOM.

The battery-powered **field-effect transistor VOM (FET VOM)** is another type of multimeter. The FET functions in the same manner as the vacuum tube in a VTVM. Most FET VOMs have a sensitivity of at least 1,000,000 ohms/volt. Some have a sensitivity as great as that provided by a VTVM. The FET VOM offers the portability of the VOM combined with the sensitivity of a VTVM.

Measuring Voltage and Current

Using a multimeter is very simple. To get ready to make a measurement, simply plug the black test lead into the negative jack on the meter and the red test lead into the positive jack. Next, set the range switch to the proper scale. Some multimeters have separate jacks for different readings. Always check the instruction sheet that came with the meter before attempting to use it.

Once you have attached the test leads and set the range switch, you're all set to make your measurement. Both voltage and resistance readings are taken by touching the test lead tips to the points between which you want to measure. To measure current, cut or unsolder the conductor the current is flowing through. Then, connect a test lead to each side of the break. We do this because the circuit current must actually flow through the meter. Figure 8-7 illustrates how to connect a VOM to a circuit to measure both voltage and current.

THE N7BH WORLD TIME FINDER

You can eliminate errors in local-to-UTC time and date conversion by keeping a two-function clock set to local time and UTC. That solution, however, doesn't help determine the date and time in time zones other than local and UTC. The circular slide rule shown here works simultaneously for all time zones. (Within certain limits; many localities deviate from the system of Time Zones.)

The outer scale shows hours in the 24-hour format with plus and minus signs to show the gain or loss of a day at midnight. The inner scale is labeled with a letter and longitude to identify each Time Zone, UTC, the International Date Line and abbreviations for Time Zones in the US. For example, 2100T indicates 9 PM Mountain Standard Time or Pacific Daylight Time. (Note that adopting daylight time has the same effect as shifting one time zone to the east, and thus one hour closer to UTC.)

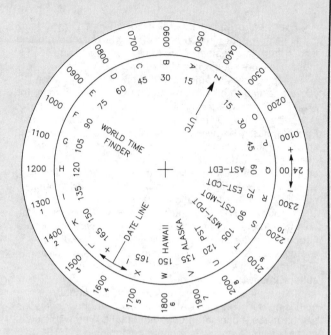

Time Zones

The system of Time Zones is based on a few facts about our planet. Because it takes 24 hours for the earth to rotate 360°, there is one hour of time change for every 15° of longitude. (There are 24 Time Zones, each 1 hour different from those adjacent.) The Prime Meridian (0° longitude) passes through Greenwich, England, and serves as a location for UTC. The International Date Line is 180° longitude and directly opposite the Prime Meridian. While this all forms a mathematical foundation for the Time Zone system, there are many deviations from a strict longitude/Time Zone correspondence for local convenience. For example, portions of Alaska and Hawaii share the same longitude, yet they are in different Time Zones.

Construction

You can assemble your own World Time Finder by cutting the two patterns from the Appendix at the back of this book. Put each circle between two pieces of clear plastic, or laminate them between sheets of clear ConTact® paper (a sticky-backed plastic material sold in many stores). Punch a hole in the center of each disk and use a 1/8-inch rivet with washers for the center pin.

Use

Operate the World Time Finder by aligning the time zone letter for your area with the current hour. In the example shown, it is 2000 hours (8 PM) at zone U (PST). Zone U is 120° W longitude, or 8 hours earlier than UTC. If the zone-U date is July 1, then the UTC time and date is 0400 (4 AM) July 2. In Japan (zone I), which is 135° E longitude and 9 hours later than UTC, it would be 1300 hours (1 PM) on July 2.

Note that this time conversion can be done by traveling either clockwise or counterclockwise around the chart. Going in a counterclockwise direction from zone U to UTC, you pass midnight (in the direction of the arrow pointing to the plus sign) on the outer scale, thus gaining a day. If traveling in a clockwise direction, you pass the International Date Line (with the arrow to plus), again gaining a day. The gain or loss of date is established easily by the + or − signs next to the arrows.

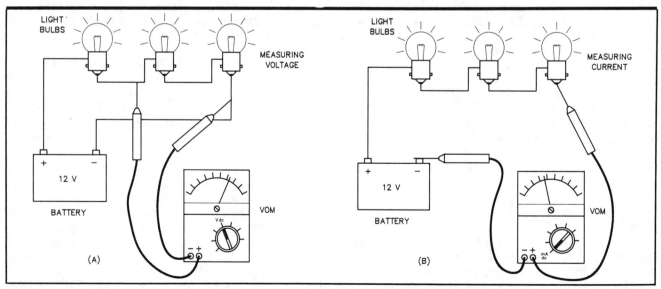

Figure 8-7—When measuring voltage with a VOM, simply connect the test leads across the circuit or component you want to check, as shown at A. To measure current, disconnect a wire at some point, and connect the meter leads at that point, as shown at B.

When you measure current, it all flows through the meter itself. Because of that, the internal resistance of the meter is very low when it is set for current measurements. If you accidentally set the meter for current measurement and connect it across a voltage, you'll almost certainly damage the meter. The low internal resistance of the meter will permit high current to flow—higher than the meter is designed to handle. Make certain the range switch is set to voltage when you're measuring a voltage.

Another point to keep in mind when measuring a voltage is that there is, in fact, a voltage present. If you're careless, you might touch something and get an electrical shock. The wire and handles provided on the test leads that came with the meter will protect you from the shock. But if you hold the probes very close to the metal tips you might touch them accidentally. Generally, the best procedure is to connect the appropriate test lead to the chassis. Then, put the hand that would have held that lead in your pocket. That way you've only got one hand near the voltage. It's a lot easier to keep track of one hand than it is to keep track of two!

SAFETY

It is important to arrange your station so it is safe for you and for any visitors. Wiring should be neat and out of the way. Make sure there is no way you can tangle your feet in loose wires. Don't leave any voltage (regardless how low) exposed.

A main power switch is a convenient item. It allows you to turn all station equipment on or off at once. This saves needless wear on the equipment power switches. More than merely convenient, however, the main power switch is an important safety item. Make sure every member of your family knows how to turn off the power to your workbench and operating position. If you ever receive an electrical shock and cannot free yourself, the main disconnect switch will help your rescuer come to your aid quickly.

You must take special safety precautions if young children can come into your shack. If you can lock your station into its own room, this is an ideal solution. Few radio amateurs can afford this luxury. There are other, less expensive ways for securing your equipment from unauthorized operation. For example, you could build your station into a closet or cabinet that can be locked. If the equipment must be in a nonsecure area, install a key-operated power switch and *keep track of the keys!* Even a simple toggle switch, if well-hidden, is effective in keeping your station secure.

The same principles apply if you set up your station for public display. FCC rules require that only a licensed control operator may put the station on the air. Therefore you must make sure that unauthorized persons will not be able to transmit. Sometimes that may require temporarily removing a tube, relay or control cable while the equipment is left unattended.

Whether you use commercially built equipment or homemade gear, you should *never* operate the equipment without proper shielding over all circuit components. Dangerous voltages may be exposed on the chassis-mounted components. Therefore, all equipment should have a protective shield on the top, bottom and all sides. An enclosure also prevents unwanted signals from entering a receiver, or from being radiated by a transmitter.

The cabinet should activate a switch that turns off the power if you remove the cover. Such a **safety interlock** reduces the danger of contacting high voltages when you open the cabinet.

Use common sense in arranging the station. Place things where they should logically be placed. Always think of safety. After you've arranged things where you think they should be, look over the arrangement. Try to find fault with your layout, both from a comfort standpoint and from a safety standpoint.

Don't feel satisfied with your station until you can't find anything left that can be improved upon.

All the equipment in your station should be connected to earth ground. Earlier in this chapter, we talked about what makes a "good ground." Briefly, you should connect your equipment to the earth by as short a cable as possible. If you live in an apartment, you may have to use a cold-water pipe rather than an outside ground rod. Don't neglect this important connection.

Lightning Protection

The lightning hazard from an antenna is often exaggerated. Ordinary amateur antennas are no more likely to be hit by a direct strike than any other object of the same height in the neighborhood. Just the same, lightning *does* strike thousands of homes each year, so it doesn't hurt to be careful. When your station is not in use, you should ground the antenna and rotator cables and unplug your equipment. An ungrounded antenna can pick up large electrical charges from storms in the area. They can damage your equipment (particularly receivers) if you don't take precautions.

Most commercial beam and vertical antennas are grounded for lightning protection through the tower itself. Of course, the tower must be grounded, too. If you use a roof mount, run a heavy ground wire from the mount to a ground rod. Dipoles and end-fed wires are not grounded. Disconnect the antenna feed line from your equipment and use an alligator-clip lead to connect both sides of it to your station ground.

Storm clouds often carry dangerous electrical charges that are coupled into high objects (like amateur antennas) *without* visible lightning. You may be operating and suddenly hear a "SNAP!" in your antenna tuner, or your receiver may go dead. You can usually hear an increase in static crashes well in advance of a thunderstorm. Be safe. When it sounds like a thunderstorm is headed your way, get off the air. If the weather forecast is for thunderstorms, don't operate! Snow and rain also generate static charges on antennas, but usually not enough to damage equipment.

The best protection against lightning is to disconnect all antennas and power cords when you aren't on the air. It takes time to hook up everything when you want to operate again, but there is little risk of damage to your equipment or your home if you follow this precaution. By the way, power companies recommend you unplug *all* electronic appliances, including TVs, VCRs and computers, when a storm threatens.

Why unplug your equipment if the antennas are disconnected? Lightning can still find its way into your equipment through the power cord. Power lines can act as long antennas, picking up sizable charges during a storm. Simply turning off the main circuit breaker is not enough—lightning can easily jump over the circuit breaker contacts and find its way into your equipment.

You may decide to leave your antennas connected and your equipment plugged in except during peak thunderstorm months. If so, you can still protect the equipment from unexpected storms. One simple step you can take is to install a grounding switch, as shown in Figure 8-8. A small knife switch will allow you to ground your feed line when you are not on the air. It will not disturb the normal operation of your station (with the switch open, of course!) if the lead from the feed line to the switch is no more than a couple of inches long. An alligator clip can be used instead of the switch. Whatever you use, don't forget to disconnect the ground when you transmit. This precaution is useful only on the HF bands. The switch will cause high SWR if used at VHF and UHF.

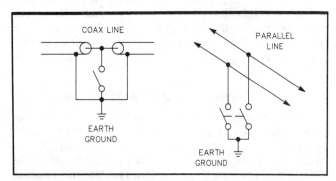

Figure 8-8—A heavy-duty knife switch can be used to connect the wires in your antenna feed line to ground. A clip lead to a ground wire can be used instead of the switch. This will prevent a large static build-up on your antenna. It will also prevent equipment damage caused by voltage on your antenna produced by a nearby lightning strike. There is no sure way to prevent a direct hit by lightning, however.

Another device that can help protect your equipment in an electrical storm is a lightning arrestor. This device connects permanently between your feed line and the ground. When the charge on your antenna builds up to a large enough potential, the lightning arrestor will "fire." This shorts the charge to ground—not through your station. A lightning arrestor can help prevent serious damage to your equipment. Most, however, don't work fast enough to protect your station completely. Lightning arrestors are useful for commercial stations and public service (fire and police) stations that must remain on the air regardless of the weather. Unless you are actually handling emergency communications, you shouldn't rely on them alone to protect your equipment, home or life.

[Now turn to Chapter 12 and study questions that begin with 2D-1, questions 2D-2.1 through 2D-2.4, and 2D-5.1 through 2D-5.2. Review this section if you have any difficulty with these questions.]

RF SAFETY

We all know basic safety precautions to follow in the ham shack or when erecting antennas. We know to pull the plug before taking the covers off a transceiver. We know to watch for power lines when hoisting an antenna into the air. Another important safety concern, one we often overlook, is radio-

frequency (RF) protection. This involves minimizing human exposure to strong RF fields. These potentially dangerous fields occur near or around antennas.

Biological effects of RF exposure have been studied for more than 20 years. Body tissues that are subjected to large amounts of RF energy may suffer heat damage. It is possible to receive an *RF burn* from touching an antenna that is being used for transmitting. You don't have to come into direct contact with an antenna to damage body tissues, however. Just being present in a strong RF field can cause problems.

Taken to extremes, we could compare the effects of RF exposure to the way a microwave oven cooks food. A typical microwave oven uses a 500-W RF source operating at 2450 MHz. Of course, the microwave oven is designed to concentrate its RF power for heating food and is not directly comparable to Amateur Radio operations. The heating effect from RF energy is also similar to the heating from an electric space heater. Some studies have shown that persons who are exposed to strong RF fields may be at increased risk to develop certain kinds of cancer.

There is no cause for alarm in most amateur installations. But be aware that exposure to strong RF fields—which we cannot see, smell, hear or touch—can cause health risks.

The amount of RF energy that the body absorbs depends on the radio frequency. The body absorbs RF energy most efficiently in the VHF range (30 to 300 MHz). Absorption is greatest if the antenna orientation is parallel to the body (vertically polarized).

Most amateur operation is with relatively low RF power and is intermittent—the transmitter is not operating continuously. Hams spend more time listening than transmitting. If you use modes such as RTTY and FM, in which the RF carrier is present continuously at full power, you'll need to pay more attention to RF safety.

RF SAFETY GUIDELINES

Take the time to study and follow these general guidelines to minimize your exposure to RF fields. Most of these guidelines are just common sense and good amateur practice.

• Confine RF radiation to the antenna, where it belongs. Provide a good earth ground for your equipment. Poor-quality feed line and improperly installed connectors can be a source of unwanted radiation. Use only good-quality coaxial cable. Be sure the connectors are of good quality and are properly installed.

• Don't operate RF power amplifiers or transmitters with the covers or shielding removed. This practice helps you avoid both electric shock hazards and RF safety hazards. This is especially important for VHF and UHF equipment. When reassembling transmitting equipment, replace all the screws that hold the RF compartment shielding in place. Tighten all the screws securely before applying power to the equipment.

• In high-power operation in the HF and VHF region, keep the antenna away from people. Humans should not be allowed within 10 to 15 feet of vertical antennas. This is especially important with higher power, high-duty-cycle operation (such as FM or RTTY). Amateur antennas that are mounted on towers and masts, away from people, pose no exposure problem.

• Always install your antennas where people and animals cannot touch them.

• When using mobile equipment with 10-W RF power output or more, do not transmit if anyone is standing within 2 feet of the antenna.

• The best location for a VHF/UHF mobile antenna—from an RF safety standpoint—is in the middle of the automobile roof. This position best protects the car's occupants.

• When using a hand-held transceiver with RF power output of several watts or more, maintain at least 1 to 2 inches separation between the antenna and your forehead. It is recommended that hand-held radios have a power of no more than 7 watts.

• Never touch an antenna that has RF power applied. Be sure RF power is off and stays off before working on or adjusting an antenna. Also, make sure any nearby antennas are deactivated. Never have someone else transmit into the antenna and monitor the SWR while you are making adjustments. When matching an antenna, you should turn the transmitter off and make the adjustment. Then, back away to a safe distance before turning the transmitter on again to check your work.

• During transmissions, never point a high-gain UHF or microwave antenna (such as a parabolic dish) toward people or animals.

• Never look into the open end of a UHF or microwave waveguide feed line that is carrying RF power. Never point the open end of a UHF waveguide that is carrying RF power toward people or animals. Make sure that all waveguide connections are tightly secured.

The following additional safety guidelines were developed in response to scientific studies done in the mid to late 1980s. (From the October 1989 *QST* article, "Is Amateur Radio Hazardous to our Health?" by Ivan A. Shulman, MD, WC2S.)

• Do not stand or sit close to your power supplies or linear amplifiers while operating, even when they are in standby mode.

• Stay at least 24 inches away from any power transformer, electrical fans or other source of high level 60-Hz magnetic fields while in operation.

• Do not tune up or operate a high powered linear amplifier while the shields or covers are off.

• Run your transmission lines away from where you or other people sit in or near your shack.

• Properly terminated coaxial transmission feed lines should be used in preference to open-wire or end-fed antenna installations that come directly into the transmitter, as the RF radiated from a coaxial feed line is much lower.

• Use common sense about placing all antennas well away from yourself and others, especially for VHF, UHF and particularly microwave applications. No one should be in the near field of an antenna.

• No person should be near any transmitting antenna while it is operating. This is especially true for mobile or ground-mounted vertical antennas. The use of indoor transmitting antennas that are close to people in a house or apartment should be reconsidered.

• Use the minimum power needed to make a QSO, especially if the antenna is less than 35 feet above the ground.

• Hand-held radios should be used on the lowest power setting needed to carry out communications.

• Hand-helds should be kept as far from the head as possible when operating. The use of a separate microphone or similar device is recommended.

• Transmissions using a hand-held radio should be kept as short as possible.

• Power density measurements should be made before running more than 25 watts in a VHF mobile installation, particularly if the antenna is rear-deck mounted and passengers may ride in the back seat. The safest mobile antenna location is in the center of the metal roof.

• The development of an accurate inexpensive power-density meter would be of major benefit to the Amateur Radio community so that RF power-density measurements could be taken in all radio installations. Because of the current high cost of such devices, groups of amateurs or clubs may wish to purchase one and share in its use.

• Soldering should only be done in a well ventilated area. A small fan should be used to blow away toxic fumes.

• When using toxic chemicals, such as when etching PC boards or repairing fiberglass, wear gloves and goggles, use proper tools, and avoid contact with any of the chemicals. If accidentally contaminated, wash off the compounds immediately with copious quantities of water. Again, the importance of always working in a well ventilated area with personal protective covering cannot be overemphasized.

• Hazardous chemicals, such as those in the PCB class, are used in some capacitors and dummy loads. Use extreme care in handling these materials, and consult with the appropriate local authorities to determine the proper means of disposing of these chemicals in an environmentally responsible way.

[Study questions in Chapter 12 that begin with 2D-4 and 2H-6. Review this section if you have difficulty answering any of these questions.]

——— NOT FOR TECHNICIANS ONLY ———

ADDITONAL STATION SET-UP INFORMATION FOR THE TECHNICIAN EXAM

——— KEY WORDS ———

Balun—Short for *bal*anced to *un*balanced. The balun is used to transform between an unbalanced feed line and a balanced antenna.

Marker generator—A high-stability oscillator that produces reference signals at known frequency intervals. It can be used to calibrate receiver and transmitter tuning dials. Also called a **crystal calibrator**.

Multimeter—An electronic test instrument used to measure current, voltage and resistance in a circuit. Describes all meters capable of making these measurements, such as the **VOM**, **VTVM** and **FET VOM**.

Reflectometer—A test instrument used to indicate standing wave ratio (SWR) by measuring the forward power (power from the transmitter) and reflected power (power returned from the antenna system).

Signal generator—A test instrument that produces a stable low-level radio-frequency signal. The signal can be set to a specific frequency and used to troubleshoot RF equipment.

S meter—A meter in a receiver that shows the relative strength of a received signal.

Wattmeter—A test instrument used to measure the power output (in watts) of a transmitter. A **directional wattmeter** measures both forward and reflected power.

———ELECTRICAL WIRING SAFETY———

Your station equipment makes use of ac line voltage. This voltage can be dangerous. The equipment also generates additional potentially lethal voltages of its own. You should be familiar with some basic precautions. Your own safety and that of others depends on it.

POWER-LINE CONNECTIONS

In most residential systems, three wires come in from outside to the distribution board. Older systems may use only two wires. In the three-wire system, the voltage between the two "hot" wires is normally 240. The third wire is neutral and is grounded. Half of the total voltage appears between each of the hot wires and neutral, as shown in Figure 8-9. Lights, appliances and 120-V outlets are divided as evenly as possible between the two sides of this circuit. Half of the load connects between one hot wire and the neutral. The other half of the load connects between the other hot wire and neutral.

Heavy appliances, such as electric stoves and most high-power amateur amplifiers, are designed for 240-V operation. Connect these across the two hot wires. *Both* ungrounded wires should be fused. The neutral wire should *never* have a fuse or switch in it.

Four-conductor appliance power cords should have the black and red wires connected to the hot wires with fuses. The white and green (or bare) wires should not have a fuse or switch. Opening a switch in the neutral wire does not disconnect the equipment from the household voltage. It places the equipment on one side of the 240-V line in series with anything across the other side. See Figure 8-10. When the neutral wire is open, the voltage will divide between the two loads. The division will be in proportion to each load resistance. The voltage will go above normal on the side with the larger load resistance. On the other side, the voltage will

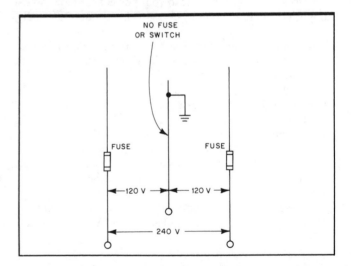

Figure 8-9—In home electrical systems, two wires carrying 240 volts are split between the house circuits carrying 120 volts each. Some heavy appliances use the full 240 V. As shown, a fuse should be placed in each hot wire, but no fuse or switch should be placed in the neutral wire.

be lower than normal. This will probably destroy the appliance. If both loads happen to be equal, the voltages will divide normally.

High-power amateur amplifiers use the full 240 V. It only takes half as much current to supply the same power as with a 120-V line. The power supply circuit efficiency improves with the higher voltage and lower current. A separate 240-V circuit for the amplifier ensures that you stay within the

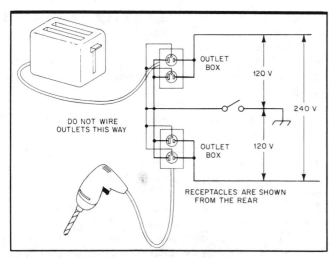

Figure 8-10—Opening the neutral wire leaves the equipment on one side of the 240-V line in series with anything connected on the other side. This is extremely dangerous! *Do not* wire outlets this way.

capacity of the 120-V circuits in your shack. An amplifier drawing more current than the house wiring can handle could cause the house lights to dim. This is because the heavy current causes the power-line voltage to drop.

Three-Wire 120-V Power Cords

State and national electrical-safety codes require three-wire power cords on many 120-V tools and appliances. Two of the conductors (the "hot" and "neutral" wires) power the device. The third conductor (the safety ground wire) connects to the metal frame of the device. See Figure 8-11. The "hot" wire is usually black or red. The "neutral" wire is white. The frame/ground wire is green or sometimes bare.

Let's look at the power cord connections for a transmitter power supply. The power supply will have a transformer in it. When you attach the power cord, the black wire will attach to one end of the fuse. The white wire will go to the side of the transformer primary winding without a fuse. The green (or bare) wire will attach to the chassis.

When plugged into a properly wired mating receptacle, a three-contact plug connects the third conductor to an earth ground. This grounds the appliance chassis or frame and

prevents the possibility of electric shock. A defective power cord that shorts to the case of the appliance will simply blow a fuse. Without the ground connection, the case could carry the full line voltage, presenting a severe shock hazard. All commercially manufactured electronic test equipment and most ac-operated amateur equipment uses these three-wire cords. Adapters are available for use where older electrical installations do not have mating receptacles. The lug of the green wire from the adapter must be attached under the cover-plate screw. The outlet (and outlet box) must be grounded for this to be effective. Power wires coming into the electric box inside a flexible metal covering provide grounding through the metal covering. The common name for this type of wire is armored cable.

A "polarized" two-wire plug has one blade that is wider than the other. The mating receptacle will accept the plug only one way. This ensures that the hot and neutral wires in the appliance connect to the appropriate wires in the house electrical system. Consider what happens without this polarized plug and receptacle. The power switch in the equipment will be in the hot wire when the plug is inserted one way. It will be in the neutral wire when inserted the other way. This can present a dangerous condition. It is possible for the equipment to be "hot" even with the switch off. With the switch in the neutral line, the hot line may be connected to the equipment chassis. An unsuspecting operator could form a path to ground by touching the case, and might receive a nasty shock!

Wiring an outlet or lamp socket properly is important. See Figure 8-12. The black (hot) wire should be connected to the brass terminal on the lamp socket or outlet. The white (neutral) wire should be connected to the white or silver-colored terminal. This will ensure that the proper blade of the plug connects to the hot wire (that the polarity is correct). This practice is especially important when wiring lamp sockets. The brass screw of the socket connects to the center pin in

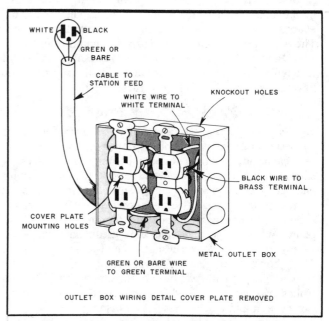

Figure 8-12—The correct way to wire a receptacle box. Connect the white wire to the white or silver terminal, and the black wire to the brass-colored terminal. This ensures that the mating plug will be connected with the proper polarization.

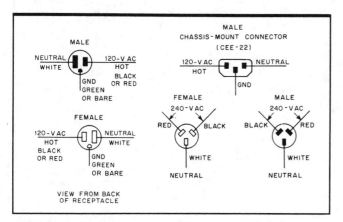

Figure 8-11—Correct wiring technique for 120-V and 240-V power cords and receptacles. The white wire is neutral, the green wire is ground and the black or red wire is the hot lead. Notice that the receptacles are shown as viewed from the back, or wiring side.

the socket. With this pin as the "hot" connection, there is much less shock hazard. Anyone unscrewing a bulb from a correctly wired socket has to reach inside the socket to get a shock. In an incorrectly wired socket, the screw threads of the bulb are "hot." A dangerous shock may result when replacing a bulb.

Current Capacity

There is another factor to take into account when you are wiring an electrical circuit. It is the current-handling capability of the wire. Table 8-1 shows the current-handling capability of some common copper-wire sizes. The table shows that number 14 wire could be used for a circuit carrying 15 A. You must use number 12 (or larger) for a circuit carrying 20 A.

Table 8-1

**Current-Carrying Capability
of Some Common Copper-Wire Sizes**

Wire Size (AWG)	Continuous-Duty Current*
8	46 A
10	33 A
12	23 A
14	17 A
16	13 A
18	10 A
20	7.5 A
22	5 A

*wires or cables in conduits or bundles

To remain safe, don't overload the ac circuits in your home. The circuit breaker or fuse rating is the maximum load for the line at any one time. Simple mathematics can be used to calculate the current your ham radio equipment will draw. Most equipment has the power requirements printed on the back. If not, the owner's manual should contain such information. Current calculations should include any other household appliances on the same line, including lights! If you put a larger fuse in the circuit, too much current could be drawn. The wires would become hot and a fire could result.

[Now turn to Chapter 13 and study questions 3AD-1-1.1 through 3AD-1-1.4. Review the material in this section if you have any difficulty with any of these questions.]

POWER-SUPPLY SAFETY

Safety must always receive careful consideration during the design and construction of any power supply. Power supplies can produce potentially lethal currents and voltages. Be careful to guard against accidental exposure to these currents and voltages. Use electrical tape, insulated tubing (spaghetti) or heat-shrink tubing to cover exposed wires. This includes component leads, component solder terminals and tie-down points. Whenever possible, connectors used to mate the power supply to the outside world should be of an insulated type. They should be designed to prevent accidental contact with the voltages present. AC power to the supply should be controlled by a clearly labeled front-panel switch. That way it can be seen and reached easily in an emergency.

All dangerous voltages in equipment should be made inaccessible. A good way to ensure this is to enclose all equipment in metal cabinets. That way no "hot" spots can be reached. Don't forget any component shafts that might protrude through the front panel. If a control shaft is hot,

protect yourself from accidental contact by using an insulated shaft extension or insulated knob.

Each metal enclosure should be connected to a good earth ground, such as a ground rod. Then, if a failure occurs inside a piece of equipment, the metal case will never present a shock hazard. The fuse will blow instead.

It's also a good idea to make it impossible for anyone to energize your equipment when you're not present. A key-operated ac-mains switch that controls all power to your station is a good way to accomplish this. Mount your switch where it can be seen and reached easily in an emergency.

You should never underestimate the potential hazard when working with electricity. Table 8-2 shows some of the effects of electric current—as little as 100 mA can be fatal! As the saying goes, "It's volts that jolts, but it's mills that kills." Low-voltage power supplies may seem safe, but even battery-powered equipment should be treated with respect. Thirty volts is the minimum voltage considered dangerous to humans. These voltage and current ratings are only general guidelines. Automobile batteries are designed to provide very high current (as much as 200 A) for short periods when starting a car. This much current can kill you, even at 12 volts. You will feel pain if the shock current is in the range of 30 to 50 mA.

Table 8-2

**Effects of Electric Current Through the Body
of an Average Person**

Current (1 Second Contact)	Effect
1 mA	Just perceptible.
5 mA	Maximum harmless current.
10-20 mA	Lower limit for sustained muscular contractions.
30-50 mA	Pain
50 mA	Pain, possible fainting. "Can't let go" current.
100-300 mA	Normal heart rhythm disrupted. Electrocution if sustained current.
6 A	Sustained heart contraction. Burns if current density is high.

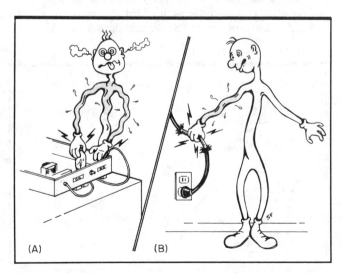

Figure 8-13—The path from the electrical source to ground affects how severe an electrical shock will be. The most dangerous path (from hand to hand directly through the heart) is shown at A. The path from one finger to the other shown at B is not quite so dangerous.

A few factors affect just how little voltage and current can be considered dangerous. One factor is skin resistance. The lower the resistance of the path, the more current that will pass through it. If you perspire heavily, you may get quite a bit more severe shock than if your skin was dry. Another factor is the path through the body to ground. As Figure 8-13 shows, the most dangerous path is from one hand to the other. This path passes directly through a person's heart. Even a very minimal current can cause heart failure and death. Current passing from one finger to another on the same hand will not have quite such a serious effect. For this reason, if you must troubleshoot a live circuit, keep one hand behind your back or in your pocket. If you do slip, the shock may not be as severe as if you were using both hands.

Bleeder Resistors

An important safety item in power-supply design is the bleeder resistor. When a power supply is turned off, the filter capacitors can store a charge for a long time. These charged capacitors present a shock hazard at the output terminals. A bleeder resistor connected across the filter capacitors will dissipate the charge stored in the capacitors when the supply is turned off. This will not affect normal operation of the supply because the bleeder resistor draws only a very small current.

[Now turn to Chapter 13 and study exam questions 3AD-1-2.1 through 3AD-1-2.3 and 3AD-1-3.1. Review any topics necessary before proceeding.]

USING TEST EQUIPMENT

THE VOLTMETER

The voltmeter is an instrument used to measure voltage. It is a basic meter movement with a resistor in series, as shown in Figure 8-14. The current multiplied by the resistance will be the voltage drop across the resistance. An instrument used this way is calibrated in terms of the voltage drop across the resistor to read voltage.

Voltage measurements are made by placing the meter in parallel with the voltage to be measured.

The range of a meter can be extended to measure a wide range of voltages. This is accomplished by adding resistance in series with it.

THE AMMETER

The ammeter depends upon a current flowing through it to deflect the needle. The ammeter is placed in series with the circuit. That way, all the current flowing in the circuit must pass through the meter. Many times the meter cannot handle all the current. The range of the meter can be extended by placing resistors in parallel with the meter to provide a path for part of the current. These shunt resistors are shown in Figure 8-15. They are calculated so that the total circuit current can be read on the meter. Most ammeters have very low resistance, but low-impedance circuits require caution. There is a chance that the slight additional resistance of the series ammeter will disturb circuit operation.

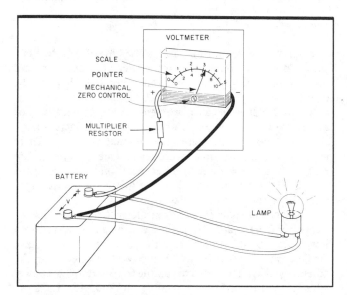

Figure 8-14—When you use a voltmeter to measure voltage, the meter must be connected in parallel with the voltage you want to measure.

A high value resistor provides a high impedance input for the meter. An ideal voltmeter would have an infinite input impedance. It would not affect the circuit under test in any way. Real-world voltmeters, however, have a finite value of input impedance. There is a possibility that the voltage you are measuring will change. This is because the meter adds some load to the circuit when you connect the voltmeter.

Use a voltmeter with a very high input impedance compared with the impedance of the circuit you are measuring. This prevents the voltmeter from drawing too much current from the circuit. Excessive current drawn from the circuit would significantly affect circuit operation. The input impedance of an ordinary voltmeter is about 20 kilohms per volt.

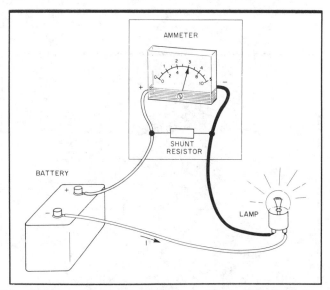

Figure 8-15—To measure current you must break the circuit at some point and connect the meter in series at the break. A shunt resistor expands the scale of the meter to measure higher currents than it could normally handle.

MULTIMETERS

A **multimeter** is a piece of test equipment that most amateurs should know how to use. The simplest kind of multimeter is the **volt-ohm-milliammeter (VOM)**. VOMs use one basic meter movement for all functions. The movement requires a fixed amount of current (often 1 mA) for a full-scale reading. As shown in the two previous sections, resistors are connected in series or parallel to provide the proper meter reading. In a VOM a switch selects various ranges for voltage, resistance and current measurements. This switch places high-value dropping resistors in series with the meter movement for voltage measurement. It connects low-value shunt resistors in parallel with the movement for current measurement. These parallel and series resistors extend the range of the basic meter movement.

If you are going to purchase a VOM, buy one with the highest ohms-per-volt rating that you can find. Stay away from meters rated under 20,000 ohms per volt if you can.

Measuring resistance with a meter involves placing the meter leads across the component or circuit you wish to measure. Make sure to select the proper resistance scale. The full-scale-reading multipliers vary from 1 to 1000 and higher. The scale is usually compressed on the higher end of the range. See Figure 8-16. For best accuracy, keep the reading in the lower-resistance half of the scale. On most meters this is the right-hand side. Thus, if you want to measure a resistance of about 5000 ohms, select the R × 1000 scale. Then the meter will indicate 5.

A **vacuum-tube voltmeter (VTVM)** operates in the same manner as an ordinary VOM. There is one important difference. The meter in a VTVM is isolated from the circuit under test by a vacuum-tube dc amplifier. As a result, the only additional circuit loading is from the tube input impedance, which is very high. The standard VTVM input impedance is 11 MΩ. This is useful for measuring voltages in high-impedance circuits, such as vacuum-tube grid circuits and FET gate circuits.

Another type of meter is a **field-effect transistor volt-ohm-milliammeter (FET VOM)**. This instrument uses a field-effect transistor (FET) to isolate the indicating meter from the circuit to be measured. FET VOMs have an input impedance of several megohms. They are the solid-state equivalent of a VTVM.

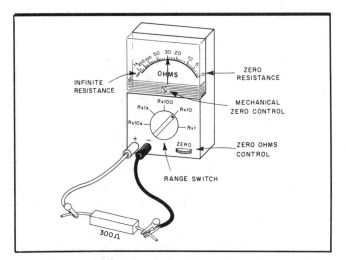

Figure 8-16—Resistance is measured across the component. For best accuracy the reading should be taken in the lower-resistance half of the scale.

[Now turn to Chapter 13 and study questions 3AD-2-1.1, 3AD-2-2.1, 3AD-3-1.1, 3AD-3-2.1 and 3AD-4.1. Review this section if you have difficulty with any of those questions.]

WATTMETERS

A **wattmeter** is a device in the transmission line to measure the power (in watts) coming out of a transmitter. Wattmeters are designed to operate at a certain line impedance, normally 50 ohms. Make sure the feed line impedance is the same as the design impedance of the wattmeter. If impedances are different, any measurements will be inaccurate. For most accurate measurement, the wattmeter should be connected directly at the transmitter (transceiver) antenna jack as shown in Figure 8-17.

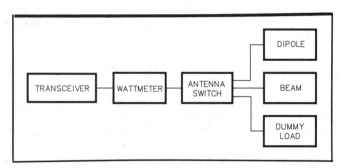

Figure 8-17—A wattmeter is connected at the transmitter output to measure power.

All wattmeters must contain some type of detection circuitry to enable you to measure power. The accuracy and upper frequency range of the wattmeter is limited by the detection device. Stray capacitance and coupling within the detection circuits can cause problems. A loss of sensitivity or accuracy occurs as the operating frequency is increased.

One type of wattmeter is a **directional wattmeter**. There are two kinds of directional wattmeters. One has a meter that reads forward power and another meter that reads reflected power. The other has a single meter that can be switched to read either forward or reflected power.

You can use a directional wattmeter to measure the output power from your transmitter. Remember that the reflected power must be subtracted from the forward reading to give you the true forward power. The power reflected from the antenna will again be reflected by the transmitter. This power adds to the forward power reading on the meter. Let's say your transmitter power output is 100 watts and 10 watts are reflected from the antenna. Those 10 watts will be added into the forward reading on your meter when they are reflected from the transmitter. Your wattmeter reading would be incorrect. To find true forward power you must subtract the reflected measurement from the forward power measurement:

True forward power =

Forward power reading − Reflected power reading

(Equation 8-1)

For example, suppose you have a wattmeter connected in the line from your transmitter. It gives a forward-power reading of 85 watts and a reflected-power reading of 15 watts. What is the true power out of your transmitter?

True forward power = 85 W − 15 W = 70 watts.

[Now turn to Chapter 13 and study exam questions

3AD-5-1.1 through 3AD-5-1.4, 3AD-5-2.1 and 3AD-5-2.2. Review this section as needed.]

SIGNAL GENERATORS

Marker Generators

The **marker generator** is a high-stability oscillator that produces an RF signal with a frequency that doesn't change. It is usually built into the receiver. This oscillator generates a series of signals that mark the exact edges of the amateur bands (and subbands, in some cases). It does this by oscillating at a low frequency that has harmonics falling on the desired frequencies. Most marker generators put out harmonics at 25, 50 or 100-kHz intervals. Since marker generators normally use crystal oscillators, they are often called **crystal calibrators**.

The marker generator is very useful. You can calibrate your receiver with it. You can then determine your precise transmitter frequency. First, turn on your marker generator (calibrator). This injects the calibrator signal into the receiver circuit. Then set your transceiver or receiver dial on the proper frequency marks. Calibration instructions are usually provided in your operator's manual. When the dial is calibrated, put your transmitter in the tune or spot position and read the frequency on the receiver dial.

The marker frequencies must be accurate. Now you know that the transmitter frequency is between the markers that show the ends of the band (or subband). In addition, the transmitter frequency must not be too close to the edge of the band (or subband). If it is, the sideband frequencies, especially in a voice transmission, will extend over the edge.

Signal Generators

A **signal generator** produces a stable, low-level signal that can be set to a specific frequency. There are two different types of signal generators. Audio frequency signal generators create signals in the audio range. Radio frequency signal generators provide radio frequency signals. These signals can be used to align or adjust circuits for best performance. One common use of a signal generator is in the alignment of receivers. The generator can be adjusted to the desired signal frequency. Then the associated circuits can be adjusted for best operation. This is indicated by the appropriate output meter (maximum signal strength, for instance).

Sometimes, a band of frequencies must be covered to chart the frequency response of a filter. For this application, a *swept frequency generator* is used. A swept frequency generator automatically sweeps back and forth over a selected range of frequencies.

You can use a signal generator to adjust the filter circuits in your transmitter. When you do, a dummy load (or dummy antenna, as it is sometimes called) must be connected to the transmitter output. The dummy load acts as a constant load for the transmitter. It replaces the antenna without radiating a signal. More about dummy loads later.

[Now turn to Chapter 13 and study questions 3AD-6.1 through 3AD-6.3, 3AD-7.1 and 3AD-7.2. Review this section as needed.]

ANTENNA MEASUREMENTS

A properly operating antenna system is essential for a top-quality amateur station. If you build your own antennas, you must be able to tune them for maximum operating efficiency. Even if you buy commercial antennas, there are tuning adjustments that must be made because of differences in mounting location. Height above ground and proximity to buildings and trees will have some effect on antenna operating characteristics.

You must be able to measure your antenna's performance. After installation, you should be able to periodically monitor your antenna system for signs of problems, and troubleshoot failures as necessary.

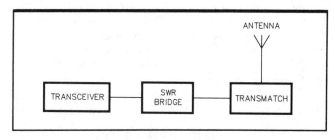

Figure 8-18—A reflectometer or SWR bridge should be connected between the transmitter and Transmatch in order to adjust the Transmatch properly.

IMPEDANCE MATCH INDICATORS

A useful metering device is the **reflectometer** (SWR meter). A reflectometer is a device used to measure *standing-wave ratio*, or *SWR*. SWR is a measure of the relationship between the amount of power traveling to the antenna and the power reflected back to the transmitter. The reflection is caused by *impedance mismatches* in the antenna system. The energy going from the transmitter to the antenna is represented by the forward, or incident, voltage. The energy reflected by the antenna is represented by the reflected voltage. A bridge circuit separates the incident and reflected voltages for measurement purposes. This is sufficient for determining SWR. Bridges designed to measure SWR are called reflectometers or SWR meters.

A reflectometer is placed in the transmission line between the transmitter and antenna. In the most common amateur application, the reflectometer is connected between the transmitter and Transmatch, as shown in Figure 8-18. A Transmatch is used to cancel out the capacitive or inductive component in the antenna impedance. With a Transmatch you can match the impedance of your antenna system to the transmitter output, normally 50 ohms. The reflectometer is used to indicate minimum reflected power as the Transmatch is adjusted. This indicates when the antenna system (including feed line) is matched to the transmitter output impedance.

To obtain a valid measure of the impedance match between an antenna and the feed line, place the SWR meter at the antenna feed point. If you put the meter at the transmitter end, feed line losses make SWR readings look lower than they really are.

[Now study questions 3AD-8-1.1, 3AD-8-1.2, 3AD-8-2.1 and 3AD-8-2.2 in Chapter 13. Review any material necessary.]

STATION ACCESSORIES

Many other station accessories are available. They make the difference between simply operating a radio and having a full awareness of the communications medium called Amateur Radio. In this section we will look at some of these accessories.

THE DUMMY LOAD

Here is some further information about the **dummy antenna**, the nonradiating load that takes the place of the antenna for testing or tuning purposes.

You can use a switch to connect the antenna or dummy load to the transmitter. See Figure 8-19. With a dummy load connected to the transmitter, you can make off-the-air tests—no signal goes out over the air.

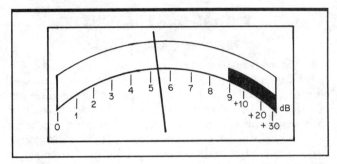

Figure 8-20—An S-meter is calibrated in S-units up to S9. Above S9 it is calibrated in decibels (dB) over S9.

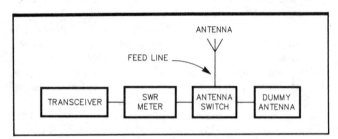

Figure 8-19—A dummy load can be switched in to provide a nonradiating load for transmitter adjustments.

For transmitter tests, remember that a dummy load is a resistor. It must be capable of safely dissipating the entire power output of the transmitter. A dummy load should provide the transmitter with a perfect load. This usually means that it has a pure resistance (with no reactance) of approximately 50 ohms. The resistors used to construct dummy loads must be noninductive. Composition resistors are usable, but wire-wound resistors are not. A single high-power resistor is best. Several lower-power resistors can be connected in parallel to obtain a 50-ohm load capable of dissipating high power.

THE S METER

S meters indicate the relative strength of a received signal. They are calibrated in S units from S1 to S9; above S9 they are calibrated in decibels (dB), as shown in Figure 8-20.

In the 1940s at least one manufacturer made an attempt to establish some significant numbers for S meters. S9 was to be equal to a signal level of 50 microvolts, with each S unit equal to 6 dB. This means that for an increase of one S unit, the received signal power would have to increase by a factor of four. Such a scale is useful for a theoretical discussion. Real S-meter circuits fall far short of this ideal for a variety of reasons.

Suppose you were working someone who was using a 25-watt transmitter, and your S meter was reading S7. If the other operator increased power to 100 watts (an increase of four times), your S meter would read S8. If the signal was S9, the operator would have to multiply his power 10-fold to make your S meter read 10 dB over S9. It would take another 10 times increase in signal strength to make the meter read 20 dB over S9.

S meters on modern transceivers may or may not respond in this manner. S-meter operation is based on the output of the automatic gain-control (AGC) circuitry; the S meter measures the AGC voltage. As a result, every S meter responds differently; no two S meters will give the same reading. The S meter is useful for giving relative signal-strength indications, however. You can see changes in signal levels on an S meter that you may not be able to detect just by listening to the audio output level.

[Now turn to Chapter 13 and study questions 3AD-9.1 through 3AD-9.6, 3AD-10.1 and 3AD-10.2. Review this section as needed.]

SAFETY WITH RF POWER

Amateur Radio is basically a safe activity but accidents can always occur if we don't use common sense. Most of us know enough not to place an antenna where it can fall on a power line. We don't insert our hand into an energized linear amplifier, or climb a tower on a windy day. We also should not venture overexposure to RF energy. Large amounts of RF energy *can* be harmful to people because it heats body tissues. The effects depend on the wavelength, energy density of the incident RF field, and on other factors such as polarization.

The most susceptible parts of the body are the tissues of the eyes. They don't have heat-sensitive receptors to warn us of the danger before the damage occurs. Symptoms of overexposure may not appear until after irreversible damage has been done. Though the problem should be taken seriously, with reasonable precaution, Amateur Radio operation can be safe.

SAFE EXPOSURE LEVELS

In recent years scientists have devoted a great deal of effort to determining safe RF-exposure limits. The problem is very complex. It's not surprising that some changes in the recommended levels have occurred as more information has become available. The American Radio Relay League believes that the 1982 "Radio Frequency Protection Guide of the American National Standards Institute (ANSI)" is a good protection standard; it took nearly five years to formulate and has undergone repeated critical review by the scientific community.

This guide recommends that special precautions be taken when transmitting with hand-held VHF and UHF radios. The antenna should be kept at least 1 to 2 inches away from the forehead, and power should be limited to no more than 7 watts.

The ANSI standards recognize the phenomenon of whole-body or geometric resonance and establishes a frequency-dependent maximum permissible RF exposure level. Exposure levels are expressed in terms of power density, measured in milliwatts per square centimeter. It is a measure of the radio frequency power that strikes a person per square centimeter of body surface.

Whole-Body Resonance

Resonance occurs at frequencies for which the human body's length (height), if parallel to the antenna (vertical), is about 0.4 wavelength long. Because of the range of human heights, the resonant region spans a broad range of frequencies. This whole-body resonance establishes the frequency range for the most stringent (lowest) permissible exposure level. Figure 8-21 shows that the lowest maximum exposure level is 1 mW/cm^2 for frequencies between 30 and 300 MHz. On either side of those "corner" frequencies the rise is gradual. At 3 MHz the maximum permissible exposure level is

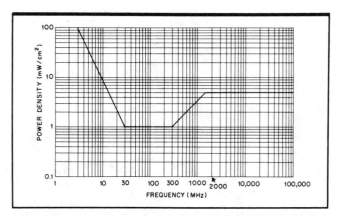

Figure 8-21—American National Standards Institute Radio Frequency Protection Guide for whole-body exposure of human beings.

100 mW/cm^2; at 1500 MHz and above, 5 mW/cm^2. The valley region includes some active amateur bands (10, 6 and 2 meters) as well as all FM and TV broadcasting. The rationale for specifying a constant 5 mW/cm^2 above 1500 MHz takes into consideration that the extremely short wavelengths don't penetrate very deep into body tissue.

[This completes your study of Chapter 8. Now turn to Chapter 13 and study questions 3AD-11-1.1, 3AD-11-1.2 , 3AD-11-2.1 through 3AD-11-2.5, 3AD-11-3.1 and 3AH-2-8.1. Review the material in this section if you have any difficulty with these questions.]

AMTOR (Amateur Teleprinting Over Radio)—AMTOR provides error-detecting capabilities. See **Automatic Repeat reQuest, Forward Error Correction** and **Selective-call identifier.**

ASCII (American National Standard Code for Information Interchange)—This is a seven-bit digital code used in computer and radioteleprinter applications.

Audio-frequency shift keying (AFSK)—A method of transmitting radioteletype information. Two switched audio tones are fed into the microphone input. AFSK RTTY is most often used on VHF.

Automatic Repeat reQuest (ARQ)—An AMTOR communication mode. In ARQ, also called Mode A, the two stations constantly confirm each other's transmissions. If information is lost, it is repeated until the receiving station confirms correct reception.

Autopatch—A device that allows repeater users to make telephone calls through a repeater.

A1A emission—The FCC emission designator used to describe Morse code telegraphy (CW) by on/off keying of a radio-frequency signal.

Baud—The unit used to describe the transmission speed of a digital signal. For a single-channel signal, one baud is equal to one digital bit per second.

Baudot—A five-bit digital code used in teleprinter applications.

Bleeder resistor—A large resistor connected across the output of a power supply. The bleeder discharges the filter capacitors when the supply is turned off.

Calling frequencies—Frequencies set aside for establishing contact. Once two stations are in contact, they should move their QSO to an unoccupied frequency.

Communications terminal—A computer-controlled device that demodulates RTTY and CW for display by a computer or ASCII terminal. The communications terminal also accepts information from a computer or terminal and modulates a transmitted signal.

Computer-Based Message System (CBMS)—A system in which a computer is used to store messages for later retrieval. Also called a RTTY mailbox.

Connected—The condition in which two packet-radio stations are sending information to each other. Each is acknowledging when the data has been received correctly.

Contests—On-the-air operating events. Different contests have different objectives: contacting as many other amateurs as possible in a given amount of time, contacting amateurs in as many different countries as possible or contacting an amateur in each county in one particular state, to name only a few.

CQ—The general call when requesting a conversation with anyone.

Digipeater—A packet-radio station used to retransmit signals that are specifically addressed to be retransmitted by that station.

Direct waves—Radio waves that travel directly from a transmitting antenna to a receiving antenna. Also called "line-of-sight" communications.

DX—Distance, foreign countries.

DX Century Club (DXCC)—A prestigious award given to amateurs who can prove contact with amateurs in at least 100 DXCC countries.

Field Day—An annual event in which amateurs set up stations in outdoor locations. Emergency power is also encouraged.

Fills—Repeats of parts of a previous transmission—usually requested because of interference.

Forward Error Correction (FEC)—A mode of AMTOR communication. In FEC mode, also called Mode B, each character is sent twice. The receiving station checks the mark/space ratio of the received characters. If an error is detected, the receiving station prints a space to show that an incorrect character was received.

Frequency-shift keying (FSK)—A method of transmitting radioteletype information by switching an RF carrier between two separate frequencies. FSK RTTY is most often used on HF.

F1B emission—The FCC emission designator used to describe frequency-shift keyed (FSK) digital communications.

F2B emission—The FCC emission designator used to describe audio-frequency shift keyed (AFSK) digital communications.

F3E emission—The FCC emission designator used to describe FM voice communications.

Ground waves—Radio waves that travel along Earth's surface.

Input frequency—A repeater's receiving frequency.

Ionosphere—A region of charged particles high in the atmosphere. The ionosphere bends radio waves as they travel through it, returning them to Earth.

J3E emission—The FCC emission designator used to describe single-sideband suppressed-carrier voice communications.

Line of sight—The term used to describe VHF and UHF propagation in a straight line directly from one station to another.

Maximum usable frequency (MUF)—The greatest frequency at which radio signals will return to a particular location from the ionosphere. The MUF may vary for radio signals sent to different destinations.

Modem—Short for modulator/demodulator. A modem modulates a radio signal to transmit data and demodulates a received signal to recover transmitted data.

Monitor mode—One type of packet-radio receiving mode. In monitor mode, everything transmitted on a packet frequency is displayed by the monitoring TNC. This occurs whether the transmissions are addressed to the monitoring station or not.

Nets—Groups of amateurs who meet on the air to pass traffic or communicate about a specific subject. One station (called the *net control station*) usually directs the net.

Network—A term used to describe several packet stations linked together to transmit data over long distances.

Output frequency—A repeater's transmitting frequency.

Packet Bulletin-Board System (PBBS)—A computer system used to store packet-radio messages for later retrieval by other amateurs.

Packet radio—A system of digital communication whereby information is broken into short bursts. The bursts ("packets") also contain addressing and error-detection information.

Procedural signal (prosign)—One or two letters sent as a single character. Amateurs use prosigns in CW QSOs as a short way to indicate the operator's intention. Some examples are K for "Go Ahead," or AR for "End of Message." (The bar over the letters indicates that we send the prosign as one character.)

Propagation—The study of how radio waves travel from one place to another.

Q signals—Three-letter symbols beginning with "Q." Q signals are used in amateur CW work to save time and for better communication.

QSO—A conversation between two radio amateurs.

Radioteletype (RTTY)—Radio signals sent from one teleprinter machine to another machine. Anything that one operator types on his teleprinter will be printed on the other machine. A type of digital communications.

Ragchew—A lengthy conversation (or QSO) between two radio amateurs.

Repeater—An amateur station that receives a signal and retransmits it for greater range.

RST—A system of numbers used for signal reports: R is readability, S is strength and T is tone.

Secondary station identifier (SSID)—A number added to a packet-radio station's call sign so that one amateur call sign can be used for several packet stations.

Selective-call identifier—A four-character AMTOR station identifier.

Simplex operation—A term normally used in relation to VHF and UHF operation. Simplex means you are receiving and transmitting on the same frequency.

Skip—Radio waves that are bent back to Earth by the ionosphere. Skip is also called **sky-wave** propagation.

Skip zone—An area past the maximum range of ground waves and before the range of waves returned from the ionosphere. An area where radio communications between stations is not possible on a certain frequency.

Sky waves—Radio waves that travel through the ionosphere and back to Earth. Sky-wave propagation is sometimes called **skip.**

Speech processor—A device that increases the average power of a sideband signal, making the voice easier to understand under weak signal conditions.

Splatter—The term used to describe a very wide-bandwidth signal. Splatter is usually caused by an improperly adjusted sideband transmitter.

Sunspots—Dark spots on the surface of the sun. When there are few sunspots, long-distance radio propagation is poor on the higher-frequency bands.

Terminal node controller (TNC)—A TNC accepts information from a computer or terminal and converts the information into packets by including address and error-checking information. The TNC also receives packet signals and extracts transmitted information for display by a computer or terminal.

Traffic—Messages passed from one amateur to another in a relay system; the amateur version of a telegram.

Tropospheric enhancement—A weather-related phenomenon. Tropo can produce unusually long-distance propagation on the VHF and UHF bands.

VOX (voice-operated switch)—Circuitry that activates a transmitter when the operator speaks into a microphone.

Zero beat—When two operators in a QSO are transmitting on the same frequency.

Chapter 9
Over the Airwaves...Painlessly

Getting on the air, tuning in and "working" other Amateur Radio operators is the goal of your efforts to obtain an amateur license. Once your ticket arrives, you'll want to indulge yourself in this fabulous communications medium. You'll be joining more than a million radio enthusiasts around the world. Instead of watching TV, you can tune in to a large global network of radio hobbyists. These people actively program their own entertainment.

The operating world is rich and varied. You can relax and enjoy a conversation (a **ragchew**) with another amateur. You can send and receive messages to anywhere in North America via the National Traffic System (handle **traffic**). You can work large numbers of stations in a very short time in

competition with other hams (**contests**). You can try to contact as many different countries as possible (chase **DX**). These are just a few of the activities that Amateur Radio operators enjoy. The more operating time you log, the more quickly your operating proficiency will improve.

In this chapter, we'll give you some tips for operating with your new Novice or Technician license. We'll discuss how radio waves travel from one place to another. Hams engage in a wide variety of operating activities. We'll show you some things you might want to try. In the last part of the chapter you'll learn about some of the more specialized operating modes and bands.

──────SAFETY FIRST──────

There is probably less danger operating a radio station than driving a car. Yet, as you know, automobile accidents do occur. There is no reason for you to involve yourself in a ham-related accident. That possibility always exists, however, if you're not thinking safety. The following safety

rules will make your ham experience more enjoyable. Read them, understand them and practice them.

1) Kill all power circuits completely before touching anything. That includes circuits behind the panel or inside the chassis or the enclosure.

2) Never allow anyone else to switch the power on and off for you while you're working on equipment.

3) Don't troubleshoot a transmitter when you're tired.

4) Never adjust internal components by hand. Use special care when checking energized circuits.

5) Avoid bodily contact with grounded metal (racks, radiators) or damp floors when working on the transmitter.

6) Never wear headphones while working on gear.

7) Follow the rule of keeping one hand in your pocket.

8) Instruct members of your household how to turn the power off and how to apply artificial respiration. Instruction sheets on the latest approved method of resuscitation can be obtained at your local Red Cross office.

9) If you must climb a tower to adjust an antenna, use a safety harness. Never work alone.

10) If you must climb into a tree or work on a roof, remember that you're not standing on the ground. That first step down can be a long one.

11) Develop your own safety technique. Take time to be careful. Death is permanent.

In addition, you should take the following precautions.

Antenna installations: Follow the advice given in Chapter 7 for installing antennas. Review the safety precautions given there. Follow them whenever you do any antenna work.

Power supplies: All power supplies should be enclosed. Be sure accidental bodily contact with power circuits is impossible. (The *ARRL Handbook for Radio Amateurs* is a good source of information concerning power-supply construction.)

All power-supply ground terminals should connect to the chassis. (This means the negative lead of a positive supply and the positive lead of a negative-voltage supply.) The chassis should connect to the electrical system ground with a three-wire line cord. If your shack does not have grounded outlets, use a water pipe or other good ground connection. See Chapter 8.

Every power supply should use a conservatively rated **bleeder resistor**. A bleeder resistor connects across the power-supply output. It discharges the filter capacitors when you turn the supply off. Some amateur equipment uses shielded wire for external power cables. Grounded shielding provides protection if the cable insulation fails.

Panel controls and metering: Every control shaft extending through the panel should be at ground potential. The frames of key or metering jacks should be fastened to the grounded panel. Meters should be recessed to avoid danger of contact with the adjusting screw.

Audio equipment: The following rule should be followed for speech equipment. Use a microphone-cable with a shield conductor connected to the microphone stand and enclosure. The other end of the cable shield must connect to chassis ground.

Lightning protection: Merely "grounding everything" is not adequate protection from lightning strikes or static build-up. Lightning has devious methods of going into the wrong places. Protect your radio by disconnecting it completely from power lines and antennas. Also, ground all disconnected antenna lines. "Pulling the big switch" is a phrase used by many hams. You can run all power to your radio equipment through one main switch. This is a good way to disconnect your equipment from the power lines. Finally, pay special attention to rotator control boxes. A lightning strike can come into the box via the control cable. It can go through the control box, out the power cord, through the outlet and up the power cord of your radio. This can happen even with the power switch off! Please handle every circuit with care.

Those lowly 120-V circuits cause more electrocutions than any other voltage. Remember these four safety rules. Know your equipment. Never work alone. Use common sense. Don't take chances or safety shortcuts. A foolhardy ham is one with a short career!

AMATEUR RADIO HF BANDS AND PROPAGATION

Amateurs enjoy the privilege of using many different frequency bands. Some of these are scattered throughout the high-frequency (HF) spectrum. Some of these frequencies work better during the day, and some work better at night. Some frequencies are good for long-distance communications. Others provide good short-range communications. Amateurs who want to work a certain part of the country or world need to know which frequency to use and when to be there. Experience combined with lots of careful listening is a good way to gain this knowledge.

Amateurs have *allocations* in certain frequency bands in the radio spectrum. Novices have privileges on four HF bands. To keep things simple, we'll refer to them as "Novice" bands, although Technicians who have passed a 5-WPM code test share these privileges.

(All Technicians have other privileges on the VHF and UHF bands.) Table 9-1 summarizes the HF privileges granted to radio amateurs. We often refer to amateur bands by approximate wavelength rather than frequency. In an average day, you can reach any part of the world using one of the Novice bands. The amateur community won new frequency allocations at 10, 18 and 24 MHz during the 1979 World Administrative Radio Conference. These bands help to ensure good worldwide communications, despite changing conditions.

Table 9-1
High-Frequency Ham Bands

HF Bands

For Full Amateur Privileges (MHz)	Novice Privileges (MHz)	Band (Meters)
1.8 - 2.0	None	160
3.5 - 4.0	3.675 - 3.725	80
7.0 - 7.3	7.10 - 7.15	40
10.10 - 10.15	None	30
14.00 - 14.35	None	20
18.068 - 18.168	None	17
21.00 - 21.45	21.1 - 21.2	15
24.89 - 24.99	None	12
28.00 - 29.70	28.1 - 28.5	10

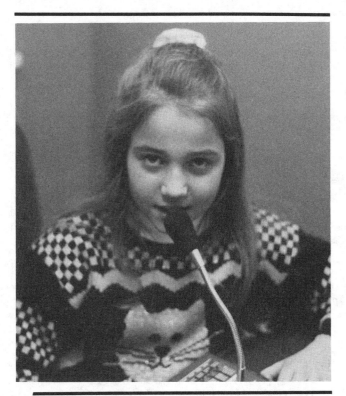

Samantha, KA1VBQ, enjoys operating on 10-meter SSB.

Radio waves travel to their destination in three ways:
- Directly from one point to another.
- Along the ground.
- Refracted, or bent, back to Earth by the **ionosphere**.

The ionosphere is a layer of charged particles in Earth's atmosphere. The study of how radio waves travel from one point to another is the science of **propagation**. Radio-wave propagation is a complicated topic. You will need to know only a few fundamentals to enjoy your new hobby.

DIRECT WAVES

Direct waves travel in a straight line from one antenna to another. Direct waves are useful mostly at VHF and higher frequencies. TV and FM broadcasts, for example, are usually received as direct waves. Direct waves travel from a hand-held transceiver to an FM repeater. From there, direct waves travel to other fixed, portable and mobile stations. This kind of radio-wave propagation is also called **line-of-sight** propagation.

GROUND WAVE

In **ground-wave** propagation, radio waves travel along the Earth's surface, even over hills. They follow the curvature of the Earth for some distance. Daytime standard AM broadcasting uses ground-wave propagation. Ground wave works best at lower frequencies. You might have an 80-meter QSO with a station a few miles away, on the other side of a hill. For that contact, you are using ground-wave propagation.

Ground-wave propagation on the ham bands means relatively short-range communications. Stations at the top of the AM broadcast band (the 1600-kHz end) do not carry far during the day. Stations near the low end of the dial (540 kHz) can be heard at much greater distances. Amateur Radio frequencies are higher than the standard broadcast band, so the ground-wave range is shorter.

SKIP

High in the atmosphere, 25 to 200 miles above the Earth, the thin air is electrically charged (ionized) by radiation from the sun. When ionized, this layer, the **ionosphere**, can refract (or bend) radio waves. If the wave is bent enough, it returns to Earth. If the wave is not bent enough, it travels off into space. Communications of as much as 2500 miles are possible with one **skip** off the ionosphere. Worldwide communications using several skips (or hops) are possible at times.

Two of the factors that determine skip-propagation possibilities between two points are: the frequency in use and the level of ionization. The higher the frequency of the radio wave, the less it is bent by the ionosphere. The specific frequency above which radio waves penetrate the ionosphere and do not return to Earth at a desired location is called the **maximum usable frequency (MUF)**. The MUF for communication between two points depends on solar radiation strength and the time of day. Radio waves that travel beyond the horizon by refraction in the ionosphere are called **sky waves**. We sometimes refer to skip propagation as sky-wave propagation.

Ionization of the ionosphere results from the sun's radiation striking the upper atmosphere. Ionization is greatest during the day and during the summer. The amount of radiation coming from the sun varies through the day, season and year. This radiation is closely related to visible **sunspots** (grayish-black blotches on the sun's surface). See Figure 9-1. Sunspots vary in number and size over an 11-year cycle. More sunspots usually mean more of the radiation that creates the ionosphere. As a result, the MUF tends also to be higher.

By contrast, when sunspots are low, radiation, and thus the MUF, is lower. That is why most hams prefer times of greater sunspot activity.

Skip propagation not only has a maximum range limit, it also has a minimum range limit. That minimum is often greater than the ground-wave range. There is an area between the maximum ground-wave distance and the minimum skip

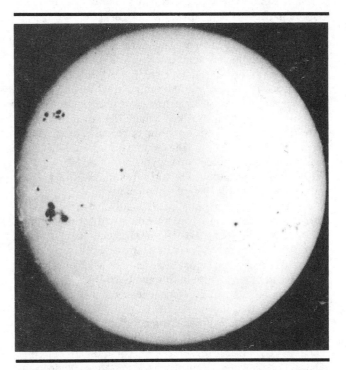

Figure 9-1—Cool sunspots allow hot propagation on Earth!

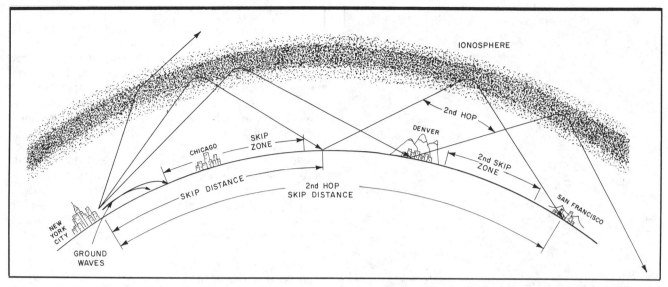

Figure 9-2—Illustration of how skip zone, skip distance and ground waves are related. See text for details.

distance where your radio signals on a particular frequency will not reach. This "dead" area is called the **skip zone**. Figure 9-2 illustrates the difference between ground-wave and skip propagation. The figure also shows the concept of skip zone and skip distance. Some radio signals may not be bent enough to bring them back to Earth.

[Before you go on to the next section, turn to Chapter 12 and study those questions with numbers that begin with 2C-1, 2C-2, 2C-3, 2C-4 and 2C-5. If you have difficulty with any of these questions, review this section before going on.]

PROPAGATION ON OUR HF BANDS

Operating on 10 meters

At times the best of bands, 10 meters also can seem the worst of bands. The highest frequency amateur HF band, 10 is more subject to the whims of the sunspot cycle. During years of high sunspot activity, 10 meters remains open all day and most of the night. Strong signals arrive from all over the world. In years of low solar activity, you may hear nothing but local signals for days at a time. Even during the peak of the sunspot cycle, the MUF doesn't always reach 28 MHz.

When operating on 10 meters, remember that the Novice CW subband is a full 200 kHz wide. The voice subband is also 200 kHz wide. Some signals may be weak, but perfectly readable. Tune the entire Novice subband carefully. If there aren't any signals in the Novice portion, listen in the rest of the band. A good place to listen is around 28.5 MHz. If the band is open, you'll likely hear someone.

During the sunspot minimum, you'll have to work a little harder to see if 10 is open. Several automated beacons operate between 28.1 and 28.3 MHz. They transmit continuous signals to test propagation. If you can hear one of these beacons, the band is open. You'll find these beacons listed occasionally in *QST* and other ham publications. Even if 10 seems dead, it may just be a case of everyone listening and no one calling! Try calling CQ.

Ten meters offers many Novices their first taste of DX: The chance to communicate with hams in foreign lands. Familiarize yourself with some of the common DX call signs. That way, you won't be surprised the first time you hear one. In a typical week, you might hear a JA (Japan), an EA (Spain)

or an LA (Norway). Some countries also use call signs beginning with a number. Don't be surprised if you work a 4Z (Israel) or a 9Y (Trinidad). Table 9-2 lists all of the currently assigned international prefixes.

In addition to DX potential, 10 meters also provides excellent short-range communications. Many clubs and local groups meet regularly on 10 meters. Check with a local radio club to find out if there are any **nets** in your area.

Ten meters is also the lowest-frequency Novice band that allows emissions other than CW (emission type **A1A**). From 28.1 to 28.3 MHz, Novices are allowed to use CW and, frequency-shift keying (FSK), which is emission type **F1B**. FSK modes include packet, Baudot radioteletype (RTTY), ASCII and AMTOR. From 28.3 to 28.5 MHz, Novices are authorized to use CW (A1A) and single-sideband, suppressed-carrier (SSB) voice (emission type **J3E**). The maximum power level that Novices may use for any mode on 10 meters is 200 watts PEP output.

Operating on 15 meters

The 15-meter band shares several characteristics with the 10-meter band. It is not, however, as dependent on high sunspot activity. The 21-MHz frequency range is still high enough so that propagation conditions change dramatically with sunspot variations. Because of its lower frequency, 15 meters is open for longer periods and more often than 10. Also, the band is more stable in years of low sunspot activity.

DX is plentiful on 15 meters, even in the lean years of the solar cycle. During the day, stations in Europe, Africa and South America may be workable. You may hear signals from the Pacific and Japan in the late afternoon through early evening hours. Fifteen meters provides good communications to areas all over the US.

Many foreign stations operate within the Novice band using phone transmissions. American hams are prohibited from doing this, but many other countries do allow it. If you hear a foreign station on voice, give him a CW call at the end of his QSO. Many are glad to work Novices. This kind of operation won't give you much practice copying CW. It will give you a chance to hear what phone DX stations sound like, though. You might even work a "new country."

Because 15 meters is so popular, you'll most likely hear

stations if the band is open. Again, listen at the bottom of the CW and phone portions if you don't hear signals in the Novice band. This is where stations usually congregate.

Fifteen is one of the best bands around because of its DX possibilities. More stable than 10 meters, it is the most reliable Novice band for DX. It's usable even at the low point of the sunspot cycle. Higher in frequency than 40 and 80 meters, it provides good long-distance contacts.

Operating on 40 meters

The 40-meter band is one of the best US ham bands. It suffers, however, from some of the worst interference you'll ever hear. International treaties allow the world outside of the Americas to use the 40-meter band above 7.1 MHz for high-power shortwave broadcasting. This causes quite a racket in North America.

During the morning and early afternoon hours, 40 meters provides good, reliable communications. Skip distance ranges from about 400 to 1200 miles. Later in the afternoon, however, the MUF drops. Skip distance then increases to several thousand miles. You'll have no trouble detecting the increase in range. You'll find yourself suddenly listening to those foreign broadcast stations.

Even though it has interference from the broadcasters, 40 meters is one of the most popular Novice bands. It is open to some part of the country 24 hours a day. During the morning and afternoon hours, you'll be able to chat with other hams to your heart's content. In the late afternoon, evening and at night, you'll be able to work more distant locations. Once you learn to live with the broadcast interference, you'll find yourself using 40 meters for many of your CW contacts.

Operating on 80 meters

At 3.5 MHz, 80 meters is the lowest in frequency of all the Novice bands. It is very popular among Novices for stateside contacts. A half-wavelength dipole antenna (see Chapter 7) for 80 is rather large. Shape, however, is not critical. Most Novices manage to put up one that works fairly well.

During the daylight hours, 80 meters provides reliable communications out to about 350 miles. Although 80 is not as heavily populated as 40 during the day, you will probably find someone eager to talk with you.

Eighty comes into its own in the evening and nighttime hours. At that time, 10 and 15 meters shut down for the night. Forty meters opens up to foreign broadcasters. Many hams switch to 80 meters. The band provides strong, reliable local propagation. It has none of the uncertainty of 10 and 15, nor the interference of 40.

The long-range capabilities of the 80-meter band are subject to seasonal changes. During the summer months, night-time communications may extend to 1000 miles. Atmospheric static levels, however, are often high. Contacts can be difficult to establish and maintain. The winter months are a different story. Static levels are usually very low, and cross-country and DX contacts are normal occurrences.

Like 40 meters, the 80-meter band is a 24-hour-a-day happening. It provides excellent local communications almost all the time. It offers long-distance possibilities at night during the winter months.

Eighty is often used to make and maintain schedules with friends. After operating on the band for a while, you will come to know many of your fellow 80-meter Novices. Plan to spend some of your evening operating time on 80 meters making

new friends. You'll likely meet them face-to-face at local conventions or hamfests.

PROPAGATION ON OUR VHF AND UHF BANDS

Normally, you'll be contacting nearby stations—within 100 miles or so—on the VHF/UHF bands. The usual propagation mode on these bands is **line of sight.** The signal travels directly between stations, so if you're using a directional antenna, you normally point it toward the station that you are trying to contact. VHF and UHF signals, however, are easily reflected by buildings, hills and even airplanes. Some of your signal reaches the other station by a direct path and some may be reflected. When such reflections occur, it is possible to contact other stations by pointing your antenna toward the reflecting object, rather than directly at the station you're trying to contact.

Reflections can cause problems for mobile operation, as the propagation path is constantly changing. The direct and reflected waves may first cancel and then reinforce each other. This causes a rapid fluttering sound called "picket fencing."

Sometimes, especially during the spring, summer and fall months, it is possible to make VHF and UHF contacts over long distances—up to 1000 miles or more. This occurs during certain weather conditions that cause **tropospheric enhancement** and tropospheric ducting. When such "tropo" openings occur, the VHF and UHF bands are filled with excited operators eager to work DX. The troposphere is the layer of the atmosphere just below the stratosphere. It extends upward approximately 7 to 10 miles. In this region clouds form and temperature decreases rapidly with altitude. You can find out more about VHF and UHF propagation from *The ARRL Handbook*.

Popular modes on the VHF/UHF bands include frequency-modulated (FM) voice (emission type **F3E**), SSB voice, CW, packet radio, and Baudot and ASCII RTTY. Unlike the HF bands, FCC rules and regulations do not usually set aside portions of these bands for specific modes. Any authorized mode may be used on any frequency within the band.

Band Plans

To avoid confusion and interference problems, amateurs have agreed to a voluntary band plan. The plan allocates segments of the band for different uses. For example, there is a section set aside around 222.1 MHz for "weak signal" CW and SSB operation. Another segment is set aside for FM voice operation, and so on. For complete information on band plans, see the latest edition of *The ARRL Repeater Directory*. While Technicians have full frequency and mode privileges on the VHF/UHF bands, Novices are allowed to use only parts of two of these bands. The 222-MHz band is very popular for FM voice and packet radio operation, and is a good place to meet other local hams. The maximum power level that Novices may use for any mode on 1.25 meters is 25 watts PEP output.

23 Centimeters

Twenty-three centimeters (1270 MHz) is the highest-frequency Novice band. It lies in the UHF portion of the radio spectrum, and is the least-populated of all Novice frequencies. Novices are allowed to operate in the segment from 1270 to 1295 MHz. They may use any and all emission modes autho-

Table 9-2

Allocation of International Call Signs

Call Sign Series	Allocated to	Call Sign Series	Allocated to
AAA-ALZ	United States of America	H8A-H9Z	Panama
AMA-AOZ	Spain	IAA-IZZ	Italy
APA-ASZ	Pakistan	JAA-JSZ	Japan
ATA-AWZ	India	JTA-JVZ	Mongolian People's Republic
AXA-AXZ	Australia	JWA-JXZ	Norway
AYA-AZZ	Argentina	JYA-JYZ	Jordan
A2A-A2Z	Botswana	JZA-JZZ	Indonesia
A3A-A3Z	Tonga	J2A-J2Z	Djibouti
A4A-A4Z	Oman	J3A-J3Z	Grenada
A5A-A5Z	Bhutan	J4A-J4Z	Greece
A6A-A6Z	United Arab Emirates	J5A-J5Z	Guinea-Bissau
A7A-A7Z	Qatar	J6A-J6Z	Saint Lucia
A8A-A8Z	Liberia	J7A-J7Z	Dominica
A9A-A9Z	Bahrain	J8A-J8Z	St. Vincent and the Grenadines
BAA-BZZ	China	KAA-KZZ	United States of America
CAA-CEZ	Chile	LAA-LNZ	Norway
CFA-CKZ	Canada	LOA-LWZ	Argentina
CLA-CMZ	Cuba	LXA-LXZ	Luxembourg
CNA-CNZ	Morocco	LYA-LYZ	Union of Soviet Socialist Republics
COA-COZ	Cuba	LZA-LZZ	Bulgaria
CPA-CPZ	Bolivia	L2A-L9Z	Argentina
CQA-CUZ	Portugal	MAA-MZZ	United Kingdom of Great Britain and Northern Ireland
CVA-CXZ	Uruguay		
CYA-CZZ	Canada	NAA-NZZ	United States of America
C2A-C2Z	Nauru	OAA-OCZ	Peru
C3A-C3Z	Andorra	ODA-ODZ	Lebanon
C4A-C4Z	Cyprus	OEA-OEZ	Austria
C5A-C5Z	Gambia	OFA-OJZ	Finland
C6A-C6Z	Bahamas	OKA-OMZ	Czechoslovakia
C7A-C7Z*	World Meteorological Organization	ONA-OTZ	Belgium
C8A-C9Z	Mozambique	OUA-OZZ	Denmark
DAA-DRZ	Germany	PAA-PIZ	Netherlands
DSA-DTZ	Republic of Korea	PJA-PJZ	Netherlands Antilles
DUA-DZZ	Philippines	PKA-POZ	Indonesia
D2A-D3Z	Angola	PPA-PYZ	Brazil
D4A-D4Z	Cape Verde	PZA-PZZ	Suriname
D5A-D5Z	Liberia	P2A-P2Z	Papua New Guinea
D6A-D6Z	Comoros	P3A-P3Z	Cyprus
D7A-D9Z	Republic of Korea	P4A-P4Z	Aruba
EAA-EHZ	Spain	P5A-P9Z	Democratic People's Republic of Korea
EIA-EJZ	Ireland	QAA-QZZ	(Service abbreviations)
EKA-EKZ	Union of Soviet Socialist Republics	RAA-RZZ	Union of Soviet Socialist Republics
ELA-ELZ	Liberia	SAA-SMZ	Sweden
EMA-EOZ	Union of Soviet Socialist Republics	SNA-SRZ	Poland
EPA-EQZ	Iran	SSA-SSM	Egypt
ERA-ESZ	Union of Soviet Socialist Republics	SSN-STZ	Sudan
ETA-ETZ	Ethiopia	SUA-SUZ	Egypt
EUA-EWZ	Byelorussian Soviet Socialist Republic	SVA-SZZ	Greece
EXA-EZZ	Union of Soviet Socialist Republics	S2A-S3Z	Bangladesh
FAA-FZZ	France	S6A-S6Z	Singapore
GAA-GZZ	United Kingdom of Great Britain and Northern Ireland	S7A-S7Z	Seychelles
		S9A-S9Z	Sao Tome and Principe
HAA-HAZ	Hungary	TAA-TCZ	Turkey
HBA-HBZ	Switzerland	TDA-TDZ	Guatemala
HCA-HDZ	Ecuador	TEA-TEZ	Costa Rica
HEA-HEZ	Switzerland	TFA-TFZ	Iceland
HFA-HFZ	Poland	TGA-TGZ	Guatemala
HGA-HGZ	Hungary	THA-THZ	France
HHA-HHZ	Haiti	TIA-TIZ	Costa Rica
HIA-HIZ	Dominican Republic	TJA-TJZ	Cameroon
HJA-HKZ	Colombia	TKA-TKZ	France
HLA-HLZ	Republic of Korea	TLA-TLZ	Central African Republic
HMA-HMZ	Democratic People's Republic of Korea	TMA-TMZ	France
HNA-HNZ	Iraq	TNA-TNZ	Congo
HOA-HPZ	Panama	TOA-TQZ	France
HQA-HRZ	Honduras	TRA-TRZ	Gabon
HSA-HSZ	Thailand	TSA-TSZ	Tunisia
HTA-HTZ	Nicaragua	TTA-TTZ	Chad
HUA-HUZ	El Salvador	TUA-TUZ	Ivory Coast
HVA-HVZ	Vatican City	TVA-TXZ	France
HWA-HYZ	France	TYA-TYZ	Benin
HZA-HZZ	Saudi Arabia	TZA-TZZ	Mali
H2A-H2Z	Cyprus	T2A-T2Z	Tuvalu
H3A-H3Z	Panama	T3A-T3Z	Kiribati
H4A-H4Z	Solomon Islands	T4A-T4Z	Cuba
H6A-H7Z	Nicaragua	T5A-T5Z	Somalia

Call Sign Series	Allocated to
T6A-T6Z	Afghanistan
T7A-T7Z	San Marino
UAA-UQZ	Union of Soviet Socialist Republics
URA-UTZ	Ukrainian Soviet Socialist Republic
UUA-UZZ	Union of Soviet Socialist Republics
VAA-VGZ	Canada
VHA-VNZ	Australia
VOA-VOZ	Canada
VPA-VSZ	United Kingdom of Great Britain and Northern Ireland
VTA-VWZ	India
VXA-VYZ	Canada
VZA-VZZ	Australia
V2A-V2Z	Antigua and Barbuda
V3A-V3Z	Belize
V4A-V4Z	St. Christopher and Nevis
V8A-V8Z	Brunei
WAA-WZZ	United States of America
XAA-XIZ	Mexico
XJA-XOZ	Canada
XPA-XPZ	Denmark
XQA-XRZ	Chile
XSA-XSZ	China
XTA-XTZ	Burkina Faso
XUA-XUZ	Kampuchea
XVA-XVZ	Viet Nam
XWA-XWZ	Laos
XXA-XXZ	Portugal
XYA-XZZ	Burma
YAA-YAZ	Afghanistan
YBA-YHZ	Indonesia
YIA-YIZ	Iraq
YJA-YJZ	New Hebrides
YKA-YKZ	Syria
YLA-YLZ	Union of Soviet Socialist Republics
YMA-YMZ	Turkey
YNA-YNZ	Nicaragua
YOA-YRZ	Romania
YSA-YSZ	El Salvador
YTA-YUZ	Yugoslavia
YVA-YYZ	Venezuela
YZA-YZZ	Yugoslavia
Y2A-Y9Z	Germany
ZAA-ZAZ	Albania
ZBA-ZJZ	United Kingdom of Great Britain and Northern Ireland
ZKA-ZMZ	New Zealand
ZNA-ZOZ	United Kingdom of Great Britain and Northern Ireland
ZPA-ZPZ	Paraguay
ZQA-ZQZ	United Kingdom of Great Britain and Northern Ireland
ZRA-ZUZ	South Africa
ZVA-ZZZ	Brazil
Z2A-Z2Z	Zimbabwe
2AA-2ZZ	United Kingdom of Great Britain and Northern Ireland
3AA-3AZ	Monaco
3BA-3AZ	Mauritius
3CA-3CZ	Equatorial Guinea
3DA-3DM	Swaziland
3DN-3DZ	Fiji
3EA-3FZ	Panama
3GA-3GZ	Chile
3HA-3UZ	China
3VA-3VZ	Tunisia
3WA-3WZ	Viet Nam
3XA-3XZ	Guinea
3YA-3YZ	Norway
3ZA-3ZZ	Poland
4AA-4CA	Mexico

Call Sign Series	Allocated to
4DA-4IZ	Philippines
4JA-4LZ	Union of Soviet Socialist Republics
4MA-4MZ	Venezuela
4NA-4OZ	Yugoslavia
4PA-4SZ	Sri Lanka
4TA-4TZ	Peru
4UA-4UZ*	United Nations Organization
4VA-4VZ	Haiti
4WA-4WZ	Yemen Republic
4XA-4XZ	Israel
4YA-4YZ*	International Civil Aviation Organization
4ZA-4ZZ	Israel
5AA-5AZ	Libya
5BA-5BZ	Cyprus
5CA-5GZ	Morocco
5HA-5IZ	Tanzania
5JA-5KZ	Colombia
5LA-5MZ	Liberia
5NA-5OZ	Nigeria
5PA-5QZ	Denmark
5RA-5SZ	Madagascar
5TA-5TZ	Mauritania
5UA-5UZ	Niger
5VA-5VZ	Togo
5WA-5WZ	Western Samoa
5XA-5XZ	Uganda
5YA-5ZZ	Kenya
6AA-6BZ	Egypt
6CA-6CZ	Syria
6DA-6JZ	Mexico
6KA-6NZ	Republic of Korea
6OA-6OZ	Somalia
6PA-6SZ	Pakistan
6TA-6UZ	Sudan
6VA-6WZ	Senegal
6XA-6XZ	Madagascar
6YA-6YZ	Jamaica
6ZA-6ZZ	Liberia
7AA-7IZ	Indonesia
7JA-7NZ	Japan
7OA-7OZ	Yemen Republic
7PA-7PZ	Lesotho
7QA-7QZ	Malawi
7RA-7RZ	Algeria
7SA-7SZ	Sweden
7TA-7YZ	Algeria
7ZA-7ZZ	Saudi Arabia
8AA-8IZ	Indonesia
8JA-8NZ	Japan
8OA-8OZ	Botswana
8PA-8PZ	Barbados
8QA-8QZ	Maldives
8RA-8RZ	Guyana
8SA-8SZ	Sweden
8TA-8YZ	India
8ZA-8ZZ	Saudi Arabia
9BA-9DZ	Iran
9EA-9FZ	Ethiopia
9GA-9GZ	Ghana
9HA-9HZ	Malta
9IA-9JZ	Zambia
9KA-9KZ	Kuwait
9LA-9LZ	Sierra Leone
9MA-9MZ	Malaysia
9NA-9NZ	Nepal
9OA-9TZ	Zaire
9UA-9UZ	Burundi
9VA-9VZ	Singapore
9WA-9WZ	Malaysia
9XA-9XZ	Rwanda
9YA-9ZZ	Trinidad and Tobago

Note

The series of call signs with an asterisk indicate the international organization to which they are allocated.

rized for that band. Popular modes on 23 cm include FM voice, SSB, CW and amateur television (ATV).

The 23-cm Novice band is similar to 1.25 meters. There are no FCC-mandated segments for the different modes. Rather, frequency usage is determined by a voluntary band plan. The 23-cm band plan calls for FM voice and ATV operation from 1270 to 1295 MHz. For complete information on the 23-cm band plan, see the latest edition of *The ARRL Repeater Directory*. The maximum power level that Novices may use for any mode on 23 cm is 5 watts PEP output. Technicians are allowed to operate on the entire band, from 1270 to 1300 MHz.

An FCC allocated amateur-satellite band is located around 1265 MHz. Weak-signal CW and SSB operation takes place around 1296 MHz, including the exotic "moonbounce" mode, where signals are actually reflected from the moon's surface!

[Now turn to Chapter 12 and study questions 2B-1-1.2, 2C-6.1 and 2C-6.2. You should also study questions 2H-1-1.1, 2H-1-1.2, 2H-1-3.1 and 2H-1-4.1. Review this section if you have any difficulty with these questions.]

OPERATING SKILL

Poor operating procedure is ham radio's version of original sin. It is a curse that will not go away. Hams call these poor operators *lids*. No one wants to be a lid or to have a QSO with a lid. Calling someone a lid is the ultimate insult. (Don't do it on the air. Just be sure your operating practices are such that no one *wants* to call *you* a lid.)

It is actually easier to be a good operator than to fall prey to sloppy habits. You can transmit a message without needless repetition and without unnecessary identification. You don't have to spell out each and every word. Good operating makes hamming more fun for everyone.

Clearly, the initial glamour of Amateur Radio is the opportunity to talk to people you can't see. It doesn't matter if they're across town or in another country. Novices and Technicians with Novice privileges have plenty of chances to get in on DX action on the 10- and 15-meter bands. The 40- and 80-meter bands (7 and 3.7 MHz) are useful primarily for domestic contacts.

Chapter 7 presents information on antennas for all types of locations. You must determine the frequency bands that you want to try. The success of your antenna installation will be quite evident once you actually get on the air. Either they'll hear you or they won't. A beam antenna is not mandatory for working DX. At times of high sunspot activity, many Novices report outstanding results using dipoles or converted CB antennas. Your goal is to put the best possible signal on the air. Of course, this will vary depending on your location and your budget. Don't worry about competing with the ham down the street who has a huge antenna atop a 70-foot tower.

In Amateur Radio, it's important to enjoy and take pride in your own accomplishment. You've heard it said "It's what you do with what you've got that really counts." That is especially true in Amateur Radio. To make up for any real or imagined lack of equipment, concentrate on improving your own operating ability.

Good operating skills can be like adding 10 dB to your signal. (That's like increasing your power by 10 times!) More detailed operating information can be found in *The ARRL Operating Manual*. This book is available from your local radio dealer or directly from ARRL.

A good rule for Amateur Radio contacts (**QSOs**) is to talk as you would during a face-to-face conversation. When you meet someone for the first time, you introduce yourself once; you don't repeat your name like a broken record. An exception would be if the other person is hard of hearing or you're meeting in a noisy place. Even then you would only repeat if the person couldn't hear you. When you are on the air, don't assume that you must continually repeat information. The other operator will tell you if she needs repeats ("**fills**"). Problem situations include static (QRN), interference (QRM) or signal fading (QSB). Table 9-3 lists many common **Q signals**. You should use Q signals on CW *only*. On voice, say what you mean.

The following example may help you. Imagine you are meeting someone for the first time. You strike up a conversation by saying "Hi, my name is John, John, Name is John. I live in Newington, Connecticut. Newington. Newington. Connecticut. Connecticut." What would you expect the other person to do? Well, don't be surprised if he or she doesn't want to talk to you anymore!

The following sections on operating procedures are important. Follow the guidelines and you'll be off to a good start.

CW OPERATING PROCEDURES

Even if you're in a rush to key the mike, don't pass up the information in this section. There are many similarities between CW and voice operation. Non-CW modes such as SSB, FM and specialized digital modes are thoroughly covered later in the chapter.

Calling CQ

There is no point in wasting words, and that includes trying to make a radio contact. Hams establish a contact when one station calls **CQ** and another replies. CQ literally means "Seek you: I'm looking for someone to talk to." You can usually tell a good ham by the length of the CQ call. A good operator sends short calls separated by concentrated listening periods. The not-so-good ham sends endless CQs. Long CQs drive away more contacts than they attract! Generally, a 3 × 3 call is more than sufficient. Here's an example:

CQ CQ CQ DE WB2UDC WB2UDC WB2UDC K

Perhaps the best way to get started is to listen for someone else's CQ. The Novice bands are usually alive with signals. You may choose to call CQ yourself, however, and that's okay. Always listen before you transmit, even if the frequency appears clear. To start, send QRL? ("Is this frequency busy?") If you hear a C ("yes") in reply, then try another frequency. It is not uncommon to hear only one of the stations in a QSO. A frequency may *seem* clear even though there is a contact in progress. It's the worst of bad manners to jump on a frequency that's already busy. Admittedly, signals on the Novice bands, especially on 40 and 80 meters, are often crowded. Even so, exercise as much courtesy as possible.

Whatever you do, don't send faster than you can reliably

Table 9-3

Q Signals

Given below are a number of Q signals whose meanings most often need to be expressed with brevity and clarity in amateur work. (Q abbreviations take the form of questions only when they are sent followed by a question mark.)

QRG   Will you tell me my exact frequency (or that of . . .)? Your exact frequency (or that of . . .) is . . . kHz.

QRL   Are you busy? I am busy (or I am busy with . . .). Please do not interfere.

QRM Is my transmission being interfered with? Your transmission is being interfered with . . . (1. Nil; 2. Slightly; 3. Moderately; 4. Severely; 5. Extremely.)

QRN   Are you troubled by static? I am troubled by static . . . (1-5 as under QRM).

QRO   Shall I increase power? Increase power.

QRP   Shall I decrease power? Decrease power.

QRQ   Shall I send faster? Send faster (. . . WPM).

QRS   Shall I send more slowly? Send more slowly (. . . WPM).

QRT   Shall I stop sending? Stop sending.

QRU   Have you anything for me? I have nothing for you.

QRV   Are you ready? I am ready.

QRX   When will you call me again? I will call you again at . . . hours (on . . . kHz).

QRZ   Who is calling me? You are being called by . . . (on . . . kHz).

QSB   Are my signals fading? Your signals are fading.

QSK   Can you hear me between your signals and if so can I break in on your transmission? I can hear you between signals; break in on my transmission.

QSL   Can you acknowledge receipt (of a message or transmission)? I am acknowledging receipt.

QSN   Did you hear me (or . . .) on . . . kHz? I did hear you (or . . .) on . . . kHz.

QSO   Can you communicate with . . . direct or by relay? I can communicate with . . . direct (or by relay through . . .).

QSP   Will you relay to . . .? I will relay to . . .

QST   General call preceding a message addressed to all amateurs and ARRL members. This is in effect "CQ ARRL."

QSX   Will you listen to . . . on . . . kHz? I am listening to . . . on . . . kHz.

QSY   Shall I change to transmission on another frequency? Change to transmission on another frequency (or on . . . kHz).

QTB   Do you agree with my counting of words? I do not agree with your counting of words. I will repeat the first letter or digit of each word or group.

QTC   How many messages have you to send? I have . . . messages for you (or for . . .).

QTH   What is your location? My location is . . .

QTR   What is the correct time? The time is . . .

CORRECT CW PROCEDURES

Establishing a contact—The best way to do this, especially at first, is to listen. When you hear someone calling CQ, answer them. If you hear a CQ, wait until the ham indicates she is listening, then call her. For example:

KA1WWP KA1WWP DE WL7AGA WL7AGA $\overline{AR}$

($\overline{AR}$ is equivalent to over.)

In answer to your call, the called station will reply WL7AGA DE KA1WWP R . . . That R means that she has received your call correctly. That's all it means—received. It does not mean (a) correct, (b) I agree, (c) I will comply, or anything else. It is not sent unless everything from the previous transmission was received correctly. Perhaps KA1WWP heard someone calling her but didn't quite catch the call because of interference (QRM) or static (QRN). In this case, she might come back with:

QRZ? DE KA1WWP $\overline{AR}$ ("Who is calling me?").

Calling CQ—CQ means "I wish to contact any amateur station." Avoid calling CQ endlessly. It clutters up the air and drives off potential new friends. The typical CQ goes like this:

CQ CQ CQ DE KA1WWP KA1WWP KA1WWP K. The letter K is an invitation for any station to go ahead.

The QSO—During a contact, it is necessary to identify your station only once every 10 minutes. Keep the contact on a friendly and cordial level. Remember, the conversation is not private. Many others, including nonamateurs, may be listening. Both on CW and phone, it is possible to be informal, friendly and conversational. This is what makes the Amateur Radio QSO enjoyable. During the contact, when you stand by, use K ("go") at the end of your transmission. If you don't want someone else to join the QSO, use $\overline{KN}$. That says you want only the contacted station to come back to you. Most of the time K is sufficient (and shorter!).

Ending the QSO—When it's time to end the contact, don't keep talking. Briefly express your pleasure at having worked the other operator. Then, sign out:

$\overline{SK}$ WL7AGA DE KA1WWP.

If you are leaving the air, add CL to the end, right after your call sign.

These ending signals establish Amateur Radio as a cordial and fraternal hobby. At the same time, they foster orderliness and organization. These signals have no legal standing, however. FCC regulations say little about our internal procedures. The procedures we ourselves adopt are even more important. They show we're not just hobbyists, but that we are an established communications service. We take pride in our distinctive procedures—tailored to our special needs.

MY FIRST ON-THE-AIR CONTACT

I slowly reach for the key, my other hand on the TR switch. All I have to do is throw the TR switch, which connects the antenna to the transmitter, and push down on the key. Then I'll be on the air and able to talk to the world. But I can't. My hand doesn't move, except to tremble slightly. It's not the rig, not the key. It's me! I can't find the nerve to do it. I can't send a signal to the world.

That's how it was for me when I tried to make my first contact. It had been weeks since I passed the Novice exam. Each day that passed without the arrival of my new ticket seemed endless. I knew that if that day would just end, the next would surely see the arrival of my license. Days, weeks passed. Then a month had gone by. The station was there waiting for me. All the equipment was in place and ready for operation. If only the license would arrive.

Finally, after what seemed to be several years, it did arrive. Can you believe it? It arrived on my birthday. What a present! The letter carrier had hardly made it to the sidewalk before I was at the rig. I turned on the transmitter and receiver. Nothing! What could be wrong? All the wires connected? Oh no! The power cords were just hanging there. I'd forgotten to plug them into the wall socket. The few seconds it took for the receiver to warm up seemed like hours. Then I heard the sound of radio. I was ready to enter the world of ham radio. Or so I thought.

After several minutes of total failure at my attempt to send CQ, I gave up. I needed help. But where to get it? Of course, the instructor of my Novice training class. He could, and would help me.

The next day I got in touch with him and explained my problem. Would he help me? Yes, he would be glad to stand behind me during that first contact. But, he was busy with something else. I'd have to wait a day or so. Another day without a contact? It might as well have been another year.

Although it didn't seem possible, the next day rolled around, and with it, my instructor. A few minutes of preparation and I was ready. I would give it my best, to sink or swim. Tuning the receiver to the frequency of my crystal-controlled transmitter, I found another station calling CQ. His sending was slow and steady. It had to be for me to copy it. "Go ahead, give him a try," advised my instructor. "What have you got to lose?"

. . . CQ CQ CQ CQ. His call seemed endless. Finally, he signed . . . CQ DE W3AOH. I flipped the TR switch and reached confidently for the key. W3AOH DE WN2VDN A̅R̅.

"That was a pretty short call you gave him. You should have sent your call sign more than once. He may have missed it." But he didn't. There it was, slow and steady. WN2VDN DE W3AOH B̅T̅ TNX CALL B̅T̅ UR
. . . He had answered my call . . . my call. I'd done it! I made a contact!

"Pay attention and copy the code!" my instructor yelled at me. "He's still sending." Dahdididit dahdidah dah dahdahdah dididah dahdahdah . . . dahdididit . . . What on Earth did that mean? I'd forgotten the code. Those strange sounds coming out of the speaker didn't make any sense at all. What was I going to do?

Fortunately, my instructor was copying it all. "He's just signed it over to you. Your turn now."

I flipped the TR switch again, and hit the key. This time there was no fear. The key was part of my hand, part of my mind. W3AOH DE WN2VDN . . . Until, that is, after I sent my call. I didn't know his name, his location, anything. So I sent the only thing I could think of. "Thanks for coming back to me OM. You're my first contact. I'm a bit nervous." Behind me, the instructor is saying, "You should have sent him your name and location, and his signal report." Too late, I was already signing it over to W3AOH.

Slow and steady came the reply. "Welcome aboard. Hope you enjoy ham radio as much as I do . . . ." This time I had no trouble copying him. After the contact was completed, I breathed a very large sigh of relief. But, I had done it. I had actually "talked" to another person via Morse code.

My instructor asked if he should hang around a little longer. But I didn't hear him. I had already begun looking around for another CQ to answer. I didn't need his help any longer; I was a ham.

copy. That will surely invite disaster! It's best to send at the speed you wish to receive. That is especially true when you call CQ. If you answer a CQ, you should answer at a speed no faster than that of the sending station. Don't be ashamed to send PSE QRS (please send more slowly).

As you gain experience, you will develop the skill of sorting out the signal you want from those of other stations. Space in the ham bands is limited. Make sure your QSO takes up as little of it as possible. When two stations are communicating, their transmitters should be on exactly the same frequency. We call this procedure "operating **zero beat**." There is no difference between the operating frequencies of the transmitters involved in the contact. Both transmissions will have the same pitch when you hear them in a receiver. When you tune in the other station, adjust your receiver for the strongest signal and the "proper" tone for your radio. This will usually be between 500 and 1000 Hz.

Zero-beat operating helps the other operator know where to listen for your signal. This is easy with a transceiver. The transmitter will automatically be close to zero beat when you tune in the received signal to a comfortable pitch. With a separate receiver and transmitter, you must be sure your transmitter is zero beat with that of the other station. This procedure limits the frequency space (bandwidth) required for your radio conversation. It also improves operating convenience and avoids needless interference.

Working "Split"

There is an exception to the zero-beat rule. Sometimes a DX station has a "pileup" of stations trying to make contact. If they are all calling on the DX station's frequency, no one (including the DX station!) can copy anything. Under these conditions, the DX station may choose to work "split." We talked about split-frequency operating in Chapter 6. When you hear a DX station, but you never hear anyone else calling or working him, chances are he's working split. Tune higher in the band, and look for the pileup. It should be easy to find. DX stations work split when operating SSB, too. (For more helpful hints on working DX, see ARRL's *The DXCC Companion*.)

For amateurs to understand each other, we must standardize our communications. You'll find, for instance, that most hams use abbreviations on CW. Why? It's faster to send a couple of letters than it is to spell out a word. But there's no point in using an abbreviation if no one else understands you. Over the years, amateurs have developed a set of standard abbreviations (Table 9-4). If you use these abbreviations, you'll find that everyone will understand you, and you'll understand them. In addition to these standards, we use a set of **procedural signals**, or **prosigns**, to help control a contact. The "Correct CW Procedures" sidebar explains these prosigns in more detail.

Table 9-4

Some Abbreviations for CW Work

Although abbreviations help to cut down unnecessary transmission, it's best not to abbreviate unnecessarily when working an operator of unknown experience.

AA	All after	GN	Good night	SASE	Self-addressed, stamped envelope
AB	All before	GND	Ground	SED	Said
ABT	About	GUD	Good	SIG	Signature; signal
ADR	Address	HI	The telegraphic laugh; high	SINE	Operator's personal initials or nickname
AGN	Again	HR	Here, hear		
ANT	Antenna	HV	Have	SKED	Schedule
BCI	Broadcast interference	HW	How	SRI	Sorry
BCL	Broadcast listener	LID	A poor operator	SSB	Single sideband
BK	Break; break me; break in	MA, MILS	Milliamperes	SVC	Service; prefix to service message
BN	All between; been	MSG	Message; prefix to radiogram	T	Zero
BUG	Semi-automatic key	N	No	TFC	Traffic
B4	Before	NCS	Net control station	TMW	Tomorrow
C	Yes	ND	Nothing doing	TNX-TKS	Thanks
CFM	Confirm; I confirm	NIL	Nothing; I have nothing for you	TT	That
CK	Check	NM	No more	TU	Thank you
CL	I am closing my station; call	NR	Number	TVI	Television interference
CLD-CLG	Called; calling	NW	Now; I resume transmission	TX	Transmitter
CQ	Calling any station	OB	Old boy	TXT	Text
CUD	Could	OC	Old chap	UR-URS	Your; You're; yours
CUL	See you later	OM	Old man	VFO	Variable-frequency oscillator
CW	Continuous wave (i.e., radiotelegraphy)	OP-OPR	Operator	VY	Very
		OT	Old-timer; old top	WA	Word after
DE	From, this is	PBL	Preamble	WB	Word before
DLD-DLVD	Delivered	PSE	Please	WD-WDS	Word; words
DR	Dear	PWR	Power	WKD-WKG	Worked; working
DX	Distance, foreign countries	PX	Press	WL	Well; will
ES	And, &	R	Received as transmitted; are	WUD	Would
FB	Fine business, excellent	RCD	Received	WX	Weather
FM	Frequency modulation	RCVR (RX)	Receiver	XCVR	Transceiver
GA	Go ahead (or resume sending)	REF	Refer to; referring to; reference	XMTR (TX)	Transmitter
GB	Good-by	RFI	Radio frequency interference	XTAL	Crystal
GBA	Give better address	RIG	Station equipment	XYL (YF)	Wife
GE	Good evening	RPT	Repeat; I repeat	YL	Young lady
GG	Going	RTTY	Radioteletype	73	Best regards
GM	Good morning	RX	Receiver	88	Love and kisses

Answering a CQ

What about our friend WB2UDC? In our last example he was calling CQ. What happened? Another ham, N2SN in Charlotte, NC, heard him and answered the CQ:

WB2UDC WB2UDC DE N2SN N2SN $\overline{AR}$

Use the prosign $\overline{AR}$ (the letters A and R run together with no separating space) in an initial call to a specific station before officially establishing contact. When calling CQ, use the prosign K, because you are inviting replies. WB2UDC is considered a good operator. He comes back to N2SN in a to-the-point manner (one you should copy).

N2SN DE WB2UDC R GE UR RST 599 EDISON NJ $\overline{BT}$ NAME BOB HW BK

In this transmission, **RST** refers to the standard readability, strength and tone system of signal-quality reporting. You'll exchange an RST signal report in nearly every Amateur Radio QSO. Don't spend a lot of time worrying about what signal report to give to a station you're in contact with. The scales are rather broad, and are simply an indication of how you are receiving the other station. As you gain experience with the descriptions given in Table 9-5, you'll be more comfortable estimating the proper signal report.

A report of RST 368 would be interpreted as "Your signal is readable with considerable difficulty, good strength, with a slight trace of modulation." The tone report is a useful indication of transmitter performance. When the RST system was developed, the tone of amateur transmitters varied widely. Today, a tone report of less than 9 is cause to ask a few other amateurs for their opinion of the transmitted signal. Consistently poor tone reports means you have problems in your transmitter.

The basic information is only transmitted once. The other station will request repeats if necessary. Notice too that $\overline{BT}$ (B and T run together) is used to separate portions of the text. This character is really the double dash (=), and is usually written as a long dash or hyphen on your copy paper. HW implies "how do you copy?" BK signifies that WB2UDC is turning it over (back) to N2SN for his basic info. WB2UDC does not sign both calls all over again. FCC rules require identification only at the end of a QSO, and once every 10 minutes.

Conversation is a two-way phenomenon. There is no reason that an Amateur Radio QSO can't be a back-and-forth process. No one wants to listen to a long, unnecessary monologue. Propagation conditions might change, hampering the QSO. WB2UDC and N2SN will relate better if each party contributes equally. Sometimes there is interference or marginal copy because of weak signals. It may help to transmit your call sign when you are turning it back to the other station.

CW Operating Summary

In summary, here are the points to keep in mind:

1) Listen before transmitting. Send QRL? ("Is this frequency busy?") before transmitting. Listen again! It's worth repeating: Listen!

2) Send short CQs and listen between each.

3) Send no faster than you can reliably copy.

4) Use standard abbreviations whenever possible—become familiar with them.

5) Use prosigns and Q-signals properly.

6) Identify at the end of a QSO (the entire contact, not each turnover) and every 10 minutes.

Table 9-5
The RST System

READABILITY
1—Unreadable.
2—Barely readable, occasional words distinguishable.
3—Readable with considerable difficulty.
4—Readable with practically no difficulty.
5—Perfectly readable.

SIGNAL STRENGTH
1—Faint signals barely perceptible.
2—Very weak signals.
3—Weak signals.
4—Fair signals.
5—Fairly good signals.
6—Good signals.
7—Moderately strong signals.
8—Strong signals.
9—Extremely strong signals.

TONE
1—Sixty-cycle ac or less, very rough and broad.
2—Very rough ac, very harsh and broad.
3—Rough ac tone, rectified but not filtered.
4—Rough note, some trace of filtering.
5—Filtered rectified ac but stongly ripple-modulated.
6—Filtered tone, definite trace of ripple modulation.
7—Near pure tone, trace of ripple modulation.
8—Near perfect tone, slight trace of modulation.
9—Perfect tone, no trace of ripple or modulation of any kind.

The "tone" report refers only to the purity of the signal. It has no connection with its stability or freedom from clicks or chirps. Most of the signals you hear will be a T-9. Other tone reports occur mainly if the power-supply filter capacitors are not doing a thorough job. If so, some trace of ac ripple finds its way onto the transmitted signal. If the signal has the characteristic steadiness of crystal control, add X to the report (eg, RST 469X). If it has a chirp or "tail" (either on "make" or "break") add C (eg, 469C). If it has clicks or noticeable other keying transients, add K (eg, 469K). Of course a signal could have both chirps and clicks, in which case both C and K could be used (eg, RST 469CK).

7) Use R only if you've received 100 percent of what the other station sent.

8) Be courteous.

9) Zero beat the other station's frequency before calling (except as noted).

TUNING UP

What is often the most exciting, most memorable and perhaps most terrifying moment in your entire ham experience? It is your first on-the-air contact with another station! Before you have that experience, you'll want to know how to operate your station equipment.

The best source of specific information about your equipment is the instruction manual. Before you even turn on your radio, study the instructions carefully so you'll be familiar with each control. Without turning on the equipment, try adjusting the controls. Nothing will happen, but you'll learn the location and feel of each important control.

After studying the manual and finding the important

controls, you're ready to tune up. You must have your FCC license in hand before you can transmit or even tune up on the air!

If your transmitter requires tuning when you change bands, connect your transmitter output to a **dummy load** or **dummy antenna** (see Chapter 8) while you tune. Never tune up your transmitter on the air because you could interfere with other hams.

Once you have tuned up the transmitter according to the instruction manual, disconnect the dummy load. Then connect the antenna (an antenna switch makes this easy). Now, you're ready to operate! If you use a Transmatch, you may have to transmit a brief low-power signal to adjust the circuit.

[Before you go on to the next section, turn to Chapter 12 and study questions 2B-1-1.1, 2B-1-1.3 and 2B-1-2.1. You should also study questions 2B-2-1.1 through 2B-2-6.5. **If you are preparing for the Technician exam,** also study questions 3AB-3.2 and 3AB-3.3 in Chapter 13. Review this section if you have any difficulty with these questions.]

VOICE OPERATING PROCEDURES

Among the most exciting amateur privileges is voice operation. To make the most of your voice privileges, you'll need to learn a new set of operating procedures. The operating procedures described here apply to voice operation on 10-meter SSB and on the "weak-signal" SSB frequencies on the VHF/UHF bands. Some, but not all, of the procedures apply to FM voice operation as well. While SSB voice operation and FM voice operation share some operating practices, there are a number of important differences. Techniques unique to FM and repeaters are covered later in this chapter.

Operating techniques and procedures vary from band to band. If you're accustomed to 80-meter CW, you may be uncertain about how to make a 10-meter SSB contact. A great way to become familiar with new techniques is to spend time listening to operators who are already using the band. Be discriminating, though. Take a few moments to understand the techniques used by the proficient operators. Proficient operators are the ones who are the most understandable (least confusing) and who sound the best. Don't simply mimic whatever you hear. This is especially true if you're going on the air for the first time.

Whatever band or mode you are undertaking, there are three fundamental things to remember. These fundamentals apply for any type of voice operating you might try. The first is that courtesy costs very little. It is often rewarded by bringing out the best in others. Second, the aim of each radio contact should be 100% effective communication. A good operator is never satisfied with anything less. Third, your "private" conversation with another station is actually open to the public. Many amateurs are uncomfortable discussing controversial subjects over the air. Also, never give any confidential information on the air. You never know who may be listening.

Keep it Plain and Simple

Correct voice operation is more challenging than it may appear. Even though it does not require the use of code or special abbreviations, the proper procedure is very important. Voice operators *say* what they want to have understood. CW operators have to spell it out or abbreviate. The speed of transmission on voice is generally between 150 and 200 words per minute. Readability and understandability are critical to good communications.

It is important to speak clearly and not too quickly. This

Table 9-6

Voice Equivalents to Code Procedure

Voice	Code	Meaning
over	$\overline{AR}$	after call to a specific station
end of message	$\overline{AR}$	end of message
wait, stand by	$\overline{AS}$	please stand by
received	R	all received correctly (This is not a promise to take any specific action.)
go, go ahead	K	any station transmit
go only	$\overline{KN}$	addressed station only
clear	$\overline{SK}$	end of contact
closing station	CL	going off the air
break or back to you	$\overline{BK}$	the receiving station's turn to transmit
stroke, portable	$\overline{DN}$	operation away from primary station location

is an excellent practice to follow. Whether you're working a DX operator who may not fully understand our language, or talking to your friend down the street, speak slowly and clearly. That way, you'll have fewer requests to repeat information.

Avoid using CW abbreviations and prosigns such as "HI" and "K" for voice communications. Also, Q-signals (QRX, QRV and so forth) are for CW, not voice, operation. The use of QSL, QSO and QRZ has become accepted practice on voice, however. Abbreviations are used on CW to say more in less time. On voice, you have plenty of time to say what you mean. On CW, for example, it's convenient to send "K" at the end of a transmission. On voice, it takes less than a second to say "go ahead." Table 9-6 shows the voice equivalents for common CW prosigns.

Use plain language and keep jargon to a minimum. In particular, avoid the use of "we" when you mean "I" and "handle" or "personal" when you mean "name." Also, don't say "that's a roger" when you mean "that's correct." Taken individually, any of these sayings is almost harmless. Combined in a conversation, however, they give a false-sounding "radioese" that is actually less effective than plain language. "Roger" for example, means "I have received what you sent." It doesn't necessarily mean that what was sent was "correct"!

Phonetic Alphabet

Sometimes you will have difficulty getting your call sign or other information across to the operator on the other end. This might be because conditions are poor, there is nearby interference, or the operator on the other end is not proficient in English. There is a standard International Telecommunication Union (ITU) *phonetic alphabet* to assist you. The standard phonetic alphabet is shown in Table 9-7. It is generally used when signing your call or passing information that must be spelled out. For example, KA5CHW signs his call Kilo Alfa Five Charlie Hotel Whiskey. WB2LZN signs Whiskey Bravo Two Lima Zulu November, and YU1EXY says Yankee Uniform One Echo X-ray Yankee.

The ITU phonetic alphabet is generally understood by hams in all countries. If you want people to understand you, stick to the standard phonetics. For example, WA2ECO should sign Whisky Alpha Two Echo Charlie Oscar, not something like Worked All Two Electron Coupled Oscillators. Use of nonstandard phonetics is often more confusing than using no phonetics at all.

Table 9-7

International Telecommunication Union Phonetics

A—Alfa (**AL** FAH)	I—India (**IN** DEE AH)	R—Romeo (**ROW** ME OH)
B—Bravo (**BRAH** VOH)	J—Juliett (**JEW** LEE ETT)	S—Sierra (SEE **AIR** RAH)
C—Charlie (**CHAR** LEE or **SHAR** LEE)	K—Kilo (**KEY** LOH)	T—Tango (**TANG** GO)
	L—Lima (**LEE** MAH)	U—Uniform (**YOU** NEE FORM or **OO** NEE FORM)
D—Delta (**DELL** TAH)	M—Mike (MIKE)	
E—Echo (**ECK** OH)	N—November (NO **VEM** BER)	V—Victor (**VIK** TAH)
F—Foxtrot (**FOKS** TROT)	O—Oscar (**OSS** CAH)	W—Whiskey (**WISS** KEY)
G—Golf (GOLF)	P—Papa (PAH **PAH**)	X—X-RAY (**ECKS** RAY)
H—Hotel (HOH **TELL**)	Q—Quebec (KEH **BECK**)	Y—Yankee (**YANG** KEY)
		Z—Zulu (**ZOO** LOO)

Note: The **Boldfaced** syllables are emphasized. The pronunciations shown in this table were designed for speakers from all international languages. The pronunciations given for "Oscar" and "Victor" may seem awkward to English-speaking people in the US.

Initiating a Contact

The procedures described in this section generally apply to SSB operation. FM and repeater operation is somewhat different. See the FM and repeaters section later in this chapter.

There are two ways to initiate an SSB voice contact: call CQ (a general call to any station) or answer a CQ. At first, you may want to tune around and find another station to answer. If activity on a band seems low, a CQ call may be worthwhile.

Before calling CQ, it is important to find a frequency that appears unoccupied by any other station. This may not be easy, particularly during crowded band conditions. Listen carefully—perhaps a weak DX station is on frequency. If you're using a beam antenna, rotate it to make sure the frequency is clear. If, after a reasonable time, the frequency seems clear, ask if the frequency is in use, then sign your call. "Is the frequency in use? This is KA1IFB." If, as far as you can determine, no one responds, you are ready to make your call.

As in CW operation, keep voice CQ calls short. Long calls are considered poor operating technique. You may interfere with stations already on frequency who didn't hear your initial frequency check. Also, stations intending to reply to the call may become impatient and move to another frequency. No one wants to listen to an endless CQ. Call CQ three times, followed by "this is," followed by your call sign three times and then listen. If no one comes back, try again. If two or three calls produce no answer, it may be that interference is present on frequency, or that the particular band is not open. At that point, change frequency and try again. If you still get no answer, try looking around and answer someone else's CQ.

An example of a good CQ call is:
"CQ CQ calling CQ. This is KA1WWP, Kilo Alfa One Whiskey Whiskey Papa, Kilo Alfa One Whiskey Whiskey Papa, calling CQ and standing by."

There is no need to say what band is being used, and certainly no need to add "tuning for any possible calls, dah-di-dah!" or "K someone please!" and the like.

When replying to a CQ, say both call signs clearly. It's not necessary to sign the other station's call phonetically. You should, however, always sign yours with standard phonetics. It is good practice to keep calls short. Say the call sign of the station you are calling once or twice only. Follow with your call sign repeated several times. For example, "W1AW, W1AW, this is WA3VIL, Whiskey Alfa Three Victor India Lima, WA3VIL, over." Depending on conditions, you may need to sign your call phonetically several times. Repeat this calling procedure as required until you receive a reply or until the station you are calling has come back to someone else.

Listening is very important. If you're using PTT (push-to-talk), be sure to let up on the transmit button between calls so you can hear what is going on. With VOX (voice operated switch), you key the transmitter simply by talking into the microphone. VOX operation is helpful because, when properly adjusted, it enables you to listen between words. Remember: It is extremely poor practice to make a long call without listening. Also, don't continue to call after the station you are trying to contact replies to someone else.

Conducting the QSO

Once you've established contact, it is no longer necessary to use the phonetic alphabet or sign the other station's call. FCC regulations stipulate that you need sign your call only every ten minutes and at the conclusion of the contact. (The exception is when handling international third-party traffic. Then, you must sign both calls.) This allows you to enjoy a normal two-way conversation without the need for continual identification. Use "over" or "go ahead" at the end of a transmission to indicate that it's the other station's turn to transmit. (During FM repeater operation, it is obvious when you or the other station stops transmitting because the repeater carrier drops. In this case it may not be necessary to say "over.")

Signal reports on SSB are two-digit numbers using the RS portion of the RST system. No tone report is required. The maximum signal report would be "59." That is, readability 5, strength 9. On FM repeaters, RS reports are not appropriate. FM signal reports are generally given in terms of quieting. "Full quieting" means that no noise is present with the signal.

Voice contacts are often similar in content to CW QSOs. Aside from signal strength, it is customary to exchange name, location and information on equipment being used. Once these routine details are out of the way, you can discuss virtually any appropriate topic.

Working DX

During the years around the sunspot maximum, 10-meter worldwide communication on a daily basis is commonplace. Ten meters is an outstanding DX band when conditions are right. A particular advantage of 10 meters for DX work is that effective beam-type antennas tend to be small and light, making for relatively easy installation.

There are a few things to keep in mind when you contact amateurs from outside the United States. While many overseas amateurs have an exceptional command of English (which is especially remarkable since very few US amateurs understand foreign languages) they may not be intimately familiar with many of our local sayings. Because of the language differences, some DX stations are more comfortable with the "bare-bones" type contact, and you should be sensitive to their preferences.

A further point is that during unsettled band conditions it may be necessary to keep the contact short in case fading or interference occurs. Take these factors into account when expanding on a basic contact. Also, during a band opening on 10 meters or on VHF, it is crucial to keep contacts brief. This allows many stations to work whatever DX is coming through.

When the time comes to end the contact, end it. Thank the other operator (once) for the pleasure of the contact and say goodbye: "This is KA9MAN, clear." This is all that is required. Unless the other amateur is a good friend, there is no need to start sending best wishes to everyone in the household including the family dog! Nor is this the time to start digging up extra comments on the contact which will require a "final final" from the other station (there may be other stations waiting to call in).

Additional Recommendations

• Listen with care. It is natural to answer the loudest

OSCAR: Amateur Radio Communications Satellites

OSCAR 1, the first Amateur Radio satellite, was launched in 1961. Since then, over 20 more amateur satellites have flown. OSCAR stands for *orbiting satellite carrying amateur radio.*

Home-Station Equipment and Modes

Amateur satellite communication takes place on the VHF/UHF bands, using voice, Morse code and data-communications modes. FM is rarely used on satellites for reasons explained later. You transmit to the satellite on its *uplink* frequency and listen on its *downlink* frequency. Uplink and downlink are on different bands. Typical satellite stations have a rig for each band, connected to separate antennas. Some manufacturers now offer multiband VHF/UHF multimode rigs that can transmit and receive on separate bands at the same time. These rigs are ideal for satellite work. Linear transverters connected to your HF or VHF rig are an alternative.

Amateur satellites don't use fixed receive and transmit frequencies. Instead, they operate like flying, high-power mixers. A typical uplink frequency range is 435.601 to 435.637 MHz. Users can access the satellite anywhere in that range. Because the satellite is a mixer, where you transmit determines where your signal is retransmitted on the downlink. For the same satellite, the downlink range might be 2400.771 to 2400.747 MHz.

Satellites are battery powered and the batteries are recharged by solar panels. Because the satellite is a linear mixer, the more stations using the satellite and the stronger they are, the greater the drain on the satellite's batteries. Running excessive power overloads the satellite and makes *all* signals weaker! Because FM voice uses a continuous carrier, it imposes a large drain on a satellite's batteries. FM is not an efficient mode for satellite operation and is almost never heard.

Antennas

Amateur satellite stations use antenna systems that can be aimed at points in the sky as well as turned like terrestrial antennas. Unlike commercial TV-satellite "dishes," amateur satellite antennas are relatively small. Amateur satellite antennas need not be mounted high in the air like terrestrial VHF/UHF antennas, although higher antennas let you "see" the satellite when it is near your horizon.

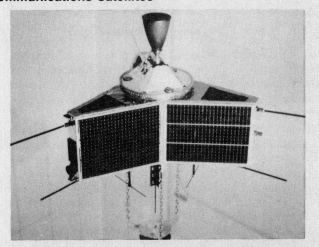

Who Can You Talk To?

Amateur Radio satellites offer hours of worldwide communications. DXing through the satellites is much easier than on the amateur HF bands where fading and interference can be very frustrating. Unlike commercial TV satellites that are parked over the equator, Amateur Radio satellites are constantly on the move, providing a wide variety of people and nations to work. Some DXpeditions to rare countries even bring along a satellite station. Another class of satellites in lower orbit offer packet-radio message forwarding. Who knows what the future will bring?

American Amateur Radio satellites are planned and built by the Radio Amateur Satellite Corporation (AMSAT). Other Amateur Radio satellites have been built by hams in the Soviet Union, Japan, France and other countries. Amateur satellite experiments involving schools around the world have introduced Amateur Radio to thousands of children.

The ARRL Operating Manual has an entire chapter dedicated to satellite communications. It's the best place to start if you'd like more information. If you think you'd like to join the thousands of satellite users around the world, see *The ARRL Satellite Anthology* and *The Satellite Experimenter's Handbook* for information on setting up and operating a station.

station that calls, but you should answer the best signal. Not all amateurs can run high power, but there is no reason every amateur cannot have a signal of the highest quality. Do not reward the operator who has cranked up the transmitter gain to the point of being unintelligible, especially if a station with a nice sounding signal is also calling.

• Use VOX or PTT. If you use VOX, don't defeat its purpose by saying "aah" to keep the transmitter on the air. If you use PTT, let go of the mike button every so often to make sure you are not "doubling" with the other station. A QSO should be an interactive conversation. Don't do all the talking.

• Don't rush. The speed of voice transmission (with perfect accuracy) depends almost entirely on the skill of the two operators concerned. Use a rate of speech that allows perfect understanding. The operator on the other end should have time to record important details of the contact. If you go too fast, you'll end up repeating a lot of information.

[Before going on to the next section, turn to Chapter 12 and study the questions with numbers that begin 2B-3-1 and **2B-3-2. If you are preparing for the Technician exam,** also study questions 3AB-1.1 through 3AB-1.3 in Chapter 13. Review this section if you have difficulty with any of these questions.]

VHF AND UHF PROCEDURES

"Weak-signal" VHF/UHF operating practices are not very different from those on HF. There are, however, some differences that you should know about. Most of these differences evolved because of the nature of VHF and UHF propagation. This is just a brief overview of VHF and UHF

procedures. See *The ARRL Operating Manual* for more information.

Grid Squares

One of the first things you'll notice when you tune the weak-signal frequencies is that most QSOs include an exchange of grid squares. Grid squares are just a way of dividing up Earth's surface into 1° latitude × 2° longitude rectangles. The grid-square designator consists of two letters and two numbers. It's a shorthand way of describing your general location. For example, W1AW in Newington, CT is in grid square FN31.

You can determine your grid square identifier from the *QST* article, "VHF/UHF Century Awards," published in January 1983, pp 49-51. (Reprints are available from the Awards Branch at ARRL HQ. Please include an SASE with your request.) ARRL also publishes a map (Figure 9-3) that shows the grid squares for the continental United States and most of Canada. This 12- × 18-inch map is available from ARRL HQ.

VHF/UHF Operating

On HF, you never know who you will run into. On any given day, the HF bands are open for cross-country contacts. At least one band will be open for transcontinental QSOs. This makes for a vast number of potential contacts. Most HF QSOs are with operators you've never met before.

It's different on VHF and UHF. Transmission range is normally limited to your local area. A lot of the activity on

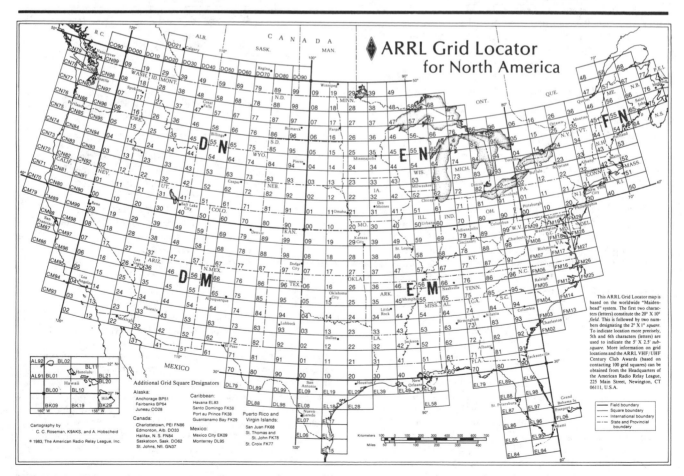

Figure 9-3—This map shows grid squares, used to specify your location for VHF and UHF SSB/CW operation.

these bands is relaxed ragchewing. Many groups meet regularly on VHF and UHF to discuss topics of mutual interest. You'll quickly identify one or more groups of "regulars." They'll probably be happy to have you join the group. These regular get-togethers are a wonderful way to meet people. The "regulars" can answer many of your questions about operating your Amateur Radio station.

When there is enhanced propagation, such as during a tropo opening, the VHF and UHF bands sound more like HF. They are teeming with operators eager to work stations not heard during normal conditions. Pileups occur during good VHF/UHF propagation conditions, just like on HF. In this case, the DX is a station from outside your local area, not from another country. Good VHF or UHF band openings are often short-lived. It's a good idea to limit the contact to the exchange of signal reports and locations. That way, everyone has a chance to work the DX. Other details can be left to the QSL card.

When conditions are good, call CQ sparingly, if at all. The old adage "if you can't hear 'em, you can't work 'em" is just as true at VHF as at HF. Stations can often be heard calling CQ DX on the same frequency as distant stations that they cannot hear.

One feature of VHF operating that is rarely found on the HF bands is the use of **calling frequencies** to provide a meeting place for operators using the same mode. Once a contact has been set up, a change to another frequency (a working frequency) is arranged. That lets others use the calling frequency.

The ARRL recommends band plans to coordinate various activities on each amateur band. For example, the 1.25-meter band plan specifies 222.1 MHz as a calling frequency. This frequency marks the bottom edge of the Novice subband, however. You should not operate right on 222.1 MHz with a Novice license. You must always be aware of the bandwidth of your transmitted signal. Also, your transmitted signal may vary from the operating frequency. You must keep your signal within your band limits.

Theoretically, by using the upper sideband for SSB operation, you could operate on a carrier frequency of 222.100 MHz and all of your transmitted signal would be within the Novice subband. In practice, however, this isn't a good idea. You should operate a few kilohertz above the bottom edge of the band, just to be safe. Check the frequencies near the bottom edge of the band for other stations doing weak-signal work.

There are also repeaters operating in this frequency range. Be certain you are not doing weak-signal work on a repeater frequency in your area. Check the latest *ARRL Repeater Directory* for repeaters in your area. You can also ask some of the other local Amateur Radio operators what frequencies are used for weak-signal work in your area.

──── FM AND REPEATERS ────

There are probably more amateurs who use FM voice than any other communications mode. Most hams have an FM rig of some type. They use it to keep in touch with their local friends. Hams often pass the time during their morning and evening commute talking on the air. In most communities, amateurs interested in a specialized topic (such as chasing DX)

have an FM frequency where they meet regularly to exchange information. At flea markets and conventions, hand-held FM units are in abundance as hams compare notes on the latest bargain.

VHF and UHF FM voice operation takes two forms: simplex and repeater. **Simplex operation** means the stations

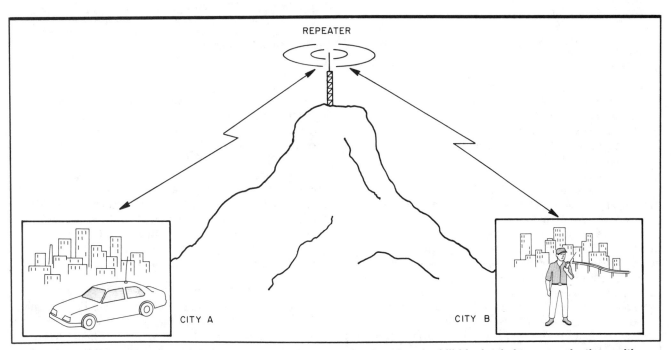

Figure 9-4—Stations in city A can easily communicate with each other, but the hill blocks their communications with city B. The hilltop repeater enables the groups to communicate with each other.

are talking to each other directly, on the same frequency. This is similar to making a contact on the HF bands.

The communications range for VHF and UHF FM simplex is usually limited to your local area. If you live high on a mountain and use a high-gain directional antenna, you may be able to extend your range considerably. Unfortunately, most of us do not have the luxury of ideal VHF/UHF operating conditions. Often, we want to make contacts even though we live in a valley, are driving in a car or are using a low-power, hand-held transceiver.

Enter repeaters. A **repeater** receives a signal on one frequency and simultaneously retransmits (repeats) it on another frequency. Often located atop a tall building or high mountain, VHF and UHF repeaters greatly extend the operating coverage of amateurs using mobile and hand-held transceivers. See Figure 9-4. If a repeater serves an area, it's not necessary for everyone to live on a hilltop. You only have to be able to hear the repeater's transmitter and reach the repeater's receiver with your transmitted signal.

EQUIPMENT CONSIDERATIONS

To use a repeater, you must have a transceiver with the capability of transmitting on the repeater's **input frequency** (the frequency that the repeater listens on) and receiving on the repeater's **output frequency** (the frequency the repeater transmits on). The input and output frequencies are spaced apart ("offset") by a predetermined amount that is different for each band. Common repeater offsets for the VHF/UHF bands are listed in Table 9-8. For example, the offset on 1.25 meters is 1.6 MHz. A repeater on 1.25 meters might have its input frequency on 222.32 MHz and its output on 223.92 MHz.

Table 9-8
Repeater Input/Output Offsets

Band	Offset
6 meters	1 MHz
2 meters	600 kHz
1.25 meters	1.6 MHz
70 cm	5 MHz
33 cm	12 MHz
23 cm	20 MHz

Most transceivers designed for FM repeater operation are set up for the correct offset. They usually have a switch to change between simplex (transmit and receive on the same frequency) and duplex (transmit and receive on different frequencies). So, if you wanted to use the repeater in the preceding example, you would switch your transceiver to the duplex mode and dial up 223.92 to listen to the repeater. When you transmit, your rig will automatically switch to 222.32 MHz (1.6 MHz away), the repeater input frequency.

When you have the correct frequency dialed in, just key your microphone button to transmit through ("access") the repeater. Most repeaters are "open"—that is, available for use by anyone in range. Some repeaters, however, have limited access. Their use is restricted to exclusive groups, such as members of a club. Such "closed" repeaters require the transmission of a continuous subaudible tone or a short "burst" of tones for access. There are also some repeaters available for use by everyone that require the use of special codes or subaudible tones to gain access. The reason for requiring access tones for "open" repeaters is to prevent interference from extraneous transmissions that might accidentally key the repeater.

FINDING A REPEATER

Most communities in the United States are served by repeaters. While the majority of repeaters (over 6000) are on 2 meters, there are more than 1600 repeaters in the 1.25-meter band, more than 5000 on the 70-cm band, over 70 on the 33-cm band and more than 200 in the 23-cm band. More repeaters are being put into service all the time.

There are several ways to find the local repeater(s). Ask local amateurs or contact the nearest radio club. Each spring, the ARRL publishes *The ARRL Repeater Directory*. This is a comprehensive listing of repeaters throughout the United States, Canada and other parts of the repeater world. Besides finding out about local repeater activity, the *Directory* is handy for finding repeaters during vacations and business trips. See Figure 9-5.

ALABAMA					
ANNISTON					
Anniston	147.09	+	WB4GNA	o(ca)xz	CARA
Jacksonville	146.78	–	N4HOA	o	N4HOA
Jacksonville	147.04	+	WD4KTY	oae	AAERC
Lincoln	145.49	–	KC4OX	o	KC4OX
Munford	146.74	–	W4NTI	otalx	W4NTI
Talladega	147.36	+	W4GBQ	o	Tldga ARC
AUBURN/OPELIKA					
Auburn	147.06	+	KA4Y	o	KA4Y
Auburn	147.24	+	K4RY	o	AbrnU ARC
Opelika	146.94	–	W4ZBA	ox	E AL ARC
Opelika	147.12	+	W4ZBA	oaez	
BIRMINGHAM					
Bessemer	145.15	–	N4AHN	oaelxz	K4GTQ
Bessemer	145.39	–	N4LJE	o	N4LJE
Birmingham	145.19	–	N4IQT	ol	N4IQT
Birmingham	145.23	–	WB4TJX	oe	UAB ARC
Birmingham	146.76	–	K4TQR	oae	H & H RA
Birmingham	146.88	–	W4CUE	oaeWx	BARC
Birmingham	146.94	–	W4CUE	oae	BARC
Birmingham	147.28	+	KD4A	o	TelPnrRC
Birmingham	147.34	+	WA4MHO	o	WA4MHO
Centerpoint	146.62	–	K4ANU	o	K4ANU
Hueytown	147.14	+	WA4CYA	o(±Offset)	HueytwnRA
Leeds	146.68	–	N4IQT	o	Leeds RG
Oneonta	146.70	–	N4KGK	oae	BlntCoARC
Palmerdale	145.45	–	WB4ZNQ	o	Cntrpt RC
Pelham	146.98	–	KC4AF	oe	ShlbyCoRC
Pell City	145.37	–	KB4LPR	oa	KB4LPR

Figure 9-5—Anyone who operates on VHF FM should have a copy of *The ARRL Repeater Directory*. *Directory* information includes the repeater call sign, location, frequency and sponsor.

Certain segments of each band are set aside for FM operation. For example, on 1.25 meters, repeater inputs are found between 222.32 and 223.28 MHz. The corresponding outputs are between 223.92 and 224.98 MHz. Frequencies between 223.42 and 223.9 MHz are set aside for simplex operation. On 70 cm, repeater inputs and outputs are located from 442 to 445 MHz and 447 to 450 MHz. On the 33-cm band, repeater inputs are mostly located from 906 to 909 MHz, with outputs from 918 to 920 MHz. On 23 cm, repeater inputs run between 1270 and 1276 MHz, with corresponding outputs between 1282 and 1288 MHz. Simplex operation is between 1294 and 1295 MHz.

REPEATER OPERATING PROCEDURES

You need to know some fundamental techniques unique to repeaters. It's worth a few minutes to listen and familiarize yourself with the procedures used by other hams before you make your first FM repeater contact. Accepted procedures can vary slightly from repeater to repeater.

Your First Transmission

Making your first transmission on a repeater is as simple as signing your call. If the repeater is quiet, just say "K1TN" or "K1TN listening"—to attract someone's attention. After you stop transmitting, you will usually hear the unmodulated repeater carrier for a second or two. This *tail* lets you know that the repeater is working. Someone interested in talking to you will call you after your initial transmission. Some repeaters have specific rules for making yourself heard. In general, however, your call sign is all you need.

Don't call CQ to initiate a conversation. It takes longer to complete a CQ than to transmit your call sign. (In some areas, a solitary "CQ" is permissible.) Efficient communication is the goal. You are not on HF, trying to attract the attention of someone who is casually tuning across the band. In the FM mode, stations are either monitoring their favorite frequency or not. Except for scanner operation, there is not much tuning across the repeater bands.

To join a conversation in progress, transmit your call sign during a break between transmissions. The station that transmits next will usually acknowledge you. Don't use the word "break" to join into a conversation. "Break" usually indicates an emergency and that all stations should stand by for the station with emergency traffic.

To call another station when the repeater is not in use, just give both calls. For example, "WA1MBK, this is W3AZD." If the repeater is in use, but the conversation sounds like it is about to end, wait before calling another station. If the conversation sounds like it is going to continue for a while, however, transmit only your call sign between their transmissions. After you are acknowledged, ask to make a quick call. Usually, the other stations will stand by. Make your call short. If your friend responds, try to meet on another repeater or a simplex frequency. Otherwise, ask your friend to stand by until the present conversation ends.

Courtesy Counts

If you are in the midst of a conversation and another station transmits his or her call sign between transmissions, the next station in line to transmit should acknowledge the new station and permit the new arrival to make a call or join the conversation. It is impolite not to acknowledge new stations, or to acknowledge them but not let them speak. The calling station may need to use the repeater immediately. He or she may have an emergency to handle, so let him or her make a transmission promptly.

A brief pause before you begin each transmission allows other stations to participate in the conversation. Don't key your microphone as soon as someone else releases hers. If your exchanges are too quick, you can prevent other stations from getting in.

The "courtesy beepers" found on some repeaters force users to leave a space between transmissions. The beeper sounds a second or two after each transmission to permit new stations to transmit their call signs in the intervening time period. The conversation may continue only after the beeper sounds. If a station is too quick and begins transmitting before the beeper sounds, the repeater may indicate the violation, sometimes by shutting down!

Keep transmissions as short as possible, so more people can use the repeater. All repeaters promote this by "timing out," (shutting down for a few minutes) when someone gets longwinded. The timer also prevents the repeater from transmitting continuously, due to distant signals or interference.

Because it has such a wide coverage area, a continuously transmitting repeater could cause unnecessary interference. Continuous operation can also damage the repeater.

You must transmit your call sign at the end of a contact and at least every 10 minutes during the course of any communication. You do not have to transmit the call sign of the station to whom you are transmitting.

Never transmit without identification. For example, keying your microphone to turn on the repeater without identifying is illegal. If you do not want to engage in conversation, but simply want to check if you are able to access a particular repeater, simply say "KJ4KB testing." Thus, you have accomplished what you wanted to do, legally.

Fixed Stations and Prime Time

Repeaters were originally intended to enhance mobile communications. During commuter rush hours, mobile stations still have preference over fixed stations on some repeaters. During mobile prime time, fixed stations should generally yield to mobile stations. When you're operating as a fixed station, don't abandon the repeater completely, though. Monitor the mobiles: your assistance may be needed in an emergency.

SIMPLEX OPERATION

After you have made a contact on a repeater, move the conversation to a simplex frequency if possible. The repeater is not a soapbox. You may like to listen to yourself, but others, who may need to use the repeater, will not be as appreciative.

The function of a repeater is to provide communications between stations that can't otherwise communicate because of terrain, equipment limitations or both. It follows that stations able to communicate without a repeater should not use one. That way, the repeater is available for stations that need it. (Besides, communication on simplex offers a degree of privacy impossible to achieve on a repeater. On simplex you can usually have extensive conversations without interruption.)

Select a frequency designated for FM simplex operation. Otherwise, you may interfere with stations operating in other modes without realizing it. Table 9-9 lists the established simplex frequencies in the 2-meter, 1.25-meter, 33-cm and 70-cm bands. Each VHF and UHF band has a frequency designated as the national FM simplex calling frequency, which is the center for most simplex operation. These frequencies are also indicated in Table 9-9.

AUTOPATCH

An **autopatch** allows repeater users to make telephone calls through the repeater. To use most repeater autopatches, you generate the standard telephone company tones to access and dial through the system. The tones are usually generated with a telephone tone pad connected to the transceiver. Tone pads are available from equipment manufacturers as standard or optional equipment. They are often mounted on the front of a portable transceiver or on the back of a fixed or mobile transceiver's microphone. Whatever equipment you use, the same autopatch operating procedures apply.

There are strict guidelines for autopatch use. The first question you should ask is "Is the call necessary?" If it is an emergency, there is no problem. Any other reason falls into a gray area. As a result, autopatch use, except for

Table 9-9

Common VHF/UHF FM Simplex Frequencies

2-Meter Band	1.25-Meter Band	70-cm Band
146.52*	223.42	446.0*
146.535	223.44	
146.55	223.46	**33-cm Band**
146.565	223.48	906.5*
146.58	223.50*	**23-cm Band**
146.595	223.52	1294.5*
147.42	223.54	
147.435	223.56	
147.45	223.58	
147.465	223.60	
147.48	223.62	
147.495	223.64	
147.51	223.66	
147.525	223.68	
147.54	223.70	
147.555	223.72	
147.57	223.74	
147.585	223.76	
	223.78	
	223.80	
	223.82	
	223.84	
	223.86	
	223.88	
	223.90	

*National Simplex Frequency

emergency situations, is expressly forbidden by some repeater groups.

Never use an autopatch where regular telephone service is available. A common example of poor operating practice can be heard most evenings in any metropolitan area. Some-

one will call home to announce departure from the office. Why not make that call from work before leaving?

Never use the autopatch for anything that could be considered business communications. The FCC strictly forbids any business communications in Amateur Radio. Don't use the autopatch to call the local radio store to find out if they have something you need in stock. Don't call to order a pizza. You may, however, call a business if the call is related to an emergency. Calling for an ambulance or a tow truck is okay.

Never use an autopatch to avoid a toll call. Autopatch operation is a privilege granted by the FCC. Abuses of autopatch privileges may lead to their loss.

You have a legitimate reason to use the autopatch? Here's how most systems are operated. First, you must access (turn on) the autopatch. This is usually done by pressing a designated key on the telephone tone pad. Ask the other hams on a repeater how to learn the access code. Many clubs provide this information only to club members. When you hear a dial tone, you know that you have successfully accessed the autopatch. Now, simply punch in the telephone number you wish to call.

Once a call is established, remember that you are still on the air. Unlike a normal telephone call, only one party at a time may speak. Both you and the other person should use the word "over" to indicate that you are finished talking and expect a reply. Keep the call short. Many repeaters shut off the autopatch after a certain time.

Turning off the autopatch is similar to accessing it. A key or combination of keys must be punched to return the repeater to normal operation. Ask the repeater group sponsoring the autopatch for specific information about access and turn-off codes, as well as timer specifics.

[Before you go on to the next section, turn to Chapter 12 and study the questions with numbers that begin 2B-6-1, 2B-6-2, 2B-6-3, 2B-6-4, and 2B-6-5. **If you are preparing for the Technician exam,** also study questions 3AB-2-1.2 through 3AB-2-2.1 in Chapter 13. Review this section if you have difficulty with any of these questions.]

━━━━━ INTERFERENCE AND SPLATTER ━━━━━

Chapter 10 covers various types of interference, and describes how to solve these problems. Voice modes require careful transmitter adjustment to produce the best signal quality. It's easy to avoid problems if you know what to do.

Most SSB transmitters and transceivers have a microphone gain control. This control may be on the front panel, or it may be inside the rig. Different microphones and different voices have different characteristics. You'll have to adjust the microphone gain control for your particular situation. Instructions for properly setting the mike gain are included in your instruction manual.

Most FM transceivers do not have a front-panel mike-gain control. The microphone gain control, sometimes called the deviation control, is preset. It requires no adjustment unless there is a problem.

Don't continuously adjust the mike gain. Set it according to the manual and leave it alone. Follow the manufacturer's instructions for use of the microphone. Some require close talking, while some need to be turned at an angle to the speaker's mouth. Always try to speak in an even amplitude, and at the same distance from the microphone. If you set the gain properly, you will minimize background room noise on your signal. You'll always hear one or two stations on the

band with their mike gain set so high that you hear people talking in the background, music playing, dogs barking and the like. This is not good practice.

If you operate with the microphone gain set too high, you will most likely cause **splatter**—interference to stations on nearby frequencies. This applies to FM voice operation as well as SSB operation. If you adjust the mike gain or deviation control on your FM rig too high, your signal will be too wide and will cause interference to stations on nearby frequencies. Your signal will *not* be easier for the station you're calling or working to hear, either. In fact, it will probably sound worse or be impossible to understand!

A **speech processor** (sometimes built into the transceiver or available as an accessory) is often a mixed blessing. It can give your audio more "punch" to help you cut through interference and noise. If you use too much processing however, your signal quality suffers greatly. You'll sometimes hear operators with their speech processor set so high that they are difficult to understand. That's exactly the opposite of what speech processing is supposed to do.

If you set the speech processing level too high, your signal will sound bad. It will also cause splatter and interfere with stations on nearby frequencies. Make tests to determine the maximum speech processing level that can be used effectively. Make a note of the control settings. Turn your speech processor control down or off if it is not required during a contact.

[It is time to turn to Chapter 12 and study a few more questions. You should be able to answer questions 2H-7.4, 2H-7.5 and 2H-7.6. If you have any difficulty, review this section.]

——RADIOTELETYPE AND PACKET COMMUNICATIONS——

Radioteletype, packet and AMTOR are terms used to describe amateur communications designed to be received and printed automatically. They are sometimes called *digital communications*, because they often involve direct transfer of information between computers. You type the information into your computer. The computer then (with the help of accessory equipment) processes the signal and sends it over the air from your transceiver. The station on the other end receives the signal, processes it and prints it out on a computer screen or printer. In this section, you will learn about two exciting forms of communication: **radioteletype (RTTY)** and **packet radio**.

EMISSION MODES

RTTY and packet communications are similar to CW. They both use two states to convey information. Instead of switching a carrier on and off as in CW operation, the carrier is left on continuously and switched between two different frequencies. The transmitter carrier frequency "shifts" between two frequencies, called MARK and SPACE. MARK is the ON state; SPACE is the OFF state. This is called **frequency-shift keying (FSK)**. The FCC emission designator used to describe FSK is **F1B**. On 10-meter RTTY, the MARK and SPACE frequencies are normally 170 Hz apart. This is known as 170-Hz-shift RTTY.

On VHF, **audio-frequency shift keying (AFSK,** or emission type **F2B)** is used. AFSK is similar to FSK, except that an FM transmitter is used. Audio tones corresponding to MARK and SPACE are fed into the microphone jack and used to modulate the carrier. The most common VHF shift is 170 Hz, but you may hear 850-Hz shift as well.

[Now turn to Chapter 12 and study questions 2H-1-2.1 and 2H-1-2.2. Review this section if you have any difficulty with these questions.]

SENDING SPEEDS

Just as you can send CW at a variety of speeds, RTTY and packet transmissions are sent at a variety of speeds. The signaling speed depends on the type of transmission and on the frequency band in use. A **baud** is the unit used to describe transmission speeds for digital signals.

For a single-channel transmission, a baud is equivalent to one digital bit of information transmitted per second. A 300-baud signaling rate represents a transmission rate of 300 bits of digital information per second in a single-channel transmission. A digital bit of information has two possible conditions, ON or OFF. We often represent a bit with a 1 for ON or a 0 for OFF. The MARK and SPACE tones of a radioteletype signal also represent the two possible bit conditions.

On HF, we use signaling rates of up to 300 bauds. Sending speeds on VHF are generally faster than on HF. A common VHF sending speed is 1200 bauds. The most important thing to remember about sending speeds is that both stations use the same speed during a contact.

——RTTY COMMUNICATIONS——

Radioteletype (RTTY) is a popular form of communications. Novices can operate RTTY on 10 meters; Novices and Technicians can operate RTTY on the 222-MHz and 1270-MHz bands. On 10 meters, Novice RTTY operation is allowed from 28.1 to 28.3 MHz. On 222 and 1270 MHz, you are allowed to operate RTTY on all of the frequencies that the FCC authorizes you to operate on. You should, however, follow the band plans as described earlier. On VHF, most RTTY activity is on repeaters. Check with local amateurs to find out where the 222-MHz RTTY activity is in your area.

This section will tell you about three popular types of RTTY: **Baudot, AMTOR** and **ASCII**. Baudot and AMTOR are the most popular RTTY modes on HF. Until recently, high-speed ASCII was most often heard on VHF, but this mode has been almost completely replaced by packet radio.

BAUDOT RADIOTELETYPE

Radioteletype communication using the **Baudot** code (also known as the International Telegraph Alphabet number 2, or ITA2) is widely used on the Amateur Radio HF bands in most areas of the world.

The Baudot code represents each character with a string of five bits of digital information. Each character has a different combination of bits. There are only 32 possible Baudot code combinations. This limits the number of possible characters. All text is in upper-case characters. To provide numbers and punctuations, you shift between the letters case (LTRS) and the figures case (FIGS).

There are three common speeds for 10-meter Baudot RTTY communications: 60 WPM (45 bauds), 75 WPM (56 bauds) and 100 WPM (75 bauds). You'll often hear 60, 75 and 100 WPM RTTY referred to as "60 speed," "75 speed," and "100 speed," respectively. Both stations must use the same sending speed to make a RTTY contact.

Setting Up

To set up a RTTY station using Baudot, the first thing you will need is a mechanical teleprinter or a computer-based RTTY terminal. Most radioteletype operators are now using computer-based **communications terminals**. One popular way of gearing up for radioteletype is to use a communications terminal designed specifically for amateur RTTY service. See

Figure 9-6—This Tono EXL-5000E is a complete RTTY communications terminal. It sends and receives CW, Baudot, ASCII and AMTOR, and has its own keyboard and display screen.

Figure 9-8—A full-feature RTTY modem, the Tono Theta-7777 has an LED bar-graph tuning indicator to help you tune in stations you're trying to contact. It is used between a computer or ASCII terminal and transceiver.

Figure 9-6. Such units are manufactured by Hal Communications, Microlog and Tono.

Another popular way of getting on RTTY is to use a personal computer, such as those manufactured by Commodore®, Apple® or IBM®, along with appropriate software. Such a system is shown in Figure 9-7. If you use a personal computer, you will also need an external **modem** (a contraction of *mo*dulator-*dem*odulator, also called a "terminal unit" or "TU"). See Figure 9-8. (Dedicated RTTY terminals usually have built-in modems.) A modem takes information from your computer and modulates the transmitted radio signal. It also demodulates the received signal. In choosing a modem or a complete RTTY system with a built-in modem, look for versatility. Look for a modem with shift capabilities of 170 and 850 Hz. Check the *QST* Product Review column, and articles and ads in *QST* and other amateur magazines for information about these products.

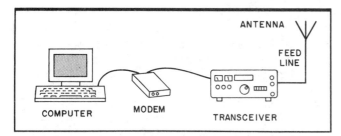

Figure 9-7—A RTTY modem connects between your transceiver and your computer.

What about a rig for RTTY? You can use almost any HF transceiver. Ideally, the receiver used for 170-Hz-shift RTTY should have the minimum practical bandwidth, preferably between 270 and 340 Hz. Many CW filters have bandwidths around 500 Hz and are good for 170-Hz RTTY reception. Many receivers (and transceivers) can use the SSB filter only in the SSB or RTTY modes. Some RTTY operators have modified their receivers to use the CW filter when the RTTY mode is selected. A switch can be added so it is possible to select the CW filter with the mode switch set for SSB opera-

tion. A transceiver with a frequency display of 10-Hz resolution is also helpful, although not a necessity.

Many modern transceivers include an FSK mode. If yours does not, you can operate RTTY with the transceiver in the SSB mode. It is normal to use the lower-sideband mode for RTTY on HF SSB radio equipment. Most transceivers have two positions on the sideband-selection knob, labeled NORMAL and REVERSE. This labeling may cause some uncertainty when you use the rig for RTTY. On 10 meters, normal SSB operation uses upper sideband, so you will have to set the switch to the REVERSE position to select the lower sideband for 10-meter RTTY.

If you are not using the correct sideband, your signal is "upside down," and other operators will have to change their normal operating setup to copy your signals. Be sure you select the lower sideband and transmit signals that are "right-side up." Consult your radio's manual for details.

On VHF, the most common practice is to use AFSK. Since most VHF RTTY work is done on local FM repeaters, almost any FM transceiver will work.

Your transmitter must be able to operate at full power for extended periods (*called 100% duty cycle*) when transmitting conventional Baudot and ASCII radioteletype, as well as AMTOR Mode B. Some transceivers, designed for SSB and CW operation (which do not require constant transmission at full power), may overheat and possibly fail if subjected to a long RTTY transmission. Many operators reduce to half power during long RTTY transmissions to avoid overheating problems. AMTOR Mode A transmits data in shorter blocks and does not require constant transmission at full power.

Receiver-tuning accuracy is important. Thus, a tuning aid can be a great help in proper receiver adjustment. Most modems have some type of tuning indicator, possibly just flashing LEDs. Some have oscilloscopes that produce patterns such as those shown in Figure 9-9. The MARK signal is dis-

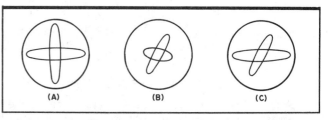

Figure 9-9—Oscilloscope RTTY tuning patterns. A shows the pattern produced by a properly tuned signal. The displays at B and C indicate improperly tuned signals.

RTTY EQUIPMENT

Years ago, all RTTY operation was done with mechanical teleprinters. You may still see some of these machines in old movies—they are big, slow and *noisy*. Today, most amateurs use a computer-based communications terminal for RTTY operation. The *communications terminal* (sometimes called a "terminal unit" or "interface") connects between a transceiver and a computer and decodes the RTTY signals for display by the computer. Most communications terminals will send and receive CW and RTTY (Baudot and ASCII). Some terminals also send and receive AMTOR, and some add packet-radio operation for "all-mode" operation.

When you shop for a communications terminal, there are a few things to keep in mind. Some terminals are computer-specific—they are designed to work with only one type of computer. Some terminals require additional software in the computer, and others require only a

simple terminal program. As always, the best way to find out about a particular unit is to ask someone who has one. The next best way is to read the product review columns in *QST* and the other ham magazines. The following list is a representative sample of what is available today. Some older used units may be available at hamfests and flea markets. If you plan to buy a used communications terminal, try to take an experienced RTTY operator along to the hamfest with you. Remember, most hams love to talk about their favorite operating mode—ask around at your local club.

The trend in RTTY equipment today is toward the "all-mode" communications terminal. The MFJ-1278 (above) and AEA PK-232 (left) provide CW, Baudot, ASCII, AMTOR, fax and packet-radio capability. They are used with any of a number of popular personal computers.

RTTY Communications Terminals

Manufacturer	Model Number	Modes	Product Review
AEA	PK-232	CW, Baudot, ASCII, AMTOR, packet	January 1988 *QST*
AEA	PK-64†	CW, Baudot, ASCII, AMTOR, packet	June 1986 *QST*
Heath	HD3030	CW, Baudot, ASCII	February 1985 *QST**
Kantronics	UTU	CW, Baudot, ASCII, AMTOR	*
Kantronics	UTU-XT/P	CW, Baudot, ASCII, AMTOR, packet	*
Kantronics	KAM	CW, Baudot, ASCII, AMTOR, packet	June 1989 *QST*
MFJ	MFJ-1224	CW, Baudot, ASCII	*
MFJ	MFJ-1278	CW, Baudot, ASCII, AMTOR	September 1989 *QST*
Tono	EXL-5000E‡	CW, Baudot, ASCII, AMTOR	July 1985 *QST*
Tono	Θ-777	CW, Baudot, ASCII, AMTOR	April 1987 *QST*

†For use with the Commodore 64 or 128 only
‡Includes display screen and keyboard. No computer needed.
*Equipment discontinued.

played as a horizontal line and the SPACE signal as a vertical line. Theoretically this should appear as a " + " sign on the 'scope screen, but in practice it may look more like a pair of crossed bananas! To avoid the high cost of an oscilloscope, some manufacturers offer LED displays that imitate the 'scope display.

Typing the Message

No one can disagree that touch typing (typing without looking at the keys) is the best way to go. But, you can have enjoyable contacts even if you can only type with two fingers! It is a good practice to keep the number of characters per line to a maximum of 69. That line length can be handled by virtually any teleprinter designed for Baudot. Many US teleprinters will print 72 or 74 characters, but some foreign printers take only 69. Computer screens and printers vary

widely and may have 22 (Commodore VIC 20™), 32 (Sinclair ZX81), 40 (Apple II® and Commodore 64™), or 80 (IBM PC® and compatibles).

After a mistake, the "oops" signal is XXXXX (some operators may use EEEEEE). There is no need to overdo this, though, because generally the other operator will figure out what you meant to say anyway, and a page filled with XXXXX can be confusing.

Station Identification

When you are transmitting RTTY, simply send your call sign at least once every 10 minutes, just as you would on any other mode. FCC rules permit a station engaged in digital communications using Baudot, AMTOR or ASCII to identify in the digital code used for the communication. On the Novice 222- and 1270-MHz bands, identification may be given using one of the methods just mentioned or by voice. (Radio-telephone operation is permitted on the same frequency being used for the RTTY communication on these bands.) Identifying the station you are communicating with, in addition to your own station, is not legally required, but it will help those monitoring your QSO to determine band conditions.

Test Messages

A message consisting of repetitive RYs is useful for local and on-the-air testing of Baudot RTTY equipment:

RYRYRYRYRYRYRYRYRYRYRYRYRYRY DE W1AW

The use of the RY sequence goes back to the early Teletype® machine days. To set the mechanical machines, it was necessary to send a string of Rs and Ys while the receiving operator adjusted a knob called the "rangefinder." The military and commercial services also used RYRYRYRYRY as a channel-holding signal during idle periods. The letters R and Y both alternate between MARK and SPACE tones in the Baudot code, so it was natural to use these letters for the range-setting operation. (If we represent the SPACE tone with a 0 and the MARK tone with a 1, then R is 01010 and Y is 10101. So you can see that a string of RY characters sends alternating SPACE and MARK tones.)

Use the RY sequence sparingly. RYs have a musical sound that is easily recognizable, and is useful for tuning a signal in properly. This makes it good for rousing attention when you are sending a CQ call, or when calling another station on schedule, but it is unnecessary during routine contacts. Don't use RY when you are working DX.

Making Contact

There are two ways of establishing contact with other amateur stations using radioteletype. You can answer someone else's call, or you can try calling CQ yourself. When you call CQ, you depend on someone else to tune your signal properly, and if you are a newcomer to the mode, that may be an advantage. By listening for other calls, you have a good chance of finding stations that you might not contact otherwise. You will want to use both methods at various times, but whichever one you choose, learn the proper procedure and follow it.

CALLING CQ

Since it is a little easier to explain, we will start by describing the procedure for calling CQ on RTTY. You must first locate a clear frequency on which to make your call. Courtesy should be the rule. Ask if the frequency is busy by sending QRL?, or by asking in clear text. There may be a QSO on frequency, but you may not hear both sides of it.

The general CQ call, like RY, has a recognizable, musical sound. Take advantage of this fact, and send CQ in a pattern something like this:

CQ CQ CQ CQ CQ DE W1HDQ W1HDQ W1HDQ K

Transmit "CQ" three to six times, followed by "DE," followed by your call sign three times. Many operators add their name and QTH to the last line of the CQ call. This is a good idea, but keep it simple and short. As on voice, several short calls with pauses to listen are much better than one long call.

CALLING ANOTHER STATION

You have just heard 9H1EL in Malta calling CQ. He is

booming in with an S9 signal, and this would be a new country for you. Make sure that he is tuned in properly, wait until he stops calling CQ and give him a call. Keep your calls short. Forget the RYs. Send 9H1EL's call sign only once, and your call sign no more than five times:

9H1EL DE KA1ION KA1ION KA1ION K

Then stand by and listen. If he doesn't answer, try another short call.

Line Feeds and Other Things

When another station answers your call, gives you a report and then turns it back to you, what should you do? Always send a line feed (L/F) and a carriage return (C/R) first. This will put his computer and/or printer into the "letters" mode, and will eliminate the possibility of part of your message being garbled by numbers and/or punctuation marks.

Next, send his call and your call once each. On your first exchange, send your name and QTH message from the computer memory, if your system has such a message. If you have a type-ahead buffer on your system, you can compose some of your reply before it is actually transmitted. This saves time, especially if you are not a fast typist.

If you give another station a signal report of RST 599, it means you're copying solid. If you receive a similar report, it is unnecessary to repeat everything twice. Give honest reports—if the copy is solid, then the readability report is five. Adapt your operating technique to the reported conditions. If copy is marginal, repeats or extra spaces are in order. But with solid copy, you can zip right along.

Don't send a string of carriage returns to clear the screen. The other operator may be copying on a printer, and the carriage returns will waste a lot of paper. The last two characters of each transmission should be carriage returns, however.

Signing Off

You have now completed your QSO and are about to sign off. What prosign do you use? Well, the standard prosigns mean the same thing on RTTY as they do on CW, and should be adequate. Table 9-10 summarizes the meaning of the most commonly used prosigns.

Table 9-10

Common Prosigns Used On RTTY

K—Invitation to transmit.
KN—Invitation to the addressed station only to transmit.
SK—Signing off. End of contact.
CL or CLEAR—I am shutting my station down.
SK QRZ—Signing off and listening on this frequency for any other calls. The idea is to indicate which station is remaining on the frequency.

Some operators use various other combinations of prosigns:

SK KN—Signing off, but listening for one last transmission from the other station.
SK SZ—Signing off and listening on this frequency for any other calls.

[It is time to turn to Chapter 12 again, to study some questions. You should be able to answer questions 2B-4-1.1 and 2B-4-2.1. Review this section if you have any difficulty.]

AMTOR OPERATION

Amateur Teleprinting Over Radio (AMTOR) is a more reliable transmission system than Baudot RTTY. AMTOR has the ability to detect errors, so you can be assured of getting perfect copy throughout the QSO. In many respects, AMTOR operation is the same as for Baudot RTTY. AMTOR characters are commonly sent at 100 bauds, and 170-Hz is the normal shift.

AMTOR Modes

There are several modes of AMTOR operation: **Automatic Repeat reQuest (ARQ)** or Mode A, and **Forward Error Correction (FEC)** or Mode B. Mode B is further subdivided into Collective B-Mode and Selective B-Mode. Amateurs have added Mode L for monitoring AMTOR transmissions.

Stations in contact using AMTOR are classified either as Information Sending Stations (ISS) or Information Receiving Stations (IRS). The stations change identities as information is exchanged during a QSO. The station that originates the communication is also called the master station and the other station is called the slave station. The master/slave relationship does not change during the contact.

Mode A

Mode A is a synchronous system in which the ISS transmits blocks of three characters to the IRS. The ISS sends the block, listens for replies from the IRS, then sends three more characters. The transmitting and listening times are less than a quarter of a second, so your transceiver must be able to change from transmit to receive very quickly. The ISS keeps the three characters in memory until it gets a receipt from the IRS. When the IRS acknowledges, the ISS moves on to the next three characters. If the IRS does not acknowledge, the ISS keeps sending the three characters until they are acknowledged. AMTOR keeps trying until it gets it right!

Mode A is used only for contacts between two stations. It should not be used for calling CQ or in nets. This mode has a characteristic "chirp" sound on the air. It has a 47% duty cycle, allowing transmitters to operate at full power output without worry about overheating. Mode L is used by stations to monitor, or listen to, Mode A contacts.

Collective B-Mode

Collective B-Mode is basically a "broadcast" mode, although most hams don't use that word because FCC rules say that we are not allowed to "broadcast" in the entertainment sense of the word. In this mode, there is only one sending station, called the Collective B Sending station (CBSS) and any number of Collective B Receiving Stations (CBRSs). The CBSS sends each character twice: the first transmission of a character, called DX, is followed by four other characters, and then the repetition, called RX, is sent.

This is the mode that W1AW uses for bulletins and the one that should be used for calling CQ, for nets and for making multi-way contacts. It has a 100% duty cycle, so you may have to reduce your transmitter power output as explained before.

Selective B-Mode

Selective B-Mode is intended for transmissions to a single station or group of stations. It is similar to collective B-Mode. Only stations set up to accept this mode and recognize the specific selective-call identifier are intended to receive Selective B-Mode transmissions.

AMTOR Selective-Calling Identities

AMTOR is designed so that four-letter identities are used as the **selective-call identifier** (similar to a call sign). Amateurs can't simply use their call signs as their AMTOR selective-call identifier because amateur call signs consist of letters and numerals. Most AMTOR stations use the first letter and the last three letters of their call sign for the selective-call identifier. Using this algorithm, the selective-call identifier for W1AW would be WWAW. This scheme doesn't provide unique selective-call identifiers for every call sign (for example, WWAW would also be used for W2AW, W2WAW and others), so be aware that someone may ask you to choose another selective-call identifier if yours is already in use.

A recent version of AMTOR does permit numbers and up to six characters for the selective-call identifier. Not all AMTOR stations use this version, however, so you should start out by using a four-character selcall.

Making Contact on AMTOR

If you try to make your first contact using Mode A (ARQ) and there is a problem somewhere in the system, you will not make contact. It takes a two-way contact to make Mode A work at all.

Try your first contact using Collective B-Mode. Use this mode for calling CQ, and include your selective-call identifier. Use of Mode B should ensure that you can get the circuit working one way. In Mode B, you can check to confirm that you are using the correct frequency-shift polarity for both receiving and transmitting.

After making contact using Mode B, ask the other station to go into the monitor (listen) mode and try to receive your Mode A transmission. If there is a problem with Mode A, the most likely cause is that your transceiver is taking too long to change between receive and transmit. If that's the case, check with other AMTOR operators having the same equipment setup. If you are using commercial AMTOR gear, the manufacturer will probably know which transceivers will switch fast enough and which require specific modification.

If the other station (in monitor mode) is copying your Mode-A transmission, ask the station to make a Mode-A call to your selective-call identifier. The other station is acting as the master and your station the slave in this case. Finally, reverse the roles and try being the master station.

Because of the timing cycle specified in the AMTOR standards, it is not practical to contact AMTOR stations on the opposite side of the earth using Mode A. Mode B can be used for communication with stations too distant for Mode-A contacts.

ASCII OPERATION

ASCII (pronounced "askee") stands for **American National Standard Code for Information Interchange**. ASCII operation differs from Baudot RTTY operation in that it has a larger character set than ITA2. This is possible because ACSII characters consist of 7 digital information bits. Besides a number of control characters, ASCII also provides both upper- and lower-case letters and a more complete set of punctuation marks. ASCII is a character set that was designed for computer and data communications uses. For more information about the complete ASCII coded character set, and for the technical details about methods and transmission rates used for the ASCII code, see the latest *ARRL Handbook*.

HF ASCII transmissions are normally sent at 110 or 300 bauds, using 170-Hz shift. Higher data rates are used on higher frequency bands. On 10 meters, the maximum permitted speed is 1200 bauds, while up to 19,600 bauds is permitted on 222 MHz and above. On VHF and UHF, 1200 bauds is the most common RTTY sending speed.

COMPUTER-BASED MESSAGE SYSTEMS

No discussion of modern radioteletype operation could be complete without some information about mailbox operation. A number of **Computer-Based Message Systems (CBMSs)** are operating on the ham bands. You may hear them called one of these terms: MSO (Message Storage Operation), bulletin board or mailbox.

All of these systems have some features in common. They will automatically respond to calls on their operating frequency if the calling station uses the correct character sequence. You can send messages to be stored in the mailbox and retrieved later by another amateur. You may also request a listing of the messages on file and read any addressed to you, as well as any bulletin messages intended for general consumption. Some systems may allow messages to have password protection to restrict access to the information.

Message handling in this manner is third-party traffic, and the system operator (SYSOP) is required to observe appropriate rules concerning message content. Also the SYSOP is responsible for maintaining control of the transmitter and removing it from the air in the event of malfunction.

─── PACKET RADIO ───

Packet radio is communications for the computer age. A computer in a ham shack is as common as a 2-meter handheld transceiver was 20 years ago. Computer programs allowed computers to send and receive CW and RTTY. Some farsighted hams, however, developed a new amateur mode of communications that unleashes the power of the computer. That mode is packet radio.

Being a child of the computer age, packet radio has the computer-age features that you would expect.

• It is data communications; high speed and error-free packet-radio communications lends itself to the transfer of large amounts of data.

• It is fast, much faster than the highest speed CW or RTTY.

• It is error-free; no "hits" or "misses" caused by propagation variations or electrical interference.

• It is spectrum efficient; several stations can share one frequency at the same time.

• It is networking; packet stations can be linked together to send messages over long distances.

• It is message storage; packet-radio bulletin boards (PBBS) provide storage of messages for later retrieval.

So, the many hams with computers in their shacks are naturally attracted to packet radio. Now, they are able to unleash the power of their machines.

HOW DOES PACKET WORK?

Packet radio uses a **terminal node controller (TNC)** as the interface between computer and transceiver. A TNC is an enhanced modem. We discussed what a modem is and what it does in the section on RTTY. The TNC accepts information from your computer or ASCII terminal and breaks the data into small pieces called *packets*. In addition to the information from your computer, each packet contains addressing, error-checking and control information. The addressing information includes the call sign of the station that sent the packet, and the call sign of the station the packet is being sent to. The address may also include call signs of stations that are being used to relay the packet. The error-checking information allows the receiving station to determine whether the received packet contains any errors. If the received packet contains errors, the receiving station asks for a repeat transmission until the packet is received error-free.

Breaking up the data into small parts allows several users to share the channel. Packets from one user are transmitted in the spaces between packets from other users. The address section allows each user's TNC to separate packets intended for him from packets intended for other users. The addresses also allow packets to be relayed through several stations before they reach their ultimate destination. Having information in the packet that tells the receiving station if the packet has been received correctly assures perfect copy.

WHAT DO I NEED TO GET ON PACKET RADIO?

All you need to set up a VHF packet-radio station is a VHF or UHF FM transceiver (with an antenna), a computer or ASCII terminal and a TNC. The TNC connects between the radio and the computer, as shown in Figure 9-10. For operation on 10 meters you'll need a 10-meter SSB transceiver in addition to the TNC and computer. The sidebar entitled "Packet Radio Equipment" list some available equipment.

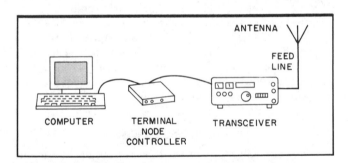

Figure 9-10—A terminal node controller connects between your transceiver and your computer, like a RTTY modem.

Your TNC manual should contain detailed instructions for wiring the TNC, radio and computer together. So many hams are on packet now that someone in the local radio club will probably be able to help you if you have problems, or ask around on the local voice repeater.

WHAT DOES IT LOOK LIKE?

So far we've talked about the equipment you need and how packet works. But what does a packet contact look like? In the following examples, we'll look at the procedures used by most of the TNCs on the market today. Some TNCs may use different command formats—consult your operating manual if you're not sure.

First, you must tell the TNC your call sign. Most TNCs allow you to change your call sign at any time and have a way to remember it when the power is switched off. Before you can enter commands into the TNC, it must be in com-

```
W1AW-4>K1CE:You have new mail, please kill after reading:
W1AW-4>K1CE:Msg# TR  Size  To      From   @ BBS  Date      Title
W1AW-4>K1CE:5807  N    420 K1CE     K1MON  W1AW     870308 HI AGAIN
W1AW-4>K1CE:K1CE de W1AW: at 2101z on 870308, 142 active msgs, last msg #5839
W1AW-4>K1CE:(A,B,D,H,I,J,K,L,R,S,T,U,W,X) >
W1AW-4>K1CE:Enter title for message:
W1AW-4>K1CE:Enter message, ^Z (CTL-Z) to end, it will be message 5840
WA3VIL>KA1MJP:Hi Leslie, are you going to the club meeting? KK
W1AW-4>K1CE:K1CE de W1AW: at 2101z on 870308, 143 active msgs, last msg #5840
W1AW-4>K1CE:(A,B,D,H,I,J,K,L,R,S,T,U,W,X) >
W1AW-4>KE3Z:Max. path length: 2 digis
W1AW-4>KE3Z:KE3Z de W1AW: at 2123z on 870308, 143 active msgs, last msg #5840
KA1MJP>WA3VIL:No, Larry, I have too much work. I have to go
W1AW-4>KE3Z:(A,B,D,H,I,J,K,L,R,S,T,U,W,X) >
W1AW-4>KE3Z:Enter title for message:
KA1MJP>WA3VIL:back in tonight. Maybe next month. KK
W1AW-4>KE3Z:Enter message, ^Z (CTL-Z) to end, it will be message 5841
```

Figure 9-11—In monitor mode, your TNC displays all the packet activity on the frequency, whether or not the packets are addressed to your station.

mand mode. When the TNC is in command mode, you will see a prompt:

cmd:

This indicates that the TNC is waiting for input. To tell the TNC her call sign, KA1MJP types:

MYCALL KA1MJP <CR>

<CR> means "carriage return." On some computers this key may be labeled "ENTER" or have an arrow (←).

As in all other modes of Amateur Radio, packet allows you to "read the mail" or monitor channel activity. This is called the **monitor mode**, and looks like this:

WA6JPR>WB6YMH: HELLO SKIP, WHEN IS THE NEXT OSCAR 10 PASS? K

WB6YMH>WA6JPR: HANG ON WALLY, I'LL TAKE A LOOK.

To enable monitor mode, simply type: MON ON at the cmd: prompt. You may also need to type MFROM ALL. Consult the operating manual for your TNC to be sure. The call signs of the stations involved appear as "FROM>TO" and the contents of the packet appear after the ":". In the monitor mode, your computer will display everything that is transmitted on the packet frequency, whether or not it is addressed to you (see Figure 9-11).

You can send a CQ by entering the converse mode of the TNC. You go to converse mode by typing:

CONV <CR>

(some TNCs allow you to type K instead of CONV)

You can then type your CQ:

MIKE IN SAN DIEGO LOOKING FOR ANYONE IN SIMI VALLEY

Your TNC adds your call sign as the FROM address and CQ as the TO address. The receiving station's TNC adds these addresses to the front of the text when it is displayed.

MAKING A CONNECTION

You answer a CQ or establish a contact by using the CONNECT command. When two packet stations are **connected**, each station sends packets specifically addressed to the other station. When a station receives an error-free packet, it transmits an acknowledgment packet to let the sender know the packet has been received correctly.

To connect to another station, you type:

Connect WA1UQC <CR>

where WA1UQC is the call sign of the station you wish to contact. (Most TNCs let you use C as an abbreviation for "connect.")

If WA1UQC's packet-radio station is on the air and receives your connect request, your station and his will ex-

PACKET RADIO EQUIPMENT
Terminal Node Controllers

There are many terminal node controllers available today, and new models are appearing almost daily. The following list is by no means complete, but it is a sample of what is available new and used. For more details on the TNCs mentioned here (and others), see "The Shopper's Guide to Packet-Radio TNCs" in March 1987 *QST* and *Your Gateway to Packet Radio,* published by ARRL.

TNC 1 or TNC 2?

Most of the TNCs on the market today can trace their roots to two designs by the Tucson Amateur Packet Radio Corporation (TAPR). The TAPR TNC 1 was released in 1981, and thousands of TNC 1 kits were built by amateurs. The TNC 1 does not provide such features as multiple connections and full-function monitoring that the TNC 2 provides.

The TAPR TNC 2 was the next logical step after the TNC 1. It is physically smaller than the TNC 1 and consumes less power. The command set of the TNC 2 was expanded to provide better monitoring features and other enhancements. The TNC 2 was supplied (in a limited production run) as a well-documented kit. TAPR then licensed manufacturers to build TNC 2 "clones" and returned to the research and development business.

TNC 2 Compatibles

AEA PK-80. This preassembled version of the TNC 2 has beefed-up circuitry to suppress RFI. Its power requirements are relatively high—12 to 15 V dc at 400 mA. Otherwise it is identical to the TNC 2.

Kantronics KPC-2. The KPC-2 is similar to the original Kantronics Packet Communicator. In addition to the standard RS-232-C serial port, it has a TTL interface (for computers like the Commodore C64™). Serial-port and radio-port data rates are software selectable.

MFJ-1270. This unit is preassembled and it provides a TTL interface (for Commodore 64 compatibility), as well as the standard RS-232-C serial port. Cosmetically it is very different from the other TNC 2 work-alikes, but it is functionally the same. (See the Product Review in September 1986 *QST*.)

The AEA-PKT-1 was the first commercial TAPR TNC 1 compatible.

The MFJ 1270 is a popular and inexpensive TAPR TNC 2 clone.

Pac-Comm TNC-200. Another TNC 2 clone, the TNC-200 is available as either a kit or an assembled and tested unit. Other than cosmetic differences, Pac-Comm's versions of the TNC 2 are the same as the original.

GLB Electronics PK2. This TNC is compatible with both the TNC 2 and the unique GLB user interfaces. GLB's plug-in modem provides software-selectable HF and VHF operation.

Computer-Specific TNCs and Multimode Communications Terminals

AEA PK-64. The PAKRATT™ Model PK-64 provides the Commodore 64 and 128 computers with packet-radio capability; in addition Morse, RTTY (Baudot and ASCII) and AMTOR operation are possible. The PK-64 plugs into

---

change packets to set up a connection. When the connection is completed, your terminal displays:

    *** CONNECTED to WA1UQC

and your TNC automatically switches to the converse mode.

Now, everything you type into the terminal keyboard is sent to the other station. A packet is sent whenever you enter a carriage return. It's a good idea to use K, BK, O or > at the end of a thought to say "Okay, I'm done. It's your turn to transmit."

When you are finished conversing with the other station, return to the command mode by typing <CTRL-C> (hold down the CONTROL key and press the C key). When the command prompt (cmd:) is displayed, type:

    Disconne <CR>

and your station will exchange packets with the other station to break the connection. (Most TNCs let you use "D" as an abbreviation.) When the connection is broken, your terminal displays:

    *** DISCONNECTED

If, for some reason, the other station does not respond to your initial connect request, your TNC will resend the request until the number of attempts equals the internal retry counter. When the number of attempts exceeds the retry counter, your TNC will stop sending connect requests and your terminal displays:

    *** retry count exceeded
    *** DISCONNECTED

A TNC can reject a connect request if it is busy or if the operator has set CONOK (short for CONnect OK) off. If this happens when you try to connect, your TNC displays:

    *** WA1UQC busy
    *** DISCONNECTED

PACKET RADIO REPEATING

Sometimes terrain or propagation prevent your signal from being received by the other station. Packet radio gets around this problem by using other packet-radio stations to relay your signal to the intended station. All you need to know is which on-the-air packet-radio stations can relay signals be-

The Kantronics KPC-2 features built-in HF and VHF modems.

The GLB TNC2A is available as a kit or assembled and tested.

the user port of a C64 or C128. (See Product Review, *QST*, June 1986. This unit has been discontinued but used PK-64s are available.)

AEA PK-232. The PAKRATT Model PK-232 provides Morse, Baudot, ASCII, AMTOR and packet-radio capability for any computer equipped with an RS-232-C serial port. The unit is preassembled and includes internal modems for HF (200 Hz frequency shift) and VHF operation. (See the Product Review in January 1988 *QST*.)

Kantronics KAM™. The "Kantronics All Mode" does just that—Morse, Baudot, ASCII, AMTOR and packet radio. It may be connected to any computer or terminal with a standard RS-232-C serial port or simultaneous TTL interface. Two radio ports are included for HF and VHF operation. (See the Product Review in June 1989 *QST*.)

MFJ 1278. MFJ's latest all-mode data controller unit features Packet, Morse, Baudot, ASCII, AMTOR, SSTV and fax capability. TTL and RS-232 ports are standard. (See the Product Review in July and September 1989 *QST*.)

RADIOS FOR PACKET OPERATION

VHF

Just about any VHF FM transceiver can be used on VHF packet. Even a small hand-held transceiver can be used, although an outside antenna is a good idea. If there is very little packet activity in your area, you may need a bit more power to reach the nearest dedicated digipeater. Many manufacturers sell amplifiers that increase the power from a hand-held transceiver to 10 or 25 watts. Most mobile FM transceivers are rated at 10 to 25 watts, and these radios make great packet rigs.

Older crystal-controlled transceivers may be used on packet, but a few words of caution are in order. Many older rigs cannot switch from receive to transmit quickly enough for packet operation. Most TNCs have an adjustable "transmit delay" that causes the TNC to key the radio and then wait a second or so before actually sending the packet. Older radios may require this transmit delay. In addition, an older rig may have passed through the hands of several amateurs, and some of the internal settings may have been "adjusted." While this

may not be a problem when you use the rig for voice communications, the rig may not work on packet. If you plan to use an older rig on packet, try to locate an experienced packet operator who can help you set up your packet station.

HF

Most SSB transceivers will work on HF packet. Again, your transceiver may require a bit of transmit delay from the TNC. Your TNC manual should cover wiring and operation guidelines in detail. On HF, packet operation uses lower sideband.

Antennas

Since many packet stations are put on the air by amateurs who have already been active on VHF FM, the same antennas are often used for both modes. As a result, vertically polarized antennas are the standard for VHF packet. Yagi antennas are usually not required, unless there is *very* little packet activity in your area or you have a particularly bad location. See the VHF FM section of this chapter for more antenna information.

---

tween your station and the station you want to contact. Once you know of a station that can relay your signals, type:

Connect WA1UQC via W1AW-5 <CR>

where WA1UQC is the call sign of the station you want to connect to and W1AW-5 is the call sign of the station that will relay your packets. The "-5" following W1AW is a **secondary station identifier (SSID)**. The SSID permits up to 16 packet stations to operate with one call sign. For example, W1AW-5 is a 2-meter packet repeater and W1AW-6 is a 222-MHz packet repeater.

When W1AW-5 receives your connect request, it stores your request in memory until the frequency is quiet. It then retransmits your request to WA1UQC on the same frequency. This action is called digipeating, a contraction of "digital repeating." If WA1UQC's packet-radio station is on the air and receives the relayed connect request, your station and his will exchange packets through W1AW-5 to set up a connection. Once the connection is established, your terminal will display:

*** CONNECTED to WA1UQC via W1AW-5

W1AW-5 will continue to relay your packets until the connection is broken (see Figure 9-12).

Digital and voice repeaters both repeat, but the similarity ends there. Notice that digital repeaters differ from typical voice repeaters in a number of ways. A digital repeater **(digipeater)** usually receives and transmits on the same frequency (whereas a voice repeater receives and transmits on different frequencies). A digipeater does not receive and transmit at the same time (as compared to a voice repeater, which immediately transmits whatever it receives). Rather, a digipeater receives a packet, stores it temporarily until the frequency is clear, and then retransmits the packet. Also, a digipeater only repeats packets that are specifically sent to be repeated by that station (the address in the packet contains the call sign of the digipeater). A voice repeater repeats everything that it receives on its input frequency.

If one digipeater is insufficient to establish a connection, you can specify as many as eight stations in your connect request. Additional digipeaters are added to the connect command separated by commas. For example, typing:

Connect WA1UQC via W1AW-5, WA2FTC-1 <CR>

```
cmd:c aa2z v wlaw-5
*** CONNECTED to AA2Z via W1AW-5
Hi Bruce, what's up? KK
hi Mark. Just wondering if we can bring the desk over tonight. KK
No problem. Got the room all set up and everything. What time
do you think you'll be here? KK
Well, that's up to Rick. Probably around 6 or so. KK
OK, see you then. SK
See you at 6.
cmd:D
*** DISCONNECTED
```

Figure 9-12—Two packet stations *connect* to have a QSO. Everything you type is sent to the other station. Packets not addressed to your station are ignored by your TNC.

after the command prompt (cmd:), causes your TNC to send the WA1UQC connect request to W1AW-5 which relays it to WA2FTC-1. Then, WA2FTC-1 relays it to WA1UQC.

Don't use more than one or two digipeaters at any one time, especially during the prime time operating hours (evenings and weekends). Each time you use a digipeater, you are competing with other stations attempting to use the same digipeater. Each station that you compete with has the potential of generating a packet that may collide with your packet (which causes your TNC to resend the packet). The more digipeaters you use, the more stations you compete with, greatly increasing the chance of a packet collision. As a result, it may be difficult to get one packet through multiple digipeaters, and your TNC will quickly reach its retry limit and disconnect the link.

Any packet-radio station can act as a digipeater. Most TNCs are set up to digipeat automatically without any intervention by the operator of the station being used as a digipeater. You do not need his permission, only his cooperation, because he can disable his station's digipeater function. (In the spirit of Amateur Radio, most packet-radio operators leave the digipeater function on, disabling it only under special circumstances.)

Similar to VHF/UHF voice repeaters, some stations are set up as dedicated digipeaters. They are usually set up in good radio locations by packet-radio clubs. Besides location, the other advantage of a dedicated digipeater is that it is always there (barring a calamity). Stations do not have to depend on the whims of other packet-radio operators, who may or may not be on the air when their stations' digipeater functions are most needed.

Although you are not allowed to be the control operator of a voice repeater until you upgrade from the Novice class, you *may* leave your TNC's digipeater function enabled. The FCC recognizes a distinction between digipeaters and voice repeaters in this case, and everyone realizes that an effective packet-radio system depends on having Novice digipeaters available.

Another form of digipeater is the *node*. To reach a distant station, first connect to the node. Then, instruct the node to connect you to the distant station. The node acknowledges packets sent from either station, then relays them to the other station. This has a number of advantages over a simple digipeater.

VHF/UHF PACKET OPERATING

Today, most amateur packet-radio activity occurs at VHF, on 2 meters, but activity on 222 MHz continues to grow. The most commonly used data rate on VHF is 1200 bauds,

with frequency-modulated AFSK tones of 1200 and 2200 Hz. This is referred to as the ''Bell 202'' telephone modem standard.

Getting on the air is usually a simple matter of turning on your radio and tuning to your favorite packet-radio frequency. On 2 meters, common packet channels are 145.01, 145.03, 145.05, 145.07 and 145.09 MHz. On 222 MHz, Novice packet activity centers on 223.4 MHz. If there is a voice repeater on that frequency in your area, ask around at a club meeting or on the repeater. Someone is bound to know where the packet activity is.

If you are conducting a direct connect (a contact without using a digipeater), move your contact to an unused simplex frequency. It is very inefficient to use a frequency where other stations, especially digipeater stations, are operating. The competition slows down your packets and, in return, you are also slowing down the other stations. You should use a frequency occupied by a digital repeater only if you are using that digital repeater. Consult the latest edition of *The ARRL Repeater Directory* for more information on recommended packet operating frequencies.

VHF/UHF packet-radio operation is similar to VHF/UHF FM voice operation. Under normal propagation conditions, you can communicate only with stations that are in line of sight of your station. By using a repeater (voice or digital), this limitation is reduced. If a repeater is within range of your station, you may communicate with other stations that are also within range of the same repeater, even though those stations may be beyond your own line of sight. Packet expands on this by permitting the simultaneous use of several digipeaters to relay a packet from one station within range of the first digipeater in the link to a station within radio coverage of the last digipeater in the chain.

HF PACKET OPERATING

HF packet radio is very different from VHF/UHF packet. An SSB transceiver is used to generate a 200-Hz-shift FSK signal, and 300 bauds is used rather than 1200 bauds.

Tuning is much more critical than it is on VHF. Tune your receiver very slowly, in as small an increment as possible (10-Hz increments are good) until your terminal begins displaying packets. Do not change frequency until a whole packet is received. If you shift frequency in midpacket, that packet will not be received properly and will not be displayed on your terminal even if you were on the correct frequency before or after the frequency shift.

Some TNCs and external modems have tuning indicators that make tuning a lot easier. Kits are also available to allow you to add a tuning indicator to a TNC without one.

```
cmd:c klce v wlaw-4
*** CONNECTED to K1CE
K1CE    BBS - West Hartford, CT
Hello Bruce, Last on 0257/870307, new 369 - 368, active 15.
KB1MW    de K1CE    BBS: (B,D,H,I,J,K,L,R,S,T,U,W,X) >
ll 5
 Msg# TR  Size To       From    @ BBS  Date    Title
  367 N    78 K1BA      K1CE    WA1RAJ 870307 Greetings
  366 N   652 ALL       KA1KRP         870306 FLEA MARKET
  360 TY  271 K1CE      WB1ASH         870305 QTC 1 K1CE
  358 BN  679 ALL       WA1OCK         870304 novice enhancement
  244 BN  319 ALL       K1CE           870228 NTS Traffic Handling Basics
KB1MW    de K1CE    BBS: (B,D,H,I,J,K,L,R,S,T,U,W,X) >
r 244
 Msg# TR  Size To       From    @ BBS  Date    Title
  244 BN  319 ALL       K1CE           870228 NTS Traffic Handling Basics
If you are interested in NTS traffic handling via packet radio,
and would like to know the basics, download a new file NTS.DOC for
information.  Good luck, and thanks for your help in handling NTS
traffic in Connecticut. If I can be of any assistance, please
leave a message.   73,   Rick K1CE NTSCT Section Node

KB1MW    de K1CE    BBS: (B,D,H,I,J,K,L,R,S,T,U,W,X) >
x
KB1MW    de K1CE    BBS: Date 870307 Time 0258 Last msg # 368, 15 active msgs
Messages: L - List, R - Read, S - Send, K - Kill
Files:    W - What, D - Download from, U - Upload to
B - Bye, G - GateWay, H - Help, T - Talk to Rick
P - Path for callsign, N - Enter/Change your name
I - Information, J - Calls heard,  X - Short/Long Menu >
b
KB1MW    Bruce de K1CE  : 73, CUL
*** DISCONNECTED
```

Figure 9-13—A packet bulletin board (PBBS) lets amateurs store messages for other amateurs. The messages may be forwarded automatically to other stations in the PBBS network.

The same rule of thumb that applies to VHF/UHF packet-radio operation also applies to HF operation. Move to an unused frequency if there is other packet-radio activity on the frequency you are presently using. Often, one frequency is used as a calling frequency where stations transmit packets to attract the attention of other stations who may wish to contact them. Once a contact/connection is established, clear the calling frequency by moving off to another unused frequency.

PACKET BULLETIN-BOARD SYSTEMS (PBBS)

We mentioned RTTY mailboxes in the section on radioteletype, and some of you may be familiar with landline telephone bulletin-board systems. The packet-radio equivalent is the **Packet Bulletin Board System (PBBS)**. The PBBS computer allows packet stations to store messages for other amateurs, download and upload computer files, and even to link one packet station through a ''gateway'' to another band (see Figure 9-13).

Some PBBS computers can automatically forward messages from one computer to another, so you can store a message at one PBBS that is ultimately meant for an amateur thousands of miles away. The message will be forwarded from one PBBS to another until it reaches its destination. A **network** is a system of packet stations that can interconnect to transmit data over long distances.

To use a PBBS, you must locate one. In any area with even a small amount of packet activity there is usually at least one PBBS. In addition, there are several HF PBBS stations, although many of the HF stations are set up for long-haul message traffic, not for individual-user connects. The *ARRL Operating Manual* contains more detailed information about using a PBBS.

THE DREADED BEACON

All TNCs have a beacon function. This function allows a station to send an unconnected packet at regular intervals. These unconnected packets usually contain a message to the effect that the station originating the beacon is on the air and is ready, willing and able to carry on a packet-radio contact.

The purpose of the beacon function is to generate activity when there is none. This purpose was legitimate when there was little packet-radio activity. Back in the early 1980s, it was a rare occurrence when a new packet-radio station appeared on the air. Without beacons, that new operator might believe that his packet-radio station was the only one active in the area. Similarly, packet-radio stations already on the air would not be aware of the new station's existence. It would be very discouraging to build a TNC (they were all kits in the early days), get on the air and find no one to contact. The beacon function was the solution to the problem. It let people know that a new packet station was on the air.

Today, beacons are usually unnecessary. There is absolutely no need to resort to beaconing in order to make your existence known. On HF, 2 meters and 222 MHz, there is plenty of activity in most areas. If you are getting on the air for the first time, monitor 145.01 or 223.4 MHz for a few minutes and you will quickly have a list of other stations that are on the air. When one of these stations disconnects, send a connect request to that station. After a few connections, your existence on the air will be known.

Instead of sending beacons, leave a message announcing your existence on your local PBBS. This is more effective than sending beacons because your message will be read even when your station is off the air.

Beacons only add congestion to already crowded packet-radio channels, so do the packet-radio community a favor and disable your TNC's beacon function by typing:

Beacon Every 0 <CR>

WHAT IF I STILL HAVE QUESTIONS?

The material presented here is only a very basic sketch of packet-radio operation. More material is presented in the *ARRL Operating Manual*. *QST* and the other ham magazines often have articles about packet radio. *Your Gateway to Packet Radio*, by Stan Horzepa, WA1LOU, is an ARRL publication that provides plenty of details about packet-radio operation. Finally, there are sure to be a few "packeteers" in your local club. For a list of clubs in your area, write to the Field Services Department at ARRL HQ.

[Now turn to Chapter 12 and study questions 2B-5-1.1, 2B-5-1.2, 2B-5-2.1 and 2B-5-2.2. If you have difficulty with any of these questions, review this section.]

─── ON-THE-AIR ACTIVITIES ───

Once your license is in hand, you'll join thousands of other active hams. You'll discover that a whole new world of on-the-air operating activities awaits you. At first, you'll probably just make contacts. Maybe you'll ragchew (chat) with other hams. After a while, however, you'll want to try your hand at specialized activities. These include handling traffic, contesting or DXing. You will probably want to exchange QSL cards with the hams you work. You may want to go after some of the various awards available to hams.

You really won't have to confine your interests to a narrow range. You'll find that certain aspects of Amateur Radio seem more appealing than others. You should at least try some of the activities. You might find you enjoy them very much.

HANDLING TRAFFIC

Passing "radiogram" messages is a vital part of an amateur's emergency communications training. A scheduled sequence of traffic **nets**, under the banner of the ARRL National Traffic System, provides an orderly path for getting messages from their origins to their destinations. These can be anywhere in the US and Canada, and some points overseas. CW traffic nets furnish an opportunity to improve your code speed. They also serve as a training ground for amateurs who want to enhance their on-the-air operating abilities. Slow-speed CW nets are particularly popular among new amateurs.

Getting started in traffic handling is a simple matter. Familiarize yourself with net procedures, and then check in. The times and frequencies of most traffic nets are listed in the *ARRL Net Directory*. The *Directory* also includes background information and instructions for typical net operations. Emergency and traffic operating are addressed in more detail in the *Public Service Communications Manual (PSCM)*. The *Net Directory* and *PSCM* are available from ARRL Headquarters for $1 each. Another source of information is *The ARRL Operating Manual*, which can be purchased from your local radio dealer or directly from ARRL.

Whether your interest is in emergency preparedness, handling messages for your friends in the community, or

Each year, volunteer hams like this one handle tens of thousands of messages. They use the National Traffic System. Sometimes these messages are fresh from disaster areas. Hams help those seeking news of friends and relatives. Other messages are from state fairs and exhibitions. Still others contain birthday greetings. You can get involved in handling traffic. Contact the Field Services Department at ARRL Headquarters for more information.

improving your code speed and operating skills, you will find traffic handling and net operation an enjoyable and educational aspect of Amateur Radio.

DX

When the DX bug bites, it bites hard, with little warning. One day as you call a casual CQ, a weak station answers. You are expecting to hear from someone in the next county or state. He sends his call sign. "Hey, that's a strange sounding call sign. Let's check the international call signs allocations list to see what country this guy might be in. Z2. That's Zimbabwe in southeastern Africa! This guy is halfway around the world!" Before you know it, you have succumbed and become a DXer.

DX is one of those loosely defined terms that means different things to different people. The term DX (distance) is generally understood to include all stations that are not in your own country. It can be a two-mile contact across the border or a 10,000-mile QSO two continents away.

DX and DXing (working fellow amateurs in foreign lands) is a fascinating and absorbing aspect of Amateur Radio. You could easily spend an entire ham radio "career" solely in pursuit of DX. And indeed, some hams do.

It's a fact that any amateur station is capable of working DX. It is true that bigger antennas, linear amplifiers (when you get your General or higher class license) and refinements in operating techniques can make the process easier. But even the newest Novice with the most basic station is capable of snagging plenty of DX.

What is the ultimate goal of the DXer? The most common answer would probably be to "work 'em all." Contact and confirm by QSL card as many of the countries on the ARRL DXCC countries list as possible (presently about 315 in number). That will ensure your high standing among fellow DXers pursuing that same goal. The **DX Century Club (DXCC)** is a prestigious award issued by the ARRL. It is recognized worldwide as the premier award for DXing achievement in all of Amateur Radio. For the basic DXCC award, you'll need to work 100 different countries from the DXCC list. QSLs are required from each of them. The cards are then sent to ARRL for verification. An official application form is required. (The ARRL DXCC list of countries is available from ARRL Headquarters for $1. It's also included in *The ARRL Operating Manual*.) After you obtain the basic award, the challenge continues. A series of endorsements for working and confirming still more DXCC countries awaits you. DXCC membership is open to amateurs worldwide (although US and Canadian amateurs must be ARRL or CRRL members to participate). It is the basis for a friendly worldwide competition. Everyone tries to work more countries than their friends across town (or across the seas).

Working all the countries on the DXCC list is not a weekend affair. Complexities of international politics and the absence of amateur activity in some of the less-populated countries work against it. Some hams with 20 years or more of DX experience are still missing quite a few DXCC countries. Some relative newcomers, on the other hand, lack only a couple of countries.

There are many resources available to the avid DXer. At the top of the list is personal on-the-air experience. Spend lots of listening time on the bands. Get to know the peculiarities of radio-wave propagation. Get to know when and where DX stations are likely to hang out. Listen to successful DXers.

Copy their good operating habits. You can develop effective strategies for working DX just by monitoring the bands.

Working DX requires a different set of operating skills. This is true from looking for DX QSOs, to sending and receiving QSL cards. Much has been printed on the art and science of working DX. Among the more useful printed materials are DX bulletins and newsletters. These bring subscribers current and helpful information on some of the "rarer" DX stations. The monthly "How's DX?" column in *QST* is chock full of useful DX news. For the beginner, ARRL publishes *The DXCC Companion, How To Work Your First 100 Countries*. This book covers every topic of interest to the DXer, including antennas, propagation, calling strategies, sending for QSL cards, coping with interference and applying for DXCC. A more general treatment of DXing techniques can be found in *The ARRL Operating Manual*. One last DX tip: Success comes only to the station that joins in the fray. After all, that's the name of the game. Good luck and good DXing.

CONTESTS AND CONTESTING

We all like to test our skills against others. In ham radio, contesting is an excellent way to learn good operating techniques. In contests, hams go "head-to-head"—and may the best operator win.

Contesting is a diverse facet of Amateur Radio. Most amateurs join in at one time or another to satisfy their competitive appetites. You might totally immerse yourself for the full 48 hours of a big contest. Those who do may come away with 2000 or more contest QSOs and the prize for first place! You can also spend but a few minutes to achieve a personal goal. Maybe you'd like to work a new DX country. Or you might try to make the most QSOs you ever made in a given time period.

Generally, a contest involves working as many different stations as possible in a given period of time. A premium is placed on working specific types of stations for "multipliers." Multipliers may be different states (or provinces) or counties in a North American contest. In international (DX) contests, multipliers may be different countries or International Telecommunication Union (ITU) Zones.

Contests come in all shapes and sizes, each tailored to one of the many different types of amateurs. There is a Novice/Technician Roundup (open to all, but awards are given only to Novice and Technician operators). There are DX contests for DXers. VHF contests exist for those who enjoy working the bands above 30 MHz. These are only a few of many types of contests...but you get the idea. "There is a contest for any taste."

"Winning" in Amateur Radio contesting is a relative term. One operator might turn in the number one score among thousands of participants. Another might significantly improve his or her operating techniques. All contests are learning experiences. Both hams are "winners." Contesting sharpens operating skill and leads to greater station efficiency, for serious contenders and casual participants.

A good contest operator wastes neither words nor motions. Contesters are likely to have some of the best signals on the band. They may not have the most elaborate stations, however. Contests encourage operators to use their equipment and skills to the best advantage.

If you want to operate in a contest, you have to know the "exchange." You may have to send a signal report and a contact number, starting with 1. Other contests require a signal report and a zone number. You can find out by reading the rules in *QST* or by listening to what local hams are saying. The station you work will give you an exchange, too. Write it in your log. You'll notice right away that most signal reports are "59" or "599"! You can give an honest signal report, but don't elaborate.

Let's say you hear W6ISQ calling CQ in the ARRL 10-Meter Contest. You give only your call: KA1RRL; he knows *his* call! W6ISQ responds: "KA1RRL 59 California" and you answer "Thanks, 59 Connecticut." The word "Thanks" indicates that you copied his exchange. W6ISQ may respond with "Thanks" or "73," or may just start calling CQ again. He's not being rude, just efficient. Wasted words in a contest result in fewer contacts and a lower score. Staying on one frequency and calling CQ is called "running stations." Experienced operators can "run" over 150 stations (contacts) an hour, so every second counts! The number of contacts per hour is called the "rate."

Tuning the band looking for contacts is called "search and pounce," abbreviated "S and P." Running almost always generates more contacts, but sometimes you have to S and P to find multipliers. At first you should S and P. Later, find a clear frequency and try running for a while. Many times, the multipliers you need will find you. If your rate starts to drop, go back to S and P for a while.

Even if you've never entered a contest before, don't be afraid to try your hand! The "Contest Corral" column in *QST*, and contest sections in most other Amateur Radio periodicals, list hundreds of contests each year. The basic rules and entry requirements are also listed. Don't be gun-shy. Choose an event you wish to participate in. Read and understand the rules. Then, jump right in and give it a shot. Don't worry about letting your inexperience show. The high-scoring stations need us to keep their rates up!

FIELD DAY

Field Day is a special event. It's fun, challenging, frustrating, exciting, exhausting and satisfying. Field Day is Amateur Radio from A to Z.

Ask 10 amateurs "What is Field Day?" and you are likely to get 12 different answers. The premier operating event of the year is held on the fourth full weekend in June. It is sponsored by the American Radio Relay League. But that's where any and all agreement ends. Field Day is a chance to take to the hills and fields. It's a chance to test our ability to communicate in adverse conditions. Field Day stations try to contact as many other stations as possible during a 30-hour period. The multiplier on Field Day is your power source and transmitter power output. The biggest multiplier goes to 5-watt-or-less transmitters operating from "natural power" sources, like solar cells or water wheels. You can operate from home, too, but you'll have more fun in the field.

Field Day is technically not a contest. Intended to test emergency preparedness and demonstrate the fun of Amateur Radio to nonhams, Field Day is a great chance to spend a weekend in the outdoors with family, friends and Amateur Radio.

One weekend spent at even a modest-sized Field Day setup is probably equal to a year's worth of "normal hamming." The experience draws heavily on ingenuity and resourcefulness. Even the newcomer is quickly pressed into service. Everyone must deal with the problems that occur in remote locations.

If Field Day sounds like your "cup of tea," we can help. Write ARRL for the name of a radio club in your area. Although you can operate Field Day by yourself, you'll miss out on a lot of fun. Field Day is an experience not to be missed. Mark your calendar now.

═══ QSL CARDS ═══

Sending a QSL card to confirm a contact is a tradition almost as old as Amateur Radio itself. QSLs are sent more frequently for HF and VHF/UHF simplex QSOs than for VHF/UHF repeater and packet QSOs. Regardless of your operating interest, a QSL can serve as your ham radio "business card" when you meet other hams at hamfests and the local radio store. If you want to chase DX or earn operating awards such as Worked All States you'll need QSLs from the stations you work. Unless you live in a less-populated state like Wyoming or Montana, you'll probably have to send a card first, and ask for a response. Including return postage will help bring a reply.

By the way, QSL sent as a "Q signal" on CW means "I acknowledge receipt," or "I will confirm this contact." QSL? asks "Can you acknowledge receipt?" or "Can you confirm this QSO for me?" QSL is an important "word" in amateur jargon. It is understood to mean a written or printed confirmation of contact.

Okay, you're just starting out in Amateur Radio. You're looking for a supply of QSL cards. You'll need to send QSLs to the stations whose call signs will soon fill your logbook. There are a few things to keep in mind as you select, fill out and, send your QSLs.

QSLs come in all sizes, shapes, colors and textures. QSLs have been silk-screened on T-shirts, and sent as commercial

telegrams. They've been molded in plastic and typed on tissue. Usually, however, they're printed on post-card sized card stock. (Remember, the US Postal Service will not accept cards smaller than 3½ by 5½ inches.)

Your QSLs can be printed professionally, or the cards can be homemade. (See the *Ham Ads* section of *QST* for suppliers.) The final design is left up to you. Keep the card's recipient in mind, however. He or she will form a lasting impression of you from your QSL card. Your QSL must also include certain information about each QSO.

The ultimate use of a QSL will be as an awards submission. There are many Amateur Radio awards. These include the DX Century Club (DXCC), Worked All States (WAS) and Worked All Continents (WAC). Most societies that issue the awards will honor your QSL as valid confirmation only if it contains the following essential information: your call sign, your specific location (QTH), confirmation that a two-way QSO has taken place, the call sign of the station worked, date of the QSO, time of the QSO (in UTC, please), frequency band used, mode (CW, SSB, RTTY, FM, and so on) used, and signal report given. When choosing the design for your QSL be sure the card has the proper layout for recording all QSO information.

There are conventions to follow when filling out QSLs. Always record times in Coordinated Universal Time (UTC).

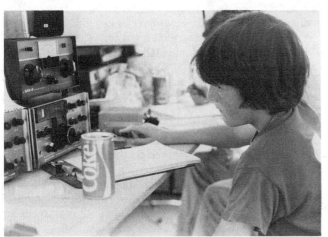

What do thousands of hams do on the fourth weekend in June every year? It's something they swear they'll never do again, but they usually do. You guessed it. It's Field Day!

Although points are awarded for various categories, it's not really a contest. Field Day is actually an emergency preparedness exercise. Many groups of amateurs literally operate out in a field. Others try the nearest mountaintop, beach or backyard. The idea is to test your readiness to operate under adverse conditions. It's a group effort, and a great deal of fun. You may be in charge of untangling a longwire antenna at 3 AM. Or you may begin operating at sunrise after being up the entire night! It's an experience you're not likely to forget. It shows what the Amateur Radio Service can do in emergencies.

Shortly after you begin your on-the-air operation, you will experience the excitement of collecting QSL cards from all over the world.

It is frustrating to receive a QSL marked in local time. You'll have to convert some obscure "local" time to UTC. Otherwise, you won't be able to find the QSO in your logbook. Amateurs around the world use UTC. There's a good rule to follow when recording the QSO date on your QSL. The date is written in Arabic numerals. The month is written in Roman numerals. The year is written in Arabic numerals. Example: July 10, 1991 would be written as 10 VII 1991. Most DX (non-US or Canadian) amateurs record the date in this manner. Standardization makes life easier for all involved. An alternative is to abbreviate the month, but use the same format (10 JUL 1991). Do not use the method of just writing Arabic numerals, such as 10/7/91 or 7/10/91. (Is that July 10 or October 7?)

When filling out your QSL card, use regular ink or permanent marker. Pencil and most felt-tipped markers tend to fade. They smudge easily and deteriorate over the years. A rainy day is all it takes to "wipe out" a hard-earned contact. If you make a mistake when filling out a QSL card, throw it away. Do not try to correct it by writing over the mistake. Destroy the card and start again. Most organizations will not accept "altered" QSLs as valid awards confirmations. There is no way to determine who altered the card. It cannot be counted for credit.

Once the QSL is made out, you must get it to the operator of the station you've worked. There are many ways to send QSLs. They depend on its destination and how quickly you want it to arrive. Domestic QSLs (US, Canada or Mexico) are sent as postcards. They can also be mailed in envelopes, as First Class mail. Hams in rarer states or provinces receive many QSL requests. They appreciate receiving an SASE (self-addressed, stamped envelope) with your QSL. That helps defray postage costs and saves time in addressing many cards.

QSLs going to DX stations do not have to be sent directly to the DX station's address. They can be sent via a DX *QSL bureau*. A QSL bureau is a system developed to help amateurs exchange QSL cards with other amateurs in foreign countries. Hams send QSLs by regular mail to one central bureau location in their country. When enough QSLs for a foreign country accumulate, a bureau staff member sends them all to that country. Once the cards arrive, someone working in an incoming QSL bureau sorts and mails them to individual amateurs. Using a QSL bureau means that each amateur does not have to send single cards overseas.

The ARRL sponsors such a system. The outgoing DX QSL Bureau (for ARRL members only) sends your QSLs to bureaus around the world. The incoming DX QSL Bureau (for use by all US and Canadian amateurs) forwards DX QSLs to their final destinations in the US and Canada. Details on the use of the ARRL DX QSL Bureau system are printed in *QST*. When mailing DX QSLs directly overseas, remember an important rule. United States stamps on your SASE will not be accepted by foreign postal authorities. Instead of using a US stamp on the return envelope, enclose one or two *International Reply Coupons*. IRCs are available at US Post Offices. They can be exchanged for the proper stamps in another country. As an added bonus, you'll start receiving beautiful foreign stamps with your DX QSLs! Many successful stamp collectors trace their "collecting" roots back to Amateur Radio DX. *The ARRL Operating Manual* has more information about sending QSLs to, and receiving them from, DX stations.

Collecting QSL cards is a satisfying hobby within a hobby. You may collect QSLs for the fun of it, or in an attempt to earn an award.

QSLs, like money, are more fun to receive than to give. In receiving a QSL, there is an implied responsibility to return the courtesy. QSLing is a worthwhile chore—do it cheerfully and promptly.

AWARDS

Working toward operating awards is a popular aspect of Amateur Radio. The ARRL sponsors many coveted awards. These include Worked All States, DX Century Club and the A-1 Operator Club. In addition, the League also administers the Worked All Continents award. This is sponsored by the International Amateur Radio Union. They're all available to licensed Amateur Radio operators throughout the world. Hams in North America must be League members to apply for most ARRL awards. Foreign amateurs need not be League members.

Perhaps the first award you'll earn is the Rag Chewers' Club award. To qualify, you need to maintain a contact for a solid half-hour. Your first contact will be quite exciting, and the first half hour will fly by. And, you'll have earned your RCC to boot! Just report your QSO to ARRL Headquarters, and we'll send you your award.

The Worked All States (WAS) award is probably the most popular achievement award, especially among US hams. Eligibility requirements are simple. You must establish two-way Amateur Radio contact with other hams in all 50 states.

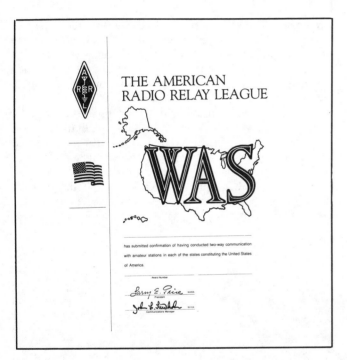

North America, South America, Europe, Africa, Asia and Oceania. Write to ARRL Headquarters and request a WAC application form and complete rules. Please include a self-addressed, stamped envelope (SASE) with your request.

All amateurs should strive for membership in the A-1 Operator Club. Membership in this elite group attests to unusual competence and performance. The A-1 Operator Club recognizes many facets of Amateur Radio operation. These include keying, modulation, procedure, copying ability, and judgment and courtesy. Members of this club are smooth, courteous operators with clean signals. They set good examples for us all. You'll run into them only occasionally. The A-1 Operator club offers no list to aid those who seek membership. You must be recommended independently by two operators who already belong. If you ask to join, you may actually "fail" the test on the basis of courtesy and judgment!

Another ARRL-sponsored award is the Certificate of Code Proficiency. To qualify, you have to build your code speed up to at least 10 words per minute. Each month, W1AW transmits an official code practice qualifying run. This consists of successive five-minute periods of text. Speeds include 10, 15, 20, 25, 30 and 35 WPM. To apply for this award, underline one minute of text. Choose the period you believe

Each contact must be confirmed by a QSL card or other written verification. As a Novice, WAS is well within your reach. Many Novices qualify. Send an SASE along with your request for the application form to ARRL Headquarters.

The DX Century Club (DXCC) is a prestigious operating achievement award. You must work and collect QSL cards from licensed hams in at least 100 different countries to qualify for this award. ("Countries" as defined by the DXCC rules, that is. Alaska and Hawaii, for example, each count as separate "countries.") Although DXCC is somewhat difficult to achieve in the Novice bands, it is possible. Years of high solar activity make it easier. Your patience and perseverance will pay off in experience and satisfaction. All DX contacts made as a Novice will count toward DXCC. You don't lose anything when you upgrade.

The Worked All Continents (WAC) award is sponsored by the International Amateur Radio Union. It's the first DX award many new hams get. To qualify, you must work and collect QSL cards from one ham in each of the continents:

you copied perfectly. Send it to ARRL Headquarters with an SASE. We'll tell you if you passed or failed. If you passed, you'll receive a free certificate. W1AW qualifying runs are announced in the "Contest Corral" section of *QST*. You can also request a W1AW operating schedule that includes a list of Qualifying Run times from League Headquarters.

Many other organizations besides the ARRL sponsor operating awards. Many Novices' first step toward WAS is the Ten American Districts Award. It's issued for working and confirming contacts in all 10 US call areas. Apply to the Lockheed Employees Recreation Club, 2814 Empire Blvd, Burbank, CA 91504. Enclose $1 with your application to cover postage and handling.

Other awards for working different US counties and international prefixes are available from *CQ* magazine, 76 North Broadway, Hicksville, NY 11801. Write them for information on their awards program. You'll find that there are a lot of certificates available. You could even wallpaper your entire shack. Decide which awards you want, tune up your rig and go get 'em!

—— LOCAL RADIO CLUBS ——

Your local Amateur Radio club is a good place to meet other hams. At club meetings, you'll meet others with similar interests. They can help you get on the air. They can introduce you to new aspects of Amateur Radio. They can also amuse you with tales of the "good old days." Through membership in your local club, you'll make fast, lifelong friendships.

Most radio clubs sponsor a wide range of activities for their members. These range from banquets to auctions, from flea markets to community service projects, and from training classes to Field Day efforts. By participating, you'll add enjoyment and dimension to your amateur experience.

Special-interest clubs may interest you as well. Some examples of these are contest clubs, DX clubs and VHF clubs. Other groups, such as Explorer posts, canoers, motorcyclists and marathoners use Amateur Radio as an integral part of their activities. If you develop a special interest within Amateur Radio, you'll want to investigate—or even help start—a local special-interest club. Often, special-interest club members are the most knowledgeable hams in your area. Many are glad to help a beginner learn the ropes.

How do you find out about these clubs? More than 2000 are affiliated with the ARRL. To find the club (or clubs) in your area, write to the Field Services Department at League Headquarters. We'll send you the information you need.

If there is no club in your area, why not start your own? If you supply the members, ARRL will supply the information. Often, hobbies are more fun if you have someone to share them with.

FIND YOURSELF A CLUB

There are 2000-plus Amateur Radio clubs scattered throughout the US and Canada. The Sheboygan (Wisconsin) ARC is one of the most active. One popular activity is helping American Field Service foreign exchange students from Latin America. The club helps the students contact their families, thousands of miles away. It's a thrill for all involved. It's rewarding to bring together homesick students and their anxious families.

The club also sponsors licensing classes and a Novice buddy program. That's where senior members of the club assist newcomers. They help in setting up stations and antennas. Big or small, problems are solved on a one-to-one basis. Long-lasting friendships are begun.

As a special project, the club visited a nearby Coast Guard station. Members learned more about the operation of marine radio and radar. Some club members were able to see the equipment in action. They traveled aboard a Coast Guard cutter (see photo).

Whether you're looking for a Novice transceiver or just want to learn more about Amateur Radio, a local club is for you. Write to the Field Services Department, ARRL, 225 Main St., Newington, CT 06111, for the name of one nearby.

The ARRL's monthly journal, *QST*, is crammed full of projects and information geared to the beginner. Whether you're into DX, simple construction projects or late-breaking news that affects all amateurs, *QST* is indispensable.

THE ARRL

In addition to participating locally, you should also take part on the national level. The American Radio Relay League (ARRL) is the membership organization of Amateur Radio operators in the United States. There are many reasons why you, as a ham, should join the League.

Each month, the ARRL sends its official journal, *QST*, to every member. In *QST* you'll find articles dealing with nearly every aspect of Amateur Radio. As a new ham, you'll appreciate the beginners' articles. They explain how transmitters, receivers, antennas and accessories work. There are easy-to-build construction projects. In addition, *QST* carries information on operating events, activities and contests. In the back of *QST*, you'll find page after page of informative ads. These can help you choose the right equipment and accessories. *QST* also brings you the very latest news from the world of Amateur Radio.

QST isn't the only reason you should join the ARRL, though. The League represents the interests of Amateur Radio in Washington. ARRL makes sure the FCC and other government agencies know where US hams stand on current issues.

ARRL also answers many questions from members. The staff at League Headquarters exists to help its members. DXers can take advantage of the ARRL Outgoing QSL Bureau. It saves considerable money in forwarding your cards to the right place. These are only a few of the services available to ARRL members.

The ARRL is much more than an organization in Newington, Connecticut. The ARRL is each local member across the country. The ARRL Field Organization depends on local volunteers to carry out various programs. The work of Amateur Radio begins at the local level by amateurs working in official elected or appointed capacities. There are jobs for those interested in many aspects of public service. These include emergency communications, communications for community events and handling routine messages. There are jobs for public relations people, government liaisons and those who will provide technical assistance. Share some of your talent and enthusiasm by becoming involved with The American Radio Relay League.

By supporting your League, you're supporting Amateur Radio. Write to us today.

───NOT FOR TECHNICIANS ONLY───
FCC EMISSION DESIGNATORS
PROPAGATION: A CLOSER LOOK
BANDWIDTH

─── **KEY WORDS** ───

Backscatter—A small amount of signal that is reflected from Earth's surface after traveling through the ionosphere. The reflected signals may go back into the ionosphere along several paths and be refracted to earth again. Backscatter can help provide communications into a station's skip zone.

Critical angle—If radio waves leave an antenna at an angle greater than the critical angle for that frequency, they will pass through the ionosphere instead of returning to earth.

Critical frequency—The highest frequency at which a vertically incident radio wave will return from the ionosphere. Above the critical frequency, radio signals pass through the ionosphere instead of returning to Earth.

D layer—The lowest layer of the ionosphere. The D layer contributes very little to short-wave radio propagation. It acts mainly to absorb energy from radio waves as they pass through it. This absorption has a significant effect on signals below about 7.5 MHz during daylight.

Deviation ratio—The ratio between the maximum change in RF-carrier frequency and the highest modulating frequency used in an FM transmitter.

Duct—A radio waveguide formed when a temperature inversion traps radio waves within a restricted layer of the atmosphere.

E layer—The second lowest ionospheric layer, the E layer exists only during the day, and under certain conditions may refract radio waves enough to return them to earth.

Emission designator—A symbol made up of two letters and a number, used to describe a radio signal.

F layer—A combination of the two highest ionospheric layers, the F1 and F2 layers. The F layer refracts radio waves and returns them to earth. The height of the F layer varies greatly depending on the time of day, season of the year and amount of sunspot activity.

Frequency deviation—The amount the carrier frequency in an FM transmitter changes as it is modulated.

Guided propagation—Radio propagation by means of ducts.

Modulation index—The ratio between the maximum carrier frequency deviation and the frequency of the modulating signal at a given instant in an FM transmitter.

Radio-path horizon—The point where radio waves are returned by tropospheric bending. The radio-path horizon is 15 percent farther away than the geometric horizon.

Reflected wave—A radio wave whose direction is changed when it bounces off some object in its path.

Refract—To bend. Electromagnetic energy is refracted when it passes through a boundary between different types of material. Light is refracted as it travels from air into water or from water into air.

Solar flux index—A measure of solar activity. The solar flux index is a measure of the radio noise on 2800 MHz.

Space wave—A radio wave arriving at the receiving antenna made up of a direct wave and one or more reflected waves.

Temperature inversion—A condition in the atmosphere in which a region of cool air is trapped beneath warmer air.

Troposphere—The region in Earth's atmosphere just above the Earth's surface and below the ionosphere.

Tropospheric bending—When radio waves are bent in the troposphere, they return to earth approximately 15 percent farther away than the geometric horizon.

True or **Geometric horizon**—The most distant point one can see by line of sight.

Virtual height—The height that radio waves appear to be reflected from when they are returned to earth by refraction in the ionosphere.

The FCC uses a special system to specify the types of signals (emissions) permitted to amateurs and other users of the radio spectrum. Each **emission designator** has three digits. Table 9-11 shows what each character in the designator stands for. The second character is a number that describes the signal used to modulate the carrier. The third character specifies the type of information being transmitted.

Some of the more common combinations are:

NØN—Unmodulated carrier (test).

A1A—Morse code telegraphy (CW) using amplitude modulation.

F1B—Telegraphy using frequency-shift keying without a modulating audio tone (FSK RTTY). F1B is designed for automatic reception.

F2A—Telegraphy produced by the on-off keying of an audio tone fed into an FM transmitter (MCW).

F2B—Telegraphy produced by modulating an FM transmitter with audio tones (AFSK RTTY). F2B is also designed for automatic reception.

F3E—Frequency-modulated telephony.

G3E—Phase-modulated telephony.

NØN is a radio-frequency signal that stays on continuously with no changes in frequency or amplitude. When heard on an SSB/CW receiver, it sounds like a steady tone. As you tune across the NØN signal, the pitch of the audio tone will change. With AM and FM receivers, no tone or other sounds are heard because there is no modulation. AM and FM receivers will simply become quieter with a lessening of background noise. Because there is no modulation of NØN transmissions, no sidebands are formed.

A1A signals are like NØN signals with the transmitter being turned on and off. In other words, A1A signals are amplitude modulated with only two amplitude levels: on and off. On an SSB/CW receiver, intermittent tones are heard, as in Morse code. AM and FM receivers cannot detect these signals properly. Usually all that is heard are thumping sounds with changes in background noise.

Morse code can be transmitted to people using FM

Table 9-11
Partial List of FCC Emission Designators

1) First Symbol—Modulation Type

Unmodulated carrier	N
Double-sideband full carrier	A
Double-sideband reduced carrier	R
Single-sideband suppressed carrier	J
Vestigial sideband	C
Frequency modulation	F
Phase modulation	G
Various forms of pulse modulation	P, K, L, M, Q, V, W, X

2) Second Symbol—Nature of Modulating Signals

No modulating signal	Ø
A single channel containing quantized or digital information without the use of a modulating subcarrier	1
A single channel containing quantized or digital information with the use of a modulating subcarrier	2
A single channel containing analog information	3
Two or more channels containing quantized or digital information	7
Two or more channels containing analog information	8

3) Third Symbol—Type of Transmitted Information

No information transmitted	N
Telegraphy—for aural reception	A
Telegraphy—for automatic reception	B
Facsimile	C
Data transmission, telemetry, telecommand	D
Telephony	E
Television	F

receivers if a keyed audio tone is fed into the microphone input of an FM transmitter. Transmissions of this kind use F2A emission.

PROPAGATION: A CLOSER LOOK

IONOSPHERIC PROPAGATION

The earth's upper atmosphere consists mainly of oxygen and nitrogen. There are traces of hydrogen, helium and several other gases. The atoms making up these gases are electrically neutral. They have no charge and exhibit no electrical force outside their own structure. The gas atoms absorb ultraviolet radiation from the sun, which knocks electrons out of the atom. In this process, the atoms become positively charged. A positively charged atom is an ion. The process by which ions are formed is *ionization*. Several ionized layers appear at different heights in the atmosphere. Each layer has a central region where the ionization is greatest. The intensity of the ionization decreases above and below this central region in each layer. See Figure 9-15.

The ionosphere consists of several layers of charged

particles. These layers have been given letter designations, as shown in Figure 9-16. Scientists started with the letter D just in case there were any undiscovered lower layers. None have been found, so there is no A,B or C layer.

The **D Layer:** The lowest layer of the ionosphere affecting propagation is the D layer. This layer is in a relatively dense part of the atmosphere. It is about 30 to 55 miles above the Earth. When the atoms in this layer absorb sunlight and form ions, they don't last very long. They quickly combine with free electrons to form neutral atoms again. The amount of ionization in this layer varies widely. It depends on how much sunlight hits the layer. At noon, D-layer ionization is maximum or very close to it. By sunset, this ionization disappears.

The D layer is ineffective in **refracting** or bending high-

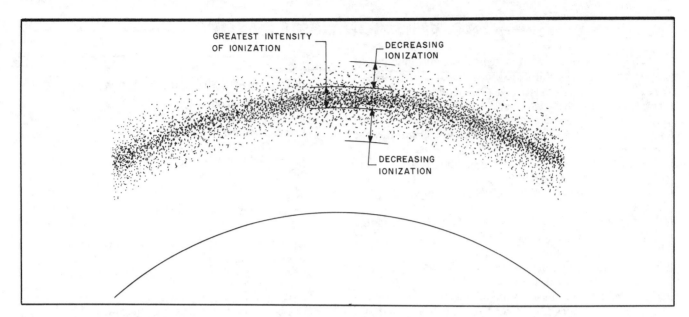

Figure 9-15—A cross section of a layer of the ionosphere. The intensity of the ionozation is greatest in the central region and decreases above and below the central region.

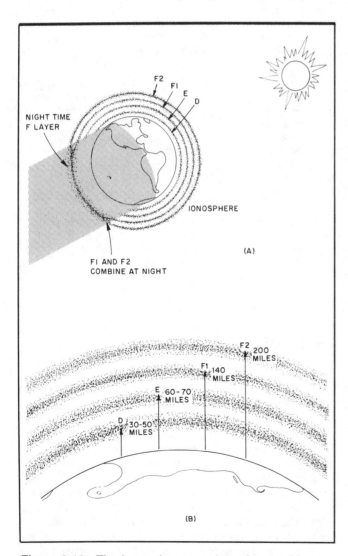

Figure 9-16—The ionosphere consists of several layers of ionized particles at different heights above Earth. At night, the D and E layers disappear and the F1 and F2 layers combine to form a single F layer.

frequency signals back to earth. The D layer's major effect is to absorb energy from radio waves. As radio waves pass through the ionosphere, they give up energy. This sets some of the ionized particles into motion. Effects of absorption on lower frequencies are greater than on higher frequencies. Absorption also increases proportionally with the amount of ionization. The more ionization, the more energy the radio waves lose passing through the ionosphere. Absorption is most pronounced at midday. It is responsible for the short daytime communications ranges on the lower amateur frequencies (160, 80 and 40 meters).

The next layer of the ionosphere is the **E layer**. The E layer appears at an altitude of about 60 to 70 miles. At this height, ionization produced by sunlight does not last very long. This makes the E layer useful for bending radio waves only when it is in sunlight. Like the D layer, the E layer reaches maximum ionization around midday. By early evening the ionization level is very low. The ionization level reaches a minimum just before sunrise, local time. Using the E layer, a radio signal can travel a maximum distance of about 1250 miles in one hop.

The **F layer**: The layer of the ionosphere most responsible for long-distance amateur communication is the F layer. This layer is a very large region. It ranges from about 100 to 260 miles above the Earth. The height depends on season, latitude, time of day and solar activity. Ionization reaches a maximum shortly after noon local standard time. It tapers off very gradually toward sunset. At this altitude, the ions and electrons recombine very slowly. The F layer remains ionized during the night, reaching a minimum just before sunrise. After sunrise, ionization increases rapidly for the first few hours. Then it increases slowly to its noontime maximum.

During the day, the F layer splits into two parts, F1 and F2. The central region of the F1 layer forms at an altitude of about 140 miles. For the F2 layer, the central region forms at about 200 miles above the Earth. These altitudes vary with the season of the year and other factors. At noon in the summer the F2 layer can reach an altitude of 300 miles. At night, the two layers recombine to form a single F layer slightly below the higher altitude. The F1 layer does not have

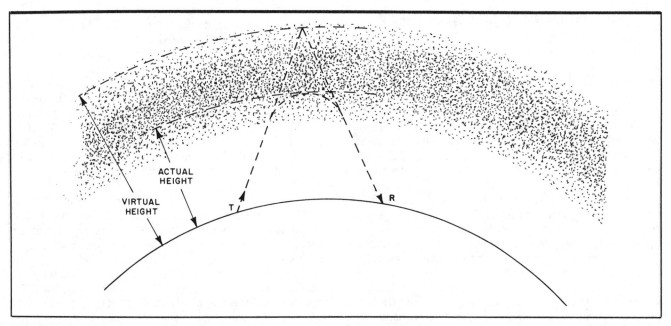

Figure 9-17—The virtual height of a layer in the ionosphere is the height at which a simple reflection would return the wave to the same point as the gradual bending that actually takes place.

much to do with long-distance communications. Its effects are similar to those caused by the E layer. The F2 layer is responsible for almost all long-distance communication on the amateur HF bands. A one-hop radio transmission travels a maximum of about 2500 miles using the F2 layer.

[Now turn to Chapter 13 and study exam questions 3AC-1-1.1 through 3AC-1-1.3, 3AC-1-2.1, 3AC-1-2.2, 3AC-1-3.1, 3AC-1-4.1 through 3AC-1-4.3, 3AC-2.1 through 3AC-2.4 and 3AC-3.1 through 3AC-3.4. Review this material as needed.]

VIRTUAL HEIGHT

An ionospheric layer is a region of considerable depth. For practical purposes, think of each layer as having a definite height. The height from which a simple reflection from the layer would give the same effects (observed from the ground) as the effects of the gradual bending that actually takes place is called the **virtual height.** See Figure 9-17.

The virtual height of an ionospheric layer for various frequencies is determined with an ionosonde. An ionosonde is a variable-frequency transmitter and receiver. It directs

radio energy vertically and measures the time required for the signal to make a round-trip. As the frequency increases, there is a point where no energy will return. The highest frequency at which vertically incident waves return to earth is the **critical frequency.**

RADIATION ANGLE AND SKIP DISTANCE

A radio wave at a low angle above the horizon requires less refraction to bring the wave back to earth. This is why we want antennas with low radiation angles to work DX.

Figure 9-18 illustrates some of the effects of radiation angle. The high-angle **sky waves** are bent only slightly in the ionosphere and pass through it. The wave at the somewhat lower angle is just able to return. In daylight it might be returned from the E layer. The point of return for high angle waves is relatively close to the transmitting station. The lowest-angle wave returns farther away, to point B.

The highest radiation angle that will return a radio wave to earth under specific ionospheric conditions is the **critical angle.** Waves meeting the ionosphere at greater than the critical angle will pass through the ionosphere into space.

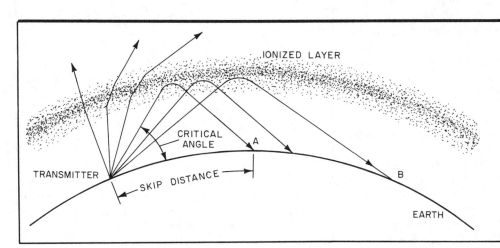

Figure 9-18—Ionospheric propagation. The waves at left leave the transmitter above the critical angle—they are refracted in the ionosphere, but not enough to return to earth. The wave at the critical angle will return to earth. The lowest-angle wave will return to earth farther away than the wave at the critical angle. This explains the emphasis on low radiation angles for DX work.

MAXIMUM USABLE FREQUENCY

There is little doubt that the critical frequency is important to amateur communication. More interesting to radio amateurs is the frequency *range* over which communication can be carried via the ionosphere. Most amateurs want to know the **maximum usable frequency** (abbreviated MUF). The MUF applies to a particular direction and distance at the time of day when you want to communicate. The MUF is the highest frequency that allows a radio wave to reach the desired destination using E- or F-layer propagation. The MUF is subject to seasonal variations as well as changes throughout the day.

Why is the MUF so important? If we know the MUF, we can make accurate predictions about which bands give the best chance for communication over a particular path. Predictions concerning amateur bands affording the best chance for communication via particular paths can be made. For example, we wish to contact a distant station. We know that the MUF for that path is 17 MHz at the time we wish to make our contact. The closest amateur band below that frequency is the 20-meter, or 14-MHz, band. The 20-meter band offers our best chance to contact that long distance location, then. There is no single MUF for a given location at any one time. The MUF will vary depending on the direction and distance to the station we wish to contact. Understanding and using the MUF is one way you can change your study of propagation from guesswork into a science.

[Now turn to Chapter 13 and study examination questions 3AC-4.1 through 3AC-4.3. Review this section as needed.]

SOLAR ACTIVITY AND RADIO-WAVE PROPAGATION

It should be clear that the sun plays the major role in the ionization of different layers in the ionosphere. The sun is the dominant factor in sky-wave communication. To communicate effectively over long distances, you must understand how solar conditions will affect your radio signals.

You know about the day-to-day sun-related cycles on earth, such as the time of day and the season of the year. Conditions affecting radio communication vary with these same cycles. Long-term and short-term solar cycles also influence propagation in ways that are not so obvious. The condition of the sun at any given moment has a very large effect on long-distance radio communication. The sun is what makes propagation prediction an inexact science.

Man's interest in the sun is older than recorded history. **Sunspots** are dark regions that appear on the surface of the sun. They were observed and described thousands of years ago. Observers noted that the number of sunspots increased and decreased in cycles. The solar observatory in Zurich, Switzerland has been recording solar data on a regular basis since 1749. The solar cycle that began in 1755 was designated cycle 1. The low sunspot numbers marking the end of cycle 21 and the beginning of cycle 22 occurred in September of 1986. Sunspot cycles also vary a great deal. For example, cycle 19 peaked with a smoothed mean sunspot number of over 200. Cycle 14 peaked at only 60.

Maximum ionization occurs during a sunspot cycle peak. High sunspot numbers usually mean good worldwide radio communications. During sunspot cycle peaks, the 20-meter amateur band is open to distant parts of the world almost continuously. The cycle 19 peak in 1957 and 1958 was responsible for the best propagation conditions in the history of

radio. Sunspot cycles do not follow consistent patterns. There can be periods of high activity that seem to come from nowhere during periods of low sunspot activity.

There is an important clue to anticipating variations in solar radiation levels. Radio propagation changes resulting from these variations can be predicted. This clue is the time it takes the sun to rotate on its axis, approximately 27 days. Active areas capable of influencing propagation can recur at four-week intervals. These active areas may last for four or five solar rotations. High MUF and good propagation for several days indicates similar conditions may develop approximately 27 days later.

Another useful indication of solar activity is solar flux, or radio energy coming from the sun. Increased solar activity produces higher levels of solar energy. More solar energy produces greater ionization in the ionosphere. Scientists use sophisticated receiving equipment and large antennas pointed at the sun to measure solar flux. A number called the **solar-flux index** is given to represent the amount of solar flux. The solar-flux index is gradually replacing the sunspot number as a means of predicting radio-wave propagation.

The solar-flux measurement is taken at 1700 UTC daily in Ottawa, Canada, on 2800 MHz (10.7 centimeters). The information is then transmitted by the National Institute of Science and Technology station WWV in Fort Collins, Colorado. Both the sunspot number and the solar flux measurements tell us similar things about solar activity. To get the sunspot number, the sun must be visible. The solar-flux measurement may be taken under any weather conditions.

Using the Solar Flux

We can use the solar flux numbers to make general daily predictions about band conditions. Figure 9-19 shows a relationship between average sunspot numbers and the 2800-MHz solar-flux measurement. The solar flux varies directly with the activity on the sun. Values range from around 60 to 250 or so. Flux values in the 60s and 70s mean fair to poor propagation conditions on the 14-MHz (20-meter) band

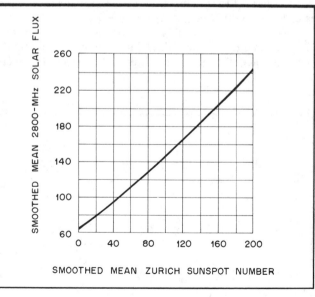

Figure 9-19—The relationship between smoothed Zurich sunspot numbers and 2800-MHz solar flux values.

and higher frequencies. Values from 90 to 110 or so indicate good conditions up to about 24 MHz (12 meters). Solar flux values over 120 indicate very good conditions on 28 MHz (10 meters) and even up to 50 MHz (6 meters) at times. On 6 meters, the flux values must be in the 200s for reliable long-range communications. The higher the frequency, the higher the flux value required for good propagation.

THE SCATTER MODES

All electromagnetic-wave propagation is subject to scattering influences. These alter idealized patterns to a great degree. The earth's atmosphere, ionospheric layers and any objects in the path of radio signals scatter the energy. Understanding how scattering takes place helps us use this propagation mode to our advantage.

Forward Scatter

There is an area between the outer limit of ground-wave propagation and the point where the first signals return from the ionosphere. We studied this area, called the **skip zone,** earlier in this chapter. See Figure 9-2. The skip zone is often described as if communications between stations in each other's skip zone were impossible. Actually, some of the transmitted signal is scattered in the atmosphere, so the signal can be heard over much of the skip zone. You usually need a very sensitive receiver and good operating techniques to hear these signals.

The troposphere is a region of the atmosphere below the ionosphere. VHF "tropo" scatter is usable out to about 500 miles from the transmitting station.

Ionospheric scatter, mostly from the height of the E region, is most marked at frequencies up to about 60 or 70 MHz. This type of forward scatter may be usable out to about 1200 miles. Ionospheric scatter propagation is most noticeable on frequencies above the MUF.

Another means of ionospheric scatter is provided by meteors entering Earth's atmosphere. As the meteor passes through the ionosphere, a trail of ionized particles forms. These particles can scatter radio energy. See Figure 9-20. This ionization is short-lived and can show up as short bursts of

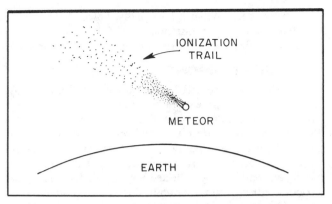

Figure 9-20—Meteors passing through the atmosphere create trails of ionized gas. These ionized trails can be used for short-duration communications.

signals with little communication value. There may be longer periods of usable signal levels, lasting up to a minute or more. Meteor scatter is most common between midnight and dawn. It peaks between 5 and 7 AM local time. Meteor scatter is an interesting method of amateur communication at 21 MHz or higher, especially during periods of low solar activity.

Backscatter

You can observe a complex form of scatter when you are working very near the MUF. The transmitted wave is refracted back to earth at some distant point. This may be an ocean area or land mass. A portion of the transmitted signal reflects back into the ionosphere. Some of this signal comes toward the transmitting station. The reflected wave helps fill in the skip zone, as shown in Figure 9-21.

Backscatter signals are generally weak and subject to distortion, because the signal may arrive at the receiver from many different directions. Backscatter is usable from just beyond the local range out to several hundred miles. Under ideal conditions, backscatter is possible over 3000 miles or more. The term "sidescatter" is more descriptive of what

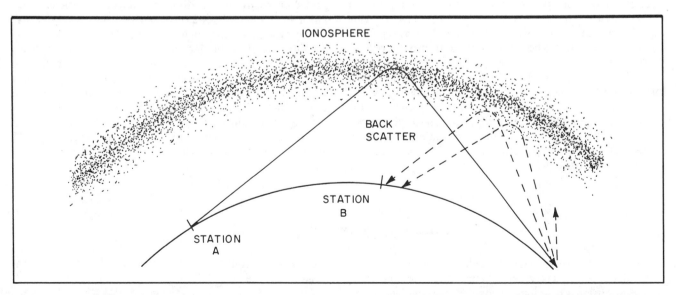

Figure 9-21—When radio waves strike the ground after passing through the ionosphere, some of the signal may reflect back into the ionosphere. If some of the signal is reflected from the ionosphere toward the transmitting station, the energy may be scattered back into the skip zone.

probably happens on such long paths, however.

[Now study exam questions 3AC-5.1 and 3AC-5.2 in Chapter 13. Review the material in this section as needed.]

LINE-OF-SIGHT PROPAGATION

In the VHF and UHF range (above 144 MHz), most propagation is by **space wave**. See Figure 9-22. Space waves are made up of a **direct wave**, and usually one or more **reflected waves**. The direct wave and reflected wave arrive at the receiving station slightly out of phase. They may cancel or reinforce each other to varying degrees. This depends on the actual path of the reflected wave(s). Effects are most pronounced when either, or both, stations are mobile. When one or both stations are moving, the paths are constantly changing. The waves may alternately reinforce and cancel each other. This causes a rapid fluttering sound (called "picket-fencing").

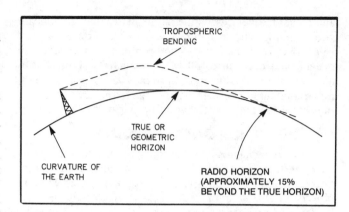

Figure 9-23—Under normal conditions, tropospheric bending causes radio waves to be returned to earth about 15% beyond the visual or geometric horizon.

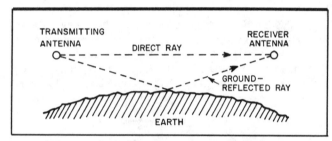

Figure 9-22—Line-of-sight propagation is accomplished by means of the space wave, a combination of a direct ray and one or more reflected rays.

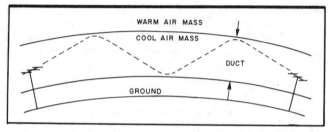

Figure 9-24—When a cool air mass is overrun by a mass of warmer air, a "duct" is formed, allowing VHF radio signals to travel great distances with little attenuation.

[At this point you should turn to Chapter 13 and study questions 3AC-6.1 and 3AC-6.2. Review any material necessary.]

TROPOSPHERIC BENDING AND DUCTING

The **troposphere** consists of atmospheric layers close to the earth's surface. **Tropospheric bending** is evident over a wide range of frequencies. It is most useful in the VHF/UHF region, especially at 144 MHz and above. Instead of gradual changes in air temperature, pressure and humidity, distinct layers may form in the troposphere. Adjacent layers having significantly different densities will bend radio waves passing between layers. Light is bent when it passes from air into water in the same way.

The **true** or **geometric horizon** is the most distant point one can see. It is limited by the height of the observer above ground. Slight bending of radio waves occurs in the troposphere. This will cause signals to return to earth somewhat beyond the geometric horizon. This **radio-path horizon** is generally about 15 percent farther away than the true horizon. See Figure 9-23.

Under normal conditions, the temperature of the air gradually decreases with increasing height above ground. Under certain conditions, however, a mass of warm air may overrun cold air. Then there is an area where cold air is covered by warm air. This is a **temperature inversion**. Radio waves can be trapped below the warm air mass. They can travel great distances with little loss. The area between the earth and the warm air mass is known as a **duct**. See Figure 9-24.

The term for radio-wave propagation through a duct is **guided propagation**, sometimes called tropospheric ducting. The manner of guiding waves through the duct is very similar to microwaves traveling in waveguides. As with tropospheric bending, we find ducting primarily at VHF frequencies, 144 MHz and higher. Ducts usually form over water, though they can form over land as well. The lowest usable frequency for duct propagation depends on two factors. One is the depth of the duct. The other is the amount the refractive index changes at the air-mass boundary.

[Now turn to Chapter 13 and study questions 3AC-7.1 through 3AC-7.6. Review this section as needed.]

━━ BANDWIDTH ━━

The amount of space in the radio-frequency spectrum that a signal occupies is called its bandwidth. The bandwidth of a transmission is determined by the information rate. Thus, a pure, continuous, unmodulated carrier (NØN) has a very small bandwidth with no sidebands. A television transmis- sion, which contains a great deal of information, is several megahertz wide.

RECEIVER BANDWIDTH

Receiver bandwidth determines how well you can receive

one signal in the presence of another signal that is very close in frequency. The enjoyment you'll experience will depend greatly on how well you can isolate the signal you are receiving from all the others nearby.

Bandwidth is a measure of selectivity: how wide a range of frequencies is received with the receiver tuned to one frequency. For example, if you can hear signals as much as 3 kHz above and 3 kHz below the frequency to which you are tuned, your receiver has a bandwidth of at least 6 kHz. If you cannot hear signals more than 200 Hz above or below the frequency to which you are tuned, the bandwidth is only 400 Hz. The narrower the bandwidth, the greater the selectivity and the easier it is to copy one signal with another one close by in frequency.

Selectivity is determined by special filters built into the receiver. Some receivers have several filters so you can choose different bandwidths. They are necessary because different emission types occupy a wider frequency range than others. A 250-Hz-bandwidth filter is excellent for separating CW signals on a crowded band, but it's useless for listening to SSB, AM or FM transmissions. A wider filter is needed to allow all the transmitted information to reach the detector.

Most receivers designed for single-sideband voice operation come standard with a filter selectivity of around 2.8 kHz. This is usable on CW, but will allow several adjacent CW signals through at the same time. F1B also is a wider emission than A1A (Morse code CW transmissions).

As we have seen in these examples, F1B radioteletype emissions are wider than CW signals, and SSB signals are even wider than that. Next, we will consider FM and PM, which can occupy even more bandwidth.

BANDWIDTH IN FM AND PM

Frequency deviation is the instantaneous change in frequency for a given signal. The frequency swings just as far in both directions, so the total frequency swing is equal to twice the deviation. In addition, there are sidebands that increase the bandwidth still further. A good estimate of the bandwidth is twice the maximum frequency deviation plus the maximum modulating audio frequency:

$$Bw = 2 \times (D + M)$$

where

    Bw = bandwidth
    D = maximum frequency deviation
    M = maximum modulating audio frequency

A transmitter using 5-kHz deviation and a maximum audio frequency of 3 kHz uses a total bandwidth of about 16 kHz. The actual bandwidth is somewhat greater than this, but it is a good approximation.

FREQUENCY DEVIATION

With direct FM, **frequency deviation** is proportional to the amplitude of the modulating signal. With phase modulation, the frequency deviation is proportional to both the amplitude and the frequency of the modulating signal. Frequency deviation is greater for higher audio frequencies. This is actually a benefit, rather than a drawback, of phase modulation. In radio communications, speech frequencies between 300 and 3000 Hz need to be reproduced for good intelligibility. In the human voice, however, speech sounds between 2000 and 3000 Hz are not as strong as at lower frequencies. Something must be done to increase the amplitude of these frequencies when a direct FM transmitter is used. A circuit

called a preemphasis network amplifies the sounds between 2000 and 3000 Hz. With phase modulation, the preemphasis network is not required, because the deviation already increases with increasing audio input frequency.

MODULATION INDEX

The **sidebands** that occur from FM or PM differ from those resulting from AM. With AM, only a single set of sidebands is produced for each modulating frequency. FM and PM sidebands occur at integral multiples of the modulating frequency on either side of the carrier, as shown in Figure 9-25. Because of these multiple sidebands, FM or PM signals inherently occupy a greater bandwidth. The additional sidebands depend on the relationship between the modulating frequency and the frequency deviation. The ratio between the peak carrier frequency deviation and the audio modulating frequency is called the **modulation index**.

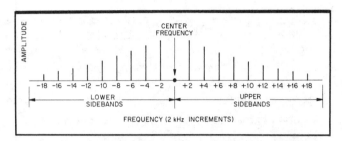

Figure 9-25—When an RF carrier is frequency-modulated by an audio signal, multiple sidebands are produced. FM sidebands are spaced above and below the center frequency of the carrier. This drawing shows a group of sidebands resulting from the application of a 2-kHz tone to the transmitter modulator. The sidebands farthest from the center frequency are the lowest in amplitude. The sidebands nearest to center frequency can be considered the significant sidebands, their amplitudes being fairly large.

Given a constant input level to the modulator, in phase modulation, the modulation index is constant regardless of the modulating frequency. For an FM signal, the modulation index varies with the modulating frequency. In an FM system, the ratio of the maximum carrier-frequency deviation to the highest modulating frequency is called the **deviation ratio**. The modulation index is a variable that depends on a set of operating conditions, but the deviation ratio is a constant. The deviation ratio for narrow-band FM is 5000 Hz (maximum deviation) divided by 3000 Hz (maximum modulation frequency) or 1.67.

Frequency multiplication offers a means for obtaining any desired amount of frequency deviation, whether or not the modulator is capable of that much deviation. Overdeviation of an FM transmitter causes **splatter**, out-of-channel emissions that can cause interference to adjacent frequencies.

A frequency-multiplier stage is an amplifier that produces harmonics of the input signal. By using a filter to select the desired harmonic, the proper output frequency is obtained. A frequency multiplier is not the same as a mixer stage, which is used to obtain the designed output frequency in an SSB or CW rig. A mixer shifts, or translates, an oscillator frequency to some new frequency.

[Now turn to Chapter 13 and study questions 3AH-6.1, 3AH-6.2, 3AH-7-1.1, 3AH-7-2.1 and 3AH-7-2.2. Review this section as needed.]

───── KEY WORDS ─────

AC power-line filter—A filter connected in the power line to an amateur transmitter or transceiver. It keeps RF energy from entering the power line and radiating from power lines near a house. A line filter in the power line to other electronic devices will keep unwanted RF energy from entering them as well.

Attenuate—To decrease or lessen in strength. Filters attenuate signals outside the frequencies they are designed to pass.

Chirp—A slight shift in transmitter frequency each time you key the transmitter.

Fundamental frequency—The desired operating frequency of an oscillator.

Harmonics—Signals from a transmitter or oscillator occurring on whole-number multiples of the desired operating frequency.

High-pass filter—A filter designed to pass high-frequency signals, while blocking lower-frequency signals.

Key click—A click or thump at the beginning or end of a CW signal.

Low-pass filter—A filter designed to pass low-frequency signals, while blocking higher-frequency signals.

Neutralization—A method of preventing oscillation in an amplifier stage.

Parasitics—Oscillations in a transmitter amplifier that are not related to the operating frequency.

Radio-frequency interference (RFI)—Disturbance to electronic equipment caused by radio-frequency signals.

Receiver overload—Interference to a receiver caused by a strong RF signal that forces its way into the equipment. A signal that overloads the receiver RF amplifier (front end) causes *front-end overload*.

Spurious emissions—Signals from a transmitter on frequencies other than the operating frequency.

Superimposed hum—A low-pitched buzz or hum on a radio signal.

Television interference (TVI)—Interruption of television reception caused by another signal.

Chapter 10

But What if I Have Trouble?

This chapter describes some common problems you may encounter when you get on the air. Although you may never have any trouble, you should be aware of possible problems and know how to cure them. We show you how to identify interference to consumer electronics equipment. We also suggest ways to cure interference problems caused by overload and harmonics. Finally, we discuss some common transmitter problems: key clicks, chirp and superimposed hum. When you finish this chapter you'll be able to identify these problems and describe their cures.

———— SPURIOUS SIGNALS ————

An ideal transmitter emits a signal only on the operating frequency and nowhere else. Real-world transmitters radiate undesired signals, or **spurious emissions**, as well. Using good design and construction practices, manufacturers and home builders can reduce spurious emissions so they cause no problems. These undesired signals can, however, cause you some problems. Spurious emissions fall into two general categories: harmonics and parasitic oscillations. On the HF

bands, you are more likely to have harmonic problems. Parasitic oscillations can occur in equipment designed for HF or VHF/UHF operation.

HARMONICS

Harmonics are multiples of a given frequency. For example, the second harmonic of 100 Hz is 200 Hz. The fifth harmonic of 100 Hz is 500 Hz. Every oscillator generates

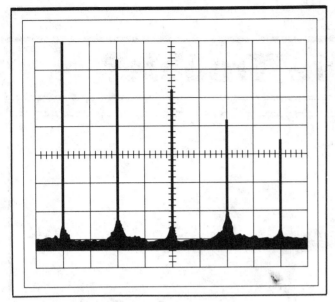

Figure 10-1—Harmonics are signals that appear at whole number multiples of the resonant, or fundamental, frequency. This drawing represents a spectrum analyzer display screen, and shows a 2-MHz signal and some of its harmonics. A spectrum analyzer is an instrument that allows you to look at energy radiated over a wide range of frequencies. Here, the analyzer is adjusted to display any RF energy between 1 MHz and 11 MHz. Each vertical line in the background grid denotes an increment of 1 MHz. The first thick black vertical "pip" represents energy from the fundamental signal of a 2-MHz oscillator. The next pip, two vertical divisions later, is the second harmonic at 4 MHz (twice the fundamental frequency). The pip at the center of the photo is the third harmonic at 6 MHz (three times the fundamental frequency). This figure shows the second, third, fourth and fifth harmonics.

harmonics in addition to a signal at its **fundamental frequency**. For example, consider an oscillator tuned to 7.125 MHz in the 40-meter band. It also generates signals at 14.250 MHz (second harmonic), 21.375 MHz (third harmonic), 28.500 MHz (fourth harmonic), and so on. Figure 10-1 shows the output of an oscillator that has many harmonics.

Harmonics can interfere with other amateurs or other users of the radio spectrum. The second through fourth harmonics of a 40-meter transmitter fall in the 20, 15 and 10-meter amateur bands. Imagine the interference (QRM) that would result if everyone transmitted two, four, six or more harmonics in addition to the desired signal!

To prevent this chaos, FCC regulations specify limits for harmonic and other spurious radiation. For example, if you are operating a 100-W-output transmitter, your harmonic signals can total no more than 10 milliwatts. As you can see, a transmitter that complies with the rules still generates some harmonic energy. Fortunately, that energy is so small that it is not likely to cause problems.

Good transmitter engineering calls for tuned circuits between the oscillator and amplifier stages in amateur transmitters. These circuits reduce or eliminate spurious signals such as harmonics. The tuned circuits allow signals at the desired frequency to pass, but they **attenuate** (reduce) harmonics.

Transmitters with vacuum tubes in the final amplifier often use a *pi-network* impedance-matching circuit at the final amplifier output. The plate-tuning and antenna-loading capacitors in the pi network are adjustable. When properly tuned, the pi network allows maximum power to pass at the frequency of operation but reduces harmonics.

Transmitters with solid-state final amplifiers usually operate over a wide range of frequencies with no external tuning controls. In these transmitters, the band switch activates a separate tuned *band-pass filter* for each band. As the name implies, this filter allows energy to pass at the desired frequency and attenuates spurious signals above and below.

How can you be sure that your transmitter does not generate excessive harmonics? The FCC requires all transmitter manufacturers to prove that their equipment complies with its regulations. This means that commercially manufactured equipment usually produces clean signals. If you build a transmitter from a magazine or book article, check for information on harmonic radiation. ARRL requires that all transmitter projects published in *QST* and our technical books meet the FCC specifications for commercially manufactured equipment.

PARASITIC OSCILLATIONS

Parasitic oscillations in the final amplifier occur on frequencies unrelated to those for which the amplifier is designed. These spurious signals, called **parasitics**, are not harmonics. They result from an unintentional tuned feedback path in the final-amplifier circuit. Parasitics happen because an amplifier tube or semiconductor often works well at frequencies much higher than those it is used on. Parasitic oscillations take place in the VHF/UHF range. Most transmit-

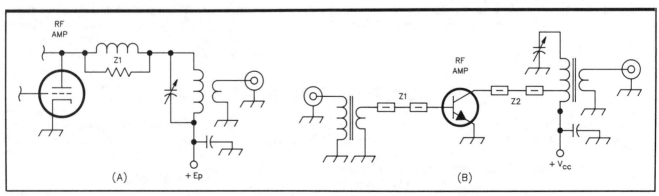

Figure 10-2—A shows the schematic diagram of a vacuum tube amplifier. The coil and resistor combination Z1 is a parasitic suppressor. B shows the schematic diagram of a transistor power amplifier. Z1 and Z2 are ferrite beads that also function as parasitic suppressors.

ters have special tuned circuits built into the final-amplifier circuit to prevent parasitic oscillations. They are called *parasitic suppressors*. Figure 10-2 shows examples of parasitic suppressors connected in amplifier circuits.

NEUTRALIZATION

Spurious signals may result from improper **neutralization** of the transmitter. An oscillator is an amplifier that has some of the output signal fed back to the input. This *positive feedback* is fine for oscillators, but we don't want positive feedback in an amplifier. Positive feedback in an audio amplifier for example, causes a howling noise. You may have heard this noise from a public-address system with the gain set too high.

We don't want positive feedback in radio amplifiers, either. In an improperly neutralized amplifier, some of the output feeds back to the input and causes the amplifier to oscillate. The signal generated may be transmitted, and can sometimes damage the transmitter. Neutralization eliminates or neutralizes this positive feedback by applying negative feedback. If you suspect that you need to neutralize your transmitter, you may have to adjust an internal control. Figure 10-3 shows a vacuum tube amplifier circuit with a neutralizing capacitor.

An amplifier that requires neutralization oscillates on the frequency band it is designed to amplify. Compare this with parasitics, which happen at much higher frequencies. You may need to operate your transmitter to check for proper neutralization, and for other transmitter adjustments and tests. You should do this without transmitting a signal on the air. The best way to adjust your transmitter is to use a *dummy load*, described in Chapter 8.

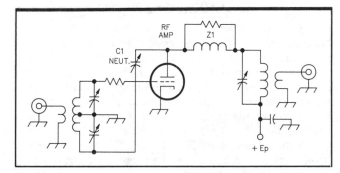

Figure 10-3—Schematic diagram of a vacuum tube amplifier. C1 is a neutralizing capacitor. It applies negative feedback to the amplifier input and prevents oscillation.

Modern solid-state transceivers don't normally require neutralization. If your transmitter or transceiver has a vacuum-tube final amplifier, you may need to adjust neutralization if you change the tubes. Often, even replacing tubes doesn't upset the adjustment. The procedure is not the same for all transmitters. Follow the instructions in your transceiver or transmitter manual, if you have it. Otherwise, ask your instructor or a local ham to help you.

Remember that you have exposed the high-voltage components of your rig when you are neutralizing it. Be extra careful to avoid the possibility of electric shock.

[Now turn to Chapter 12 and study questions 2H-7.1 and 2H-7.2. Review this section if you have any difficulty with those questions.]

━━━━━INTERFERENCE WITH OTHER SERVICES━━━━━

Radio frequency interference (RFI) has given radio amateurs headaches for years. It can occur whenever an electronic device is surrounded by a field of RF energy. Your rig emits RF energy each time you transmit. This RF energy may interfere with your own or your neighbor's television set (causing **television interference—TVI**). You may also have problems with a stereo system, electronic organ, video cassette recorder or any other piece of consumer electronic equipment.

If you have a very obvious antenna in your yard, your neighbors may blame you for any interference they experience, even when you're not on the air! If you have any problems with interference to your own equipment, it's a good bet that your neighbors do too. On the other hand, if you can show your neighbors that you don't interfere with *your* television, they may be more open to your suggestions for curing problems.

So what should you do if someone complains of interference? First, make sure that your equipment is operating properly. Check for interference to your own TV. If you see it, stop operating and cure the problem before you go back on the air.

Even if you don't interfere with your own TV, don't stop there. Simply telling your neighbors you're not at fault can cause even more problems. Try to work with your neighbors to determine if your rig is actually causing the interference. If so, try to help solve the problem. A more-experienced ham can be a great help. If you don't know any other hams in your

Figure 10-4—There has been a boom in home electronic devices since the 1950s. Many more amateur and CB antennas are close to a growing number of home-entertainment devices. The result: an RFI problem that shows little sign of disappearing.

area, write to ARRL HQ. We'll try to help you find a knowledgeable local ham.

[Now go back to Chapter 12 and study those questions with numbers that begin 2D-8-3. Review this section if you have any problems.]

RECEIVER OVERLOAD

Receiver overload is a common type of TV and FM-broadcast interference. It happens most often to consumer electronic equipment near an amateur station or other transmitter. When the RF signal (at the fundamental frequency) enters the receiver, it overloads one or more circuits. The receiver front end (first RF amplifier stage after the antenna) is most commonly affected. For this reason, we sometimes call this interference *front-end overload*.

A strong enough RF field may produce spurious signals in the receiver, which cause the interference. Receiver overload interference may occur in your neighbor's house or just your own. Receiver overload can be caused by transmitters operating on any frequency.

Receiver overload usually has a dramatic effect on the television picture. Whenever you key your transmitter, the picture may be completely wiped out. The screen may go black, or it might just become light with traces of color. The sound (audio) will probably be affected also. In an FM receiver, the audio may be blocked each time you transmit. More often than not, overload affects only TV channels 2 through 13. In cases of severe interference, however, it may also affect the UHF channels.

The objective in curing receiver overload is to prevent the amateur signal from entering the front end of the entertainment receiver. The first step is to have the equipment owner or a qualified service technician install a **high-pass filter**. See Figure 10-5.

Install the filter at the TV or FM receiver input. The best location is where the antenna feed line connects to the TV or FM tuner. It is *not* a good idea for an Amateur Radio operator to install a filter on a neighbor's entertainment equipment. Only the owner or a qualified technician should install

the filter. If you install the filter, you might later be blamed for other problems with the TV set. A high-pass filter is a tuned circuit that passes high frequencies (TV channels start at 54 MHz). The filter blocks low frequencies (the HF amateur bands are in the range of 1.8-30 MHz).

[Now study the questions in Chapter 12 with numbers that begin 2D-8-1. Review this section as needed.]

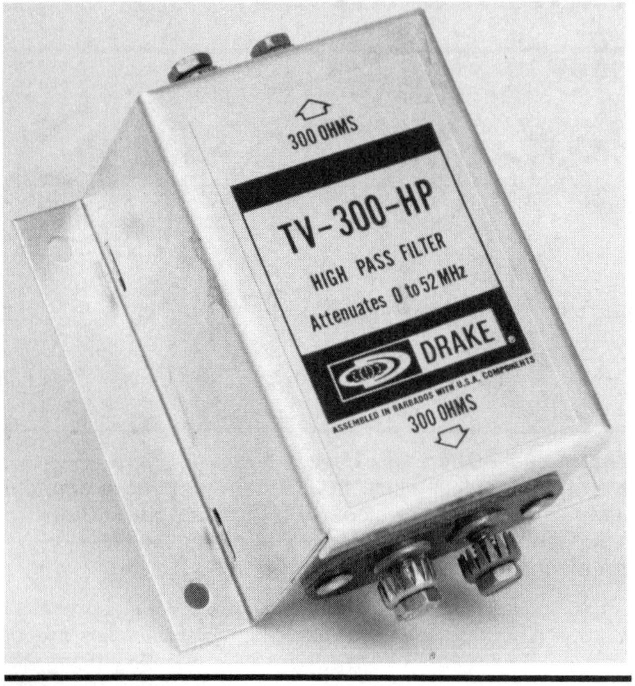

HARMONIC INTERFERENCE

Another problem for hams is harmonic interference to entertainment equipment. As we learned before, harmonics are multiples of a given frequency. Your HF transmitter radiates undesired harmonics along with your signal. Your transmitting frequency is much lower than the TV or FM channels. Some harmonics will fall within the home entertainment bands, however.

The entertainment receiver cannot distinguish between the TV or FM signals (desired signals) and your harmonics (undesirable intruders). If your harmonics are strong enough, they can seriously interfere with the received signal. Harmonic interference shows up as crosshatch or a herringbone pattern on the TV screen. See Figure 10-6.

Figure 10-6—"Crosshatching," caused by harmonics radiated from an amateur transmitter.

Unlike receiver overload, harmonic interference seldom affects all channels. Rather, it may bother the one channel that has a harmonic relationship to the band you're on. Generally, harmonics from amateur transmitters operating below 30 MHz affect the lower TV channels (2 through 6). Ten-meter transmitters usually bother channels 2 and 6, and channels 3 and 6 experience trouble from 15-meter transmitters.

Harmonic interference must be cured at your transmitter. As a licensed amateur, you must take steps to see that harmonics from your transmitter do not interfere with other services. All harmonics generated by your transmitter must be attenuated well below the strength of the fundamental frequency. If harmonics from your transmitting equipment exceed these limits, you are at fault.

In this section we will discuss some of the several possible cures for harmonic interference. Try each step in order and the chances are good that your problem will be solved quickly.

Figure 10-5—A high-pass filter can prevent fundamental energy from an amateur signal from entering a television set. This type of high-pass filter goes in the 300-ohm feed line that connects the television with the antenna.

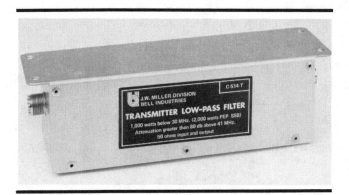

Figure 10-7—A low-pass filter. When connected in the coaxial cable feed line between an amateur transmitter and the antenna, a low-pass filter can reduce the strength of transmitted harmonics.

The first step you should take is to install a **low-pass filter** like the one shown in Figure 10-7. The filter goes in the transmission line between your transmitter and antenna or antenna tuner. As the name implies, a low-pass filter is the opposite of a high-pass filter. A low-pass filter allows RF energy in the amateur bands to pass freely. It blocks very high frequency harmonics that can fall in the TV and FM bands. Low-pass filters usually have a specified cutoff frequency, often 40 MHz, above which they severely attenuate the passage of RF energy.

Even if your transmitter is working well within FCC specifications, you may need additional attenuation to reduce harmonics. Remember, your goal is to eliminate interference. Good-quality low-pass filters often attenuate signals falling in the entertainment bands by 70 or 80 dB. This is significantly better than the 40 to 50 dB typical of amateur transmitters. A decibel (dB) is a number (the logarithm of a ratio) used to describe how effective the filter is. Larger numbers indicate better filtering. Figure 10-8 shows the output of a transmitter before and after filtering.

Another source of interference is RF energy from your transmitter that enters the ac power lines. The **ac power-line filter** is another kind of low-pass network. It prevents RF energy from entering the ac line and radiating from power lines near your house.

Multiband Antennas

You can also run into trouble if you use a multiband antenna. If your antenna works on two or three different bands, it will radiate any harmonics present on those frequencies. After all, we *want* the antenna to radiate energy at a given frequency. It cannot tell the difference between desired signal energy and unwanted harmonic energy. This problem does not usually affect home entertainment equipment. It may cause interference to other amateurs or to other radio services operating near the amateur bands, however.

For example, a multiband dipole antenna that covers 80 and 40 meters may radiate 40-meter energy while you operate on 80 meters. The second harmonic of a 3.7-MHz signal falls above the 40-meter amateur band, at 7.4 MHz. If your transmitter is free of excessive harmonic output, you will probably not have a problem.

Proper shielding and grounding are essential to reduce harmonic radiation. The only place you want RF to leave your transmitter is through the antenna connection. Your transmitter must be fully enclosed in a metal cabinet. The various shields that make up the metal cabinet should be securely screwed or welded together at the seams. You must also connect the transmitter to a good ground.

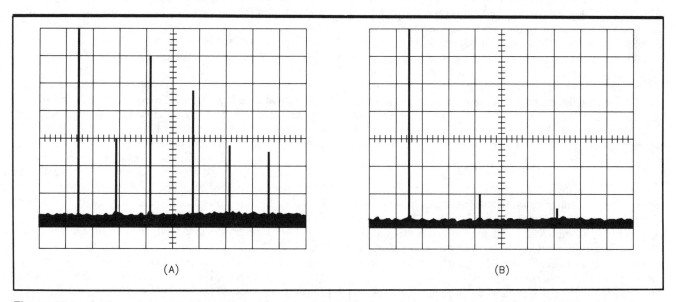

(A)   (B)

Figure 10-8—A shows a spectrum-analyzer display of the signals emitted from an amateur transmitter. The pip at the left of the display (the one that extends to the top horizontal line) is the fundamental. All other pips represent harmonics. This particular transmitter generates several harmonics. On an analyzer display, stronger signals create taller pips. Here, the harmonic signals are quite strong. In fact, the third harmonic is about one-tenth as strong as the fundamental. The fundamental signal is 100 W, so the transmitter is radiating a potent 10-W signal at the third harmonic. Most of these harmonics will cause interference to other services. B shows the output from the same transmitter, operating at the same power level at the same frequency, after installation of a low-pass filter between the transmitter and the analyzer. The harmonics have all but disappeared from the display. The stronger of the two remaining harmonics is only about 100 microwatts—weak enough that it is unlikely to cause interference.

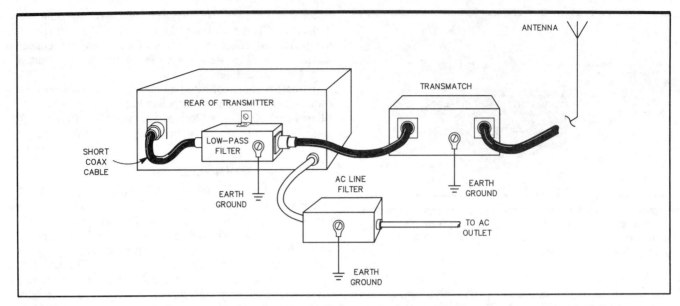

Figure 10-9—Suggested techniques for filtering harmonic energy from the leads of an amateur transmitter.

Remember: A low-pass filter will only block harmonics from reaching your antenna. It will do nothing for a poorly shielded transmitter that leaks stray RF from places other than the antenna connector. Figure 10-9 summarizes the steps you can take to reduce harmonic radiation from your station.

[Now turn to Chapter 12 and study the questions that begin 2H-5, question 2H-7.3, and the questions that begin 2D-8-2. Review this section as necessary.]

═══ SIGNAL PURITY ═══

As a licensed Amateur Radio operator, you're responsible for the quality of the signal transmitted from your station. The rules require your transmitted signal to be stable in frequency and pure in tone. Stations receiving your signal should hear a single, pure, unwavering note. If your signal is not "clean," it is unpleasant to listen to. It may also cause interference to others sharing the band.

Unfortunately, however, some problems can creep up and give you a "dirty" signal. Three of the most common problems with CW signals are **key clicks, chirp** and **superimposed hum**.

KEY CLICKS

As you listen on the air, you will notice that some signals have a click or thump on *make* (the instant the key contacts close) or *break* (the instant they open) or both. This **key click** is more than just annoying; it can interfere with other stations.

If you use an oscilloscope to monitor a CW signal with key clicks, you will see excessively square CW keyed waveforms. Imagine a good, stable transmitter sending a CW signal on 3.720 MHz. What happens when we turn the transmitter on and off with a telegraph key? You'd think that the only frequency the output energy could have would be 3.720 MHz. If you turn the transmitter output on and off rapidly, however, something else happens. Unwanted energy in the form of key clicks appears for several kilohertz on either side of the operating frequency. The transmitter creates these clicks during the instant that it is turned on and off.

When we say "keyed rapidly," we don't mean that we're sending fast (like 35 WPM) CW. We mean that the transmitter

goes from zero power to full power and back again very quickly and abruptly. We call the time it takes to go from no power to full power the *rise time*. We call the return trip from full power to zero power the *fall time*.

An oscilloscope display of a CW signal with short rise and fall times is shown in Figure 10-10A. This signal has key clicks. A click-free signal is shown in part B. Notice how the beginning and ending of this CW pulse are soft and round. Compare this with the square shoulders of the signal with clicks. Part C shows a string of dots and dashes that will generate interference from key clicks.

We use a key-click filter or *shaping filter* to eliminate this unwanted and bothersome energy. The filter makes the transmitter output increase to maximum more slowly on make, and fall from full output more slowly on break. The keying waveform is softer, limiting the output energy to a few hundred hertz on either side of the operating frequency.

[Turn to Chapter 12 now and study the questions with numbers that begin 2H-2. Review this section if any of those questions confuse you.]

CHIRP

Chirp is another common transmitter problem. Chirp occurs when the oscillator in your transmitter shifts frequency slightly whenever you close your telegraph key. The result is that other stations receive your transmitted signal as a chirping sound rather than as a pure tone. Your "dahdidahdit" will sound like "whoopwhiwhoopwhip." It isn't very much fun to copy a chirpy CW signal!

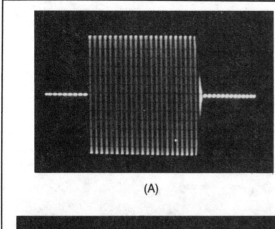

(A)

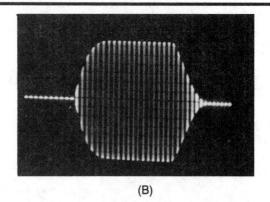

(B)

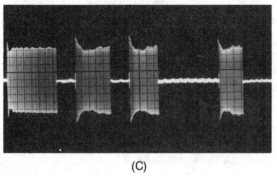

(C)

Figure 10-10—CW signals viewed on an oscilloscope. A shows a CW dot with no intentional wave shaping. This signal has key clicks. B shows a similar dot, shaped to eliminate key clicks. Notice how the signal at B builds and decays gradually. Compare this with the abrupt on-and-off characteristics at A. C shows a string of unshaped CW characters. Notice the sharp *spikes* at the beginning of each pulse. These spikes are audible in a receiver as key clicks. Such spikes can appear at either end of a CW character.

Chirp usually happens when the oscillator power supply voltage changes as you transmit. Your transmitter may also chirp if the load on the oscillator changes when you transmit. If the supply voltage changes, you must improve the *voltage regulation*. With better regulation, the voltage won't shift when you key your transmitter.

If it's not a voltage problem, then what? Amplifier stages after the oscillator may be loading it down and pulling its frequency. You may need a better buffer (isolation) or driver stage between the oscillator and the next stage in your transmitter. Some oscillators are sensitive to temperature changes. If there is too much current through the frequency-determining components, their temperature may increase and the resonant frequency will change.

[Time for another trip to the Question Pool. Study the questions in Chapter 12 with numbers that begin 2H-3. Review this section if you have any problems.]

SUPERIMPOSED HUM

The last kind of signal problem we discuss is superimposed hum. Power supplies contain filters that remove the ac present in the rectifier output. The result is a pure, filtered dc output. If a filter capacitor fails, then the filtering action will be incomplete.

If the filter doesn't work properly, ac will be present in the power supply output. This ac will also work its way into the transmitter output. Instead of hearing a pure tone, stations receiving your signal would hear a low-pitched hum as well. If enough ac is present, the signal will have a raspy tone. It may even buzz as if you were keying an electric razor! To cure hum, check the power-supply filter circuit. A bad filter capacitor can cause superimposed hum.

[Now study the questions in Chapter 12 with numbers beginning 2H-4. Review this section as necessary.]

HOW TO GET HELP

Transmitting a signal with chirp, key clicks or hum is a violation of both the letter and spirit of the regulations governing Amateur Radio. The best way to find out if you have a bad-sounding signal is from the stations you work. If another operator tells you about a problem with your signal, don't be offended. He cares about the image of the Amateur Service and only wants to help you. You might never be aware of a problem otherwise.

Don't let this chapter scare you. Spurious signals, unwanted harmonics, poor neutralization, key clicks, parasitic oscillations, television interference (TVI) or other equipment difficulties can all be solved. Two ARRL publications will be helpful: *The ARRL Handbook for Radio Amateurs* and *Radio Frequency Interference*. Check with your Amateur Radio instructor or any experienced ham for help. There's no substitute for experience. Another ham may know just how to solve your problem and return you to the air as soon as possible.

——— KEY WORDS ———

A1A emission—The FCC emission type designator that describes international Morse code telegraphy **(CW)** communications without audio modulation of the carrier.

Bandwidth—A range of associated frequencies (measured in hertz). For example, bandwidth is used to describe the range of frequencies in the radio spectrum that a radio transmission occupies.

Code key—A device used as a switch to generate Morse code.

Code-practice oscillator—A device that produces an audio tone, used for learning the code.

CW (continuous wave)—The FCC emission type that describes international Morse code telegraphy communication without audio modulation of the carrier. Hams usually produce Morse code signals by interrupting the continuous-wave signal from a transmitter to form the dots and dashes.

Dash—The long sound used in Morse code. Pronounce this as "dah" when verbally sounding Morse code characters. Dashes are three times longer than dots.

Dot—The short sound used in Morse code. Pronounce this as "dit" when verbally sounding Morse code characters if the dot comes at the end of the character. If the dot comes at the beginning or in the middle of the character, pronounce it as "di."

Emission—RF signals transmitted from a radio station.

Emission privileges—Permissible types of transmitted signals.

Fist—The unique rhythm of an individual amateur's Morse code sending.

Phone—Voice communications.

Q signals—Three-letter symbols beginning with "Q," used in amateur CW work to save time and for better comprehension.

Traffic net—An on-the-air meeting of amateurs, for the purpose of relaying messages.

W1AW—The headquarters station of the American Radio Relay League. This station is a memorial to the League's cofounder, Hiram Percy Maxim. The station provides daily on-the-air code practice and bulletins of interest to hams.

Chapter 11

Morse Code—The Amateur's International Language

To qualify for a Novice license, you must pass a written exam about FCC Rules, electronics theory and basic amateur operating practices. In addition, you will have to show your ability to communicate using the international Morse code. The code exam is given at 5 words per minute.

To earn the Technician license, you do not have to pass the Morse code exam. That license does not include privileges on the amateur high-frequency bands, which provide world-wide communications. As a Technician class licensee, you *can* earn those privileges, however. To join the excitement of communicating with other Amateur Radio operators around the world, you simply pass the 5-WPM Morse code exam.

This book won't teach you the Morse code. The code is best learned by listening to sounds, and for that you'll need either cassette tapes or a computer program (or both). The ARRL offers a code-teaching package of cassette tapes, called *Your Introduction to Morse Code*. That package contains two 90-minute cassette tapes to teach you all of the code characters

required by the FCC. Practice text at 5 WPM ensures that you are prepared for the 5-WPM code exam.

The ARRL also offers two computer programs to teach Morse code. If you have a Commodore 64™ or 128™ computer, the AEA *Morse University* program is for you. This excellent program comes on a ROM cartridge that plugs into the back of your computer. For the IBM® PC and compatible computers, the ARRL sells the GGTE *Morse Tutor* program, another excellent Morse-code training program.

The cassette tapes and both programs are available directly from ARRL Headquarters or from the many dealers who sell ARRL publications. See the advertising section at the back of this book for an ARRL publications order form.

CODE IS FUN!

Using the code is an exciting way to communicate. Many long-time hams beam with pride when they proclaim that they don't even own a microphone! You are fluent in another

A FAMILY OF HAMS

The Dalton family of Duluth, Minnesota is a special group of hams. David (NØLOG), and Elaine (KBØFLB) began to study for Amateur Radio licenses in 1989. Two of their children, Sarah (10 at the time) and Daniel (then 8) also became interested when they saw mom and dad studying. Both children passed their Novice exams in January 1990.

Encouraged by the excitement of the Novice bands and the interest of other hams in their local radio club, both children upgraded to Technician in May. Less than a year after first being licensed, Daniel (NØMAT) upgraded to General and Sarah (NØMAS) passed the General written exam. David has upgraded to Amateur Extra and Elaine to General.

Sarah and Daniel have become very excited about ham radio. They have taken their hand-held 2-meter radios to school and demonstrated them to their classes, they attend club meetings and enjoy participating in nets. Daniel takes his hand-held radio along when he goes out selling popcorn for his Cub Scout Pack and on other Webelos Scout activities. Both children carry their radios while on their newspaper routes. This may be Elaine's favorite aspect of ham radio—keeping in touch with her busy family. The family has helped their local radio club provide public-service communications at several local events.

James, another member of the Dalton family, began to study Morse code at the age of 6, and knows over half

the Morse code characters after only a few weeks of studying. James hopes to have his Novice license before he completes the first grade!

---

complete language when you know the code. You can chat with hams from all around the world using this common language. With the practice you will gain by making on-the-air contacts, your speed will increase quickly. With more advanced licenses, you'll be operating on more portions of the bands, increasing your realm of contacts.

Amateur Radio operators must know the international Morse code if their license permits them to transmit on frequencies below 30 MHz. An international treaty sets this rule, and the United States must follow the treaty. Because of this, the Federal Communications Commission requires you to pass a code test to earn your Novice license.

There's a lot more to the code than just satisfying the terms of a treaty, however. Morse code goes back to the very beginning of radio, and is still one of the most effective radio-communication methods. We send Morse code by interrupting the **continuous-wave** signal generated by a transmitter, and so we call it **CW** for short.

For one thing, it takes far less power to establish reliable communications with CW than it does with voice (**phone**). On phone, we sometimes need high power and elaborate antennas to communicate with distant stations, or *DX* in the ham's lingo. On CW, less power and more modest stations will provide the same contacts. Finally, there is great satisfaction in being able to communicate using Morse code. This is similar to the satisfaction you might feel from using any acquired skill.

CONSERVE TIME AND SPECTRUM SPACE

Another advantage of CW over phone is its very narrow **bandwidth**. Morse code makes efficient use of spectrum space. The group of frequencies where hams operate, the *ham bands*, are narrow portions of the whole spectrum. Many stations use the bands, and because they are so crowded, interference

is sometimes a problem. A CW signal occupies only about one-tenth the bandwidth of a phone signal. This means 10 CW signals can fit into the space taken up by one phone signal.

Over the years, radiotelegraph operators have developed a vocabulary of three-letter **Q signals**, which other radio-telegraphers throughout the world understand. For example, the Q signal *QRM* means "you are being interfered with." Just imagine how hard it would be to communicate that thought to someone who didn't understand one word of English. (Chapter 9 includes a list of common Q signals.)

Another advantage to using Q signals is speed. It's much faster to send three letters than to spell out each word. That's why you'll use these Q signals even when you're chatting by code with another English-speaking ham. Speed of transmission is also the reason radiotelegraphers use a code "shorthand." For example, to acknowledge that you heard what was transmitted to you, send the letter R. This means "I have received your transmission okay."

Standard Q signals and shorthand abbreviations reduce the total time necessary to send a message. When radio conditions are poor and signals are marginal, a short message is much more likely to get through.

Many hams prefer to use CW in **traffic nets**. (A net is a regular on-the-air meeting of a group of hams.) Using these nets, hams send messages across the country for just about anyone. When they send messages using CW, there is no confusion about the spelling of names such as Lee, Lea or Leigh.

CW: SOMETIMES THE ONLY CHOICE

When WA6INJ's jeep went over a cliff in a February snowstorm, he was able to call for help using his mobile rig. This worked well at first, but as the search for him continued,

Morse Code From the Heart

The power of modern medicine kept one ham alive; the power of Morse code kept him in touch with loved ones.

Reprinted from July 1990 QST.

Have you ever felt Morse code rather than heard it?

Although I've been a licensed amateur for 34 years and have had many wonderful experiences in this hobby, none can compare to the one I'll never forget. It happened on Monday, August 26, 1985.

My husband Ralph, W8LCU, went to the hospital the Friday before for an ECG and heart catheterization. He was told that an immediate quadruple bypass was needed and he could not leave the hospital. Arrangements were made for the following Monday. Ralph had always been healthy and never showed an inkling of heart problems, so this came as quite a shock to us. The doctors told us that after his surgery he would not be speaking or doing much else, until perhaps the next day or until he was off the respirator, heart pump and everything else that goes with this type of surgery.

Over the weekend we had many things to discuss and Amateur Radio never entered my mind.

Monday evening, in the intensive-care unit (ICU) after surgery, I held Ralph's hand. He began tapping on my palm. I didn't think much of it, but his eyes opened and seemed to be telling me something. He moved his fingers to my wrist and suddenly, as clear as if I was hearing CW on the radio, came the letters P A (tears coming down my face) I N (pause) IS HELL. "Pain is hell."

Before I could say or do anything, four nurses were in the room. I told them what Ralph had just said to me in Morse code. I think they were ready to have me taken to the mental ward, but they gave him a shot. Then they stood by in disbelief as he tapped out a short message to our son and daughter and a final I LUV U before drifting off to sleep.

Meanwhile, in another hospital across the state, a friend of ours, Vanessa, KA8TRH, was back in her room after major surgery. Her first words to her husband, Chuck, N8EOJ, were "How is Ralph doing?" Sure enough, through the wonders of CW, hand-held transceivers, repeaters and many hams along the way, relays of Ralph's progress were sent to N8EOJ all day long. When Ralph tapped CW to me, within moments hams all across the state knew all was well.

The ICU and other units were buzzing for days as doctors came into Ralph's room to find out about this "new" form of communication. They told Ralph that they thought more people should know Morse code, themselves included. Of course, Ralph told them that with a little study and determination any one can do it.

Needless to say, CW will always be important to me, either in an emergency or just for plain fun.

Today, Ralph is doing fine and I, while I was an Advanced at the time, have gone on to earn my Amateur Extra Class license.—*Donna Burch, W8QOY*

---

he became unable to speak. The nearly frozen man managed to tap out Morse code signals with his microphone push-to-talk button. That was all his rescuers had to work with to locate him. Morse code saved this ham's life.

For some types of transmissions, CW (also called type **A1A emission** by the FCC) is the only available choice. As a Novice, CW is the only **emission privilege** you may use on the 80, 40 and 15-meter amateur bands. (One exception to this rule is if you are in Alaska, and involved in some emergency communications. In that case you may use single sideband [J3E or R3E] on 5167.5 kHz.) CW is the only mode that may be used on *all* amateur frequencies.

Some hams like to bounce VHF and UHF signals off the surface of the moon to another ham station on the earth. Because of its efficiency, hams use CW in most of this *moon-bounce* work. They could use voice signals, but this increases the power and antenna-gain requirements quite a bit.

On some frequencies, amateurs communicate by bouncing their signals off an auroral curtain in the northern sky. (Stations in the Southern Hemisphere would use an auroral curtain in the southern sky.) Phone signals become so distorted in the process of reflecting off an auroral curtain that they are difficult or impossible to understand. CW is the most effective way to communicate using signals bounced off an aurora.

You will feel a special thrill and a warm satisfaction when

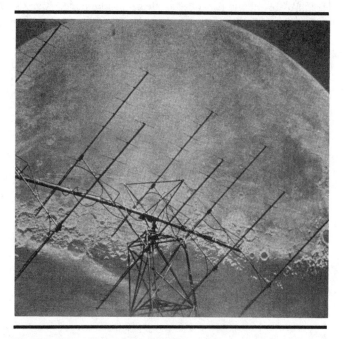

Figure 11-1—Even the moon isn't immune from ever-ambitious hams, and code is the most efficient type of signal to bounce off its surface and be reflected back to earth.

you use the Morse code to communicate with someone. This feeling comes partly from sending messages to another part of the world without regard to language barriers. Sending and receiving Morse code is a skill that helps set amateurs apart from other people. It provides a common bond between amateurs worldwide.

—— GETTING ACQUAINTED WITH THE CODE ——

The basic element of a Morse code character is a **dot**. The length of the dot determines how long a **dash** should be. The dot length also determines the length of the spaces between elements, characters and words. Figure 11-2 shows the proper timing of each piece. Notice that a dash is three times as long as a dot. The time between dots and dashes in a character is equal to the length of a dot. The time between letters in a word is equal to three dot lengths and the space between words is seven dot lengths.

The lengths of Morse code characters are not all the same, of course. Samuel Finley Breese Morse (1791-1872) developed the system of dots and dashes in 1838. He assigned the shortest combinations to the most-used letters in plain-language text. The letter E has the shortest sound, because it is the most-used letter. T and I are the next most-used characters, and they are also short. Character lengths get longer for letters used less often.

An analysis of English plain-language text shows that the average word (including the space after the word) is 50 units long. By a unit we mean the time of a single dot or space between the parts of a character. The word PARIS is 50 units long, so we use it as a standard word to check code speed accurately. For example, to transmit at 5 words per minute (WPM), adjust your code-speed timing to send PARIS five times in one minute. To transmit at 10 WPM, adjust your timing to send PARIS 10 times in one minute.

As you can see, the correct dot length (and the length of dashes and spaces) changes for each code speed. As a result, the characters sound different when the speed changes. This leads to problems for a person learning the code. Also, at slower speeds, the characters seem long and drawn out. The slow pace encourages students to count dots and dashes, and to learn the code through this counting method.

Unfortunately, learning the code by counting dots and dashes introduces an extra translation in your brain. (Learning the code by memorizing Morse-code-character dot/dash patterns from a printed copy introduces a similar extra translation.) That extra translation may not seem so bad at first. As you try to increase your speed, however, you will soon find out what a problem it is. You won't be able to count the dots and dashes and then make the translation to a character fast enough!

People learning the Morse code with either of these methods often reach a learning plateau at about 10 words per minute. Unfortunately, this is just below the 13-WPM speed required to upgrade to the General class license. That frustration (I just can't copy faster than 10 WPM!) is overcome by other methods, however.

LEARNING MORSE CODE

Many studies have been done, and various techniques tried, to teach Morse code. The method that has met with the most success is the Farnsworth method. That is the method used on the ARRL code-teaching tapes included in the package, *Your Introduction to Morse Code*. With this technique, we send each character at a faster speed (we use an 18-WPM character speed at ARRL). At speeds in this range, the characters—and even some short words—begin to take on a distinctive rhythmic pattern.

With this faster character speed, we use longer spaces between characters and words to slow the overall code speed. The ARRL code-teaching tapes send code at an overall speed of 5 WPM. (You can still measure this timing by using the word PARIS, as described earlier.) Once you learn the character sounds, and can copy at 5 WPM, it will be easy to increase your speed. Just decrease the spaces between letters and words, and your code speed increases without changing the rhythmic pattern of the characters.

Learn to recognize that rhythmic pattern, and associate it directly with the character. You'll learn the code in the shortest possible time, and it will be much easier to increase your code speed. Decreasing the space between characters and

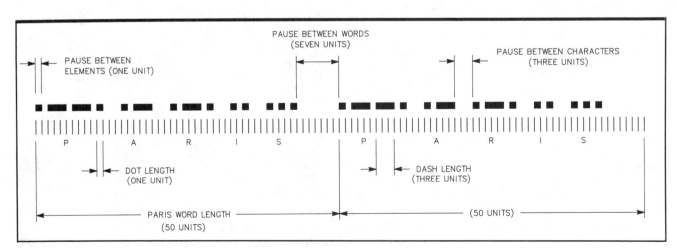

Figure 11-2—Whether you are a beginner or an expert, good sending depends on maintaining proper time ratios or "weight" among the dots, dashes and spaces, as shown.

words provides a natural progression to increase your code speed. The ARRL *Increasing Your Code Speed* series offers code-practice tapes from 5 to 10 WPM, 10 to 15 WPM and 15 to 22 WPM using this technique.

Morse code is a communications method that depends on sounds. To understand the communications you must hear the sounds and interpret their meaning. This is why most code-teaching methods repeat the sounds for you to listen to and associate the characters with the sounds. It is also why you will not find a copy of the Morse code dots and dashes printed in this book. Cassette tapes, computer programs and even classroom or individual practice with a **code-practice oscillator** and a **code key** all rely on sounds to teach you the Morse code characters.

There are many computer programs around for teaching Morse code, and some of them may be very helpful. The ARRL sells *Morse Tutor* for the IBM® PC and compatibles and *Morse University* for the Commodore 64™ and 128™ computers. Both are excellent teaching programs. Beware of programs written in BASIC, however. Because of the way BASIC operates, the timing is often not quite right. Also beware of programs written ''to teach myself Morse code.'' While such writers may be excellent programmers, they are often unaware of the finer points of code training.

Several other techniques have also been successful for teaching Morse code. Some of these methods involve memorizing a printed copy of the code. There are even a few commercial packages that picture the dots and dashes of the code characters in various ''creative'' patterns to help you remember them. You *can* learn Morse code by following any of these methods. Most people will learn faster, and be able to increase their code speed easier, however, by using a ''listening'' method. For those who seem unable to learn the Morse code using tapes or a computer program, one of these ''printed'' methods may prove helpful. Save that as a last resort, however. Practice faithfully with your cassette tapes or a computer program every day for at least three to four weeks. Then, if you have not learned many of the characters, you may want to try one of the visual, or printed, methods.

Morse Code: The Essential Language, by L. Peter Carron, Jr, W3DKV (published by ARRL) contains other suggestions for learning Morse code. That book also describes the history of Morse code. It includes several stories about lives saved because of emergency messages transmitted over the radio.

Sounding the Code

Some people find it helpful to say the sounds of Morse code characters, especially when they are first learning the code. Instead of saying the names of the Morse code elements, dot and dash, we use the sounds ''dit'' and ''dah.'' If the dot is at the beginning or in the middle of the character, we sound it out as ''di'' instead of ''dit.''

Listen to the difference between the sounds you make saying the word ''dit'' and saying ''dah.'' If you can tell the difference between those sounds, you have all the ability you need to learn the code. Being able to receive Morse code is really nothing more than being able to recognize a sound. Try it yourself. Say ''didah.'' Now say ''dididah.'' Can you hear the difference? Congratulations! You now know the sounds for the letters A and U, and are on your way to learning the Morse code.

Using this method, you hear the sound ''didah'' and associate that sound with the letter A. With practice, you'll

learn all the sounds and associate them with the correct letters, numbers and punctuation.

The 26 letters of the alphabet and the numbers 0 through 9 each have a different sound. There are also different sounds for the period, comma, question mark, double dash (=), fraction bar (/) and some procedural signals that hams use. The + sign, which hams call $\overline{AR}$, means ''end of message.'' $\overline{SK}$ means ''end of work,'' or ''end of contact.'' Hams sometimes refer to the double dash as $\overline{BT}$ and the fraction bar as $\overline{DN}$. These two-letter combinations are written with a line over the letters to indicate that two letters are sent as one character to form these symbols. That's a total of 43 character sounds that you will have to learn for your 5-WPM Morse code exam. You'll learn the sounds of all these characters as you practice with your code cassettes or computer program.

Learning to Write

To learn the code, you train your hand to write a certain letter, number or punctuation mark whenever you hear a specific sound. You are forming a habit through your practice. After all, forming a habit is nothing more than doing something the same way time after time. Eventually, whenever you want to do that thing, you automatically do it the same way; it has become a habit.

You will need lots of practice writing the specific characters each time you hear a sound. Eventually you'll copy the code without thinking about it. In other words, you'll respond automatically to the sound by writing the corresponding character.

As you copy code sent at faster speeds, you may find that your ability to write the letters limits you. Practice writing the characters as quickly as possible. If you normally print, look for ways to avoid retracing lines. Don't allow yourself to be sloppy, though, because you may not be able to read your writing later.

Many people find that script, or cursive writing is faster than printing. Experiment with different writing methods, and find one that works for you. Then practice writing with that method so you don't have to think about forming the characters when you hear the sounds.

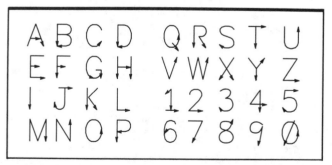

Figure 11-3—A method of hand-printing letters and numbers with minimum effort and maximum speed.

Figure 11-3 shows a systematic method of printing numbers and the letters of the alphabet. This system requires a minimum of pencil movement or retraced lines. You may find this technique helpful to increase your writing speed. Whatever method you choose, practice so it becomes second nature.

ASSEMBLING A CODE-PRACTICE OSCILLATOR

It is not difficult to construct a code-practice oscillator. A complete oscillator that mounts on a small piece of wood is shown in Figure A. Figure B shows all the parts and tools you will need for this project. The circuit board alone or the entire parts kit can be ordered from Circuit Board Specialists, PO Box 951, Pueblo, CO 81002, tel. 719-542-4525.

Please read all instructions carefully before mounting any parts. Check the parts-placement diagram for the location of each part.

Figure A

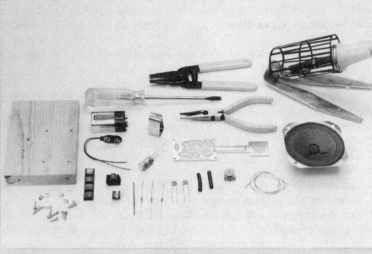

Figure B

Parts List

[ ] Check box as each part is installed and soldered

	Quantity	Description	Radio Shack Part Number	Component Number	Used in Step Number
Capacitors					
[ ]	1	0.01-μF	272-131	C1	3
[ ]	1	0.01-μF	272-131	C2	6
[ ]	1	220-μF, 35-V electrolytic	272-1029	C3	5
Resistors					
[ ]	1	10-kilohm, ¼ W (brown-black-orange stripes)	271-1335	R2	4
[ ]	1	68-kilohm, ¼ W (blue-gray-orange stripes)	271-1345	R3	8
[ ]	1	10-kilohm, ¼ W (brown-black-orange-stripes)	271-1335	R1	9
Miscellaneous					
[ ]	1	100-kilohm potentiometer	271-220	R4	7
[ ]	1	7555 CMOS IC Timer (or 555 timer IC)	276-1718	U1	2
[ ]	1	Loudspeaker—3-inch, 8-ohm	40-245	LS1	11
[ ]	1	9-V Battery connector	23-553	BT1	10
[ ]	1	9-V Battery			
[ ]	1	Brass rod 2 inches long, approximately 18 gauge (about the diameter of a wire coat hanger). (Available at hobby shops.)			
[ ]	4	¼-inch spacers	64-3024		
[ ]	1	U-shaped battery holder	270-326		
[ ]	1	2 × 4 × ½-inch piece of wood for base			
[ ]	6	No. 6 wood screws			

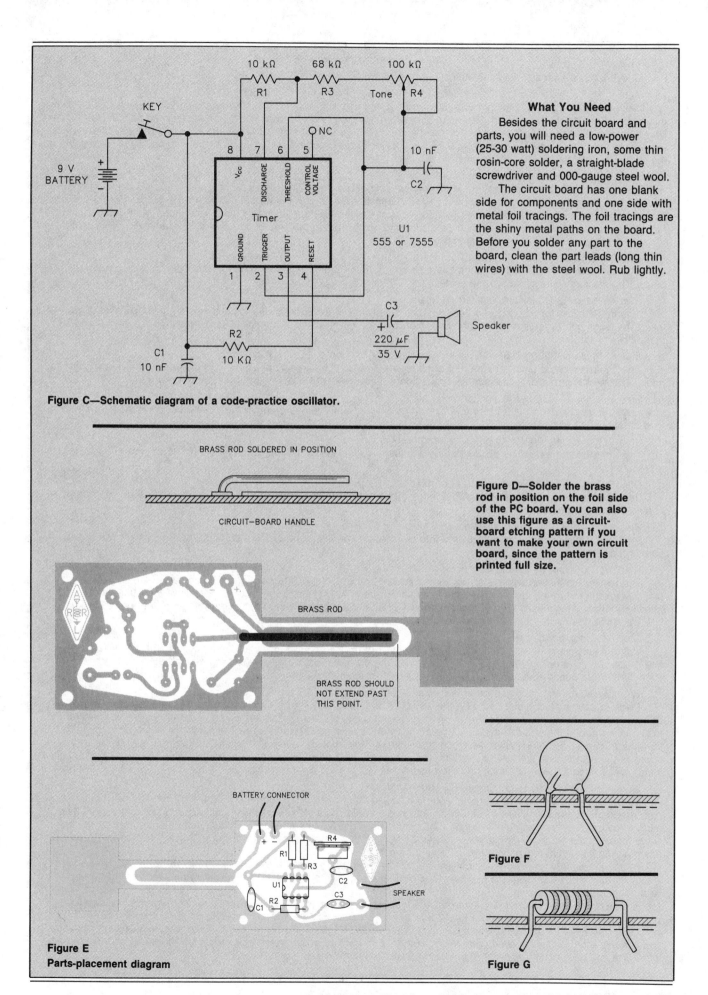

What You Need

Besides the circuit board and parts, you will need a low-power (25-30 watt) soldering iron, some thin rosin-core solder, a straight-blade screwdriver and 000-gauge steel wool.

The circuit board has one blank side for components and one side with metal foil tracings. The foil tracings are the shiny metal paths on the board. Before you solder any part to the board, clean the part leads (long thin wires) with the steel wool. Rub lightly.

Figure C—Schematic diagram of a code-practice oscillator.

BRASS ROD SOLDERED IN POSITION

CIRCUIT—BOARD HANDLE

Figure D—Solder the brass rod in position on the foil side of the PC board. You can also use this figure as a circuit-board etching pattern if you want to make your own circuit board, since the pattern is printed full size.

BRASS ROD

BRASS ROD SHOULD NOT EXTEND PAST THIS POINT.

BATTERY CONNECTOR

SPEAKER

Figure E
Parts-placement diagram

Figure F

Figure G

Assembly Instructions

(Check box as each step is completed)

☐ Step 1: Attach the brass rod. Check parts-placement diagram (Figure E) for location.

Clean the brass rod with sandpaper or steel wool. Bend one end of the rod slightly less than 90 degrees. Lay the circuit board on the table with foil side up. Place the hooked end of the brass rod over the large hole near the handle (see Figure D). Make sure the rod extends out over the handle area. Solder the rod to the board on the foil side. The end of the brass rod should not extend past the marked oval on the handle. This is your contact point. If it does extend beyond this point, cut the rod off just before the end of the oval.

☐ Step 2: Solder the IC socket to the board.

The socket for the IC is placed on the component side of the board first. Do not plug the IC into the socket now. After all the other parts are soldered to the board you will be instructed to plug the IC into the socket (Step 13). Identify the notched end of the socket. Insert the socket into the circuit board on the component side. Make sure the notched end is facing the handle of the board. Turn the board over and gently spread the pins on the socket so they make contact with the foil side of the board. Solder the socket in place.

☐ Step 3: Place C1 (0.01-µF capacitor) on board.

Thread the wire leads on C1 through holes on board. (See Figure F.) Solder the wires onto the foil side of the board. Cut the extra wire off above the solder joint.

☐ Step 4: Place R2 (10-kilohm resistor) on board.

Prepare resistors for mounting by bending each lead (wire) of the resistor to approximately a 90° angle. (See Figure G.) Insert the leads into the board holes and bend them over to hold the resistor in place. Solder the leads to the foil and trim them close to the foil.

☐ Step 5: Place C3 (220-µF, 35-volt electrolytic capacitor) on board.

This capacitor has a plus (+) side and a negative (−) side. The (−) side is placed on the board facing away from the handle. Insert the capacitor leads into the circuit board holes, solder in place and trim off the extra wire.

☐ Step 6: Place C2 (0.01-µF capacitor) on board.

Thread C2 wire leads through holes on board. (See Step 3, and Figure F.) Solder the wires onto the board. Cut the extra wire off above the solder joint.

☐ Step 7: Place R4 (100-kilohm potentiometer) on board.

This component has three pins. All three pins must be plugged into the holes on the board. (It fits only one way.) Solder them in place.

☐ Step 8: Place R3 (68-kilohm resistor) on board.

Bend the wires on the resistor to plug it into the board. (See Step 4 and Figure G.) Plug the resistor into the board, spread the wires and solder in place.

☐ Step 9: Place R1 (10-kilohm resistor) on board.

Bend the wires on the resistor to plug it into the board. (See Step 4 and Figure G.) Plug the resistor into the board, spread the wires and solder in place.

☐ Step 10: Hook up the battery connector leads.

The battery connector consists of two wires, one red and one black, attached to a snap-on cap. Remove ¼ inch of plastic insulation from the end of both wires. The black wire is negative and the red wire is positive. The positive and negative battery connections are marked on the solder side of the board. Be sure the red wire goes in the hole marked "+", and the black wire goes in the hole marked "−". Solder the wires in place.

☐ Step 11: Hook up the speaker.

Cut the speaker wire into two equal lengths. Remove ¼ inch of plastic insulation from each end of both wires. Solder one piece of wire to one of the speaker terminals and the other wire to the other speaker terminal. Solder the other end of each wire to the board at the points marked on the parts-placement diagram.

☐ Step 12: Attach the circuit board to the wood base.

Place the completed circuit board on the wood. Trace through the four holes with a pencil. Take the board off the wood and lay it aside. Place the spacers on the wood, standing upright. Carefully put the circuit board on top of the spacers. Put the screws through the holes in the circuit board and through the spacers and screw them into the board until snug. Be sure not to overtighten the screws, which could crack the circuit board. Attach the speaker to the front end of the board opposite the handle with the two screws left over. Attach the U-shaped metal battery holder to the wooden base. You can either use glue or a screw to attach it to the base.

☐ Step 13: Plug the integrated circuit (IC) into the socket.

CAUTION—The static electricity from your body could destroy the IC. Before touching the IC, be sure you have discharged any static that may be built up on your body. While sitting at your table or workbench, touch a metal pipe or other large metal object for a few seconds. Carefully remove the IC from its foam padding. Hold it by the black body and avoid touching the wires. Plug it into the socket, being sure that the notched end of the IC is facing towards the handle. The notch on the IC should line up with the notch on the socket.

Attach the battery to the snap-on battery connector, and place it in the U-shaped metal battery holder. This unit uses electricity only when the telegraph key handle is pushed down. No ON/OFF switch is necessary and you may leave the battery connected at all times.

You're done! The oscillator should produce a tone when you press the key. If your oscillator does not work, check all your connections carefully. Make sure the IC is positioned correctly in the socket, and that you have a fresh battery.

Once you have the oscillator working, you're ready to use it to practice Morse code. If you are studying with a friend, you can use the oscillator to send code to each other. If you are studying alone, tape record your sending and play it back later. Can you copy what you sent? How would it sound on the air? Good luck!

SOME STUDY SUGGESTIONS

The secret to easy and painless mastery of the Morse code is regular practice. Set aside two 15- to 30-minute periods every day to practice the code. If you try longer sessions, you may become over tired, and you will not learn as quickly. Likewise, if you only practice every other day or even less often, you will tend to forget more between practice sessions. It's a good idea to work your practice sessions into your daily routine. For instance, practice first thing in the morning and before dinner. Daily practice gives quick results.

Learn the sound of each letter. Morse code character elements sound like dits and dahs, so that's what we call them. Each character has its own pattern of dits and dahs, so learn to associate the sound of that pattern with the character. Don't try to remember how many dots and dashes make up each character. Practice until you automatically recognize each Morse code character.

Feel free to review. You're learning a new way of communicating, by using the Morse code. If you are having trouble with a particular character, spend some extra time with it. If you are using the cassette tapes from ARRL's *Your Introduction to Morse Code*, rewind the tape and play that section again. If you are using one of the computer programs, spend some extra time drilling on the problem character. After you've listened to the practice on one character two or three times, however, go on to the next one. You will get more practice with the problem character later, because you will be constantly reviewing all of the characters learned so far. You can even come back to the problem character again in a later practice session. Be sure to listen to the practice for at least 3 characters during each practice session, however.

If you hear a Morse code character you don't immediately know, just draw a short line on your copy paper. Then get ready for the next letter. If you ignore your mistakes now, you'll make fewer of them. If you sit there worrying about the letter you missed, you'll miss a lot more! You shouldn't expect to copy perfectly while you are learning the code. You will get better with more practice.

When you think you've recognized a word after copying a few letters, concentrate all the more on the actual code sent. If you try to anticipate what comes next, your guess may turn out to be wrong. When that happens, you'll probably get confused and miss the next few letters as well. Write each letter just after it is sent. With more practice, you'll learn to "copy

---

AMATEUR RADIO EXCITEMENT

Seven-year-old Luke Ward of Alexandria, Virginia and his dad Keith saw an article about how to convert a small AM radio to receive shortwave broadcasts. After completing the project over a weekend, they were able to hear shortwave stations from all around the world! When Luke asked about the strange sounds they often heard, his dad explained that they were Morse code messages being sent by Amateur Radio operators. (Keith had been a ham when he was a boy, but was no longer licensed.) When Luke learned that there was no minimum age to become a ham, he and his dad began studying for their Novice exams. They also bought a used shortwave receiver and became avid shortwave listeners (SWLs). Luke and Keith also joined the Mt Vernon (VA) Amateur Radio Club.

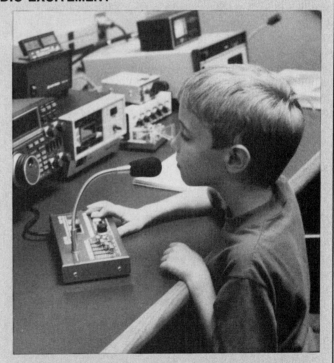

About six weeks later, in August 1990, Luke and Keith passed their Novice exams. The next morning they left for a vacation trip to Cape Cod, and stopped at ARRL Headquarters in Newington, Connecticut on the way. Luke and his parents were thrilled to see the W1AW facilities, many of which they had read about in *Tune in the World with Ham Radio* (the ARRL's previous book for the Novice license). Luke was in third grade that fall when the tickets arrived from the FCC, and Luke (now KC4UJS) and Keith (now KC4TZJ) were soon on the air. Luke's first contact was with VE1VAZ in Nova Scotia, Canada! Within a month Luke had 60 CW contacts on 80, 40 and 15 meters. Luke and his dad have been competing for most states and countries worked.

Luke wasted no time in studying for his Technician license, and he and Keith passed their Technician exams in October 1990, about six weeks before Luke's eighth birthday.

"Learning Morse code took a lot of practice and so was harder than learning the other stuff necessary to pass the written exams," says Luke, who was already technically inclined before he got involved with ham radio. "Besides ham radio, I enjoy BASIC computer programming. Math and PE are my favorite school subjects," he adds. Luke also enjoys soccer and Cub Scouts.

After their 10-meter antenna was tuned, Luke tried SSB phone, and came to enjoy that as much as CW. His first phone contact was with CU1AC on Santa Maria Island in the Azores (a chain of islands in the North Atlantic that belong to Portugal)! "Eighty meters used to be my favorite band, but now I like 10 meters best because of the DX. I really like to get QSL cards, especially from foreign countries. My CW QSOs helped improve my code speed. I think I am about ready to take my General exam, once I finish studying the radio theory part. I want a General ticket so that I can use the extra band space, and I hope I can do moonbounce QSOs with it, too." (Luke did pass his General class exam in February 1991, at the age of eight.)

behind,'' hearing and writing whole words at one time. For now, when you are just learning the code, concentrate on writing each character as it is sent. This helps reinforce the association of a sound and a character in your mind.

Practice sending code. To communicate with Morse code you must be able to send it as well as receive it! You will need a **code-practice oscillator** and a **code key**. The sidebar, "Assembling A Code-Practice Oscillator" describes a simple oscillator that you can build. It even includes a simple key that you can use to practice sending.

One trick that some people use while learning the code is to whistle or hum the code while walking or driving. You can also say the sounds di, dit and dah to sound out the characters. Send the words on street signs, billboards and store windows. This extra practice may be just the help you need to master the code!

Morse code is a language. Eventually you'll begin to recognize common syllables and words. With practice you will know many complete words, and won't even listen to the individual letters. When you become this familiar with the code, it really starts to be fun!

Don't be discouraged if you don't seem to be breaking any speed records. Some people have an ear for code and can learn the entire code in a week or less. Others require a month or more to learn it. Be patient, continue to practice and you will reach your goal.

To pass the Novice class code examination, you must be able to understand a plain-language message sent at 5 WPM. As you know, in the English language some words are just one or two letters long, others 10 or more letters long. To standardize the code test, the FCC defines a word as a group of five letters. Numbers and punctuation marks normally count as two characters for this purpose.

COMFORTABLE SENDING

There's more to the code than just learning to receive it; you'll also have to learn to send it. To accomplish this, you'll need a telegraph key and a code-practice oscillator. You can get these items at most electronics-parts stores, or you can build your own simple oscillator. The "Assembling A Code-Practice Oscillator" sidebar gives you step-by-step instructions for building one simple oscillator that even includes a key for you to practice with. The key with this project is *not* the best key you could use, but it will allow you to do some practice sending. You may want to consider adding a real straight key to the project—just connect the wires to the key across the contacts of the circuit-board key.

Many experienced amateurs prefer to use an electronic keyer to send Morse code. An electronic keyer produces properly timed dots and dashes, because it uses one circuit to produce dots and another circuit to produce dashes. In general, it is probably better to learn to send Morse code with a hand key at first. Some students may have good success with a keyer. Commercial keyers range from simple, basic units to full-featured Morse code machines. While they are comparatively expensive, some of the full-featured machines offer features that are quite helpful to a beginner. The keyers shown in Figure 11-4 can send random-character code practice at any speed you desire. The AEA MM-3 keyer even has a program built in that will allow you to contact imaginary amateurs and carry on a typical amateur conversation with the keyer.

Figure 11-5 shows two different standard straight key models (one in the foreground and one to the left). There is a semiautomatic "bug" in the background and a popular Bencher paddle used with modern electronic keyers on the right. You'll want to obtain some type of code key to practice with before you're ready for your Novice code test. You'll need the key for some of your on-the-air operating after the license arrives from the FCC as well! Most new hams start with an inexpensive straight key.

Just as with receiving, it is important that you be comfortable when sending. It helps to rest your arm on the table, letting your wrist and hand do all the work. Grasp the key lightly with your fingertips. Don't grip it tightly. If you do, you'll soon discover a few muscles you didn't know you

Figure 11-4—Electronic keyers shown here can store messages in memory to be sent at the touch of a button and also offer various training features to help you learn Morse code and increase your speed. The MFJ-486 keyer sends 5-character random-letter groups, random 1- to 8-character groups and plain text in the format of an on-the-air Amateur Radio contact (QSO). In addition to sending random characters, the AEA MM-3 can connect to a computer to send text from a keyboard or text file. The MM-3 also contains a program that allows you to "contact" other stations in the keyer and exchange QSO information.

had, and each one will ache. With a light grasp, you'll be able to send for long periods without fatigue. See Figure 11-6.

Another important part of sending code is the proper adjustment of your telegraph key. There are only two adjustments to make on a straight key, but you'll find they are very important. Figure 11-7 illustrates these adjustments.

The first adjustment is the spacing between the contacts, which determines the distance the key knob must move to send a letter. Adjust the contacts so the knob moves about the thickness of a dime (1/16 inch). Try it. If you're not satisfied with this setting, try a wider space. If that doesn't do it, try reducing the space. Eventually, you'll find a spacing that works best for you. Don't be surprised if your feelings change from time to time, however, especially when your sending speed increases.

The second adjustment you must make is the spring tension that keeps the contacts apart. Just as there is no "correct" contact spacing, there is no correct tension adjustment for everyone. You will find, however, that adjusting the spacing

Figure 11-5—Older than radio itself, code still reigns as the most efficient and effective communications mode; many hams use it almost exclusively. A modern straight key, the device most beginners use, is in the foreground.

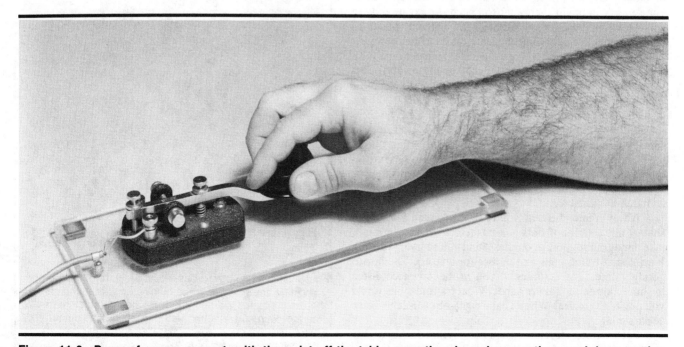

Figure 11-6—Proper forearm support, with the wrist off the table, a gentle grip and a smooth up-and-down motion make for clean, effortless sending.

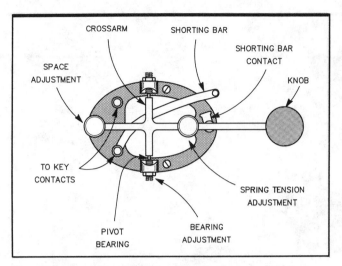

Figure 11-7—A few simple adjustments to suit your style allow you to send for hours without fatigue. The contact spacing and spring tension should be set to provide the most comfortable feel.

may also require a tension adjustment. Adjust the tension to provide what you think is the best "feel" when sending.

Some straight keys have ball bearing pivot points on either side of the crossarms. These normally need no adjustment, but you should be sure the crossarms move freely in these pivots. If the bearings are too tight the key will bind or stick. If they are too loose there will be excessive play in the bearings. The side screws also adjust the crossarms from side to side so the contact points line up.

All of these adjustment screws have lock nuts, so be sure you loosen them before you make any adjustments. Tighten the lock nuts securely after making the adjustment.

Some better-quality keys have a shorting bar like the one shown in Figure 11-7. This shorting bar can be used to close the key contacts for transmitter tuning or adjustments.

You'll probably want to fasten the key to a piece of wood or other heavy weight to prevent it from sliding around as you send. You might even want to fasten the key directly to the table. It's best to experiment with different positions before permanently attaching the key to any surface, however.

Some operators use a board that extends under their forearm and allows their arm to hold the key in position. This way the key can be moved aside for storage, or to clean off the table for other activities. A piece of ¼-inch Plexiglas® about 12 inches long works well for this type of key base. This technique also allows you to reposition the key to find the most comfortable sending position.

Learning to send good code, like learning to receive, requires practice. A good way to start is to send along with your code tapes or computer program. Try to duplicate the sounds as much as possible.

Always remember that you're trying to send a complete sound, not a series of dots and dashes. With that in mind, take a moment to think about the sound you're trying to send. It consists of dits, dahs and pauses (or spaces). The key to good sending, then, is timing. If you're not convinced, listen to some code on the Novice bands. What transmissions would you prefer to receive? Why? That's right—because they have good timing.

Each person develops a unique rhythm in his or her sending. It's almost impossible to describe what makes one person's rhythm different from another person's. No two people send code exactly the same way, though. This unique rhythm, or **fist** is like the signature of the operator sending the code. Some experienced CW operators can even identify their friends without hearing call signs.

Some people send code that is very easy and enjoyable to copy. Others are not so good, and require a lot of concentration to understand. Since your fist is your on-the-air signature, try to make it as easy to read as possible. Learn to send code that is easy to copy. Then you'll have a fist you can be proud of. It can make a big difference in your success as an amateur operator.

One of the best ways to learn to send and receive code is to work with another person. That person may be another member of your own family, a friend who is also studying the code or a licensed ham. If you're attending an organized class, you may be able to get together with another student several times a week.

If you must work alone, make good use of your tape recorder. Try recording your sending. After waiting a day or two, try receiving what you sent. The wait between sending and receiving will help prevent you from writing down the

---

CODE IS THEIR COMMON BOND

When Anne Harlan asked, on the air, how she could join a CW net Scott Prather responded. (A net is a group of hams who meet on a certain frequency on a regular schedule to pass messages.) Scott said, "Since I was the resident expert of sorts on CW nets, I called Anne and gave her the information. I then asked how I could contact her in the future, and she gave me a list of her operating frequencies."

From there, it wasn't long before Scott and Anne were working side by side passing messages during the annual Simulated Emergency Test. Their common interest in Morse code had led to a mutual interest in each other. Anne (KA9EHV) and Scott (KB9Y) Prather now compete for operating time at the same Amateur Radio station as husband and wife.

Scott runs an electronics-repair business part time. He recently arranged radio communications for a church-sponsored bike trip. Anne's operating interests are in CW ragchewing and weather nets. She says, "No matter what else we do, it seems that CW and public service are eventually a part of it."

Table 11-1

W1AW Schedule

MTWThFSSn = Days of Week   Dy = Daily

W1AW code practice and bulletin transmissions are sent on the following schedule:

ET	Slow Code Practice	MWF: 9 AM, 7 PM; TThSSn: 4 PM, 10 PM
	Fast Code Practice	MWF: 4 PM, 10 PM; TTh: 9 AM; TThSSn: 7 PM
	CW Bulletins	Dy: 5 PM, 8 PM, 11 PM; MTWThF: 10 AM
	Teleprinter Bulletins	Dy: 6 PM, 9 PM, 12 PM; MTWThF: 11 AM
	Voice Bulletins	Dy: 9:45 PM, 12:45 AM
CT	Slow Code Practice	MWF: 8 AM, 6 PM; TThSSn: 3 PM, 9 PM
	Fast Code Practice	MWF: 3 PM, 9 PM; TTh: 8 AM; TThSSn: 6 PM
	CW Bulletins	Dy: 4 PM, 7 PM, 10 PM; MTWThF: 9 AM
	Teleprinter Bulletins	Dy: 5 PM, 8 PM, 11 PM; MTWThF: 10 AM
	Voice Bulletins	Dy: 8:45 PM, 11:45 PM
MT	Slow Code Practice	MWF: 7 AM, 5 PM; TThSSn: 2 PM, 8 PM
	Fast Code Practice	MWF: 2 PM, 8 PM; TTh: 7 AM; TThSSn: 5 PM
	CW Bulletins	Dy: 3 PM, 6 PM, 9 PM; MTWThF: 8 AM
	Teleprinter Bulletins	Dy: 4 PM, 7 PM, 10 PM; MTWThF: 9 AM
	Voice Bulletins	Dy: 7:45 PM, 10:45 PM
PT	Slow Code Practice	MWF: 6 AM, 4 PM; TThSSn: 1 PM, 7 PM
	Fast Code Practice	MWF: 1 PM, 7 PM; TTh: 6 AM; TThSSn: 4 PM
	CW Bulletins	Dy: 2 PM, 5 PM, 8 PM; MTWThF: 7 AM
	Teleprinter Bulletins	Dy: 3 PM, 6 PM, 9 PM; MTWThF: 8 AM
	Voice Bulletins	Dy: 6:45 PM, 9:45 PM

Code practice, Qualifying Run and CW bulletin frequencies: 1.818, 3.5815, 7.0475, 14.0475, 18.0975, 21.0675, 28.0675, 147.555 MHz.

Teleprinter bulletin frequencies: 3.625, 7.095, 14.095, 18.1025, 21.095, 28.095, 147.555 MHz.

Voice bulletin frequencies: 3.99, 7.29, 14.29, 18.160, 21.39, 28.59, 147.555 MHz.

Slow code practice is at 5, 7½, 10, 13 and 15 WPM. Fast code practice is at 35, 30, 25, 20, 15, 13 and 10 WPM.

Code practice texts are from *QST*, and the source of each practice is given at the beginning of each practice and at the beginning of alternate speeds. For example, "Text is from August 1990 *QST*, pages 16 and 80" indicates that the main text is from the article on page 16 and the mixed number/letter groups at the end of each speed are from the contest scores on page 80.

Some of the slow practice sessions are sent with each line of text from *QST* reversed. For example, "Last October, the ARRL Board of Directors" would be sent as DIRECTORS OF BOARD ARRL THE, OCTOBER LAST.

Teleprinter bulletins are 45.45-baud Baudot, 110-baud ASCII and 100-baud AMTOR, FEC mode.

CW bulletins are sent at 18 WPM.

W1AW is open for visitors Monday through Friday from 11 AM to 11 PM ET and on Saturday and Sunday from 4:30 PM to 11 PM ET. If you desire to operate W1AW, be sure to bring a copy of your license with you. W1AW is available for operation by visitors between 1 and 4 PM Monday through Friday.

In a communications emergency, monitor W1AW for special bulletins as follows: voice on the hour, teleprinter at 15 minutes past the hour, and CW on the half hour.

---

message from memory. Not only will this procedure provide practice in receiving, but it will also let you hear exactly how your sending sounds. If your timing is off, you'll hear it. If you're having trouble with a specific letter or number or punctuation mark, you'll soon know about it. If you can't understand your own sending, neither will anyone else!

Regardless of whether you're sending or receiving, the key to your success with Morse code is regular practice. After you've learned all the characters you will want to continue your regular practice to gain confidence and increase your speed.

If you can, listen to actual contacts between hams. Make use of the code-practice material transmitted daily by **W1AW**, the ARRL station heard nationwide from Newington, Connecticut. Table 3-1 lists the code-practice schedule for W1AW. When we change from Standard Time to Daylight Saving Time, the code-practice is sent at the same local times.

——— THE CODE TEST ———

To pass the Novice code test, you must demonstrate your ability to send and receive Morse code at 5 words per minute. Your Novice test examiners will give you the code test. The

FCC specifies that the exam message should be at least 5 minutes long. The message must contain all letters of the alphabet, all numbers, period, comma, question mark and fraction bar (/). The exam message must also include some common procedural signals. These are the + sign ($\overline{AR}$), the = sign ($\overline{BT}$) and $\overline{SK}$.

The two hams giving you the test have several options in deciding if you pass the exam. If you have one minute of solid (perfect) copy out of a five-minute test, you pass. The examiners may also give you a 10-question multiple-choice or fill-in-the-blank test about the exam content. A passing grade on such a written exam is 70%. Your examiners may devise other fair and reasonable standards for taking the code test. Again, the examiners are simply certifying that you have proven your ability to send and receive code at 5 words per minute.

EXAMINATION NERVES

If you have prepared properly, the code exam should be easy—a pleasant experience, not an agonizing one. The key to a successful exam is to relax. One of the biggest reasons people fail the code examination is because they become nervous. You can be confident of passing, however, because you have studied hard and are properly prepared.

The exam isn't *that* important. You can always take the test again soon. It won't kill you even if you don't pass. But you are going to pass! You can copy 5 WPM at home with only a couple of errors every few minutes. The code test will be even easier.

Think positively: "I will pass!" Relax. Before you know it, you'll be grinning from ear to ear as you hear the words, "You've passed!"

HEADING ON UP

Once you obtain your Novice ticket, you'll soon set your sights on a Technician or General class license. The ARRL's *Increasing Your Code Speed* series of code-practice tapes will help you increase your code speed. There are tapes to go from 5 to 10 WPM, from 10 to 15 WPM and from 15 to 22 WPM. Each set of tapes includes two 90-minute cassettes, which provide practice with words, sentences, random code groups, related text and QSO practice. The space between characters decreases gradually to increase the overall code speed. You'll be copying faster code before you know it! W1AW also provides practice at a variety of speeds. Contact the ARRL, 225 Main Street, Newington, CT 06111 for the tapes you'll need to reach your desired code speed.

Chapter 12

Element 2 Question Pool —With Answers

———— DON'T START HERE ————

This chapter contains the complete question pool for the Element 2 exam. Element 2 is the written part of the Novice exam, and is also part of the Technician exam. The Technician exam also includes Element 3A. Chapter 13 contains the entire Element 3A question pool, with answers. To obtain a Novice license you must also pass a 5-WPM Morse code test. The Technician license does not require a code test.

Before you read the questions and answers printed in this chapter, be sure to read the text in the previous chapters. Use these questions as review exercises, when the text tells you to study them. Don't try to memorize all the questions and answers. This book was carefully written and prepared to guide you step by step as you learn about Amateur Radio. By understanding the electronics principles and Amateur Radio concepts in this book, you will enjoy our hobby more. You will also better appreciate the privileges granted by an Amateur Radio license.

This pool will be used until further notice from the Volunteer Examiner Coordinator's Question Pool Committee.

HOW MANY QUESTIONS?

Your Element 2 exam will consist of 30 of these questions, selected by the Volunteer Examiners giving you the test. The ARRL/VEC and most other VECs have agreed to use the multiple-choice answers. Some VECs may use the questions printed here with different answers and/or distractors (incorrect answers).

WHO GIVES THE TEST?

You may take your exam at a session coordinated by a Volunteer Examiner Coordinator. If so, check with that VEC to find out if they use these multiple-choice answers.

You might also take your Element 2 exam from two Volunteer Examiners with General class or higher licenses, but who are not part of the VEC program. These examiners must still use the questions exactly as printed. They may choose other answer formats, however. Ask your examiners what answer format they will use before you take the exam. Note that *only* the Novice license exam may be given by examiners who are not registered with a Volunteer Examiner program.

Volunteer Examiners for Novice licenses can request a Novice exam from the Educational Activities Department at ARRL Headquarters. They should include their own call signs, license classes and expiration dates, so the staff can verify that they are eligible to give the exam. If your examiners select the questions for your exam, we recommend the multiple-choice answers printed in this chapter. They have been carefully worded to provide the best answer and good distractors for each question. The examiners are free to choose another answer format, such as fill-in-the-blank or even to give an oral exam, however.

QUESTION POOL SECTIONS

The question pool is divided into nine sections, called subelements. (A subelement is a portion of the exam element, in this case Element 2.) The FCC specifies how many questions from each section must be on your test. For example, there must be ten questions from the Commission's Rules section, Subelement 2A. There must also be two questions from the Operating Procedures section, Subelement 2B, and so on. Table 12-1 summarizes the number of questions that make up an exam. The number of questions on an exam appears at the beginning of each subelement in the question pool, too. The subelements are broken into smaller groups, with one question specified to come from each smaller group. These sections are clearly shown in the questions pool.

Table 12-1
Novice Exam Content

Subelement	Topic	Number of questions
2A	Commission's Rules	10
2B	Operating Procedures	2
2C	Radio-Wave Propagation	1
2D	Amateur Radio Practices	4
2E	Electrical Principles	4
2F	Circuit Components	2
2G	Practical Circuits	2
2H	Signals and Emissions	2
2I	Antennas and Feed Lines	3

The question numbers used in the question pool relate to the syllabus or study guide printed at the end of Chapter 1. The syllabus is an outline of topics covered by the exam. The first part of each question number (up to the decimal point) lists the syllabus point covered by that question. The number after the decimal point identifies the individual questions that go with that point. For example, question 2C-4.2 is the second question in the series about syllabus point 2C-4, sunspot cycle.

Good luck with your studies.

Withdrawn Questions

FCC Rules changes sometimes make it necessary to withdraw certain questions from the pool. Withdrawn questions are noted in the following pages.

Subelement 2A—Rules and Regulations (10 Questions)

One question must be from the following:

2A-1.1 What are the five principles that express the fundamental purpose for which the amateur service rules are designed?
A. Recognition of emergency communications, advancement of the radio art, improvement of communication and technical skills, increase in the number of trained radio operators and electronics experts, and the enhancement of international goodwill
B. Recognition of business communications, advancement of the radio art, improvement of communication and business skills, increase in the number of trained radio operators and electronics experts, and the enhancement of international goodwill
C. Recognition of emergency communications, preservation of the earliest radio techniques, improvement of communication and technical skills, maintain a pool of people familiar with early tube-type equipment, and the enhancement of international goodwill
D. Recognition of emergency communications, advancement of the radio art, improvement of communication and technical skills, increase in the number of trained radio operators and electronics experts, and the enhancement of a sense of patriotism

2A-1.2 Which of the following is *not* one of the basic principles for which the *amateur service* rules are designed?
A. Providing emergency communications
B. Improvement of communication and technical skills
C. Advancement of the radio art
D. Enhancement of a sense of patriotism and nationalism

2A-1.3 The amateur service rules were designed to provide a radio communications service that meets five fundamental purposes. Which of the following is *not* one of those principles?
A. Improvement of communication and technical skills
B. Enhancement of international goodwill
C. Increase the number of trained radio operators and electronics experts
D. Preserving the history of radio communications

2A-1.4 The amateur service rules were designed to provide a radio communications service that meets five fundamental purposes. What are those principles?
A. Recognition of business communications, advancement of the radio art, improvement of communication and business skills, increase in the number of trained radio operators and electronics experts, and the enhancement of international goodwill
B. Recognition of emergency communications, advancement of the radio art, improvement of communication and technical skills, increase in the number of trained radio operators and electronics experts, and the enhancement of international goodwill
C. Recognition of emergency communications, preservation of the earliest radio techniques, improvement of communication and technical skills, maintain a pool of people familiar with early tube-type equipment, and the enhancement of international goodwill
D. Recognition of emergency communications, advancement of the radio art, improvement of communication and technical skills, increase in the number of trained radio operators and electronics experts, and the enhancement of a sense of patriotism

2A-2.1 What is the definition of the *amateur service*?
A. A private radio service used for personal gain and public benefit
B. A public radio service used for public service communications
C. A radio communication service for the purpose of self-training, intercommunication and technical investigations
D. A private radio service intended for the furtherance of commercial radio interests

2A-2.2 What name is given to the radio communication service that is designed for self-training, intercommunication, and technical investigation?
A. The amateur service
B. The Citizen's Radio Service
C. The Experimenter's Radio Service
D. The Maritime Radio Service

2A-3.1 What document contains the specific rules and regulations governing the amateur service in the United States?
A. Part 97 of title 47 CFR (Code of Federal Regulations)
B. The Communications Act of 1934 (as amended)
C. The Radio Amateur's Handbook
D. The minutes of the International Telecommunication Union meetings

2A-3.2 Which one of the following topics is *not* addressed in the rules and regulations of the amateur service?
A. Station operation standards
B. Technical standards
C. Providing emergency communications
D. Station construction standards

2A-4.1 What is the definition of an *amateur operator*?
A. A person who has not received any training in radio operations
B. A person holding a written authorization to be the control operator of an amateur station
C. A person who performs private radio communications for hire
D. A trainee in a commercial radio station

2A-4.2 What term describes a person holding a written authorization to be the control operator of an amateur station?
A. A Citizen Radio operator
B. A Personal Radio operator
C. A Radio Service operator
D. An amateur operator

One question must be from the following:

2A-5.1 What is the portion of an amateur operator/primary station license that conveys operator privileges?
A. The verification section
B. Form 610
C. The operator license
D. The station license

2A-5.2 What authority is derived from an operator/primary station license?
A. The authority to operate any shortwave radio station
B. The authority to be the control operator of an amateur station
C. The authority to have an amateur station at a particular location
D. The authority to transmit on either amateur or Class D citizen's band frequencies

2A-6.1 What authority is derived from a written authorization for an amateur station?
A. The authority to use specified operating frequencies
B. The authority to operate an amateur station
C. The authority to enforce FCC Rules when violations are noted on the part of other operators
D. The authority to transmit on either amateur or Class D citizen's band frequencies

2A-6.2 What part of your amateur license gives you authority to have an amateur station?
A. The operator license
B. The FCC Form 610
C. The station license
D. An amateur operator/primary station license does not specify a station location

2A-7.1 What is an *amateur station*?
A. A licensed radio station engaged in broadcasting to the public in a limited and well-defined area
B. A radio station used to further commercial radio interests
C. A private radio service used for personal gain and public service
D. A station in an amateur service consisting of the apparatus necessary for carrying on radio communications

2A-8.1 Who is a *control operator*?
A. An amateur operator designated by the licensee of a station to be responsible for the transmissions from that station to assure compliance with the FCC rules
B. A person, either licensed or not, who controls the emissions of an amateur station
C. An unlicensed person who is speaking over an amateur station's microphone while a licensed person is present
D. A government official who comes to an amateur station to take control for test purposes

2A-8.2 If you designate another amateur operator to be responsible for the transmissions from your station, what is the other operator called?
A. Auxiliary operator
B. Operations coordinator
C. Third party
D. Control operator

2A-9.1 List the five United States amateur operator/primary station license classes in order of increasing privileges.
A. Novice, General, Technician, Advanced, Amateur Extra
B. Novice, Technician, General, Advanced, Digital
C. Novice, Technician, General, Amateur, Extra
D. Novice, Technician, General, Advanced, Amateur Extra

2A-9.2 This question has been withdrawn.

2A-9.3 What is the license class immediately above Novice class?
A. The Digital class license
B. The Technician class license
C. The General class license
D. The Experimenter's class license

One question must be from the following:

2A-10.1 This question has been withdrawn

2A-10.2 What frequencies are available in the amateur 40-meter wavelength band for a control operator holding a Novice class operator license in ITU Region 2?
A. 3500 to 4000 kHz
B. 3700 to 3750 kHz
C. 7100 to 7150 kHz
D. 7000 to 7300 kHz

2A-10.3 What frequencies are available in the amateur 15-meter wavelength band for a control operator holding a Novice class operator license?
A. 21.100 to 21.200 MHz
B. 21.000 to 21.450 MHz
C. 28.000 to 29.700 MHz
D. 28.100 to 28.200 MHz

2A-10.4 What frequencies are available in the amateur 10-meter wavelength band for a control operator holding a Novice class operator license?
A. 28.000 to 29.700 MHz
B. 28.100 to 28.300 MHz
C. 28.100 to 28.500 MHz
D. 28.300 to 28.500 MHz

2A-10.5 What frequencies are available in the amateur 220-MHz band for a control operator holding a Novice class operator license in ITU Region 2?
- A. 225.0 to 230.5 MHz
- B. 222.1 to 223.91 MHz
- C. 224.1 to 225.1 MHz
- D. 222.2 to 224.0 MHz

2A-10.6 What frequencies are available in the amateur 1270-MHz band for a control operator holding a Novice class operator license?
- A. 1260 to 1270 MHz
- B. 1240 to 1300 MHz
- C. 1270 to 1295 MHz
- D. 1240 to 1246 MHz

2A-10.7 If you are operating your amateur station on 3725 kHz, in what meter band are you operating?
- A. 80 meters
- B. 40 meters
- C. 15 meters
- D. 10 meters

2A-10.8 If you are operating your amateur station on 7125 kHz, in what meter band are you operating?
- A. 80 meters
- B. 40 meters
- C. 15 meters
- D. 10 meters

2A-10.9 If you are operating your amateur station on 21150 kHz, in what meter band are you operating?
- A. 80 meters
- B. 40 meters
- C. 15 meters
- D. 10 meters

2A-10.10 If you are operating your amateur station on 28150 kHz, in what meter band are you operating?
- A. 80 meters
- B. 40 meters
- C. 15 meters
- D. 10 meters

One question must be from the following:

2A-11.1 Who is eligible to obtain a US amateur *operator/primary station* license?
- A. Anyone except a representative of a foreign government
- B. Only a citizen of the United States
- C. Anyone
- D. Anyone except an employee of the United States Government

2A-11.2 Who is *not* eligible to obtain a US amateur *operator/primary station* license?
- A. Any citizen of a country other than the United States
- B. A representative of a foreign government
- C. No one
- D. An employee of the United States Government

2A-12.1 What FCC examination elements are required for a Novice class license?
- A. Elements 1(A) and 2(A)
- B. Elements 1(A) and 3(A)
- C. Elements 1(A) and 2
- D. Elements 2 and 4

2A-12.2 What is an FCC Element 1(A) examination intended to prove?
- A. The applicant's ability to send and receive texts in the international Morse code at not less than 5 words per minute
- B. The applicant's ability to send and receive texts in the international Morse code at not less than 13 words per minute
- C. The applicant's knowledge of Novice class theory and regulations
- D. The applicant's ability to recognize Novice frequency assignments and operating modes

2A-12.3 What is an FCC Element 2 examination?
- A. A test of the applicant's ability to send and receive Morse code at 5 words per minute
- B. The written examination concerning the privileges of a Technician class operator license
- C. A test of the applicant's ability to recognize Novice frequency assignments
- D. The written examination concerning the privileges of a Novice class operator license

2A-13.1 Who is eligible to obtain an FCC-issued written authorization for an amateur station?
- A. A licensed amateur operator
- B. Any unlicensed person, except an agent of a foreign government
- C. Any unlicensed person, except an employee of the United States Government
- D. Any unlicensed United States Citizen

2A-14.1 Why is an amateur operator required to furnish the FCC with a current mailing address served by the US Postal service?
- A. So the FCC has a record of the location of each amateur station
- B. In order to comply with the Commission's rules and so the FCC can correspond with the licensee
- C. So the FCC can send license-renewal notices
- D. So the FCC can compile a list for use in a call sign directory

2A-15.1 Which one of the following call signs is a valid US amateur call?
- A. UA4HAK
- B. KBL7766
- C. KA9OLS
- D. BY7HY

2A-15.2 Which one of the following call signs is a valid US amateur call?
- A. CE2FTF
- B. G3GVA
- C. UA1ZAM
- D. AA2Z

2A-15.3 Which one of the following call signs is *not* a valid US amateur call?
- A. KDV5653
- B. WA1DVU
- C. KA5BUG
- D. NTØZ

2A-15.4 What letters may be used for the first letter in a valid US amateur call sign?
- A. K, N, U and W
- B. A, K, N and W
- C. A, B, C and D
- D. A, N, V and W

2A-15.5 Excluding special-event call signs that may be issued by the FCC, what numbers may be used in a valid US call sign?
A. Any double-digit number, 10 through 99
B. Any double-digit number, 22 through 45
C. Any single digit, 1 though 9
D. A single digit, 0 through 9

2A-16.1 Your Novice license was issued on November 1, 1988. When will it expire?
A. On the date specified on the license
B. November 30, 1998
C. November 1, 1993
D. November 1, 1990

One question must be from the following:

2A-17.1 What does the term *emission* mean?
A. RF signals transmitted from a radio station
B. Signals refracted by the E layer
C. Filter out the carrier of a received signal
D. Baud rate

2A-17.2 What emission types are Novice control operators permitted to use on the 80-meter wavelength band?
A. CW only
B. Data only
C. RTTY only
D. Phone only

2A-17.3 What emission types are Novice control operators permitted to use in the 40-meter wavelength band?
A. CW only
B. Data only
C. RTTY only
D. Phone only

2A-17.4 What emission types are Novice control operators permitted to use in the 15-meter wavelength band?
A. CW only
B. Data only
C. RTTY only
D. Phone only

2A-17.5 This question has been withdrawn.

2A-17.6 What emission types are Novice control operators permitted to use from 7100 to 7150 kHz in ITU Region 2?
A. CW and data
B. Phone
C. All amateur emission privileges authorized for use on those frequencies
D. CW only

2A-17.7 What emission types are Novice control operators permitted to use on frequencies from 21.1 to 21.2 MHz?
A. CW and data only
B. CW and phone only
C. All amateur emission privileges authorized for use on those frequencies
D. CW only

2A-17.8 What emission types are Novice control operators permitted to use on frequencies from 28.1 to 28.3 MHz?
A. All authorized amateur emission privileges
B. Data or phone only
C. CW, RTTY and data
D. CW and phone only

2A-17.9 What emission types are Novice control operators permitted to use on frequencies from 28.3 to 28.5 MHz?
A. All authorized amateur emission privileges
B. CW and data only
C. CW and single-sideband phone only
D. Data and phone only

2A-17.10 What emission types are Novice control operators permitted to use on the amateur 220-MHz band in ITU Region 2?
A. CW and phone only
B. CW and data only
C. Data and phone only
D. All amateur emission privileges authorized for use on 220 MHz

2A-17.11 What emission types are Novice control operators permitted to use on the amateur 1270-MHz band?
A. Data and phone only
B. CW and data only
C. CW and phone only
D. All amateur emission privileges authorized for use on 1270 MHz

2A-17.12 On what frequencies in the 10-meter wavelength band may a Novice control operator use single-sideband phone?
A. 3700 to 3750 kHz
B. 7100 to 7150 kHz
C. 21100 to 21200 kHz
D. 28300 to 28500 kHz

2A-17.13 On what frequencies in the 1.25-meter wavelength band in ITU Region 2 may a Novice control operator use FM phone emission?
A. 28.3 to 28.5 MHz
B. 144.0 to 148.0 MHz
C. 222.1 to 223.91 MHz
D. 1240 to 1270 MHz

One question must be from the following:

2A-18.1 What amount of output transmitting power may a Novice class control operator use when operating below 30 MHz?
A. 200 watts input
B. 250 watts output
C. 1500 watts PEP output
D. The minimum legal power necessary to carry out the desired communications

2A-18.2 What is the maximum transmitting power ever permitted to be used by an amateur station transmitting in the 80, 40 and 15-meter Novice bands?
A. 75 watts PEP output
B. 100 watts PEP output
C. 200 watts PEP output
D. 1500 watts PEP output

2A-18.3 What is the maximum transmitting power permitted an amateur station transmitting on 3725 kHz?
A. 75 watts PEP output
B. 100 watts PEP output
C. 200 watts PEP output
D. 1500 watts PEP output

2A-18.4 What is the maximum transmitting power permitted an amateur station transmitting on 7125 kHz?
A. 75 watts PEP output
B. 100 watts PEP output
C. 200 watts PEP output
D. 1500 watts PEP output

2A-18.5 What is the maximum transmitting power permitted an amateur station transmitting on 21.125 MHz?
A. 75 watts PEP output
B. 100 watts PEP output
C. 200 watts PEP output
D. 1500 watts PEP output

2A-19.1 What is the maximum transmitting power permitted an amateur station with a Novice control operator transmitting on 28.125 MHz?
A. 75 watts PEP output
B. 100 watts PEP output
C. 200 watts PEP output
D. 1500 watts PEP output

2A-19.2 What is the maximum transmitting power permitted an amateur station with a Novice control operator transmitting in the amateur 10-meter wavelength band?
A. 25 watts PEP output
B. 200 watts PEP output
C. 1000 watts PEP output
D. 1500 watts PEP output

2A-19.3 What is the maximum transmitting power permitted an amateur station with a Novice control operator transmitting in the amateur 220-MHz band?
A. 5 watts PEP output
B. 10 watts PEP output
C. 25 watts PEP output
D. 200 watts PEP output

2A-19.4 What is the maximum transmitting power permitted an amateur station with a Novice control operator transmitting in the amateur 1270-MHz band?
A. 5 milliwatts PEP output
B. 500 milliwatts PEP output
C. 1 watt PEP output
D. 5 watts PEP output

2A-19.5 What amount of transmitting power may an amateur station with a Novice control operator use in the amateur 220-MHz band?
A. Not less than 5 watts PEP output
B. The minimum legal power necessary to maintain reliable communications
C. Not more than 50 watts PEP output
D. Not more than 200 watts PEP output

2A-20.1 What term is used to describe narrow-band direct-printing telegraphy emissions?
A. Teleport communications
B. Direct communications
C. RTTY communications
D. Third-party communications

2A-20.2 What term is used to describe telemetry, telecommand and computer communications emissions?
A. Teleport communications
B. Direct communications
C. Data communications
D. Third-party communications

2A-20.3 On what frequencies in the 10-meter wavelength band are Novice control operators permitted to transmit RTTY?
A. 28.1 to 28.5 MHz
B. 28.0 to 29.7 MHz
C. 28.1 to 28.2 MHz
D. 28.1 to 28.3 MHz

One question must be from the following:

2A-21.1 Who is held responsible for the proper operation of an amateur station?
A. Only the control operator
B. Only the station licensee
C. Both the control operator and the station licensee
D. The person who owns the property where the station is located

2A-21.2 You allow another amateur operator to use your amateur station. What are your responsibilities, as the station licensee?
A. You and the other amateur operator are equally responsible for the proper operation of your station
B. Only the control operator is responsible for the proper operation of the station
C. As the station licensee, you must be at the control point of your station whenever it is operated
D. You must notify the FCC when another amateur will be the control operator of your station

2A-21.3 What is your primary responsibility as the station licensee?
A. You must permit any licensed amateur radio operator to operate your station at any time upon request
B. You must be present whenever the station is operated
C. You must notify the FCC in writing whenever another amateur radio operator will act as the control operator
D. You are responsible for the proper operation of the station for which you are licensed

2A-21.4 If you are the licensee of an amateur station when are you *not* responsible for its proper operation?
A. Only when another licensed amateur is the control operator
B. The licensee is responsible for the proper operation of the station for which he or she is licensed
C. Only after notifying the FCC in writing that another licensed amateur will assume responsibility for the proper operation of your station
D. Only when your station is in repeater operation

2A-22.1 When must an amateur station have a control operator?
A. A control operator is only required for training purposes
B. Whenever the station receiver is operated
C. Whenever the station is transmitting
D. A control operator is not required

2A-22.2 Another amateur gives you permission to use her amateur station. What are your responsibilities, as the control operator?
A. Both you and she are equally responsible for the proper operation of her station
B. Only the station licensee is responsible for the proper operation of the station, not you the control operator
C. You must be certain the station licensee has given proper FCC notice that you will be the control operator
D. You must inspect all antennas and related equipment to ensure they are working properly

2A-23.1 Who may be the control operator of an amateur station?
A. Any person over 21 years of age
B. Any properly licensed amateur operator that is designated by the station licensee
C. Any licensed amateur operator with an Advanced class license or higher
D. Any person over 21 years of age with a General class license or higher

2A-24.1 Where must an amateur operator be when he or she is performing the duties of control operator?
A. Anywhere in the same building as the transmitter
B. At the control point of the amateur station
C. At the station entrance, to control entry to the room
D. Within sight of the station monitor, to view the output spectrum of the transmitter

2A-25.1 Where must you keep your amateur operator license when you are operating a station?
A. Your original operator license must always be posted in plain view
B. Your original operator license must always be taped to the inside front cover of your station log
C. You must have the original or a photocopy of your operator license in your possession
D. You must have the original or a photocopy of your operator license posted at your primary station location. You need not have the original license nor a copy in your possession to operate another station

2A-26.1 Where must you keep your written authorization for an amateur station?
A. Your original station license must always be taped to the inside front cover of your station log
B. Your original station license must always be posted in plain view
C. You must post the original or a photocopy of your station license at the main entrance to the transmitter building
D. The original or a photocopy of the written authorization for an amateur station must be retained at the station

One question must be from the following:

2A-27.1 How often must an amateur station be identified?
A. At the beginning of the contact and at least every ten minutes during a contact
B. At least once during each transmission
C. At least every ten minutes during a contact and at the end of the contact
D. Every 15 minutes during a contact and at the end of the contact

2A-27.2 As an amateur operator, how should you correctly identify your station?
A. With the name and location of the control operator
B. With the station call sign
C. With the call of the control operator, even when he or she is visiting another radio amateur's station
D. With the name and location of the station licensee, followed by the two-letter designation of the nearest FCC Field Office

2A-27.3 What station identification, if any, is required at the beginning of communication?
A. The operator originating the contact must transmit both call signs
B. No identification is required at the beginning of the contact
C. Both operators must transmit their own call signs
D. Both operators must transmit both call signs

2A-27.4 What station identification, if any, is required at the end of a communication?
A. Both stations must transmit their own call sign, assuming they are FCC-licensed
B. No identification is required at the end of the contact
C. The station originating the contact must always transmit both call signs
D. Both stations must transmit their own call sign followed by a two-letter designator for the nearest FCC field office

2A-27.5 What do the FCC rules for amateur station identification generally require?
A. Each amateur station shall give its call sign at the beginning of each communication, and every ten minutes or less during a communication
B. Each amateur station shall give its call sign at the end of each communication, and every ten minutes or less during a communication
C. Each amateur station shall give its call sign at the beginning of each communication, and every five minutes or less during a communication
D. Each amateur station shall give its call sign at the end of each communication, and every five minutes or less during a communication

2A-27.6 What is the fewest number of times you must transmit your amateur station identification during a 25 minute QSO?
A. 1
B. 2
C. 3
D. 4

2A-27.7 What is the longest period of time during a QSO that an amateur station does not need to transmit its station identification?
A. 5 minutes
B. 10 minutes
C. 15 minutes
D. 20 minutes

2A-28.1 With which amateur stations may an FCC-licensed amateur station communicate?
A. All amateur stations
B. All public noncommercial radio stations unless prohibited by the station's government
C. Only with US amateur stations
D. All amateur stations, unless prohibited by the amateur's government

2A-28.2 With which non-amateur radio stations may an FCC-licensed amateur station communicate?
- A. No non-amateur stations
- B. All such stations
- C. Only those authorized by the FCC
- D. Only those who use the International Morse code

2A-29.1 When must the licensee of an amateur station in portable or mobile operation notify the FCC?
- A. One week in advance if the operation will last for more than 24 hours
- B. FCC notification is not required for portable or mobile operation
- C. One week in advance if the operation will last for more than a week
- D. One month in advance of any portable or mobile operation

2A-29.2 When may you operate your amateur station at a location within the United States, its territories or possessions other than the one listed on your station license?
- A. Only during times of emergency
- B. Only after giving proper notice to the FCC
- C. During an emergency or an FCC-approved emergency preparedness drill
- D. Whenever you want to

2A-30.1 When are communications pertaining to the business or commercial affairs of any party permitted in the amateur service?
- A. Only when the immediate safety of human life or immediate protection of property is threatened
- B. There are no rules against conducting business communications in the amateur service
- C. No business communications of any kind are ever permitted in the amateur service
- D. Business communications are permitted between the hours of 9 AM to 5 PM, only on weekdays

2A-30.2 You wish to obtain an application for membership in the American Radio Relay League. When would you be permitted to send an amateur radio message requesting the application?
- A. At any time, since the ARRL is a not-for-profit organization
- B. Never. This would facilitate the commercial affairs of the ARRL
- C. Only during normal business hours, between 9 AM and 5 PM
- D. At any time, since there are no rules against conducting business communications in the amateur service

2A-30.3 On your way home from work you decide to order pizza for dinner. When would you be permitted to use the autopatch on your radio club repeater to order the pizza?
- A. At any time, since you will not profit from the communications
- B. Only during normal business hours, between 9 AM and 5 PM
- C. At any time, since there are no rules against conducting business communications in the amateur service
- D. Never. This would facilitate the commercial affairs of a business

One question must be from the following:

2A-31.1 When may an FCC-licensed amateur operator communicate with an amateur operator in a foreign country?
- A. Only when the foreign operator uses English as his primary language
- B. All the time, except on 28.600 to 29.700 MHz
- C. Only when a third party agreement exists between the US and the foreign country
- D. At any time unless prohibited by either the US or the foreign government

2A-32.1 When may an amateur station be used to transmit messages for hire?
- A. Under no circumstances may an amateur station be hired to transmit messages
- B. Modest payment from a non-profit charitable organization is permissible
- C. No money may change hands, but a radio amateur may be compensated for services rendered with gifts of equipment or services rendered as a returned favor
- D. All payments received in return for transmitting messages by amateur radio must be reported to the IRS

2A-32.2 When may the control operator be paid to transmit messages from an amateur station?
- A. The control operator may be paid if he or she works for a public service agency such as the Red Cross
- B. The control operator may not be paid under any circumstances
- C. The control operator may be paid if he or she reports all income earned from operating an amateur station to the IRS as receipt of tax-deductible contributions
- D. The control operator may accept compensation if he or she works for a club station during the period in which the station is transmitting telegraphy practice or information bulletins if certain exacting conditions are met

2A-33.1 When is an amateur operator permitted to broadcast information intended for the general public?
- A. Amateur operators are not permitted to broadcast information intended for the general public
- B. Only when the operator is being paid to transmit the information
- C. Only when such transmissions last less than 1 hour in any 24-hour period
- D. Only when such transmissions last longer than 15 minutes

2A-34.1 What is *third-party communications*?
- A. A message passed from the control operator of an amateur station to another control operator on behalf of another person
- B. Public service communications handled on behalf of a minor political party
- C. Only messages that are formally handled through amateur radio channels
- D. A report of highway conditions transmitted over a local repeater

2A-34.2 Who is a *third party* in amateur communications?
  A. The amateur station that breaks into a two-way contact between two other amateur stations
  B. Any person for whom a message is passed through amateur communication channels other than the control operators of the two stations handling the message
  C. A shortwave listener monitoring a two-way amateur communication
  D. The control operator present when an unlicensed person communicates over an amateur station

2A-34.3 When is an amateur operator permitted to transmit a message to a foreign country for a third party?
  A. Anytime
  B. Never
  C. Anytime, unless there is a third-party communications agreement between the US and the foreign government
  D. When there is a third-party communications agreement between the US and the foreign government, or when the third party is eligible to be the control operator of the station

2A-35.1 Is an amateur station permitted to transmit music?
  A. The transmission of music is not permitted in the amateur service
  B. When the music played produces no dissonances or spurious emissions
  C. When it is used to jam an illegal transmission
  D. Only above 1280 MHz

2A-36.1 Is the use of codes or ciphers where the intent is to obscure the meaning permitted during a two-way communication in the amateur service?
  A. Codes and ciphers are permitted during ARRL-sponsored contests
  B. Codes and ciphers are permitted during nationally declared emergencies
  C. The transmission of codes and ciphers where the intent is to obscure the meaning is not permitted in the amateur service
  D. Codes and ciphers are permitted above 1280 MHz

2A-36.2 When is an operator in the amateur service permitted to use abbreviations that are intended to obscure the meaning of the message?
  A. Only during ARRL-sponsored contests
  B. Only on frequencies above 222.5 MHz
  C. Only during a declared communications emergency
  D. Abbreviations that are intended to obscure the meaning of the message may never be used in the amateur service

One question must be from the following:

2A-37.1 Under what circumstances, if any, may the control operator cause *false or deceptive signals or communications* to be transmitted?
  A. Under no circumstances
  B. When operating a beacon transmitter in a "fox hunt" exercise
  C. When playing a harmless "practical joke" without causing interference to other stations that are not involved
  D. When you need to obscure the meaning of transmitted information to ensure secrecy

2A-37.2 If an amateur operator transmits the word "MAYDAY" when no actual emergency has occurred, what is this called?
  A. A traditional greeting in May
  B. An Emergency Action System test transmission
  C. False or deceptive signals
  D. "MAYDAY" has no significance in an emergency situation

2A-38.1 When may an amateur station transmit unidentified communications?
  A. A transmission need not be identified if it is restricted to brief tests not intended for reception by other parties
  B. A transmission need not be identified when conducted on a clear frequency or "dead band" where interference will not occur
  C. An amateur operator may never transmit unidentified communications
  D. A transmission need not be identified unless two-way communications or third-party communications handling are involved

2A-38.2 What is the meaning of the term *unidentified radio communications or signals*?
  A. Radio communications in which the transmitting station's call sign is transmitted in modes other than CW and voice
  B. Radio communications approaching a receiving station from an unknown direction
  C. Radio communications in which the operator fails to transmit his or her name and QTH
  D. Radio communications in which the station identification is not transmitted

2A-38.3 What is the term used to describe a transmission from an amateur station that does not transmit the required station identification?
  A. Unidentified communications or signals
  B. Reluctance modulation
  C. NØN emission
  D. Tactical communication

2A-39.1 When may an amateur operator willfully or maliciously interfere with a radio communication or signal?
  A. You may jam another person's transmissions if that person is not operating in a legal manner
  B. You may interfere with another station's signals if that station begins transmitting on a frequency already occupied by your station
  C. You may never willfully or maliciously interfere with another station's transmissions
  D. You may expect, and cause, deliberate interference because it is unavoidable during crowded band conditions

2A-39.2 What is the meaning of the term *malicious interference*?
  A. Accidental interference
  B. Intentional interference
  C. Mild interference
  D. Occasional interference

2A-39.3 What is the term used to describe an amateur radio transmission that is intended to disrupt other communications in progress?
  A. Interrupted CW
  B. Malicious interference
  C. Transponded signals
  D. Unidentified transmissions

2A-40.1 As an amateur operator, you receive an *Official Notice of Violation* from the FCC. How promptly must you respond?
A. Within 90 days
B. Within 30 days
C. As specified in the Notice
D. The next day

2A-40.2 If you were to receive a voice distress signal from a station on a frequency outside your operator privileges, what restrictions would apply to assisting the station in distress?
A. You would not be allowed to assist the station because the frequency of its signals were outside your operator privileges
B. You would be allowed to assist the station only if your signals were restricted to the nearest frequency band of your privileges
C. You would be allowed to assist the station on a frequency outside of your operator privileges only if you used international Morse code
D. You would be allowed to assist the station on a frequency outside of your operator privileges using any means of radio communications at your disposal

2A-40.3 If you were in a situation where normal communication systems were disrupted due to a disaster, what restrictions would apply to essential communications you might provide in connection with the immediate safety of human life?
A. You would not be allowed to communicate at all except to the FCC Engineer in Charge of the area concerned
B. You would be restricted to communications using only the emissions and frequencies authorized to your operator privileges
C. You would be allowed to communicate on frequencies outside your operator privileges only if you used international Morse code
D. You would be allowed to use any means of radio communication at your disposal

Subelement 2B—Operating Procedures (2 Questions)

One question must be from the following:

2B-1-1.1 What is the most important factor to consider when selecting a transmitting frequency within your authorized subband?
A. The frequency should not be in use by other amateurs
B. You should be able to hear other stations on the frequency to ensure that someone will be able to hear you
C. Your antenna should be resonant at the selected frequency
D. You should ensure that the SWR on the antenna feed line is high enough at the selected frequency

2B-1-1.2 You wish to contact an amateur station more than 1500 miles away on a summer afternoon. Which band is most likely to provide a successful contact?
A. The 80- or 40-meter wavelength bands
B. The 40- or 15-meter wavelength bands
C. The 15- or 10-meter wavelength bands
D. The 1¼ meter or 23-centimeter wavelength bands

2B-1-1.3 How can on-the-air transmitter tune-up be kept as short as possible?
A. By using a random wire antenna
B. By tuning up on 40 meters first, then switching to the desired band
C. By tuning the transmitter into a dummy load
D. By using twin lead instead of coaxial-cable feed lines

2B-1-2.1 You are having a QSO with your uncle in Pittsburgh when you hear an emergency call for help on the frequency you are using. What should you do?
A. Inform the station that the frequency is in use
B. Direct the station to the nearest emergency net frequency
C. Call your local Civil Preparedness Office and inform them of the emergency
D. Immediately stand by to copy the emergency communication

2B-2-1.1 What is the format of a standard Morse code CQ call?
A. Transmit the procedural signal "CQ" three times, followed by the procedural signal "DE", followed by your call three times
B. Transmit the procedural signal "CQ" three times, followed by the procedural signal "DE", followed by your call one time
C. Transmit the procedural signal "CQ" ten times, followed by the procedural signal "DE", followed by your call one time
D. Transmit the procedural signal "CQ" continuously until someone answers your call

2B-2-1.2 How should you answer a Morse code CQ call?
A. Send your call sign four times
B. Send the other station's call sign twice, followed by the procedural signal "DE", followed by your call sign twice
C. Send the other station's call sign once, followed by the procedural signal "DE", followed by your call sign four times
D. Send your call sign followed by your name, station location and a signal report

2B-2-2.1 At what telegraphy speed should a "CQ" message be transmitted?
A. Only speeds below five WPM
B. The highest speed your keyer will operate
C. Any speed at which you can reliably receive
D. The highest speed at which you can control the keyer

2B-2-3.1 What is the meaning of the Morse code character AR?
A. Only the called station transmit
B. All received correctly
C. End of transmission
D. Best regards

2B-2-3.2 What is the meaning of the Morse code character SK?
A. Received some correctly
B. Best regards
C. Wait
D. End of contact

2B-2-3.3 What is the meaning of the Morse code character BT?
A. Double dash " = "
B. Fraction bar "/"
C. End of contact
D. Back to you

2B-2-3.4 What is the meaning of the Morse code character DN?
A. Double dash " = "
B. Fraction bar "/"
C. Done now (end of contact)
D. Called station only transmit

2B-2-3.5 What is the meaning of the Morse code character KN?
A. Fraction bar "/"
B. End of contact
C. Called station only transmit
D. Key now (go ahead to transmit)

2B-2-4.1 What is the procedural signal "CQ" used for?
A. To notify another station that you will call on the quarter hour
B. To indicate that you are testing a new antenna and are not listening for another station to answer
C. To indicate that only the called station should transmit
D. A general call when you are trying to make a contact

2B-2-4.2 What is the procedural signal "DE" used for?
A. To mean "from" or "this is," as in "W9NGT de N9BTT"
B. To indicate directional emissions from your antenna
C. To indicate "received all correctly"
D. To mean "calling any station"

2B-2-4.3 What is the procedural signal "K" used for?
A. To mean "any station transmit"
B. To mean "all received correctly"
C. To mean "end of message"
D. To mean "called station only transmit"

2B-2-5.1 What does the R in the RST signal report mean?
A. The recovery of the signal
B. The resonance of the CW tone
C. The rate of signal flutter
D. The readability of the signal

2B-2-5.2 What does the S in the RST signal report mean?
A. The scintillation of a signal
B. The strength of the signal
C. The signal quality
D. The speed of the CW transmission

2B-2-5.3 What does the T in the RST signal report mean?
A. The tone of the signal
B. The closeness of the signal to "telephone" quality
C. The timing of the signal dot to dash ratio
D. The tempo of the signal

2B-2-6.1 What is one meaning of the Q signal "QRS"?
A. Interference from static
B. Send more slowly
C. Send RST report
D. Radio station location is

2B-2-6.2 What is one meaning of the Q signal "QRT"?
A. The correct time is
B. Send RST report
C. Stop sending
D. Send more slowly

2B-2-6.3 What is one meaning of the Q signal "QTH"?
A. Time here is
B. My name is
C. Stop sending
D. My location is

2B-2-6.4 What is one meaning of the Q signal "QRZ," when it is followed with a question mark?
A. Who is calling me?
B. What is your radio zone?
C. What time zone are you in?
D. Is this frequency in use?

2B-2-6.5 What is one meaning of the Q signal "QSL," when it is followed with a question mark?
A. Shall I send you my log?
B. Can you acknowledge receipt (of my message)?
C. Shall I send more slowly?
D. Who is calling me?

2B-3-1.1 What is the format of a standard radiotelephone CQ call?
A. Transmit the phrase "CQ" at least ten times, followed by "this is," followed by your call sign at least two times
B. Transmit the phrase "CQ" at least five times, followed by "this is," followed by your call sign once
C. Transmit the phrase "CQ" three times, followed by "this is," followed by your call sign three times
D. Transmit the phrase "CQ" at least ten times, followed by "this is," followed by your call sign once

2B-3-1.2 How should you answer a radiotelephone CQ call?
A. Transmit the other station's call sign at least ten times, followed by "this is," followed by your call sign at least twice
B. Transmit the other station's call sign at least five times phonetically, followed by "this is," followed by your call sign at least once
C. Transmit the other station's call sign at least three times, followed by "this is," followed by your call sign at least five times phonetically
D. Transmit the other station's call sign once, followed by "this is," followed by your call sign given phonetically

2B-3-2.1 How is the call sign "KA3BGQ" stated in Standard International Phonetics?
A. Kilo Alfa Three Bravo Golf Quebec
B. King America Three Bravo Golf Quebec
C. Kilowatt Alfa Three Bravo George Queen
D. Kilo America Three Baker Golf Quebec

2B-3-2.2 How is the call sign "WE5TZD" stated phonetically?
A. Whiskey Echo Foxtrot Tango Zulu Delta
B. Washington England Five Tokyo Zanzibar Denmark
C. Whiskey Echo Five Tango Zulu Delta
D. Whiskey Easy Five Tear Zebra Dog

2B-3-2.3 How is the call sign "KC4HRM" stated phonetically?
A. Kilo Charlie Four Hotel Romeo Mike
B. Kilowatt Charlie Four Hotel Roger Mexico
C. Kentucky Canada Four Honolulu Radio Mexico
D. King Charlie Foxtrot Hotel Roger Mary

2B-3-2.4 How is the call sign "AF6PSQ" stated phonetically?
A. America Florida Six Portugal Spain Quebec
B. Adam Frank Six Peter Sugar Queen
C. Alfa Fox Sierra Papa Santiago Queen
D. Alfa Foxtrot Six Papa Sierra Quebec

2B-3-2.5 How is the call sign "NB8LXG" stated phonetically?
A. November Bravo Eight Lima Xray Golf
B. Nancy Baker Eight Love Xray George
C. Norway Boston Eight London Xray Germany
D. November Bravo Eight London Xray Germany

2B-3-2.6 How is the call sign "KJ1UOI" stated phonetically?
A. King John One Uncle Oboe Ida
B. Kilowatt George India Uncle Oscar India
C. Kilo Juliette One Uniform Oscar India
D. Kentucky Juliette One United Ontario Indiana

2B-3-2.7 How is the call sign "WV2BPZ" stated phonetically?
A. Whiskey Victor Two Bravo Papa Zulu
B. Willie Victor Two Baker Papa Zebra
C. Whiskey Victor Tango Bravo Papa Zulu
D. Willie Virginia Two Boston Peter Zanzibar

2B-3-2.8 How is the call sign "NY3CTJ" stated phonetically?
A. Norway Yokohama Three California Tokyo Japan
B. Nancy Yankee Three Cat Texas Jackrabbit
C. Norway Yesterday Three Charlie Texas Juliette
D. November Yankee Three Charlie Tango Juliette

2B-3-2.9 How is the call sign "KG7DRV" stated phonetically?
A. Kilo Golf Seven Denver Radio Venezuela
B. Kilo Golf Seven Delta Romeo Victor
C. King John Seven Dog Radio Victor
D. Kilowatt George Seven Delta Romeo Video

2B-3-2.10 How is the call sign "WX9HKS" stated phonetically?
A. Whiskey Xray Nine Hotel Kilo Sierra
B. Willie Xray November Hotel King Sierra
C. Washington Xray Nine Honolulu Kentucky Santiago
D. Whiskey Xray Nine Henry King Sugar

2B-3-2.11 How is the call sign "AE0LQY" stated phonetically?
A. Able Easy Zero Lima Quebec Yankee
B. Arizona Equador Zero London Queen Yesterday
C. Alfa Echo Zero Lima Quebec Yankee
D. Able Easy Zero Love Queen Yoke

One question must be from the following:

2B-4-1.1 What is the format of a standard RTTY CQ call?
A. Transmit the phrase "CQ" three times, followed by "DE", followed by your call sign two times
B. Transmit the phrase "CQ" three to six times, followed by "DE", followed by your call sign three times
C. Transmit the phrase "CQ" ten times, followed by the procedural signal "DE", followed by your call one time
D. Transmit the phrase "CQ" continuously until someone answers your call

2B-4-2.1 You receive an RTTY CQ call at 45 bauds. At what speed should you respond?
A. 22½ bauds
B. 45 bauds
C. 90 bauds
D. Any speed, since radioteletype systems adjust to any signal rate

2B-5-1.1 What does the term *connected* mean in a packet-radio link?
A. A telephone link has been established between two amateurs
B. An amateur radio message has reached the station for local delivery
C. The transmitting station is sending data specifically addressed to the receiving station, and the receiving station is acknowledging that the data has been received correctly
D. The transmitting station and a receiving station are using a certain digipeater, so no other contacts can take place until they are finished

2B-5-1.2 What does the term *monitoring* mean on a frequency used for packet radio?
A. The FCC is copying all messages to determine their content
B. A member of the Amateur Auxiliary to the FCC's Field Operations Bureau is copying all messages to determine their content
C. The receiving station's video monitor is displaying all messages intended for that station, and is acknowledging correct receipt of the data
D. The receiving station is displaying information that may not be addressed to that station, and is not acknowledging correct receipt of the data

2B-5-2.1 What is a *digipeater*?
A. A packet-radio station used to retransmit data that is specifically addressed to be retransmitted by that station
B. An amateur radio repeater designed to retransmit all audio signals in a digital form
C. An amateur radio repeater designed using only digital electronics components
D. A packet-radio station that retransmits any signals it receives

2B-5-2.2 What is the meaning of the term *network* in packet radio?
A. A system of telephone lines interconnecting packet-radio stations to transfer data
B. A method of interconnecting packet-radio stations so that data can be transferred over long distances
C. The interlaced wiring on a terminal-node-controller board
D. The terminal-node-controller function that automatically rejects another caller when the station is connected

2B-6-1.1 What is a good way to establish contact on a repeater?
- A. Give the call sign of the station you want to contact three times
- B. Call the other operator by name and then give your call sign three times
- C. Call the desired station and then identify your own station
- D. Say, "Breaker, breaker," and then give your call sign

2B-6-2.1 What is the main purpose of a repeater?
- A. To provide a station that makes local information available 24 hours a day
- B. To provide a means of linking amateur radio stations with the telephone system
- C. To retransmit NOAA weather information during severe storm warnings
- D. Repeaters extend the operating range of portable and mobile stations

2B-6-3.1 What does it mean to say that a repeater has an *input* and an *output* frequency?
- A. The repeater receives on one frequency and transmits on another
- B. All repeaters offer a choice of operating frequency, in case one is busy
- C. One frequency is used to control repeater functions and the other frequency is the one used to retransmit received signals
- D. Repeaters require an access code to be transmitted on one frequency while your voice is transmitted on the other

2B-6-4.1 When should simplex operation be used instead of using a repeater?
- A. Whenever greater communications reliability is needed
- B. Whenever a contact is possible without using a repeater
- C. Whenever you need someone to make an emergency telephone call
- D. Whenever you are traveling and need some local information

2B-6-5.1 What is an *autopatch*?
- A. A repeater feature that automatically selects the strongest signal to be repeated
- B. An automatic system of connecting a mobile station to the next repeater as it moves out of range of the first
- C. A device that allows repeater users to make telephone calls from their portable or mobile stations
- D. A system that automatically locks other stations out of the repeater when there is a QSO in progress

2B-6-5.2 What is the purpose of a repeater *time-out timer*?
- A. It allows the repeater to have a rest period after heavy use
- B. It logs repeater transmit time to determine when the repeater mean time between failure rating is exceeded
- C. It limits repeater transmission time to no more than ten minutes
- D. It limits repeater transmission time to no more than three minutes

Subelement 2C—Radio-Wave Propagation (1 Question)

One question must be from the following:

2C-1.1 What type of radio-wave propagation occurs when the signal travels in a straight line from the transmitting antenna to the receiving antenna?
- A. Line-of-sight propagation
- B. Straight-line propagation
- C. Knife-edge diffraction
- D. Tunnel propagation

2C-1.2 What path do radio waves usually follow from a transmitting antenna to a receiving antenna at VHF and higher frequencies?
- A. A bent path through the ionosphere
- B. A straight line
- C. A great circle path over either the north or south pole
- D. A circular path going either east or west from the transmitter

2C-2.1 What type of propagation involves radio signals that travel along the surface of the Earth?
- A. Sky-wave propagation
- B. Knife-edge diffraction
- C. E-layer propagation
- D. Ground-wave propagation

2C-2.2 What is the meaning of the term *ground-wave propagation*?
- A. Signals that travel along seismic fault lines
- B. Signals that travel along the surface of the earth
- C. Signals that are radiated from a ground-plane antenna
- D. Signals that are radiated from a ground station to a satellite

2C-2.3 Two amateur radio stations a few miles apart and separated by a low hill blocking their line-of-sight path are communicating on 3.725 MHz. What type of propagation is probably being used?
- A. Tropospheric ducting
- B. Ground wave
- C. Meteor scatter
- D. Sporadic E

2C-2.4 When compared to sky-wave propagation, what is the usual effective range of ground-wave propagation?
- A. Much smaller
- B. Much greater
- C. The same
- D. Dependent on the weather

2C-3.1 What type of propagation uses radio signals refracted back to earth by the ionosphere?
- A. Sky wave
- B. Earth-moon-earth
- C. Ground wave
- D. Tropospheric

2C-3.2 What is the meaning of the term *sky-wave propagation*?
- A. Signals reflected from the moon
- B. Signals refracted by the ionosphere
- C. Signals refracted by water-dense cloud formations
- D. Signals retransmitted by a repeater

2C-3.3 What does the term *skip* mean?
- A. Signals are reflected from the moon
- B. Signals are refracted by water-dense cloud formations
- C. Signals are retransmitted by repeaters
- D. Signals are refracted by the ionosphere

2C-3.4 What is the area of weak signals between the ranges of ground waves and the first hop called?
A. The skip zone
B. The hysteresis zone
C. The monitor zone
D. The transequatorial zone

2C-3.5 What is the meaning of the term *skip zone*?
A. An area covered by skip propagation
B. The area where a satellite comes close to the earth, and skips off the ionosphere
C. An area that is too far for ground-wave propagation, but too close for skip propagation
D. The area in the atmosphere that causes skip propagation

2C-3.6 What type of radio wave propagation makes it possible for amateur stations to communicate long distances?
A. Direct-inductive propagation
B. Knife-edge diffraction
C. Ground-wave propagation
D. Sky-wave propagation

2C-4.1 How long is an average *sunspot cycle*?
A. 2 years
B. 5 years
C. 11 years
D. 17 years

2C-4.2 What is the term used to describe the long-term variation in the number of visible sunspots?
A. The 11-year cycle
B. The Solar magnetic flux cycle
C. The hysteresis count
D. The sunspot cycle

2C-5.1 What effect does the number of sunspots have on the maximum usable frequency (MUF)?
A. The more sunspots there are, the higher the MUF will be
B. The more sunspots there are, the lower the MUF will be
C. The MUF is equal to the square of the number of sunspots
D. The number of sunspots effects the lowest usable frequency (LUF) but not the MUF

2C-5.2 What effect does the number of sunspots have on the ionization level in the atmosphere?
A. The more sunspots there are, the lower the ionization level will be
B. The more sunspots there are, the higher the ionization level will be
C. The ionization level of the ionosphere is equal to the square root of the number of sunspots
D. The ionization level of the ionosphere is equal to the square of the number of sunspots

2C-6.1 Why can a VHF or UHF radio signal that is transmitted toward a mountain often be received at some distant point in a different direction?
A. You can never tell what direction a radio wave is traveling in
B. These radio signals are easily bent by the ionosphere
C. These radio signals are easily reflected by objects in their path
D. These radio signals are sometimes scattered in the ectosphere

2C-6.2 Why can the direction that a VHF or UHF radio signal is traveling be changed if there is a tall building in the way?
A. You can never tell what direction a radio wave is traveling in
B. These radio signals are easily bent by the ionosphere
C. These radio signals are easily reflected by objects in their path
D. These radio signals are sometimes scattered in the ectosphere

Subelement 2D—Amateur Radio Practice (4 Questions)

One question must be from the following:

2D-1.1 How can you prevent the use of your amateur station by unauthorized persons?
A. Install a carrier-operated relay in the main power line
B. Install a key-operated "ON/OFF" switch in the main power line
C. Post a "Danger - High Voltage" sign in the station
D. Install AC line fuses in the main power line

2D-1.2 What is the purpose of a key-operated "ON/OFF" switch in the main power line?
A. To prevent the use of your station by unauthorized persons
B. To provide an easy method for the FCC to put your station off the air
C. To prevent the power company from inadvertently turning off your electricity during an emergency
D. As a safety feature, to kill all power to the station in the event of an emergency

2D-2.1 Why should all antenna and rotator cables be grounded when an amateur station is not in use?
A. To lock the antenna system in one position
B. To avoid radio frequency interference
C. To save electricity
D. To protect the station and building from damage due to a nearby lightning strike

2D-2.2 How can an antenna system be protected from damage caused by a nearby lightning strike?
A. Install a balun at the antenna feed point
B. Install an RF choke in the feed line
C. Ground all antennas when they are not in use
D. Install a line fuse in the antenna wire

2D-2.3 How can amateur station equipment be protected from damage caused by voltage induced in the power lines by a nearby lightning strike?
A. Use heavy insulation on the wiring
B. Keep the equipment on constantly
C. Disconnect the ground system
D. Disconnect all equipment after use, either by unplugging or by using a main disconnect switch

2D-2.4 For proper protection from lightning strikes, what equipment should be grounded in an amateur station?
A. The power supply primary
B. All station equipment
C. The feed line center conductors
D. The AC power mains

2D-3.1 What is a convenient indoor grounding point for an amateur station?
A. A metallic cold water pipe
B. PVC plumbing
C. A window screen
D. A natural gas pipe

2D-3.2 To protect against electrical shock hazards, what should you connect the chassis of each piece of your equipment to?
A. Insulated shock mounts
B. The antenna
C. A good ground connection
D. A circuit breaker

2D-3.3 What type of material should a driven ground rod be made of?
A. Ceramic or other good insulator
B. Copper or copper-clad steel
C. Iron or steel
D. Fiberglass

2D-3.4 What is the shortest ground rod you should consider installing for your amateur station RF ground?
A. 4 foot
B. 6 foot
C. 8 foot
D. 10 foot

One question must be from the following:

2D-4.1 What precautions should you take when working with 1270-MHz waveguide?
A. Make sure that the RF leakage filters are installed at both ends of the waveguide
B. Never look into the open end of a waveguide when RF is applied
C. Minimize the standing wave ratio before you test the waveguide
D. Never have both ends of the waveguide open at the same time when RF is applied

2D-4.2 What precautions should you take when you mount a UHF antenna in a permanent location?
A. Make sure that no one can be near the antenna when you are transmitting
B. Make sure that the RF field screens are in place
C. Make sure that the antenna is near the ground to maximize directional effect
D. Make sure you connect an RF leakage filter at the antenna feed point

2D-4.3 What precautions should you take before removing the shielding on a UHF power amplifier?
A. Make sure all RF screens are in place at the antenna
B. Make sure the feed line is properly grounded
C. Make sure the amplifier cannot be accidentally energized
D. Make sure that the RF leakage filters are connected

2D-4.4 Why should you use only good-quality, well-constructed coaxial cable and connectors for a UHF antenna system?
A. To minimize RF leakage
B. To reduce parasitic oscillations
C. To maximize the directional characteristics of your antenna
D. To maximize the standing wave ratio of the antenna system

2D-4.5 Why should you be careful to position the antenna of your 220-MHz hand-held transceiver away from your head when you are transmitting?
A. To take advantage of the directional effect
B. To minimize RF exposure
C. To use your body to reflect the signal, improving the directional characteristics of the antenna
D. To minimize static discharges

2D-4.6 Which of the following types of radiation produce health risks most like the risks produced by radio frequency radiation?
A. Microwave oven radiation and ultraviolet radiation
B. Microwave oven radiation and radiation from an electric space heater
C. Radiation from Uranium or Radium and ultraviolet radiation
D. Sunlight and radiation from an electric space heater

2D-5.1 Why is there a switch that turns off the power to a high-voltage power supply if the cabinet is opened?
A. To prevent RF from escaping from the supply
B. To prevent RF from entering the supply through the open cabinet
C. To provide a way to turn the power supply on and off
D. To reduce the danger of electrical shock

2D-5.2 What purpose does a safety interlock on an amateur transmitter serve?
A. It reduces the danger that the operator will come in contact with dangerous high voltages when the cabinet is opened while the power is on
B. It prevents the transmitter from being turned on accidentally
C. It prevents RF energy from leaking out of the transmitter cabinet
D. It provides a way for the station licensee to ensure that only authorized operators can turn the transmitter on

2D-6.1 What type of safety equipment should you wear when you are working at the top of an antenna tower?
A. A grounding chain
B. A reflective vest
C. Loose clothing
D. A carefully inspected safety belt

2D-6.2 Why should you wear a safety belt when you are working at the top of an antenna tower?
A. To provide a way to safely hold your tools so they don't fall and injure someone on the ground
B. To maintain a balanced load on the tower while you are working
C. To provide a way to safely bring tools up and down the tower
D. To prevent an accidental fall

2D-6.3 For safety purposes, how high should you locate all portions of your horizontal wire antenna?
A. High enough so that a person cannot touch them from the ground
B. Higher than chest level
C. Above knee level
D. Above electrical lines

2D-6.4 What type of safety equipment should you wear when you are on the ground assisting someone who is working on an antenna tower?
A. A reflective vest
B. A safety belt
C. A grounding chain
D. A hard hat

2D-6.5 Why should you wear a hard hat when you are on the ground assisting someone who is working on an antenna tower?
A. To avoid injury from tools dropped from the tower
B. To provide an RF shield during antenna testing
C. To avoid injury if the tower should accidentally collapse
D. To avoid injury from walking into tower guy wires

One question must be from the following:

2D-7-1.1 What accessory is used to measure standing wave ratio?
A. An ohm meter
B. An ammeter
C. An SWR meter
D. A current bridge

2D-7-1.2 What instrument is used to indicate the relative impedance match between a transmitter and antenna?
A. An ammeter
B. An ohmmeter
C. A voltmeter
D. An SWR meter

2D-7-2.1 What does an SWR-meter reading of 1:1 indicate?
A. An antenna designed for use on another frequency band is probably connected
B. An optimum impedance match has been attained
C. No power is being transferred to the antenna
D. An SWR meter never indicates 1:1 unless it is defective

2D-7-2.2 What does an SWR-meter reading of less than 1.5:1 indicate?
A. An unacceptably low reading
B. An unacceptably high reading
C. An acceptable impedance match
D. An antenna gain of 1.5

2D-7-2.3 What does an SWR-meter reading of 4:1 indicate?
A. An unacceptably low reading
B. An acceptable impedance match
C. An antenna gain of 4
D. An impedance mismatch, which is not acceptable; it indicates problems with the antenna system

2D-7-2.4 What does an SWR-meter reading of 5:1 indicate?
A. The antenna will make a 10-watt signal as strong as a 50-watt signal
B. Maximum power is being delivered to the antenna
C. An unacceptable mismatch is indicated
D. A very desirable impedance match has been attained

2D-7-3.1 What kind of SWR-meter reading may indicate poor electrical contact between parts of an antenna system?
A. An erratic reading
B. An unusually low reading
C. No reading at all
D. A negative reading

2D-7-3.2 What does an unusually high SWR-meter reading indicate?

A. That the antenna is not the correct length, or that there is an open or shorted connection somewhere in the feed line

B. That the signals arriving at the antenna are unusually strong, indicating good radio conditions

C. That the transmitter is producing more power than normal, probably indicating that the final amplifier tubes or transistors are about to go bad

D. That there is an unusually large amount of solar white-noise radiation, indicating very poor radio conditions

2D-7-3.3 The SWR-meter reading at the low-frequency end of an amateur band is 2.5:1, and the SWR-meter reading at the high-frequency end of the same band is 5:1. What does this indicate about your antenna?

A. The antenna is broadbanded

B. The antenna is too long for operation on this band

C. The antenna is too short for operation on this band

D. The antenna has been optimized for operation on this band

2D-7-3.4 The SWR-meter reading at the low-frequency end of an amateur band is 5:1, and the SWR-meter reading at the high-frequency end of the same band is 2.5:1. What does this indicate about your antenna?

A. The antenna is broadbanded

B. The antenna is too long for operation on this band

C. The antenna is too short for operation on this band

D. The antenna has been optimized for operation on this band

One question must be from the following:

2D-8-1.1 What is meant by *receiver overload*?

A. Interference caused by transmitter harmonics

B. Interference caused by overcrowded band conditions

C. Interference caused by strong signals from a nearby transmitter

D. Interference caused by turning the receiver volume too high

2D-8-1.2 What is a likely indication that radio-frequency interference to a receiver is caused by front-end overload?

A. A low pass filter at the transmitter reduces interference sharply

B. The interference is independent of frequency

C. A high pass filter at the receiver reduces interference little or not at all

D. Grounding the receiver makes the problem worse

2D-8-1.3 Your neighbor reports interference to his television whenever you are transmitting from your amateur station. This interference occurs regardless of your transmitter frequency. What is likely to be the cause of the interference?

A. Inadequate transmitter harmonic suppression

B. Receiver VR tube discharge

C. Receiver overload

D. Incorrect antenna length

2D-8-1.4 What type of filter should be installed on a TV receiver as the first step in preventing RF overload from an amateur HF station transmission?

A. Low pass

B. High pass

C. Band pass

D. Notch

2D-8-2.1 What is meant by *harmonic radiation*?

A. Transmission of signals at whole number multiples of the fundamental (desired) frequency

B. Transmission of signals that include a superimposed 60-Hz hum

C. Transmission of signals caused by sympathetic vibrations from a nearby transmitter

D. Transmission of signals to produce a stimulated emission in the air to enhance skip propagation

2D-8-2.2 Why is harmonic radiation from an amateur station undesirable?

A. It will cause interference to other stations and may result in out-of-band signal radiation

B. It uses large amounts of electric power

C. It will cause sympathetic vibrations in nearby transmitters

D. It will produce stimulated emission in the air above the transmitter, thus causing aurora

2D-8-2.3 What type of interference may radiate from a multi-band antenna connected to an improperly tuned transmitter?

A. Harmonic radiation

B. Auroral distortion

C. Parasitic excitation

D. Intermodulation

2D-8-2.4 What is the purpose of shielding in a transmitter?

A. It gives the low pass filter structural stability

B. It enhances the microphonic tendencies of radiotelephone transmitters

C. It prevents unwanted RF radiation

D. It helps maintain a sufficiently high operating temperature in circuit components

2D-8-2.5 Your neighbor reports interference on one or two channels of her television when you are transmitting from your amateur station. This interference only occurs when you are operating on 15 meters. What is likely to be the cause of the interference?

A. Excessive low-pass filtering on the transmitter

B. Sporadic E de-ionization near your neighbor's TV antenna

C. TV Receiver front-end overload

D. Harmonic radiation from your transmitter

2D-8-2.6 What type of filter should be installed on an amateur transmitter as the first step in reducing harmonic radiation?

A. Key click filter

B. Low pass filter

C. High pass filter

D. CW filter

2D-8-3.1　If you are notified that your amateur station is causing television interference, what should you do first?
- A. Make sure that your amateur equipment is operating properly, and that it does not cause interference to your own television
- B. Immediately turn off your transmitter and contact the nearest FCC office for assistance
- C. Install a high-pass filter at the transmitter output and a low-pass filter at the antenna-input terminals of the TV
- D. Continue operating normally, since you have no legal obligation to reduce or eliminate the interference

2D-8-3.2　Your neighbor informs you that you are causing television interference, but you are sure your amateur equipment is operating properly and you cause no interference to your own TV. What should you do?
- A. Immediately turn off your transmitter and contact the nearest FCC office for assistance
- B. Work with your neighbor to determine that you are actually the cause of the interference
- C. Install a high-pass filter at the transmitter output and a low-pass filter at the antenna-input terminals of the TV
- D. Continue operating normally, since you have no legal obligation to reduce or eliminate the interference

Subelement 2E—Electrical Principles (4 questions)

One question must be from the following:

2E-1-1.1　Your receiver dial is calibrated in megahertz and shows a signal at 1200 MHz. At what frequency would a dial calibrated in gigahertz show the signal?
- A. 1,200,000 GHz
- B. 12 GHz
- C. 1.2 GHz
- D. 0.0012 GHz

2E-1-2.1　Your receiver dial is calibrated in kilohertz and shows a signal at 7125 kHz. At what frequency would a dial calibrated in megahertz show the signal?
- A. 0.007125 MHz
- B. 7.125 MHz
- C. 71.25 MHz
- D. 7,125,000 MHz

2E-1-2.2　Your receiver dial is calibrated in gigahertz and shows a signal at 1.2 GHz. At what frequency would a dial calibrated in megahertz show the same signal?
- A. 1.2 MHz
- B. 12 MHz
- C. 120 MHz
- D. 1200 MHz

2E-1-3.1　Your receiver dial is calibrated in megahertz and shows a signal at 3.525 MHz. At what frequency would a dial calibrated in kilohertz show the signal?
- A. 0.003525 kHz
- B. 3525 kHz
- C. 35.25 kHz
- D. 3,525,000 kHz

2E-1-3.2　Your receiver dial is calibrated in kilohertz and shows a signal at 3725 kHz. At what frequency would a dial calibrated in Hertz show the same signal?
- A. 3,725 Hz
- B. 3.725 Hz
- C. 37.25 Hz
- D. 3,725,000 Hz

2E-1-4.1　How long (in meters) is an antenna that is 400 centimeters long?
- A. 0.0004 meters
- B. 4 meters
- C. 40 meters
- D. 40,000 meters

2E-1-5.1　What reading will be displayed on a meter calibrated in amperes when it is being used to measure a 3000-milliampere current?
- A. 0.003 amperes
- B. 0.3 amperes
- C. 3 amperes
- D. 3,000,000 amperes

2E-1-5.2　What reading will be displayed on a meter calibrated in volts when it is being used to measure a 3500-millivolt potential?
- A. 350 volts
- B. 35 volts
- C. 3.5 volts
- D. 0.35 volts

2E-1-6.1　How many farads is 500,000 microfarads?
- A. 0.0005 farads
- B. 0.5 farads
- C. 500 farads
- D. 500,000,000 farads

2E-1-7.1 How many microfarads is 1,000,000 picofarads?
A. 0.001 microfarads
B. 1 microfarad
C. 1,000 microfarads
D. 1,000,000,000 microfarads

One question must be from the following:

2E-2-1.1 What is the term used to describe the flow of electrons in an electric circuit?
A. Voltage
B. Resistance
C. Capacitance
D. Current

2E-2-2.1 What is the basic unit of electric current?
A. The volt
B. The watt
C. The ampere
D. The ohm

2E-3-1.1 What supplies the force that will cause electrons to flow through a circuit?
A. Electromotive force, or voltage
B. Magnetomotive force, or inductance
C. Farad force, or capacitance
D. Thermodynamic force, or entropy

2E-3-1.2 The pressure in a water pipe is comparable to what force in an electrical circuit?
A. Current
B. Resistance
C. Gravitation
D. Voltage

2E-3-1.3 An electric circuit must connect to two terminals of a voltage source. What are these two terminals called?
A. The north and south poles
B. The positive and neutral terminals
C. The positive and negative terminals
D. The entrance and exit terminals

2E-3-2.1 What is the basic unit of voltage?
A. The volt
B. The watt
C. The ampere
D. The ohm

2E-4.1 List at least three good electrical conductors.
A. Copper, gold, mica
B. Gold, silver, wood
C. Gold, silver, aluminum
D. Copper, aluminum, paper

2E-5.1 List at least four good electrical insulators.
A. Glass, air, plastic, porcelain
B. Glass, wood, copper, porcelain
C. Paper, glass, air, aluminum
D. Plastic, rubber, wood, carbon

2E-6-1.1 There is a limit to the electric current that can pass through any material. What is this current limiting called?
A. Fusing
B. Reactance
C. Saturation
D. Resistance

2E-6-1.2 What is an electrical component called that opposes electron movement through a circuit?
A. A resistor
B. A reactor
C. A fuse
D. An oersted

2E-6-2.1 What is the basic unit of resistance?
A. The volt
B. The watt
C. The ampere
D. The ohm

One question must be from the following:

2E-7.1 What electrical principle relates voltage, current and resistance in an electric circuit?
A. Ampere's Law
B. Kirchhoff's Law
C. Ohm's Law
D. Tesla's Law

2E-7.2 There is a 2-amp current through a 50-ohm resistor. What is the applied voltage?
A. 0.04 volts
B. 52 volts
C. 100 volts
D. 200 volts

2E-7.3 If 200 volts is applied to a 100-ohm resistor, what is the current through the resistor?
A. 0.5 amps
B. 2 amps
C. 50 amps
D. 20000 amps

2E-7.4 There is a 3-amp current through a resistor and we know that the applied voltage is 90 volts. What is the value of the resistor?
A. 0.03 ohms
B. 10 ohms
C. 30 ohms
D. 2700 ohms

2E-8.1 What is the term used to describe the ability to do work?
A. Voltage
B. Power
C. Inertia
D. Energy

2E-8.2 What is converted to heat and light in an electric light bulb?
A. Electrical energy
B. Electrical voltage
C. Electrical power
D. Electrical current

2E-9-1.1 What term is used to describe the rate of energy consumption?
A. Energy
B. Current
C. Power
D. Voltage

2E-9-1.2 You have two lamps with different wattage light bulbs in them. How can you determine which bulb uses electrical energy faster?
A. The bulb that operates from the higher voltage will consume energy faster
B. The physically larger bulb will consume energy faster
C. The bulb with the higher wattage rating will consume energy faster
D. The bulb with the lower wattage rating will consume energy faster

2E-9-2.1 What is the basic unit of electrical power?
A. Ohm
B. Watt
C. Volt
D. Ampere

2E-10.1 What is the term for an electrical circuit in which there can be no current?
A. A closed circuit
B. A short circuit
C. An open circuit
D. A hyper circuit

2E-11.1 What is the term for a failure in an electrical circuit that causes excessively high current?
A. An open circuit
B. A dead circuit
C. A closed circuit
D. A short circuit

One question must be from the following:

2E-12-1.1 What is the term used to describe a current that flows only in one direction?
A. Alternating current
B. Direct current
C. Periodic current
D. Pulsating current

2E-12-2.1 What is the term used to describe a current that flows first in one direction, then in the opposite direction, over and over?
A. Alternating current
B. Direct current
C. Negative current
D. Positive current

2E-12-3.1 What is the term for the number of complete cycles of an alternating waveform that occur in one second?
A. Pulse repetition rate
B. Hertz
C. Frequency per wavelength
D. Frequency

2E-12-3.2 A certain AC signal makes 2000 complete cycles in one second. What property of the signal does this number describe?
A. The frequency of the signal
B. The pulse repetition rate of the signal
C. The wavelength of the signal
D. The hertz per second of the signal

2E-12-3.3 What is the basic unit of frequency?
A. The hertz
B. The cycle
C. The kilohertz
D. The megahertz

2E-12-4.1 What range of frequencies are usually called *audio frequencies*?
A. 0 to 20 Hz
B. 20 to 20,000 Hz
C. 200 to 200,000 Hz
D. 10,000 to 30,000 Hz

2E-12-4.2 A signal at 725 Hz is in what frequency range?
A. Audio frequency
B. Intermediate frequency
C. Microwave frequency
D. Radio frequency

2E-12-4.3 Why do we call signals in the range 20 Hz to 20,000 Hz *audio frequencies*?
A. Because the human ear rejects signals in this frequency range
B. Because the human ear responds to sounds in this frequency range
C. Because frequencies in this range are too low for a radio to detect
D. Because a radio converts signals in this range directly to sounds the human ear responds to

2E-12-5.1 Signals above what frequency are usually called *radio-frequency* signals?
A. 20 Hz
B. 2000 Hz
C. 20,000 Hz
D. 1,000,000 Hz

2E-12-5.2 A signal at 7125 kHz is in what frequency range?
A. Audio frequency
B. Radio frequency
C. Hyper-frequency
D. Super-high frequency

2E-13.1 What is the term for the distance an AC signal travels during one complete cycle?
A. Wave velocity
B. Velocity factor
C. Wavelength
D. Wavelength per meter

2E-13.2 In the time it takes a certain radio signal to pass your antenna, the leading edge of the wave travels 12 meters. What property of the signal does this number refer to?
A. The signal frequency
B. The wave velocity
C. The velocity factor
D. The signal wavelength

Subelement 2F—Circuit Components (2 Questions)

One question must be from the following:

2F-1.1   What is the symbol used on schematic diagrams to represent a resistor?

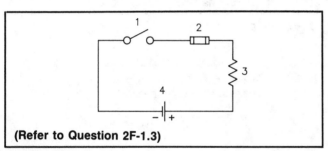

2F-1.2   What is the symbol used on schematic diagrams to represent a variable resistor or potentiometer?

A.

B.

C.

D.

(Refer to Question 2F-1.3)

Figure 2F-1

2F-1.3   In diagram 2F-1, which component is a resistor?
   A. 1
   B. 2
   C. 3
   D. 4

2F-2.1   What is the symbol used on schematic diagrams to represent a single-pole, single-throw switch?

2F-2.2   What is the symbol used on schematic diagrams to represent a single-pole, double-throw switch?

2F-2.3   What is the symbol used on schematic diagrams to represent a double-pole, double-throw switch?

2F-2.4   What is the symbol used on schematic diagrams to represent a single-pole 5-position switch?

2F-2.5   In diagram 2F-2, which component is a switch?
   A. 1
   B. 2
   C. 3
   D. 4

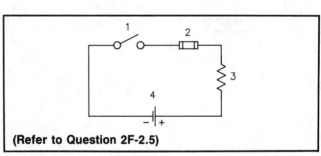

(Refer to Question 2F-2.5)

Figure 2F-2

2F-3.1 What is the symbol used on schematic diagrams to represent a fuse?

A.

B. ⊣◻⊢

C.

D.

2F-4.1 What is the symbol used on schematic diagrams to represent a single-cell battery?

A. −‖+

B. −▯+

C. +‖−

D. +☐−

2F-4.2 What is the symbol used on schematic diagrams to represent a multiple-cell battery?

A. +☐—☐—☐−

B. +‖‖+

C. +‖‖‖☐−

D. −‖‖+

One question must be from the following:

2F-5.1 What is the symbol normally used to represent an earth-ground connection on schematic diagrams?

A.

B.

C.

D.

2F-5.2 What is the symbol normally used to represent a chassis-ground connection on schematic diagrams?

A.

B.

C.

D.

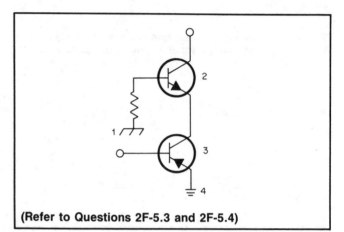

(Refer to Questions 2F-5.3 and 2F-5.4)

Figure 2F-5

2F-5.3 In diagram 2F-5, which symbol represents a chassis ground connection?
A. 1
B. 2
C. 3
D. 4

2F-5.4 In diagram 2F-5, which symbol represents an earth ground connection?
A. 1
B. 2
C. 3
D. 4

2F-6.1 What is the symbol used to represent an antenna on schematic diagrams?

A.

B.

C.

D.

2F-7.1   What is the symbol used to represent an NPN bipolar transistor on schematic diagrams?

 A.

 B.

 C.

 D.

2F-7.2   What is the symbol used to represent a PNP bipolar transistor on schematic diagrams?

 A.

 B.

 C.

 D.

2F-7.4   In diagram 2F-7, which symbol represents an NPN bipolar transistor?
    A. 1
    B. 2
    C. 3
    D. 4

2F-8.1   What is the symbol used to represent a triode vacuum tube on schematic diagrams?

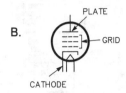

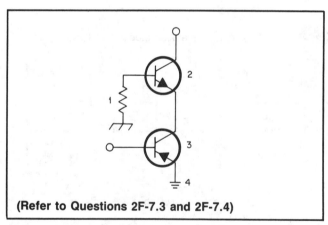

(Refer to Questions 2F-7.3 and 2F-7.4)

Figure 2F-7

2F-7.3   In diagram 2F-7, which symbol represents a PNP bipolar transistor?
    A. 1
    B. 2
    C. 3
    D. 4

Subelement 2G—Practical Circuits (2 Questions)

One question must be from the following:

2G-1-1.1   What is the unlabeled block (?) in this diagram?

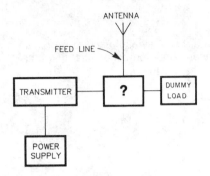

A. A terminal-node controller
B. An antenna switch
C. A telegraph key
D. A TR switch

2G-1-1.2   What is the unlabeled block (?) in this diagram?

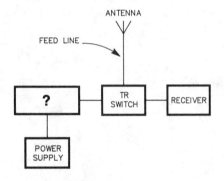

A. A microphone
B. A receiver
C. A transmitter
D. An SWR meter

2G-1-1.3   What is the unlabeled block (?) in this diagram?

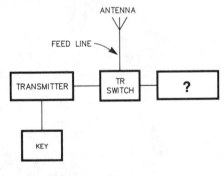

A. A key click filter
B. An antenna tuner
C. A power supply
D. A receiver

2G-1-1.4   What is the unlabeled block (?) in this diagram?

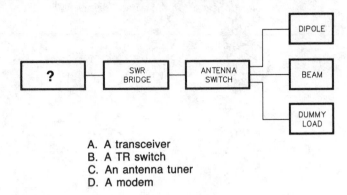

A. A transceiver
B. A TR switch
C. An antenna tuner
D. A modem

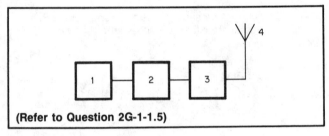

(Refer to Question 2G-1-1.5)

Figure 2G-1

2G-1-1.5   In block diagram 2G-1, which symbol represents an antenna?
A. 1
B. 2
C. 3
D. 4

2G-1-2.1   What is the unlabeled block (?) in this diagram?

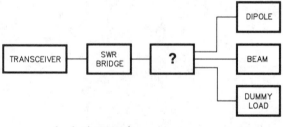

A. A pi network
B. An antenna switch
C. A key click filter
D. A mixer

2G-1-2.2   What is the unlabeled block (?) in this diagram?

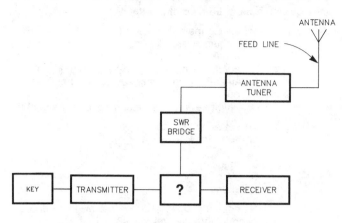

A. A TR switch
B. A variable frequency oscillator
C. A linear amplifier
D. A microphone

2G-1-2.3   What is the unlabeled block (?) in this diagram?

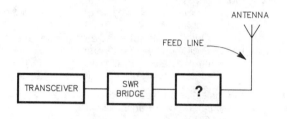

A. An antenna switch
B. An impedance-matching network
C. A key click filter
D. A terminal-node controller

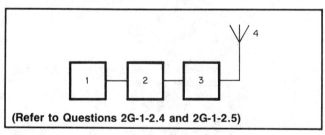

(Refer to Questions 2G-1-2.4 and 2G-1-2.5)

Figure 2G-1

2G-1-2.4   In block diagram 2G-1, if component 1 is a transceiver and component 2 is an SWR meter, what is component 3?
A. A power supply
B. A receiver
C. A microphone
D. An impedance matching device

2G-1-2.5   In block diagram 2G-1, if component 2 is an SWR meter and component 3 is an impedance matching device, what is component 1?
A. A power supply
B. An antenna
C. An antenna switch
D. A transceiver

One question must be from the following:

2G-2.1   In an amateur station designed for Morse radiotelegraph operation, what station accessory will you need to go with your transmitter?
A. A terminal-node controller
B. A telegraph key
C. An SWR meter
D. An antenna switch

2G-2.2   What is the unlabeled block (?) in this diagram of a Morse telegraphy station?

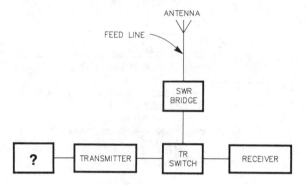

A. A sidetone oscillator
B. A microphone
C. A telegraph key
D. A DTMF keypad

2G-2.3   What station accessory do many amateurs use to help form good Morse code characters?
A. A sidetone oscillator
B. A key-click filter
C. An electronic keyer
D. A DTMF keypad

2G-3.1   In an amateur station designed for radiotelephone operation, what station accessory will you need to go with your transmitter?
A. A splatter filter
B. A terminal-voice controller
C. A receiver audio filter
D. A microphone

2G-3.2   What is the unlabeled block (?) in this diagram of a radiotelephone station?

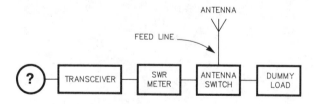

A. A splatter filter
B. A terminal-voice controller
C. A receiver audio filter
D. A microphone

2G-4.1   In an amateur station designed for radioteletype operation, what station accessories will you need to go with your transmitter?
A. A modem and a teleprinter or computer system
B. A computer, a printer and a RTTY refresh unit
C. A terminal-node controller
D. A modem, a monitor and a DTMF keypad

2G-4.2   What is the unlabeled block (?) in this diagram?

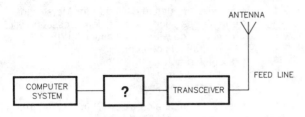

A. An RS-232 interface
B. SWR bridge
C. Modem
D. Terminal-network controller

2G-5.1   In a packet-radio station, what device connects between the radio transceiver and the computer terminal?
A. A terminal-node controller
B. An RS-232 interface
C. A terminal refresh unit
D. A tactical network control system

2G-5.2   What is the unlabeled block (?) in this diagram of a packet-radio station?

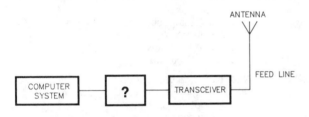

A. A terminal-node controller
B. An RS-232 interface
C. A terminal refresh unit
D. A tactical network control system

2G-5.3   Where does a terminal-node controller connect in an amateur packet-radio station?
A. Between the antenna and the radio
B. Between the computer and the monitor
C. Between the computer or terminal and the radio
D. Between the keyboard and the computer

Subelement 2H—Signals and Emissions (2 Questions)

One question must be from the following:

2H-1-1.1   What keying method is used to transmit CW?
A. Frequency-shift keying of a radio-frequency signal
B. On/off keying of a radio-frequency signal
C. Audio-frequency-shift keying of an oscillator tone
D. On/off keying of an audio-frequency signal

2H-1-1.2   What emission type describes international Morse code telegraphy messages?
A. RTTY
B. Image
C. CW
D. Phone

2H-1-2.1   What emission type describes narrow-band direct-printing telegraphy emissions?
A. RTTY
B. Image
C. CW
D. Phone

2H-1-2.2   What keying method is used to transmit RTTY messages?
A. Frequency-shift keying of a radio-frequency signal
B. On/off keying of a radio-frequency signal
C. Digital pulse-code keying of an unmodulated carrier
D. On/off keying of an audio-frequency signal

2H-1-3.1   What emission type describes frequency-modulated voice transmissions?
A. FM phone
B. Image
C. CW
D. Single-sideband phone

2H-1-4.1   What emission type describes single-sideband suppressed-carrier (SSB) voice transmissions?
A. FM phone
B. Image
C. CW
D. Single-sideband phone

2H-2.1   What does the term *key click* mean?
A. The mechanical noise caused by closing a straight key too hard
B. The clicking noise from an excessively square CW keyed waveform
C. The sound produced in a receiver from a CW signal faster than 20 WPM
D. The sound of a CW signal being copied on an AM receiver

2H-2.2   How can key clicks be eliminated?
A. By reducing your keying speed to less than 20 WPM
B. By increasing power to the maximum allowable level
C. By using a power supply with better regulation
D. By using a key-click filter

2H-3.1   What does the term *chirp* mean?
A. A distortion in the receiver audio circuits
B. A high-pitched audio tone transmitted with a CW signal
C. A slight shift in oscillator frequency each time a CW transmitter is keyed
D. A slow change in transmitter frequency as the circuit warms up

2H-3.2 What can be done to the power supply of a CW transmitter to avoid chirp?
A. Resonate the power supply filters
B. Regulate the power supply output voltages
C. Use a buffer amplifier between the transmitter output and the feed line
D. Hold the power supply current to a fixed value

2H-4.1 What is a common cause of superimposed hum?
A. Using a nonresonant random-wire antenna
B. Sympathetic vibrations from a nearby transmitter
C. Improper neutralization of the transmitter output stage
D. A defective filter capacitor in the power supply

2H-4.2 What type of problem can a bad power-supply filter capacitor cause in a transmitter or receiver?
A. Sympathetic vibrations in nearby receivers
B. A superimposed hum or buzzing sound
C. Extreme changes in antenna resonance
D. Imbalance in the mixers

One question must be from the following:

2H-5.1 What is the 4th harmonic of a 7160-kHz signal?
A. 28,640 kHz
B. 35,800 kHz
C. 28,160 kHz
D. 1790 kHz

2H-5.2 You receive an FCC Notice of Violation stating that your station was heard on 21,375 kHz. At the time listed on the notice, you were operating on 7125 kHz. What is a possible cause of this violation?
A. Your transmitter has a defective power-supply filter capacitor
B. Your CW keying speed was excessively fast
C. Your transmitter was radiating excess harmonic signals
D. Your transmitter has a defective power-supply filter choke

2H-6.1 What may happen to body tissues that are exposed to large amounts of UHF or microwave RF energy?
A. The tissue may be damaged because of the heat produced
B. The tissue may suddenly be frozen
C. The tissue may be immediately destroyed because of the Maxwell Effect
D. The tissue may become less resistant to cosmic radiation

2H-6.2 What precaution should you take before working near a high-gain UHF or microwave antenna (such as a parabolic, or dish antenna)?
A. Be certain the antenna is FCC type accepted
B. Be certain the antenna and transmitter are properly grounded
C. Be certain the transmitter cannot be operated
D. Be certain the antenna safety interlocks are in place

2H-6.3 You are installing a VHF or UHF mobile radio in your vehicle. What is the best location to mount the antenna on the vehicle to minimize any danger from RF exposure to the driver or passengers?
A. In the middle of the roof
B. Along the top of the windshield
C. On either front fender
D. On the trunk lid

2H-7.1 You discover that your tube-type transmitter power amplifier is radiating spurious emissions. What is the most likely cause of this problem?
A. Excessively fast keying speed
B. Undermodulation
C. Improper neutralization
D. Tank-circuit current dip at resonance

2H-7.2 Your transmitter radiates signals outside the amateur band where you are transmitting. What term describes this radiation?
A. Off-frequency emissions
B. Transmitter chirp
C. Incidental radiation
D. Spurious emissions

2H-7.3 What problem can occur if you operate your transmitter without the cover and other shielding in place?
A. Your transmitter can radiate spurious emissions
B. Your transmitter may radiate a "chirpy" signal
C. The final amplifier efficiency of your transmitter may decrease
D. You may cause splatter interference to other stations operating on nearby frequencies

2H-7.4 What type of interference will you cause if you operate your SSB transmitter with the microphone gain adjusted too high?
A. You may cause digital interference to computer equipment in your neighborhood
B. You may cause splatter interference to other stations operating on nearby frequencies
C. You may cause atmospheric interference in the air around your antenna
D. You may cause processor interference to the microprocessor in your rig

2H-7.5 What may happen if you adjust the microphone gain or deviation control on your FM transmitter too high?
A. You may cause digital interference to computer equipment in your neighborhood
B. You may cause interference to other stations operating on nearby frequencies
C. You may cause atmospheric interference in the air around your antenna
D. You may cause processor interference to the microprocessor in your rig

2H-7.6 What type of interference can excessive amounts of speech processing in your SSB transmitter cause?
A. You may cause digital interference to computer equipment in your neighborhood
B. You may cause splatter interference to other stations operating on nearby frequencies
C. You may cause atmospheric interference in the air around your antenna
D. You may cause processor interference to the microprocessor in your rig

Subelement 2I—Antennas and Feed Lines (3 Questions)

One question must be from the following:

2I-1.1   What is the approximate length (in feet) of a half-wavelength dipole antenna for 3725 kHz?
A. 126 ft
B. 81 ft
C. 63 ft
D. 40 ft

2I-1.2   What is the approximate length (in feet) of a half-wavelength dipole antenna for 7125 kHz?
A. 84 ft
B. 42 ft
C. 33 ft
D. 66 ft

2I-1.3   What is the approximate length (in feet) of a half-wavelength dipole antenna for 21,125 kHz?
A. 44 ft
B. 28 ft
C. 22 ft
D. 14 ft

2I-1.4   What is the approximate length (in feet) of a half-wavelength dipole antenna for 28,150 kHz?
A. 22 ft
B. 11 ft
C. 17 ft
D. 34 ft

2I-1.5   How is the approximate length (in feet) of a half-wavelength dipole antenna calculated?
A. By substituting the desired operating frequency for f in the formula:

$$\frac{150}{f \text{ (in MHz)}}$$

B. By substituting the desired operating frequency for f in the formula:

$$\frac{234}{f \text{ (in MHz)}}$$

C. By substituting the desired operating frequency for f in the formula:

$$\frac{300}{f \text{ (in MHz)}}$$

D. By substituting the desired operating frequency for f in the formula:

$$\frac{468}{f \text{ (in MHz)}}$$

2I-2.1   What is the approximate length (in feet) of a quarter-wavelength vertical antenna for 3725 kHz?
A. 20 ft
B. 32 ft
C. 40 ft
D. 63 ft

2I-2.2   What is the approximate length (in feet) of a quarter-wavelength vertical antenna for 7125 kHz?
A. 11 ft
B. 16 ft
C. 21 ft
D. 33 ft

2I-2.3   What is the approximate length (in feet) of a quarter-wavelength vertical antenna for 21,125 kHz?
A. 7 ft
B. 11 ft
C. 14 ft
D. 22 ft

2I-2.4   What is the approximate length (in feet) of a quarter-wavelength vertical antenna for 28,150 kHz?
A. 5 ft
B. 8 ft
C. 11 ft
D. 17 ft

2I-2.5   When a vertical antenna is lengthened, what happens to its resonant frequency?
A. It decreases
B. It increases
C. It stays the same
D. It doubles

2I-3.1   Why do many amateurs use a 5/8-wavelength vertical antenna rather than a 1/4-wavelength vertical antenna for their VHF or UHF mobile stations?
A. A 5/8-wavelength antenna can handle more power than a 1/4-wavelength antenna
B. A 5/8-wavelength antenna has more gain than a 1/4-wavelength antenna
C. A 5/8-wavelength antenna exhibits less corona loss than a 1/4-wavelength antenna
D. A 5/8-wavelength antenna looks more like a CB antenna, so it does not attract as much attention as a 1/4-wavelength antenna

2I-3.2   What type of radiation pattern is produced by a 5/8-wavelength vertical antenna?
A. A pattern with most of the transmitted signal concentrated in two opposite directions
B. A pattern with the transmitted signal going equally in all compass directions, with most of the radiation going high above the horizon
C. A pattern with the transmitted signal going equally in all compass directions, with most of the radiation going close to the horizon
D. A pattern with more of the transmitted signal concentrated in one direction than in other directions

One question must be from the following:

2I-4-1.1   What type of antenna produces a radiation pattern with more of the transmitted signal concentrated in a particular direction than in other directions?
A. A dipole antenna
B. A vertical antenna
C. An isotropic antenna
D. A beam antenna

2I-4-1.2   What type of radiation pattern is produced by a Yagi antenna?
A. A pattern with the transmitted signal spread out equally in all compass directions
B. A pattern with more of the transmitted signal concentrated in one direction than in other directions
C. A pattern with most of the transmitted signal concentrated in two opposite directions
D. A pattern with most of the transmitted signal concentrated at high radiation angles

2I-4-1.3 Approximately how long (in wavelengths) is the driven element of a Yagi antenna?
A. 1/4 wavelength
B. 1/3 wavelength
C. 1/2 wavelength
D. 1 wavelength

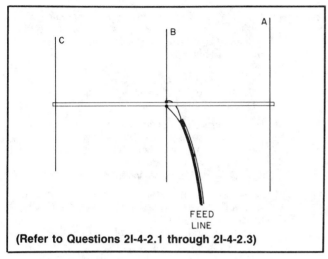

FEED LINE

(Refer to Questions 2I-4-2.1 through 2I-4-2.3)

Figure 2I-4

2I-4-2.1 On the Yagi antenna shown in Figure 2I-4, what is the name of section B?
A. Director
B. Reflector
C. Boom
D. Driven element

2I-4-2.2 On the Yagi antenna shown in Figure 2I-4, what is the name of section C?
A. Director
B. Reflector
C. Boom
D. Driven element

2I-4-2.3 On the Yagi antenna shown in Figure 2I-4, what is the name of section A?
A. Director
B. Reflector
C. Boom
D. Driven element

2I-4-2.4 What are the names of the elements in a 3-element Yagi antenna?
A. Reflector, driven element and director
B. Boom, mast and reflector
C. Reflector, base and radiator
D. Driven element, trap and feed line

2I-5.1 How should the antenna on a hand-held transceiver be positioned while you are transmitting?
A. Away from your head and away from others standing nearby
B. Pointed in the general direction of the repeater or other station you are transmitting to
C. Pointed in a general direction 90 degrees away from the repeater or other station you are transmitting to
D. With the top of the antenna angled down slightly to take the most advantage of ground reflections

2I-5.2 Why should you always locate your antennas so that no one can come in contact with them while you are transmitting?
A. Such contact can detune the antenna, causing television interference
B. To prevent RF burns and excessive exposure to RF energy
C. The antenna is more likely to radiate harmonics when it is touched
D. Such contact may reflect the transmitted signal back to the transmitter, damaging the final amplifier

2I-5.3 You are going to purchase a new antenna for your VHF or UHF hand-held radio. Which type of antenna is the best choice to produce a radiation pattern that will be least hazardous to your face and eyes?
A. A 1/8-wavelength whip
B. A 7/8-wavelength whip
C. A 1/2-wavelength whip
D. A short, helically wound, flexible antenna

One question must be from the following:

2I-6.1 What is a *coaxial cable*?
A. Two parallel conductors encased along the edges of a flat plastic ribbon
B. Two parallel conductors held at a fixed distance from each other by insulating rods
C. Two conductors twisted around each other in a double spiral
D. A center conductor encased in insulating material which is covered by a conducting sleeve or shield

2I-6.2 What kind of antenna feed line is constructed of a center conductor encased in insulation which is then covered by an outer conducting shield and weatherproof jacket?
A. Twin lead
B. Coaxial cable
C. Open-wire feed line
D. Wave guide

2I-6.3 What are some advantages of using coaxial cable as an antenna feed line?
A. It is easy to make at home, and it has a characteristic impedance in the range of most common amateur antennas
B. It is weatherproof, and it has a characteristic impedance in the range of most common amateur antennas
C. It can be operated at a higher SWR than twin lead, and it is weatherproof
D. It is unaffected by nearby metallic objects, and has a characteristic impedance that is higher than twin lead

2I-6.4 What commonly available antenna feed line can be buried directly in the ground for some distance without adverse effects?
A. Twin lead
B. Coaxial cable
C. Parallel conductor
D. Twisted pair

2I-6.5 When an antenna feed line must be located near grounded metal objects, which commonly available feed line should be used?
A. Twisted pair
B. Twin lead
C. Coaxial cable
D. Ladder-line

2I-7.1   What is parallel-conductor feed line?
          A. Two conductors twisted around each other
             in a double spiral
          B. Two parallel conductors held a uniform
             distance apart by insulating material
          C. A conductor encased in insulating material
             which is then covered by a conducting
             shield and a weatherproof jacket
          D. A metallic pipe whose diameter is equal to
             or slightly greater than the wavelength of
             the signal being carried

2I-7.2   How can *TV-type twin lead* be used as a feed
          line?
          A. By carefully running the feed line parallel to
             a metal post to ensure self resonance
          B. TV-type twin lead cannot be used in an
             amateur station
          C. By installing an impedance-matching
             network between the transmitter and feed
             line
          D. By using a high-power amplifier and
             installing a power attenuator between the
             transmitter and feed line

2I-7.3   What are some advantages of using parallel-
          conductor feed line?
          A. It has a lower characteristic impedance than
             coaxial cable, and will operate at a higher
             SWR than coaxial cable
          B. It will operate at a higher SWR than coaxial
             cable, and it is unaffected by nearby metal
             objects
          C. It has a lower characteristic impedance than
             coaxial cable, and has less loss than
             coaxial cable
          D. It will operate at higher SWR than coaxial
             cable and it has less loss than coaxial cable

2I-7.4   What are some disadvantages of using parallel-
          conductor feed line?
          A. It is affected by nearby metallic objects, and
             it has a characteristic impedance that is too
             high for direct connection to most amateur
             transmitters
          B. It is more difficult to make at home than
             coaxial cable and it cannot be operated at a
             high SWR
          C. It is affected by nearby metallic objects, and
             it cannot handle the power output of a
             typical amateur transmitter
          D. It has a characteristic impedance that is too
             high for direct connection to most amateur
             transmitters, and it will operate at a high
             SWR

2I-7.5   What kind of antenna feed line is constructed of
          two conductors maintained a uniform distance
          apart by insulated spreaders?
          A. Coaxial cable
          B. Ladder-line open conductor line
          C. Twin lead in a plastic ribbon
          D. Twisted pair

2I-8.1   A certain antenna has a feed-point impedance of
          35 ohms. You want to use a 50-ohm-impedance
          coaxial cable to feed this antenna. What type of
          device will you need to connect between the
          antenna and the feed line?
          A. A balun
          B. An SWR bridge
          C. An impedance matching device
          D. A low-pass filter

2I-8.2   A certain antenna system has an impedance of
          1000 ohms on one band. What must you use to
          connect this antenna system to the 50-ohm
          output on your transmitter?
          A. A balun
          B. An SWR bridge
          C. An impedance matching device
          D. A low-pass filter

2I-9.1   The word *balun* is a contraction for what phrase?
          A. Balanced-antenna-lobe use network
          B. Broadband-amplifier linearly unregulated
          C. Balanced unmodulator
          D. Balanced to unbalanced

2I-9.2   Where would you install a balun if you wanted to
          feed your dipole antenna with 450-ohm parallel-
          conductor feed line?
          A. At the transmitter end of the feed line
          B. At the antenna feed point
          C. In only one conductor of the feed line
          D. From one conductor of the feed line to
             ground

2I-9.3   Where might you install a balun if you wanted to
          feed your dipole antenna with 50-ohm coaxial
          cable?
          A. You might install a balun at the antenna
             feed point
          B. You might install a balun at the transmitter
             output
          C. You might install a balun ½ wavelength
             from the transmitter
          D. You might install baluns in the middle of
             each side of the dipole

2I-10-1.1 A four-element Yagi antenna is mounted with its
          elements parallel to the ground. A signal
          produced by this antenna will have what type of
          polarization?
          A. Broadside polarization
          B. Circular polarization
          C. Horizontal polarization
          D. Vertical polarization

2I-11-1.1 A four-element Yagi antenna is mounted with its
          elements perpendicular to the ground. A signal
          produced by this antenna will have what type of
          polarization?
          A. Broadside polarization
          B. Circular polarization
          C. Horizontal polarization
          D. Vertical polarization

SUBELEMENT 2A

Numbers in this section refer to pages in *Now You're Talking!*

2A-1.1	A	2-3
2A-1.2	D	2-3
2A-1.3	D	2-3
2A-1.4	B	2-3
2A-2.1	C	2-4
2A-2.2	A	2-4
2A-3.1	A	2-3
2A-3.2	D	2-4
2A-4.1	B	2-4
2A-4.2	D	2-5
2A-5.1	C	2-5
2A-5.2	B	2-5
2A-6.1	B	2-5
2A-6.2	C	2-5
2A-7.1	D	2-4
2A-8.1	A	2-5
2A-8.2	D	2-5
2A-9.1	D	2-6
2A-9.2		(withdrawn)
2A-9.3	B	2-6
2A-10.1		(withdrawn)
2A-10.2	C	2-6
2A-10.3	A	2-6
2A-10.4	C	2-6
2A-10.5	B	2-6
2A-10.6	C	2-6
2A-10.7	A	2-6
2A-10.8	B	2-6
2A-10.9	C	2-6
2A-10.10	D	2-6
2A-11.1	A	2-6
2A-11.2	B	2-6
2A-12.1	C	2-9
2A-12.2	A	2-9
2A-12.3	D	2-9
2A-13.1	A	2-6
2A-14.1	B	2-11
2A-15.1	C	2-14
2A-15.2	D	2-14
2A-15.3	A	2-14
2A-15.4	B	2-14
2A-15.5	D	2-14
2A-16.1	A	2-5
2A-17.1	A	2-7
2A-17.2	A	2-7
2A-17.3	A	2-7
2A-17.4	A	2-7
2A-17.5		(withdrawn)

2A-17.6	D	2-7
2A-17.7	D	2-7
2A-17.8	C	2-7
2A-17.9	C	2-7
2A-17.10	D	2-7
2A-17.11	D	2-7
2A-17.12	D	2-7
2A-17.13	C	2-7
2A-18.1	D	2-7
2A-18.2	C	2-7
2A-18.3	C	2-7
2A-18.4	C	2-7
2A-18.5	C	2-7
2A-19.1	C	2-7
2A-19.2	B	2-7
2A-19.3	C	2-7
2A-19.4	D	2-7
2A-19.5	B	2-7
2A-20.1	C	2-7
2A-20.2	C	2-7
2A-20.3	D	2-7
2A-21.1	C	2-5
2A-21.2	A	2-5
2A-21.3	D	2-5
2A-21.4	B	2-5
2A-22.1	C	2-5
2A-22.2	A	2-5
2A-23.1	B	2-5
2A-24.1	B	2-5
2A-25.1	C	2-5
2A-26.1	D	2-5
2A-27.1	C	2-15
2A-27.2	B	2-15
2A-27.3	B	2-15
2A-27.4	A	2-15
2A-27.5	B	2-15
2A-27.6	C	2-15
2A-27.7	B	2-15
2A-28.1	D	2-15
2A-28.2	C	2-15
2A-29.1	B	2-17
2A-29.2	D	2-17
2A-30.1	A	2-16
2A-30.2	B	2-16
2A-30.3	D	2-16
2A-31.1	D	2-16
2A-32.1	A	2-16
2A-32.2	D	2-16
2A-33.1	A	2-16
2A-34.1	A	2-16
2A-34.2	B	2-16
2A-34.3	D	2-16
2A-35.1	A	2-17

2A-36.1	C	2-17
2A-36.2	D	2-17
2A-37.1	A	2-17
2A-37.2	C	2-17
2A-38.1	C	2-15
2A-38.2	D	2-15
2A-38.3	A	2-15
2A-39.1	C	2-17
2A-39.2	B	2-17
2A-39.3	B	2-17
2A-40.1	C	2-17
2A-40.2	D	2-17
2A-40.3	D	2-17

SUBELEMENT 2B

2B-1-1.1	A	9-8
2B-1-1.2	C	9-4
2B-1-1.3	C	9-12
2B-1-2.1	D	9-11
2B-2-1.1	A	9-8
2B-2-1.2	B	9-12
2B-2-2.1	C	9-8
2B-2-3.1	C	9-12
2B-2-3.2	D	9-12
2B-2-3.3	A	9-12
2B-2-3.4	B	9-13
2B-2-3.5	C	9-13
2B-2-4.1	D	9-8
2B-2-4.2	A	9-13
2B-2-4.3	A	9-13
2B-2-5.1	D	9-12
2B-2-5.2	B	9-12
2B-2-5.3	A	9-12
2B-2-6.1	B	9-9
2B-2-6.2	C	9-9
2B-2-6.3	D	9-9
2B-2-6.4	A	9-9
2B-2-6.5	B	9-9
2B-3-1.1	C	9-14
2B-3-1.2	D	9-14
2B-3-2.1	A	9-14
2B-3-2.2	C	9-14
2B-3-2.3	A	9-14
2B-3-2.4	D	9-14
2B-3-2.5	A	9-14
2B-3-2.6	C	9-14
2B-3-2.7	A	9-14
2B-3-2.8	D	9-14
2B-3-2.9	B	9-14
2B-3-2.10	A	9-14
2B-3-2.11	C	9-14
2B-4-1.1	B	9-24

2B-4-2.1	B	9-24
2B-5-1.1	C	9-27
2B-5-1.2	D	9-27
2B-5-2.1	A	9-29
2B-5-2.2	B	9-31
2B-6-1.1	C	9-19
2B-6-2.1	D	9-18
2B-6-3.1	A	9-18
2B-6-4.1	B	9-19
2B-6-5.1	C	9-19
2B-6-5.2	D	9-19

SUBELEMENT 2C

2C-1.1	A	9-3
2C-1.2	B	9-3
2C-2.1	D	9-3
2C-2.2	B	9-3
2C-2.3	B	9-3
2C-2.4	A	9-3
2C-3.1	A	9-3
2C-3.2	B	9-3
2C-3.3	D	9-3
2C-3.4	A	9-4
2C-3.5	C	9-4
2C-3.6	D	9-3
2C-4.1	C	9-3
2C-4.2	D	9-3
2C-5.1	A	9-3
2C-5.2	B	9-3
2C-6.1	C	9-5
2C-6.2	C	9-5

SUBELEMENT 2D

2D-1.1	B	8-9
2D-1.2	A	8-9
2D-2.1	D	8-9
2D-2.2	C	8-9
2D-2.3	D	8-9
2D-2.4	B	8-9
2D-3.1	A	8-3
2D-3.2	C	8-3
2D-3.3	B	8-3
2D-3.4	C	8-3
2D-4.1	B	8-11
2D-4.2	A	8-10
2D-4.3	C	8-10
2D-4.4	A	8-10
2D-4.5	B	8-10
2D-4.6	B	8-10
2D-5.1	D	8-9
2D-5.2	A	8-9
2D-6.1	D	7-21
2D-6.2	D	7-21
2D-6.3	A	7-21
2D-6.4	D	7-21
2D-6.5	A	7-21
2D-7-1.1	C	8-17

2D-7-1.2	D	8-17
2D-7-2.1	B	7-6
2D-7-2.2	C	7-6
2D-7-2.3	D	7-6
2D-7-2.4	C	7-6
2D-7-3.1	A	7-7
2D-7-3.2	A	7-6
2D-7-3.3	B	7-7
2D-7-3.4	C	7-7
2D-8-1.1	C	10-4
2D-8-1.2	B	10-4
2D-8-1.3	C	10-4
2D-8-1.4	B	10-5
2D-8-2.1	A	10-4
2D-8-2.2	A	10-4
2D-8-2.3	A	10-4
2D-8-2.4	C	10-6
2D-8-2.5	D	10-4
2D-8-2.6	B	10-5
2D-8-3.1	A	10-3
2D-8-3.2	B	10-3

SUBELEMENT 2E

2E-1-1.1	C	3-2
2E-1-2.1	B	3-2
2E-1-2.2	D	3-2
2E-1-3.1	B	3-2
2E-1-3.2	D	3-2
2E-1-4.1	B	3-13
2E-1-5.1	C	3-2
2E-1-5.2	C	3-2
2E-1-6.1	B	3-2
2E-1-7.1	B	3-2
2E-2-1.1	D	3-4
2E-2-2.1	C	3-5
2E-3-1.1	A	3-4
2E-3-1.2	D	3-4
2E-3-1.3	C	3-4
2E-3-2.1	A	3-4
2E-4.1	C	3-5
2E-5.1	A	3-5
2E-6-1.1	D	3-6
2E-6-1.2	A	3-6
2E-6-2.1	D	3-6
2E-7.1	C	3-7
2E-7.2	C	3-7
2E-7.3	B	3-7
2E-7.4	C	3-7
2E-8.1	D	3-10
2E-8.2	A	3-10
2E-9-1.1	C	3-10
2E-9-1.2	C	3-10
2E-9-2.1	B	3-10
2E-10.1	C	3-9
2E-11.1	D	3-9
2E-12-1.1	B	3-12
2E-12-2.1	A	3-12
2E-12-3.1	D	3-12

2E-12-3.2	A	3-12
2E-12-3.3	A	3-12
2E-12-4.1	B	3-12
2E-12-4.2	A	3-12
2E-12-4.3	B	3-12
2E-12-5.1	C	3-12
2E-12-5.2	B	3-12
2E-13.1	C	3-12
2E-13.2	D	3-13

SUBELEMENT 2F

2F-1.1	B	4-2
2F-1.2	C	4-2
2F-1.3	C	4-2
2F-2.1	A	4-2
2F-2.2	A	4-2
2F-2.3	B	4-2
2F-2.4	D	4-2
2F-2.5	A	4-2
2F-3.1	C	4-3
2F-4.1	C	4-4
2F-4.2	B	4-4
2F-5.1	D	4-4
2F-5.2	B	4-4
2F-5.3	A	4-4
2F-5.4	D	4-4
2F-6.1	D	4-4
2F-7.1	C	4-5
2F-7.2	A	4-5
2F-7.3	C	4-5
2F-7.4	B	4-5
2F-8.1	A	4-6

SUBELEMENT 2G

2G-1-1.1	B	5-2
2G-1-1.2	C	5-2
2G-1-1.3	D	5-2
2G-1-1.4	A	5-3
2G-1-1.5	D	5-3
2G-1-2.1	B	5-3
2G-1-2.2	A	5-4
2G-1-2.3	B	5-3
2G-1-2.4	D	5-3
2G-1-2.5	D	5-3
2G-2.1	B	5-4
2G-2.2	C	5-4
2G-2.3	C	5-3
2G-3.1	D	5-4
2G-3.2	D	5-4
2G-4.1	A	5-5
2G-4.2	C	5-5
2G-5.1	A	5-5
2G-5.2	A	5-5
2G-5.3	C	5-5

SUBELEMENT 2H

2H-1-1.1	B	2-7

2H-1-1.2	C	2-7
2H-1-2.1	A	2-7
2H-1-2.2	A	2-7
2H-1-3.1	A	2-7
2H-1-4.1	D	2-7
2H-2.1	B	10-6
2H-2.2	D	10-6
2H-3.1	C	10-6
2H-3.2	B	10-6
2H-4.1	D	10-7
2H-4.2	B	10-7
2H-5.1	A	10-1
2H-5.2	C	10-1
2H-6.1	A	8-11
2H-6.2	C	8-11
2H-6.3	A	8-11
2H-7.1	C	10-3
2H-7.2	D	10-1
2H-7.3	A	10-6
2H-7.4	B	9-20
2H-7.5	B	9-20

2H-7.6	B	9-20

SUBELEMENT 2I

2I-1.1	A	7-7
2I-1.2	D	7-7
2I-1.3	C	7-7
2I-1.4	C	7-7
2I-1.5	D	7-7
2I-2.1	D	7-14
2I-2.2	D	7-14
2I-2.3	B	7-14
2I-2.4	B	7-14
2I-2.5	A	7-14
2I-3.1	B	7-21
2I-3.2	C	7-21
2I-4-1.1	D	7-19
2I-4-1.2	B	7-19
2I-4-1.3	C	7-20
2I-4-2.1	D	7-20
2I-4-2.2	A	7-20
2I-4-2.3	B	7-20

2I-4-2.4	A	7-20
2I-5.1	A	7-21
2I-5.2	B	7-21
2I-5.3	C	7-22
2I-6.1	D	7-2
2I-6.2	B	7-2
2I-6.3	B	7-2
2I-6.4	B	7-2
2I-6.5	C	7-2
2I-7.1	B	7-3
2I-7.2	C	7-3
2I-7.3	D	7-3
2I-7.4	A	7-4
2I-7.5	B	7-5
2I-8.1	C	7-4
2I-8.2	C	7-4
2I-9.1	D	7-5
2I-9.2	A	7-5
2I-9.3	A	7-5
2I-10-1.1	C	7-21
2I-11-1.1	D	7-24

Chapter 13

Element 3A Question Pool
—With Answers

——— DON'T START HERE ———

This chapter contains the complete question pool for the Element 3A exam. Element 3A is part of the Technician exam. To earn a Technician license, you must also pass the Element 2 exam (Chapter 12). The Technician license does not require a code test.

Before you read the questions and answers printed in this chapter, be sure to read the text in the previous chapters. Use these questions as review exercises, when the text tells you to study them. Don't try to memorize all the questions and answers.

HOW MANY QUESTIONS?

The FCC specifies that an Element 3A exam must include 25 questions, and also specifies that a certain number of questions from each subelement must appear on the exam. The number of questions to be selected from each section is printed at the beginning of each subelement, and is summarized in Table 13-1.

Table 13-1
Technician Exam Content

Subelement	3AA	3AB	3AC	3AD	3AE	3AF	3AG	3AH	3AI
Number of Questions	5	3	3	4	2	2	1	2	3

WHO PICKS THE QUESTIONS?

The FCC allows Volunteer-Examiner teams to select the questions that will be used on amateur exams. If your test is coordinated by the ARRL/VEC, however, your test will be prepared by the VEC. The questions with multiple-choice answers and distractors (incorrect answers) printed here were released by the Volunteer Examiner Coordinator's Question Pool Committee for use until further notice. Most VECs have agreed to use these multiple-choice answers and distractors. If your test is coordinated by the ARRL/VEC or one of the other VECs using these multiple-choice answers, they will appear on your exam exactly as they are printed here. Some VECs may use the questions printed here with different answers and/or distractors; check with the VEC coordinating your test session.

PAGE REFERENCES

We have listed page references along with the answers in the answer key section of this chapter. These page numbers indicate where you will find the text discussion related to each question. If you have any problems with a question, refer to the page listed for that question. You may have to study beyond the listed page numbers.

Good luck with your studies.

Withdrawn Questions

FCC Rules changes sometimes make it necessary to withdraw certain questions from the pool. Withdrawn questions are noted in the following pages.

3AA-1.1   What is the *control point* of an amateur station?
- A. The location at which the control operator function is performed
- B. The operating position of any amateur station operating as a repeater user station
- C. The physical location of any Amateur Radio transmitter, even if it is operated by radio link from some other location
- D. The variable frequency oscillator (VFO) of the transmitter

3AA-1.2   What is the term for the location at which the control operator function is performed?
- A. The operating desk
- B. The control point
- C. The station location
- D. The manual control location

3AA-2.1   This question has been withdrawn.

3AA-2.2   Which operator licenses authorize privileges on 52.525 MHz?
- A. Extra, Advanced only
- B. Extra, Advanced, General only
- C. Extra, Advanced, General, Technician only
- D. Extra, Advanced, General, Technician, Novice

3AA-2.3   Which operator licenses authorize privileges on 146.52 MHz?
- A. Extra, Advanced, General, Technician, Novice
- B. Extra, Advanced, General, Technician only
- C. Extra, Advanced, General only
- D. Extra, Advanced only

3AA-2.4   Which operator licenses authorize privileges on 223.50 MHz?
- A. Extra, Advanced, General, Technician, Novice
- B. Extra, Advanced, General, Technician only
- C. Extra, Advanced, General only
- D. Extra, Advanced only

3AA-2.5   Which operator licenses authorize privileges on 446.0 MHz?
- A. Extra, Advanced, General, Technician, Novice
- B. Extra, Advanced, General, Technician only
- C. Extra, Advanced, General only
- D. Extra, Advanced only

3AA-3.1   How often do amateur service licenses generally need to be renewed?
- A. Every 10 years
- B. Every 5 years
- C. Every 2 years
- D. They are lifetime licenses

3AA-3.2   The FCC currently issues amateur licenses carrying 10-year terms. What is the "grace period" during which the FCC will renew an expired 10-year license?
- A. 2 years
- B. 5 years
- C. 10 years
- D. There is no grace period

3AA-3.3   What action would you take to modify your operator/primary station license?
- A. Properly fill out FCC Form 610 and send it to the FCC in Gettysburg, PA
- B. Properly fill out FCC Form 610 and send it to the nearest FCC field office
- C. Write the FCC at their nearest field office
- D. There is no need to modify an amateur license between renewals

3AA-4.1   On what frequencies within the 6-meter wavelength band may FM phone emissions be transmitted?
- A. 50.0-54.0 MHz only
- B. 50.1-54.0 MHz only
- C. 51.0-54.0 MHz only
- D. 52.0-54.0 MHz only

3AA-4.2   On what frequencies within the 2-meter wavelength band may FM image emissions be transmitted?
- A. 144.1-148.0 MHz only
- B. 146.0-148.0 MHz only
- C. 144.0-148.0 MHz only
- D. 146.0-147.0 MHz only

3AA-4.3   What emission type may always be used for station identification, regardless of the transmitting frequency?
- A. CW
- B. RTTY
- C. MCW
- D. Phone

3AA-5.1   If you are using a frequency within a band designated to the amateur service on a secondary basis and another station assigned to a primary service on that band causes interference, what action should you take?
- A. Notify the FCC's regional Engineer in Charge of the interference
- B. Increase your transmitter's power to overcome the interference
- C. Attempt to contact the station and request that it stop the interference
- D. Change frequencies; you may also be causing interference to the other station and that would be a violation of FCC rules

3AA-5.2   What is the basic principle of frequency sharing between two stations allocated to a primary service within a frequency band, but each in a different ITU Region or Subregion?
- A. The station with a control operator holding a lesser class of license must yield the frequency to the station with a control operator holding a higher class license
- B. The station with a lower power output must yield the frequency to the station with a higher power output
- C. Both stations have an equal right to operate on the frequency
- D. Stations in ITU Regions 1 and 3 must yield the frequency to stations in ITU Region 2

3AA-6-1.1   FCC Rules specify the maximum transmitter power that you may use with your amateur station. At what point in your station is the transmitter power measured?
- A. By measuring the final amplifier supply voltage inside the transmitter or amplifier
- B. By measuring the final amplifier supply current inside the transmitter or amplifier
- C. At the antenna terminals of the transmitter or amplifier
- D. On the antenna itself, after the feed line

3AA-6-1.2 What is the term used to define the average power supplied to the antenna transmission line during one RF cycle at the crest of the modulation envelope?
A. Peak transmitter power
B. Peak output power
C. Average radio-frequency power
D. Peak envelope power

3AA-6-2.1 Notwithstanding the numerical limitations in the FCC Rules, how much transmitting power shall be used by an amateur station?
A. There is no regulation other than the numerical limits
B. The minimum power level required to achieve S9 signal reports
C. The minimum power necessary to carry out the desired communication
D. The maximum power available, as long as it is under the allowable limit

3AA-6-3.1 What is the maximum transmitting power permitted an amateur station on 146.52 MHz?
A. 200 watts PEP output
B. 500 watts ERP
C. 1000 watts DC input
D. 1500 watts PEP output

3AA-6-4.1 What is the maximum transmitting power permitted an amateur station in beacon operation?
A. 10 watts PEP output
B. 100 watts PEP output
C. 500 watts PEP output
D. 1500 watts PEP output

3AA-7-1.1 What is the maximum sending speed permitted for a RTTY transmission between 28 and 50 MHz?
A. 56 kilobauds
B. 19.6 kilobauds
C. 1200 bauds
D. 300 bauds

3AA-7-1.2 What is the maximum sending speed permitted for a RTTY transmission between 50 and 220 MHz?
A. 56 kilobauds
B. 19.6 kilobauds
C. 1200 bauds
D. 300 bauds

3AA-7-1.3 What is the maximum sending speed permitted for a RTTY transmission above 220 MHz?
A. 300 bauds
B. 1200 bauds
C. 19.6 kilobauds
D. 56 kilobauds

3AA-7-2.1 What is the maximum frequency shift permitted for RTTY when transmitted below 50 MHz?
A. 100 Hz
B. 500 Hz
C. 1000 Hz
D. 5000 Hz

3AA-7-2.2 What is the maximum frequency shift permitted for RTTY when transmitted above 50 MHz?
A. 100 Hz or the sending speed, in bauds, whichever is greater
B. 500 Hz or the sending speed, in bauds, whichever is greater
C. The FCC rules do not specify a maximum frequency shift above 50 MHz
D. 5000 Hz or the sending speed, in bauds, whichever is greater

3AA-7-3.1 What is the authorized bandwidth of a RTTY, data or multiplexed emission using a specified digital code within the frequency range of 50 to 220 MHz?
A. 20 kHz
B. 50 kHz
C. The total bandwidth shall not exceed that of a single-sideband emission
D. The total bandwidth shall not exceed 10 times that of a CW emission

3AA-7-3.2 What is the authorized bandwidth of a RTTY, data or multiplexed emission using an unspecified digital code within the frequency range of 220 to 450 MHz?
A. 50 kHz
B. 150 kHz
C. 200 kHz
D. 100 kHz

3AA-7-3.3 What is the maximum authorized bandwidth of a RTTY, data or multiplexed emission using an unspecified digital code within the 420 to 450 MHz amateur band?
A. 50 kHz
B. 200 kHz
C. 300 kHz
D. 100 kHz

3AA-8-1.1 How must a control operator who has a Novice license and a Certificate of Successful Completion of Examination for Technician privileges identify the station when transmitting on 146.34 MHz?
A. The new Technician may not operate on 146.34 until his or her new license arrives
B. The licensee gives his or her call sign, followed by any suitable word that denotes the slant mark and the identifier "KT"
C. No special form of identification is needed
D. The license gives his or her call sign and states the location of the VE examination where he or she obtained the certificate of successful completion

3AA-8-2.1 Which language(s) must be used when making the station identification by telephony?
A. The language being used for the contact may be used if it is not English, providing the US has a third-party communications agreement with that country
B. English must be used for identification
C. Any language may be used, if the country which uses that language is a member of the International Telecommunication Union
D. The language being used for the contact must be used for identification purposes

3AA-8-3.1 What does the FCC recommend to aid correct station identification when using phone?
A. A speech compressor
B. Q signals
C. A recognized phonetic alphabet
D. Unique words of the operator's choice

3AA-9-1.1 What is the term used to describe an amateur station transmitting communications for the purpose of observation of propagation and reception or other related experimental activities?
A. Beacon operation
B. Repeater operation
C. Auxiliary operation
D. Radio control operation

3AA-9-2.1 What class of amateur operator license must you hold to operate a beacon station?
A. Technician, General, Advanced or Amateur Extra class
B. General, Advanced or Amateur Extra class
C. Amateur Extra class only
D. Any license class

3AA-10.1 What is the maximum transmitter power an amateur station is permitted when transmitting signals to control a model craft?
A. One watt
B. One milliwatt
C. Two watts
D. Three watts

3AA-10.2 What minimum information must be indicated on the label affixed to a transmitter transmitting signals to control a model craft?
A. Station call sign
B. Station call sign and operating times
C. Station call sign and the station licensee's name and address
D. Station call sign, class of license, and operating times

3AA-10.3 What are the station identification requirements for an amateur station transmitting signals to control a model craft?
A. Once every ten minutes, and at the beginning and end of each transmission
B. Once every ten minutes
C. At the beginning and end of each transmission
D. Station identification is not required provided that a label indicating the station call sign and the station licensee's name and address is affixed to the station transmitter

3AA-10.4 Where must the writing indicating the station call sign and the licensee's name and address be affixed in order to operate under the special rules for radio control of remote model craft and vehicles?
A. It must be in the operator's possession
B. It must be affixed to the transmitter
C. It must be affixed to the craft or vehicle
D. It must be filed with the nearest FCC Field Office

3AA-11-1.1 If an amateur repeater is causing harmful interference to another amateur repeater and a frequency coordinator has coordinated (recommends) the operation of one station and not the other, who is primarily responsible for resolving the interference?
A. The licensee of the non-coordinated (unrecommended) repeater
B. Both repeater licensees
C. The licensee of the coordinated (recommended) repeater
D. The frequency coordinator

3AA-11-1.2 If an amateur repeater is causing harmful interference to another amateur repeater and a frequency coordinator has coordinated (recommends) the operation of both stations, who is primarily responsible for resolving the interference?
A. The licensee of the repeater which has been coordinated for the longest period of time
B. Both repeater licensees
C. The licensee of the repeater which has been coordinated the most recently
D. The frequency coordinator

3AA-11-1.3 If an amateur repeater is causing harmful interference to another amateur repeater and a frequency coordinator has not coordinated the operation of either station, who is primarily responsible for resolving the interference?
A. Both repeater licensees
B. The licensee of the repeater which has been in operation for the longest period of time
C. The licensee of the repeater which has been in operation for the shortest period of time
D. The frequency coordinator

3AA-11-2.1 Under what circumstances does the FCC declare a *temporary state of communication emergency*?
A. When a declaration of war is received from Congress
B. When the maximum usable frequency goes above 28 MHz
C. When communications facilities in Washington, DC, are disrupted
D. When a disaster disrupts normal communications systems in a particular area

3AA-11-2.2 By what means should a request for a declaration of a *temporary state of communication emergency* be initiated?
A. Communication with the FCC Engineer-In-Charge of the affected area
B. Communication with the US senator or congressman for the area affected
C. Communication with the local Emergency Coordinator
D. Communication with the Chief of the FCC Private Radio Bureau

3AA-11-2.3 What information is included in an FCC declaration of a *temporary state of communication emergency*?
A. Designation of the areas affected and of organizations authorized to use radio communications in the affected area
B. Designation of amateur frequency bands for use only by amateurs participating in emergency communications in the affected area, and complete suspension of Novice operating privileges for the duration of the emergency
C. Any special conditions and special rules to be observed during the communication emergency
D. Suspension of amateur rules regarding station identification and business communication

3AA-11-2.4 If a disaster disrupts normal communication systems in an area where the amateur service is regulated by the FCC, what kinds of transmissions are authorized to amateur stations in such an area?
A. Communications which are necessary to meet essential communication needs and facilitate relief actions
B. Communications which allow a commercial business to continue to operate in the affected area
C. Communications for which material compensation has been paid to the amateur operator for delivery into the affected area
D. Communications which are to be used for program production or newsgathering for broadcasting purposes

3AA-12.1 What is meant by the term *broadcasting*?
- A. Transmissions intended for reception by the general public, either direct or relayed
- B. Retransmission by automatic means of programs or signals emanating from any class of station other than amateur
- C. The transmission of any one-way radio communication, regardless of purpose or content
- D. Any one-way or two-way radio communication involving more than two stations

3AA-12.2 Which of the following is an amateur station that cannot automatically retransmit radio signals of other amateur stations?
- A. Auxiliary station
- B. Repeater station
- C. Beacon station
- D. Space station

3AA-12.3 Which of the following is an amateur station that is permitted to automatically retransmit radio signals of other amateur stations?
- A. Beacon station
- B. Space station
- C. Official bulletin station
- D. RACES station

3AA-12.4 What type of radio signals may be directly retransmitted by an amateur station?
- A. AM radio station
- B. Police or fire department radio station
- C. NOAA weather station
- D. US Government communications between the space shuttle and associated Earth stations with prior approval from the National Aeronautics and Space Administration (NASA)

3AA-12.5 When may US Government communications between the space shuttle and associated Earth stations be directly retransmitted by an amateur station?
- A. After prior approval has been obtained from the FCC in Washington, DC
- B. No radio stations other than amateur may be retransmitted in the amateur service
- C. After prior approval has been obtained from the National Aeronautics and Space Administration (NASA)
- D. After prior approval has been obtained from the nearest FCC Engineer-In-Charge

3AA-13.1 What kinds of one-way communications by amateur stations are not considered broadcasting?
- A. All types of one-way communications by amateurs are considered by the FCC as broadcasting
- B. Beacon operation, remote control of a device, emergency communications, information bulletins consisting solely of subject matter of direct interest to the amateur service, and telegraphy practice
- C. Only code-practice transmissions conducted simultaneously on all available amateur bands below 30 MHz and conducted for more than 40 hours per week are not considered broadcasting
- D. Only actual emergency communications during a declared communications emergency are exempt

3AA-13.2 Which of the following one-way communications may not be transmitted in the amateur service?
- A. Transmissions to remotely control a device at a distant location
- B. Transmissions to assist persons learning or improving their proficiency in Morse code
- C. Brief transmissions to make adjustments to the station
- D. Transmission of music

3AA-13.3 What kinds of one-way information bulletins may be transmitted by amateur stations?
- A. NOAA weather bulletins
- B. Commuter traffic reports from local radio stations
- C. Regularly scheduled announcements concerning Amateur Radio equipment for sale or trade
- D. Messages directed only to amateur operators consisting solely of subject matter of direct interest to the amateur service

3AA-13.4 What types of one-way amateur communications may be transmitted by an amateur station?
- A. Beacon operation, radio control, code practice, retransmission of other services
- B. Beacon operation, radio control, transmitting an unmodulated carrier, NOAA weather bulletins
- C. Beacon operation, remote control of a device, information bulletins consisting solely of subject matter of direct interest to the amateur service, telegraphy practice and emergency communications
- D. Beacon operation, emergency-drill-practice transmissions, automatic retransmission of NOAA weather transmissions, code practice

3AA-14.1 What types of material compensation, if any, may be involved in third-party communications transmitted by an amateur station?
- A. Payment of an amount agreed upon by the amateur operator and the parties involved
- B. Assistance in maintenance of auxiliary station equipment
- C. Donation of amateur equipment to the control operator
- D. No compensation may be accepted

3AA-14.2 What types of business communications, if any, may be transmitted by an amateur station on behalf of a third party?
- A. The FCC rules specifically prohibit communications with a business for any reason
- B. Business communications involving the sale of Amateur Radio equipment
- C. Communications to a business may be provided during an emergency as provided by the FCC rules
- D. Business communications aiding a broadcast station

3AA-14.3 Does the FCC allow third-party messages when communicating with Amateur Radio operators in a foreign country?
- A. Third-party messages with a foreign country are only allowed on behalf of other amateurs.
- B. Yes, provided the third-party message involves the immediate family of one of the communicating amateurs
- C. Under no circumstances may US amateurs exchange third-party messages with an amateur in a foreign country
- D. Yes, when communicating with a person in a country with which the US shares a third-party agreement

3AA-15.1 Under what circumstances, if any, may a third party participate in radio communications from an amateur station if the third party is ineligible to be a control operator of one of the stations?
- A. A control operator must be present at the control point and continuously monitor and supervise the third party participation. Also, contacts may only be made with amateurs in the US and countries with which the US has a third-party communications agreement
- B. A control operator must be present and continuously monitor and supervise the radio communication to ensure compliance with the rules only if contacts are made with amateurs in countries with which the US has no third-party communications agreement
- C. A control operator must be present and continuously monitor and supervise the radio communication to ensure compliance with the rules. In addition, the control operator must key the transmitter and make the station identification.
- D. A control operator must be present and continuously monitor and supervise the radio communication to ensure compliance with the rules. In addition, if contacts are made on frequencies below 30 MHz, the control operator must transmit the call signs of both stations involved in the contact at 10-minute intervals

3AA-15.2 Where must the control operator be situated when a third party is participating in radio communications from an amateur station?
- A. If a radio remote control is used, the control operator may be physically separated from the control point, when provisions are incorporated to shut off the transmitter by remote control
- B. If the control operator supervises the third party until he or she is satisfied of the competence of the third party, the control operator may leave the control point
- C. The control operator must be present at the control point
- D. If the third party holds a valid radiotelegraph license issued by the FCC, no supervision is necessary

3AA-15.3 What must the control operator do while a third party is participating in radio communications?
- A. If the third party holds a valid commercial radiotelegraph license, no supervision is necessary
- B. The control operator must tune up and down 5 kHz from the transmitting frequency on another receiver, to ensure that no interference is taking place
- C. If a radio control link is available, the control operator may leave the room
- D. The control operator must continuously monitor and supervise the third party's participation

3AA-15.4 In an exchange of international third-party communications, when is the station identification procedure required?
- A. Only at the beginning of the communications
- B. At the end of each exchange of communications
- C. The station identification procedure is not required during international third-party communications
- D. Only at the end of multiple exchanges of communications

3AA-16.1 Under what circumstances, if any, may an amateur station transmit radio communications containing obscene words?
- A. Obscene words are permitted when they do not cause interference to any other radio communication or signal
- B. Obscene words are prohibited in Amateur Radio transmissions
- C. Obscene words are permitted when they are not retransmitted through repeater or auxiliary stations
- D. Obscene words are permitted, but there is an unwritten rule among amateurs that they should not be used on the air

3AA-16.2 Under what circumstances, if any, may an amateur station transmit radio communications containing indecent words?
- A. Indecent words are permitted when they do not cause interference to any other radio communication or signal
- B. Indecent words are permitted when they are not retransmitted through repeater or auxiliary stations
- C. Indecent words are permitted, but there is an unwritten rule among amateurs that they should not be used on the air
- D. Indecent words are prohibited in Amateur Radio transmissions

3AA-16.3 Under what circumstances, if any, may an amateur station transmit radio communications containing profane words?
- A. Profane words are permitted when they are not retransmitted through repeater or auxiliary stations
- B. Profane words are permitted, but there is an unwritten rule among amateurs that they should not be used on the air
- C. Profane words are prohibited in Amateur Radio transmissions
- D. Profane words are permitted when they do not cause interference to any other radio communication or signal

3AA-17.1　Which of the following VHF/UHF bands may not be used by Earth stations for satellite communications?
- A. 6 meters
- B. 2 meters
- C. 23 centimeters
- D. 70 centimeters

SUBELEMENT 3AB—Operating Procedures
(3 Exam Questions)

3AB-1.1　What is the meaning of: "Your report is five seven..."?
- A. Your signal is perfectly readable and moderately strong
- B. Your signal is perfectly readable, but weak
- C. Your signal is readable with considerable difficulty
- D. Your signal is perfectly readable with near pure tone

3AB-1.2　What is the meaning of: "Your report is three three..."?
- A. The contact is serial number thirty-three
- B. The station is located at latitude 33 degrees
- C. Your signal is readable with considerable difficulty and weak in strength
- D. Your signal is unreadable, very weak in strength

3AB-1.3　What is the meaning of: "Your report is five nine plus 20 dB..."?
- A. Your signal strength has increased by a factor of 100
- B. Repeat your transmission on a frequency 20 kHz higher
- C. The bandwidth of your signal is 20 decibels above linearity
- D. A relative signal-strength meter reading is 20 decibels greater than strength 9

3AB-2-1.1　How should a QSO be initiated through a station in repeater operation?
- A. Say "breaker, breaker 79"
- B. Call the desired station and then identify your own station
- C. Call "CQ" three times and identify three times
- D. Wait for a "CQ" to be called and then answer it

3AB-2-1.2　Why should users of a station in repeater operation pause briefly between transmissions?
- A. To check the SWR of the repeater
- B. To reach for pencil and paper for third-party communications
- C. To listen for any hams wanting to break in
- D. To dial up the repeater's autopatch

3AB-2-1.3　Why should users of a station in repeater operation keep their transmissions short and thoughtful?
- A. A long transmission may prevent someone with an emergency from using the repeater
- B. To see if the receiving station operator is still awake
- C. To give any non-hams that are listening a chance to respond
- D. To keep long-distance charges down

3AB-2-1.4　What is the proper procedure to break into an on-going QSO through a station in repeater operation?
- A. Wait for the end of a transmission and start calling
- B. Shout, "break, break!" to show that you're eager to join the conversation
- C. Turn on your 100-watt amplifier and over-ride whoever is talking
- D. Send your call sign during a break between transmissions

3AB-2-1.5 What is the purpose of repeater operation?
- A. To cut your power bill by using someone's higher power system
- B. To enable mobile and low-power stations to extend their usable range
- C. To reduce your telephone bill
- D. To call the ham radio distributor 50 miles away

3AB-2-1.6 What is meant by "making the repeater time out"?
- A. The repeater's battery supply has run out
- B. The repeater's transmission time limit has expired during a single transmission
- C. The warranty on the repeater duplexer has expired
- D. The repeater is in need of repairs

3AB-2-1.7 During commuting rush hours, which types of operation should relinquish the use of the repeater?
- A. Mobile operators
- B. Low-power stations
- C. Highway traffic information nets
- D. Third-party communications nets

3AB-2-2.1 Why should simplex be used where possible instead of using a station in repeater operation?
- A. Farther distances can be reached
- B. To avoid long distance toll charges
- C. To avoid tying up the repeater unnecessarily
- D. To permit the testing of the effectiveness of your antenna

3AB-2-2.2 When a frequency conflict arises between a simplex operation and a repeater operation, why does good amateur practice call for the simplex operation to move to another frequency?
- A. The repeater's output power can be turned up to ruin the front end of the station in simplex operation
- B. There are more repeaters than simplex operators
- C. Changing the repeater's frequency is not practical
- D. Changing a repeater frequency requires the authorization of the Federal Communications Commission

3AB-2-3.1 What is the usual input/output frequency separation for stations in repeater operation in the 2-meter wavelength band?
- A. 1 MHz
- B. 1.6 MHz
- C. 170 Hz
- D. 0.6 MHz

3AB-2-3.2 What is the usual input/output frequency separation for stations in repeater operation in the 70-centimeter band?
- A. 1.6 MHz
- B. 5 MHz
- C. 600 kHz
- D. 5 kHz

3AB-2-3.3 What is the usual input/output frequency separation for a 6-meter station in repeater operation?
- A. 1 MHz
- B. 600 kHz
- C. 1.6 MHz
- D. 20 kHz

3AB-2-3.4 What is the usual input/output frequency separation for a 1.25-meter station in repeater operation?
- A. 1000 kHz
- B. 600 kHz
- C. 1600 kHz
- D. 1.6 GHz

3AB-2-4.1 What is a *repeater frequency coordinator*?
- A. Someone who coordinates the assembly of a repeater station
- B. Someone who provides advice on what kind of system to buy
- C. The club's repeater trustee
- D. A person or group that recommends frequency pairs for repeater usage

3AB-3.1 Why should local amateur communications be conducted on VHF and UHF frequencies?
- A. To minimize interference on HF bands capable of long-distance sky-wave communication
- B. Because greater output power is permitted on VHF and UHF
- C. Because HF transmissions are not propagated locally
- D. Because absorption is greater at VHF and UHF frequencies

3AB-3.2 How can on-the-air transmissions be minimized during a lengthy transmitter testing or loading up procedure?
- A. Choose an unoccupied frequency
- B. Use a dummy antenna
- C. Use a non-resonant antenna
- D. Use a resonant antenna that requires no loading up procedure

3AB-3.3 What is the proper Q signal to use to determine whether a frequency is in use before making a transmission?
- A. QRV?
- B. QRU?
- C. QRL?
- D. QRZ?

3AB-4.1 What is the proper distress calling procedure when using telephony?
- A. Transmit MAYDAY
- B. Transmit QRRR
- C. Transmit QRZ
- D. Transmit SOS

3AB-4.2 What is the proper distress calling procedure when using telegraphy?
- A. Transmit MAYDAY
- B. Transmit QRRR
- C. Transmit QRZ
- D. Transmit SOS

3AB-5-1.1 What is one requirement you must meet before you can participate in RACES drills?
- A. You must be registered with ARRL
- B. You must be registered with a local racing organization
- C. You must be registered with the responsible civil defense organization
- D. You need not register with anyone to operate RACES

3AB-5-1.2 What is the maximum amount of time allowed per week for RACES drills?
- A. Eight hours
- B. One hour
- C. As many hours as you want
- D. Six hours, but not more than one hour per day

3AB-5-2.1 How must you identify messages sent during a RACES drill?
A. As emergency messages
B. As amateur traffic
C. As official government messages
D. As drill or test messages

3AB-6-1.1 What is the term used to describe first-response communications in an emergency situation?
A. Tactical communications
B. Emergency communications
C. Formal message traffic
D. National Traffic System messages

3AB-6-1.2 What is one reason for using tactical call signs such as "command post" or "weather center" during an emergency?
A. They keep the general public informed about what is going on
B. They promote efficiency and coordination in public-service communications activities
C. They are required by the FCC
D. They promote goodwill among amateurs

3AB-6-2.1 What is the term used to describe messages sent into or out of a disaster area that pertain to a person's well being?
A. Emergency traffic
B. Tactical traffic
C. Formal message traffic
D. Health and welfare traffic

3AB-6-3.1 Why is it important to provide a means of operating your amateur station separate from the commercial AC power lines?
A. So that you can take your station mobile
B. So that you can provide communications in an emergency
C. So that you can operate field day
D. So that you will comply with Subpart 97.169 of the FCC Rules

3AB-6-3.2 Which type of antenna would be a good choice as part of a portable HF amateur station that could be set up in case of a communications emergency?
A. A three-element quad
B. A three-element Yagi
C. A dipole
D. A parabolic dish

SUBELEMENT 3AC—Radio-Wave Propagation
(3 Exam Questions)

3AC-1-1.1 What is the *ionosphere*?
A. That part of the upper atmosphere where enough ions and free electrons exist to affect radio-wave propagation
B. The boundary between two air masses of different temperature and humidity, along which radio waves can travel
C. The ball that goes on the top of a mobile whip antenna
D. That part of the atmosphere where weather takes place

3AC-1-1.2 What is the region of the outer atmosphere that makes long-distance radio communications possible as a result of bending of radio waves?
A. Troposphere
B. Stratosphere
C. Magnetosphere
D. Ionosphere

3AC-1-1.3 What type of solar radiation is most responsible for ionization in the outer atmosphere?
A. Thermal
B. Ionized particle
C. Ultraviolet
D. Microwave

3AC-1-2.1 Which ionospheric layer limits daytime radio communications in the 80-meter wavelength band to short distances?
A. D layer
B. F1 layer
C. E layer
D. F2 layer

3AC-1-2.2 What is the lowest ionospheric layer?
A. The A layer
B. The D layer
C. The E layer
D. The F layer

3AC-1-3.1 What is the lowest region of the ionosphere that is useful for long-distance radio wave propagation?
A. The D layer
B. The E layer
C. The F1 layer
D. The F2 layer

3AC-1-4.1 Which layer of the ionosphere is mainly responsible for long-distance sky-wave radio communications?
A. D layer
B. E layer
C. F1 layer
D. F2 layer

3AC-1-4.2 What are the two distinct sub-layers of the F layer of the ionosphere during the daytime?
A. Troposphere and stratosphere
B. F1 and F2
C. Electrostatic and electromagnetic
D. D and E

3AC-1-4.3 Which two daytime ionospheric layers combine into one layer at night?
A. E and F1
B. D and E
C. F1 and F2
D. E1 and E2

3AC-2.1 Which layer of the ionosphere is most responsible for absorption of radio signals during daylight hours?
A. The E layer
B. The F1 layer
C. The F2 layer
D. The D layer

3AC-2.2 When is ionospheric absorption most pronounced?
A. When tropospheric ducting occurs
B. When radio waves enter the D layer at low angles
C. When radio waves travel to the F layer
D. When a temperature inversion occurs

3AC-2.3 During daylight hours, what effect does the D layer of the ionosphere have on 80-meter radio waves?
A. The D layer absorbs the signals
B. The D layer bends the radio waves out into space
C. The D layer refracts the radio waves back to earth
D. The D layer has little or no effect on 80-meter radio wave propagation

3AC-2.4 What causes *ionospheric absorption* of radio waves?
A. A lack of D layer ionization
B. D layer ionization
C. The presence of ionized clouds in the E layer
D. Splitting of the F layer

3AC-3.1 What is usually the condition of the ionosphere just before sunrise?
A. Atmospheric attenuation is at a maximum
B. Ionization is at a maximum
C. The E layer is above the F layer
D. Ionization is at a minimum

3AC-3.2 At what time of day does maximum ionization of the ionosphere occur?
A. Dusk
B. Midnight
C. Midday
D. Dawn

3AC-3.3 Minimum ionization of the ionosphere occurs daily at what time?
A. Shortly before dawn
B. Just after noon
C. Just after dusk
D. Shortly before midnight

3AC-3.4 When is E layer ionization at a maximum?
A. Dawn
B. Midday
C. Dusk
D. Midnight

3AC-4.1 What is the name for the highest radio frequency that will be refracted back to earth?
A. Lowest usable frequency
B. Optimum working frequency
C. Ultra high frequency
D. Critical frequency

3AC-4.2 What causes the *maximum usable frequency* to vary?
A. Variations in the temperature of the air at ionospheric levels
B. Upper-atmospheric wind patterns
C. The amount of ultraviolet and other types of radiation received from the sun
D. Presence of ducting

3AC-4.3 What does the term *maximum usable frequency* refer to?
A. The maximum frequency that allows a radio signal to reach its destination in a single hop
B. The minimum frequency that allows a radio signal to reach its destination in a single hop
C. The maximum frequency that allows a radio signal to be absorbed in the lowest ionospheric layer
D. The minimum frequency that allows a radio signal to be absorbed in the lowest ionospheric layer

3AC-5.1 When two stations are within each other's skip zone on the frequency being used, what mode of propagation would it be desirable to use?
A. Ground wave propagation
B. Sky wave propagation
C. Scatter-mode propagation
D. Ionospheric ducting propagation

3AC-5.2 You are in contact with a distant station and are operating at a frequency close to the maximum usable frequency. If the received signals are weak and somewhat distorted, what type of propagation are you probably experiencing?
A. Tropospheric ducting
B. Line-of-sight propagation
C. Backscatter propagation
D. Waveguide propagation

3AC-6.1 What is the transmission path of a wave that travels directly from the transmitting antenna to the receiving antenna called?
A. Line of sight
B. The sky wave
C. The linear wave
D. The plane wave

3AC-6.2 How are VHF signals within the range of the visible horizon propagated?
A. By sky wave
B. By direct wave
C. By plane wave
D. By geometric wave

3AC-7.1 Ducting occurs in which region of the atmosphere?
A. F2
B. Ionosphere
C. Troposphere
D. Stratosphere

3AC-7.2 What effect does tropospheric bending have on 2-meter radio waves?
A. It increases the distance over which they can be transmitted
B. It decreases the distance over which they can be transmitted
C. It tends to garble 2-meter phone transmissions
D. It reverses the sideband of 2-meter phone transmissions

3AC-7.3 What atmospheric phenomenon causes tropospheric ducting of radio waves?
A. A very low pressure area
B. An aurora to the north
C. Lightning between the transmitting and receiving station
D. A temperature inversion

3AC-7.4 Tropospheric ducting occurs as a result of what phenomenon?
A. A temperature inversion
B. Sun spots
C. An aurora to the north
D. Lightning between the transmitting and receiving station

3AC-7.5 What atmospheric phenomenon causes VHF radio waves to be propagated several hundred miles through stable air masses over oceans?
A. Presence of a maritime polar air mass
B. A widespread temperature inversion
C. An overcast of cirriform clouds
D. Atmospheric pressure of roughly 29 inches of mercury or higher

3AC-7.6 In what frequency range does tropospheric ducting occur most often?
A. LF
B. MF
C. HF
D. VHF

SUBELEMENT 3AD—Amateur Radio Practice
(4 Exam Questions)

3AD-1-1.1 Where should the green wire in an AC line cord be attached in a power supply?
A. To the fuse
B. To the "hot" side of the power switch
C. To the chassis
D. To the meter

3AD-1-1.2 Where should the black (or red) wire in a three-wire line cord be attached in a power supply?
A. To the filter capacitor
B. To the DC ground
C. To the chassis
D. To the fuse

3AD-1-1.3 Where should the white wire in a three-wire line cord be attached in a power supply?
A. To the side of the transformer's primary winding that has a fuse
B. To the side of the transformer's primary winding without a fuse
C. To the black wire
D. To the rectifier junction

3AD-1-1.4 Why is the retaining screw in one terminal of a light socket made of brass while the other one is silver colored?
A. To prevent galvanic action
B. To indicate correct wiring polarity
C. To better conduct current
D. To reduce skin effect

3AD-1-2.1 How much electrical current flowing through the human body is usually fatal?
A. As little as 100 milliamperes may be fatal
B. Approximately 10 amperes is required to be fatal
C. More than 20 amperes is needed to kill a human being
D. No amount of current will harm you. Voltages of over 2000 volts are always fatal, however

3AD-1-2.2 What is the minimum voltage considered to be dangerous to humans?
A. 30 volts
B. 100 volts
C. 1000 volts
D. 2000 volts

3AD-1-2.3 How much electrical current flowing through the human body is usually painful?
A. As little as 50 milliamperes may be painful
B. Approximately 10 amperes is required to be painful
C. More than 20 amperes is needed to be painful to a human being
D. No amount of current will be painful. Voltages of over 2000 volts are always painful, however

3AD-1-3.1 Where should the main power-line switch for a high voltage power supply be situated?
A. Inside the cabinet, to interrupt power when the cabinet is opened
B. On the rear panel of the high-voltage supply
C. Where it can be seen and reached easily
D. This supply should not be switch-operated

3AD-2-1.1 How is a voltmeter typically connected to a circuit under test?
A. In series with the circuit
B. In parallel with the circuit
C. In quadrature with the circuit
D. In phase with the circuit

Element 3A Question Pool—With Answers   13-11

3AD-2-2.1　How can the range of a voltmeter be extended?
A. By adding resistance in series with the circuit under test
B. By adding resistance in parallel with the circuit under test
C. By adding resistance in series with the meter
D. By adding resistance in parallel with the meter

3AD-3-1.1　How is an ammeter typically connected to a circuit under test?
A. In series with the circuit
B. In parallel with the circuit
C. In quadrature with the circuit
D. In phase with the circuit

3AD-3-2.1　How can the range of an ammeter be extended?
A. By adding resistance in series with the circuit under test
B. By adding resistance in parallel with the circuit under test
C. By adding resistance in series with the meter
D. By adding resistance in parallel with the meter

3AD-4.1　What is a *multimeter*?
A. An instrument capable of reading SWR and power
B. An instrument capable of reading resistance, capacitance and inductance
C. An instrument capable of reading resistance and reactance
D. An instrument capable of reading voltage, current and resistance

3AD-5-1.1　Where in the antenna transmission line should a peak-reading wattmeter be attached to determine the transmitter output power?
A. At the transmitter output
B. At the antenna feed point
C. One-half wavelength from the antenna feed point
D. One-quarter wavelength from the transmitter output

3AD-5-1.2　For the most accurate readings of transmitter output power, where should the RF wattmeter be inserted?
A. The wattmeter should be inserted and the output measured one-quarter wavelength from the antenna feed point
B. The wattmeter should be inserted and the output measured one-half wavelength from the antenna feed point
C. The wattmeter should be inserted and the output power measured at the transmitter antenna jack
D. The wattmeter should be inserted and the output power measured at the Transmatch output

3AD-5-1.3　At what line impedance are RF wattmeters usually designed to operate?
A. 25 ohms
B. 50 ohms
C. 100 ohms
D. 300 ohms

3AD-5-1.4　What is a *directional wattmeter*?
A. An instrument that measures forward or reflected power
B. An instrument that measures the directional pattern of an antenna
C. An instrument that measures the energy consumed by the transmitter
D. An instrument that measures thermal heating in a load resistor

3AD-5-2.1　If a directional RF wattmeter indicates 90 watts forward power and 10 watts reflected power, what is the actual transmitter output power?
A. 10 watts
B. 80 watts
C. 90 watts
D. 100 watts

3AD-5-2.2　If a directional RF wattmeter indicates 96 watts forward power and 4 watts reflected power, what is the actual transmitter output power?
A. 80 watts
B. 88 watts
C. 92 watts
D. 100 watts

3AD-6.1　What is a *marker generator*?
A. A high-stability oscillator that generates a series of reference signals at known frequency intervals
B. A low-stability oscillator that "sweeps" through a band of frequencies
C. An oscillator often used in aircraft to determine the craft's location relative to the inner and outer markers at airports
D. A high-stability oscillator whose output frequency and amplitude can be varied over a wide range

3AD-6.2　What type of circuit is used to inject a frequency calibration signal into a communications receiver?
A. A product detector
B. A receiver incremental tuning circuit
C. A balanced modulator
D. A crystal calibrator

3AD-6.3　How is a *marker generator* used?
A. To calibrate the tuning dial on a receiver
B. To calibrate the volume control on a receiver
C. To test the amplitude linearity of an SSB transmitter
D. To test the frequency deviation of an FM transmitter

3AD-7.1　What piece of test equipment produces a stable, low-level signal that can be set to a specific frequency?
A. A wavemeter
B. A reflectometer
C. A signal generator
D. A balanced modulator

3AD-7.2　What is an *RF signal generator* commonly used for?
A. Measuring RF signal amplitude
B. Aligning receiver tuned circuits
C. Adjusting the transmitter impedance-matching network
D. Measuring transmission line impedance

3AD-8-1.1 What is a *reflectometer*?
A. An instrument used to measure signals reflected from the ionosphere
B. An instrument used to measure radiation resistance
C. An instrument used to measure transmission-line impedance
D. An instrument used to measure standing wave ratio

3AD-8-1.2 What is the device that can indicate an impedance mismatch in an antenna system?
A. A field-strength meter
B. A set of lecher wires
C. A wavemeter
D. A reflectometer

3AD-8-2.1 For best accuracy when adjusting the impedance match between an antenna and feed line, where should the match-indicating device be inserted?
A. At the antenna feed point
B. At the transmitter
C. At the midpoint of the feed line
D. Anywhere along the feed line

3AD-8-2.2 Where should a reflectometer be inserted into a long antenna transmission line in order to obtain the most valid standing wave ratio indication?
A. At any quarter-wavelength interval along the transmission line
B. At the receiver end
C. At the antenna end
D. At any even half-wavelength interval along the transmission line

3AD-9.1 When adjusting a transmitter filter circuit, what device is connected to the transmitter output?
A. A multimeter
B. A set of Litz wires
C. A receiver
D. A dummy antenna

3AD-9.2 What is a *dummy antenna*?
A. An isotropic radiator
B. A nonradiating load for a transmitter
C. An antenna used as a reference for gain measurements
D. The image of an antenna, located below ground

3AD-9.3 Of what materials may a dummy antenna be made?
A. A wire-wound resistor
B. A diode and resistor combination
C. A noninductive resistor
D. A coil and capacitor combination

3AD-9.4 What station accessory is used in place of an antenna during transmitter tests so that no signal is radiated?
A. A Transmatch
B. A dummy antenna
C. A low-pass filter
D. A decoupling resistor

3AD-9.5 What is the purpose of a *dummy load*?
A. To allow off-the-air transmitter testing
B. To reduce output power for QRP operation
C. To give comparative signal reports
D. To allow Transmatch tuning without causing interference

3AD-9.6 How many watts should a dummy load for use with a 100-watt single-sideband phone transmitter be able to dissipate?
A. A minimum of 100 watts continuous
B. A minimum of 141 watts continuous
C. A minimum of 175 watts continuous
D. A minimum of 200 watts continuous

3AD-10.1 What is an *S-meter*?
A. A meter used to measure sideband suppression
B. A meter used to measure spurious emissions from a transmitter
C. A meter used to measure relative signal strength in a receiver
D. A meter used to measure solar flux

3AD-10.2 A meter that is used to measure relative signal strength in a receiver is known as what?
A. An S-meter
B. An RST-meter
C. A signal deviation meter
D. An SSB meter

3AD-11-1.1 Large amounts of RF energy may cause damage to body tissue, depending on the wavelength of the signal, the energy density of the RF field, and other factors. How does RF energy effect body tissue?
A. It causes radiation poisoning
B. It heats the tissue
C. It cools the tissue
D. It produces genetic changes in the tissue

3AD-11-1.2 Which body organ is most susceptible to damage from the heating effects of radio frequency radiation?
A. Eyes
B. Hands
C. Heart
D. Liver

3AD-11-2.1 Scientists have devoted a great deal of effort to determine safe RF exposure limits. What organization has established an RF protection guide?
A. The Institute of Electrical and Electronics Engineers
B. The American Radio Relay League
C. The Environmental Protection Agency
D. The American National Standards Institute

3AD-11-2.2 What is the purpose of the ANSI RF protection guide?
A. It protects you from unscrupulous radio dealers
B. It sets RF exposure limits under certain circumstances
C. It sets transmitter power limits
D. It sets antenna height requirements

3AD-11-2.3 The American National Standards Institute RF protection guide sets RF exposure limits under certain circumstances. In what frequency range is the maximum exposure level the most stringent (lowest)?
A. 3 to 30 MHz
B. 30 to 300 MHz
C. 300 to 3000 MHz
D. Above 1.5 GHz

3AD-11-2.4 The American National Standards Institute RF protection guide sets RF exposure limits under certain circumstances. Why is the maximum exposure level the most stringent (lowest) in the ranges between 30 MHz and 300 MHz?
A. There are fewer transmitters operating in this frequency range
B. There are more transmitters operating in this frequency range
C. Most transmissions in this frequency range are for an extended time
D. Human body lengths are close to whole-body resonance in that range

3AD-11-2.5 The American National Standards Institute RF protection guide sets RF exposure limits under certain circumstances. What is the maximum safe power output to the antenna terminal of a hand-held VHF or UHF radio, as set by this RF protection guide?
A. 125 milliwatts
B. 7 watts
C. 10 watts
D. 25 watts

3AD-11-3.1 After you make internal tuning adjustments to your VHF power amplifier, what should you do before you turn the amplifier on?
A. Remove all amplifier shielding to ensure maximum cooling
B. Connect a noise bridge to eliminate any interference
C. Be certain all amplifier shielding is fastened in place
D. Be certain no antenna is attached so that you will not cause any interference

SUBELEMENT 3AE—Electrical Principles
(3 Exam Questions)

3AE-1-1.1 What is meant by the term *resistance*?
A. The opposition to the flow of current in an electric circuit containing inductors
B. The opposition to the flow of current in an electric circuit containing capacitance
C. The opposition to the flow of current in an electric circuit containing reactance
D. The opposition to the flow of current in an electric circuit that does not contain reactance

3AE-1-2.1 What is an *ohm*?
A. The basic unit of resistance
B. The basic unit of capacitance
C. The basic unit of inductance
D. The basic unit of admittance

3AE-1-2.2 What is the unit measurement of resistance?
A. Volt
B. Ampere
C. Joule
D. Ohm

3AE-1-3.1 Two equal-value resistors are connected in series. How does the total resistance of this combination compare with the value of either resistor by itself?
A. The total resistance is half the value of either resistor
B. The total resistance is twice the value of either resistor
C. The total resistance is the same as the value of either resistor
D. The total resistance is the square of the value of either resistor

3AE-1-3.2 How does the total resistance of a string of series-connected resistors compare to the values of the individual resistors?
A. The total resistance is the square of the sum of all the individual resistor values
B. The total resistance is the square root of the sum of the individual resistor values
C. The total resistance is the sum of the squares of the individual resistor values
D. The total resistance is the sum of all the individual resistance values

3AE-1-4.1 Two equal-value resistors are connected in parallel. How does the total resistance of this combination compare with the value of either resistor by itself?
A. The total resistance is twice the value of either resistor
B. The total resistance is half the value of either resistor
C. The total resistance is the square of the value of either resistor
D. The total resistance is the same as the value of either resistor

3AE-1-4.2 How does the total resistance of a string of parallel-connected resistors compare to the values of the individual resistors?
A. The total resistance is the square of the sum of the resistor values
B. The total resistance is more than the highest-value resistor in the combination
C. The total resistance is less than the smallest-value resistor in the combination
D. The total resistance is the same as the highest-value resistor in the combination

3AE-2.1 What is *Ohm's Law*?
  A. A mathematical relationship between resistance, voltage and power in a circuit
  B. A mathematical relationship between current, resistance and power in a circuit
  C. A mathematical relationship between current, voltage and power in a circuit
  D. A mathematical relationship between resistance, current and applied voltage in a circuit

3AE-2.2 How is the current in a DC circuit calculated when the voltage and resistance are known?
  A. $I = E / R$
  B. $P = I \times E$
  C. $I = R \times E$
  D. $I = E \times R$

3AE-2.3 What is the input resistance of a load when a 12-volt battery supplies 0.25 amperes to it?
  A. 0.02 ohms
  B. 3 ohms
  C. 48 ohms
  D. 480 ohms

3AE-2.4 The product of the current and what force gives the electrical power in a circuit?
  A. Magnetomotive force
  B. Centripetal force
  C. Electrochemical force
  D. Electromotive force

3AE-2.5 What is the input resistance of a load when a 12-volt battery supplies 0.15 amperes to it?
  A. 8 ohms
  B. 80 ohms
  C. 100 ohms
  D. 800 ohms

3AE-2.6 When 120 volts is measured across a 4700-ohm resistor, approximately how much current is flowing through it?
  A. 39 amperes
  B. 3.9 amperes
  C. 0.26 ampere
  D. 0.026 ampere

3AE-2.7 When 120 volts is measured across a 47000-ohm resistor, approximately how much current is flowing through it?
  A. 392 A
  B. 39.2 A
  C. 26 mA
  D. 2.6 mA

3AE-2.8 When 12 volts is measured across a 4700-ohm resistor, approximately how much current is flowing through it?
  A. 2.6 mA
  B. 26 mA
  C. 39.2 A
  D. 392 A

3AE-2.9 When 12 volts is measured across a 47000-ohm resistor, approximately how much current is flowing through it?
  A. 255 μA
  B. 255 mA
  C. 3917 mA
  D. 3917 A

3AE-3-1.1 What is the term used to describe the ability of a component to store energy in a magnetic field?
  A. Admittance
  B. Capacitance
  C. Inductance
  D. Resistance

3AE-3-2.1 What is the basic unit of inductance?
  A. Coulomb
  B. Farad
  C. Henry
  D. Ohm

3AE-3-2.2 What is a *henry*?
  A. The basic unit of admittance
  B. The basic unit of capacitance
  C. The basic unit of inductance
  D. The basic unit of resistance

3AE-3-2.3 What is a *microhenry*?
  A. A basic unit of inductance equal to 10^{-12} henrys
  B. A basic unit of inductance equal to 10^{-6} henrys
  C. A basic unit of inductance equal to 10^{-3} henrys
  D. A basic unit of inductance equal to 10^6 henrys

3AE-3-2.4 What is a *millihenry*?
  A. A basic unit of inductance equal to 10^{-12} henrys
  B. A basic unit of inductance equal to 10^{-6} henrys
  C. A basic unit of inductance equal to 10^{-3} henrys
  D. A basic unit of inductance equal to 10^6 henrys

3AE-3-3.1 Two equal-value inductors are connected in series. How does the total inductance of this combination compare with the value of either inductor by itself?
  A. The total inductance is half the value of either inductor
  B. The total inductance is twice the value of either inductor
  C. The total inductance is equal to the value of either inductor
  D. No comparison can be made without knowing the exact inductances

3AE-3-3.2 How does the total inductance of a string of series-connected inductors compare to the values of the individual inductors?
  A. The total inductance is equal to the average of all the individual inductances
  B. The total inductance is equal to less than the value of the smallest inductance
  C. The total inductance is equal to the sum of all the individual inductances
  D. No comparison can be made without knowing the exact inductances

3AE-3-4.1 Two equal-value inductors are connected in parallel. How does the total inductance of this combination compare with the value of either inductor by itself?
  A. The total inductance is half the value of either inductor
  B. The total inductance is twice the value of either inductor
  C. The total inductance is equal to the square of either inductance
  D. No comparison can be made without knowing the exact inductances

3AE-3-4.2 How does the total inductance of a string of parallel-connected inductors compare to the values of the individual inductors?
- A. The total inductance is equal to the sum of the inductances in the combination
- B. The total inductance is less than the smallest inductance value in the combination
- C. The total inductance is equal to the average of the inductances in the combination
- D. No comparison can be made without knowing the exact inductances

3AE-4-1.1 What is the term used to describe the ability of a component to store energy in an electric field?
- A. Capacitance
- B. Inductance
- C. Resistance
- D. Tolerance

3AE-4-2.1 What is the basic unit of capacitance?
- A. Farad
- B. Ohm
- C. Volt
- D. Ampere

3AE-4-2.2 What is a *microfarad*?
- A. A basic unit of capacitance equal to 10^{-12} farads
- B. A basic unit of capacitance equal to 10^{-6} farads
- C. A basic unit of capacitance equal to 10^{-2} farads
- D. A basic unit of capacitance equal to 10^{6} farads

3AE-4-2.3 What is a *picofarad*?
- A. A basic unit of capacitance equal to 10^{-12} farads
- B. A basic unit of capacitance equal to 10^{-6} farads
- C. A basic unit of capacitance equal to 10^{-2} farads
- D. A basic unit of capacitance equal to 10^{6} farads

3AE-4-2.4 What is a *farad*?
- A. The basic unit of resistance
- B. The basic unit of capacitance
- C. The basic unit of inductance
- D. The basic unit of admittance

3AE-4-3.1 Two equal-value capacitors are connected in series. How does the total capacitance of this combination compare with the value of either capacitor by itself?
- A. The total capacitance is twice the value of either capacitor
- B. The total capacitance is equal to the value of either capacitor
- C. The total capacitance is half the value of either capacitor
- D. No comparison can be made without knowing the exact capacitances

3AE-4-3.2 How does the total capacitance of a string of series-connected capacitors compare to the values of the individual capacitors?
- A. The total capacitance is equal to the sum of the capacitances in the combination
- B. The total capacitance is less than the smallest value of capacitance
- C. The total capacitance is equal to the average of the capacitances in the combination
- D. No comparison can be made without knowing the exact capacitances

3AE-4-4.1 Two equal-value capacitors are connected in parallel. How does the total capacitance of this combination compare with the value of either capacitor by itself?
- A. The total capacitance is twice the value of either capacitor
- B. The total capacitance is half the value of either capacitor
- C. The total capacitance is equal to the value of either capacitor
- D. No comparison can be made without knowing the exact capacitances

3AE-4-4.2 How does the total capacitance of a string of parallel-connected capacitors compare to the values of the individual capacitors?
- A. The total capacitance is equal to the sum of the capacitances in the combination
- B. The total capacitance is less than the smallest value of capacitance in the combination
- C. The total capacitance is equal to the average of the capacitances in the combination
- D. No comparison can be made without knowing the exact capacitances

SUBELEMENT 3AF—Circuit Components
(2 Exam Questions)

3AF-1-1.1 What are the four common types of resistor construction?
- A. Carbon-film, metal-film, micro-film and wire-film
- B. Carbon-composition, carbon-film, metal-film and wire-wound
- C. Carbon-composition, carbon-film, electrolytic and metal-film
- D. Carbon-film, ferrite, carbon-composition and metal-film

3AF-1-2.1 What is the primary function of a resistor?
- A. To store an electric charge
- B. To store a magnetic field
- C. To match a high-impedance source to a low-impedance load
- D. To limit the current in an electric circuit

3AF-1-2.2 What is a *variable resistor*?
- A. A resistor that changes value when an AC voltage is applied to it
- B. A device that can transform a variable voltage into a constant voltage
- C. A resistor with a slide or contact that makes the resistance adjustable
- D. A resistor that changes value when it is heated

3AF-1-3.1 What do the first three color bands on a resistor indicate?
- A. The value of the resistor in ohms
- B. The resistance tolerance in percent
- C. The power rating in watts
- D. The value of the resistor in henrys

3AF-1-3.2 How can a carbon resistor's electrical tolerance rating be found?
- A. By using a wavemeter
- B. By using the resistor's color code
- C. By using Thevenin's theorem for resistors
- D. By using the Baudot code

3AF-1-3.3 What does the fourth color band on a resistor indicate?
- A. The value of the resistor in ohms
- B. The resistance tolerance in percent
- C. The power rating in watts
- D. The resistor composition

3AF-1-3.4 When the color bands on a group of resistors indicate that they all have the same resistance, what further information about each resistor is needed in order to select those that have nearly equal value?
- A. The working voltage rating of each resistor
- B. The composition of each resistor
- C. The tolerance of each resistor
- D. The current rating of each resistor

3AF-1-4.1 Why do resistors generate heat?
- A. They convert electrical energy to heat energy
- B. They exhibit reactance
- C. Because of skin effect
- D. To produce thermionic emission

3AF-1-4.2 Why would a large size resistor be substituted for a smaller one of the same resistance?
- A. To obtain better response
- B. To obtain a higher current gain
- C. To increase power dissipation capability
- D. To produce a greater parallel impedance

3AF-1-5.1 What is the symbol used to represent a fixed resistor on schematic diagrams?

3AF-1-5.2 What is the symbol used to represent a variable resistor on schematic diagrams.

3AF-2-1.1 What is an inductor *core*?
- A. The point at which an inductor is tapped to produce resonance
- B. A tight coil of wire used in a transformer
- C. An insulating material placed between the plates of an inductor
- D. The central portion of a coil; may be made from air, iron, brass or other material

3AF-2-1.2 What are the component parts of a coil?
- A. The wire in the winding and the core material
- B. Two conductive plates and an insulating material
- C. Two or more layers of silicon material
- D. A donut-shaped iron core and a layer of insulating tape

3AF-2-1.3 Describe an *inductor*.
- A. A semiconductor in a conducting shield
- B. Two parallel conducting plates
- C. A straight wire conductor mounted inside a Faraday shield
- D. A coil of conducting wire

3AF-2-1.4 For radio frequency power applications, which type of inductor has the least amount of loss?
- A. Magnetic wire
- B. Iron core
- C. Air core
- D. Slug tuned

3AF-2-2.1 What is an *inductor*?
- A. An electronic component that stores energy in an electric field
- B. An electronic component that converts a high voltage to a lower voltage
- C. An electronic component that opposes DC while allowing AC to pass
- D. An electronic component that stores energy in a magnetic field

3AF-2-2.2 What are the electrical properties of an inductor?
- A. An inductor stores a charge electrostatically and opposes a change in voltage
- B. An inductor stores a charge electrochemically and opposes a change in current
- C. An inductor stores a charge electromagnetically and opposes a change in current
- D. An inductor stores a charge electromechanically and opposes a change in voltage

3AF-2-3.1 What factors determine the amount of inductance in a *coil?*
- A. The type of material used in the core, the diameter of the core and whether the coil is mounted horizontally or vertically
- B. The diameter of the core, the number of turns of wire used to wind the coil and the type of metal used in the wire
- C. The type of material used in the core, the number of turns used to wind the core and the frequency of the current through the coil
- D. The type of material used in the core, the diameter of the core, the length of the coil and the number of turns of wire used to wind the coil

3AF-2-3.2 What can be done to raise the inductance of a 5-microhenry air-core coil to a 5-millihenry coil with the same physical dimensions?
- A. The coil can be wound on a non-conducting tube
- B. The coil can be wound on an iron core
- C. Both ends of the coil can be brought around to form the shape of a donut, or toroid
- D. The coil can be made of a heavier-gauge wire

3AF-2-3.3 As an iron core is inserted in a coil, what happens to the inductance?
- A. It increases
- B. It decreases
- C. It stays the same
- D. It becomes voltage-dependent

3AF-2-3.4 As a brass core is inserted in a coil, what happens to the inductance?
- A. It increases
- B. It decreases
- C. It stays the same
- D. It becomes voltage-dependent

3AF-2-4.1 What is the symbol used to represent an adjustable inductor on schematic diagrams?

A.   B.

C.   D.

3AF-2-4.2 What is the symbol used to represent an iron-core inductor on schematic diagrams?

A.   B.

C.   D.

3AF-2-4.3 What is the symbol used to represent an inductor wound over a toroidal core on schematic diagrams?

A.   B.

C.   D.

3AF-3-1.1 What is a capacitor *dielectric?*
- A. The insulating material used for the plates
- B. The conducting material used between the plates
- C. The ferrite material that the plates are mounted on
- D. The insulating material between the plates

3AF-3-1.2 What are the component parts of a capacitor?
- A. Two or more conductive plates with an insulating material between them
- B. The wire used in the winding and the core material
- C. Two or more layers of silicon material
- D. Two insulating plates with a conductive material between them

3AF-3-1.3 What is an *electrolytic capacitor?*
- A. A capacitor whose plates are formed on a thin ceramic layer
- B. A capacitor whose plates are separated by a thin strip of mica insulation
- C. A capacitor whose dielectric is formed on one set of plates through electrochemical action
- D. A capacitor whose value varies with applied voltage

3AF-3-1.4 What is a *paper capacitor?*
- A. A capacitor whose plates are formed on a thin ceramic layer
- B. A capacitor whose plates are separated by a thin strip of mica insulation
- C. A capacitor whose plates are separated by a layer of paper
- D. A capacitor whose dielectric is formed on one set of plates through electrochemical action

3AF-3-2.1 What is a *capacitor?*
- A. An electronic component that stores energy in a magnetic field
- B. An electronic component that stores energy in an electric field
- C. An electronic component that converts a high voltage to a lower voltage
- D. An electronic component that converts power into heat

3AF-3-2.2 What are the electrical properties of a capacitor?
  A. A capacitor stores a charge electrochemically and opposes a change in current
  B. A capacitor stores a charge electromagnetically and opposes a change in current
  C. A capacitor stores a charge electromechanically and opposes a change in voltage
  D. A capacitor stores a charge electrostatically and opposes a change in voltage

3AF-3-2.3 What factors must be considered when selecting a capacitor for a circuit?
  A. Type of capacitor, capacitance and voltage rating
  B. Type of capacitor, capacitance and the kilowatt-hour rating
  C. The amount of capacitance, the temperature coefficient and the KVA rating
  D. The type of capacitor, the microscopy coefficient and the temperature coefficient

3AF-3-2.4 How are the characteristics of a capacitor usually *specified*?
  A. In volts and amperes
  B. In microfarads and volts
  C. In ohms and watts
  D. In millihenrys and amperes

3AF-3-3.1 What factors determine the amount of capacitance in a *capacitor*?
  A. The dielectric constant of the material between the plates, the area of one side of one plate, the separation between the plates and the number of plates
  B. The dielectric constant of the material between the plates, the number of plates and the diameter of the leads connected to the plates
  C. The number of plates, the spacing between the plates and whether the dielectric material is N type or P type
  D. The dielectric constant of the material between the plates, the surface area of one side of one plate, the number of plates and the type of material used for the protective coating

3AF-3-3.2 As the plate area of a capacitor is increased, what happens to its capacitance?
  A. Decreases
  B. Increases
  C. Stays the same
  D. Becomes voltage dependent

3AF-3-3.3 As the plate spacing of a capacitor is increased, what happens to its capacitance?
  A. Increases
  B. Stays the same
  C. Becomes voltage dependent
  D. Decreases

3AF-3-4.1 What is the symbol used to represent an electrolytic capacitor on schematic diagrams?

3AF-3-4.2 What is the symbol used to represent a variable capacitor on schematic diagrams?

SUBELEMENT 3AG—Practical Circuits
(1 Exam Question)

3AG-1-1.1 Which frequencies are attenuated by a low-pass filter?
A. Those above its cut-off frequency
B. Those within its cut-off frequency
C. Those within 50 kHz on either side of its cut-off frequency
D. Those below its cut-off frequency

3AG-1-1.2 What circuit passes electrical energy below a certain frequency and blocks electrical energy above that frequency?
A. A band-pass filter
B. A high-pass filter
C. An input filter
D. A low-pass filter

3AG-1-2.1 Why does virtually every modern transmitter have a built-in low-pass filter connected to its output?
A. To attenuate frequencies below its cutoff point
B. To attenuate low frequency interference to other amateurs
C. To attenuate excess harmonic radiation
D. To attenuate excess fundamental radiation

3AG-1-2.2 You believe that excess harmonic radiation from your transmitter is causing interference to your television receiver. What is one possible solution for this problem?
A. Install a low-pass filter on the television receiver
B. Install a low-pass filter at the transmitter output
C. Install a high-pass filter on the transmitter output
D. Install a band-pass filter on the television receiver

3AG-2-1.1 What circuit passes electrical energy above a certain frequency and attenuates electrical energy below that frequency?
A. A band-pass filter
B. A high-pass filter
C. An input filter
D. A low-pass filter

3AG-2-2.1 Where is the proper place to install a high-pass filter?
A. At the antenna terminals of a television receiver
B. Between a transmitter and a Transmatch
C. Between a Transmatch and the transmission line
D. On a transmitting antenna

3AG-2-2.2 Your Amateur Radio transmissions cause interference to your television receiver even though you have installed a low-pass filter at the transmitter output. What is one possible solution for this problem?
A. Install a high-pass filter at the transmitter terminals
B. Install a high-pass filter at the television antenna terminals
C. Install a low-pass filter at the television antenna terminals also
D. Install a band-pass filter at the television antenna terminals

3AG-3-1.1 What circuit attenuates electrical energy above a certain frequency and below a lower frequency?
A. A band-pass filter
B. A high-pass filter
C. An input filter
D. A low-pass filter

3AG-3-1.2 What general range of RF energy does a band-pass filter reject?
A. All frequencies above a specified frequency
B. All frequencies below a specified frequency
C. All frequencies above the upper limit of the band in question
D. All frequencies above a specified frequency and below a lower specified frequency

3AG-3-2.1 The IF stage of a communications receiver uses a filter with a peak response at the intermediate frequency. What term describes this filter response?
A. A band-pass filter
B. A high-pass filter
C. An input filter
D. A low-pass filter

3AG-4-1.1 What circuit is likely to be found in all types of receivers?
A. An audio filter
B. A beat frequency oscillator
C. A detector
D. An RF amplifier

3AG-4-1.2 What type of transmitter does this block diagram represent?

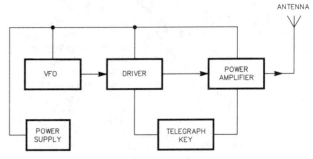

A. A simple packet-radio transmitter
B. A simple crystal-controlled transmitter
C. A single-sideband transmitter
D. A VFO-controlled transmitter

3AG-4-1.3 What type of transmitter does this block diagram represent?

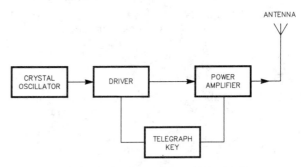

A. A simple packet-radio transmitter
B. A simple crystal-controlled transmitter
C. A single-sideband transmitter
D. A VFO-controlled transmitter

3AG-4-1.4 What is the unlabeled block (?) in this diagram?

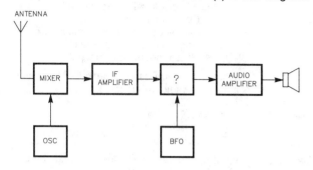

    A. An AGC circuit
    B. A detector
    C. A power supply
    D. A VFO circuit

3AG-4-1.5 What type of device does this block diagram represent?

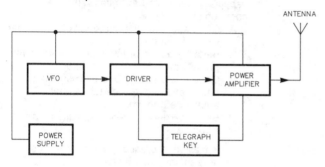

    A. A double-conversion receiver
    B. A variable-frequency oscillator
    C. A simple superheterodyne receiver
    D. A simple CW transmitter

3AG-4-2.1 What type of device does this block diagram represent?

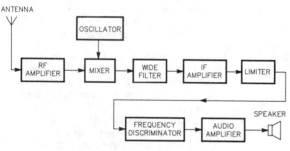

    A. A double-conversion receiver
    B. A variable-frequency oscillator
    C. A simple superheterodyne receiver
    D. A simple FM receiver

3AG-4-2.2 What is the unlabeled block (?) in this diagram?

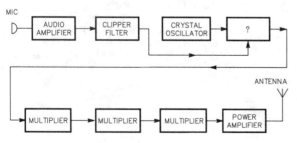

    A. A band-pass filter
    B. A crystal oscillator
    C. A reactance modulator
    D. A rectifier modulator

SUBELEMENT 3AH—Signals and Emissions
(2 Exam Questions)

3AH-1.1 What is the meaning of the term *modulation*?
    A. The process of varying some characteristic of a carrier wave for the purpose of conveying information
    B. The process of recovering audio information from a received signal
    C. The process of increasing the average power of a single-sideband transmission
    D. The process of suppressing the carrier in a single-sideband transmitter

3AH-2-1.1 If the modulator circuit of your FM transmitter fails, what emission type would likely result?
    A. An unmodulated carrier wave
    B. A phase modulated carrier wave
    C. An amplitude modulated carrier wave
    D. A frequency modulated carrier wave

3AH-2-1.2 What emission does not have sidebands resulting from modulation?
    A. AM phone
    B. Test
    C. FM phone
    D. RTTY

3AH-2-2.1 What is the FCC emission designator for a Morse code telegraphy signal produced by switching the transmitter output on and off?
    A. Test
    B. AM phone
    C. CW
    D. RTTY

3AH-2-2.2 What is CW?
    A. Morse code telegraphy using amplitude modulation
    B. Morse code telegraphy using frequency modulation
    C. Morse code telegraphy using phase modulation
    D. Morse code telegraphy using pulse modulation

3AH-2-3.1 What is RTTY?
    A. Amplitude-keyed telegraphy
    B. Frequency-shift-keyed telegraphy
    C. Frequency-modulated telephony
    D. Phase-modulated telephony

3AH-2-3.2 What is the emission designation for telegraphy by frequency shift keying without the use of a modulating tone?
    A. RTTY
    B. MCW
    C. CW
    D. Single-sideband phone

3AH-2-4.1 What emission type results when an on/off keyed audio tone is applied to the microphone input of an FM transmitter?
    A. RTTY
    B. MCW
    C. CW
    D. Single-sideband phone

3AH-2-4.2 What is tone-modulated international Morse code telegraphy?
    A. Telephony produced by audio fed into an FM transmitter
    B. Telegraphy produced by an on/off keyed audio tone fed into a CW transmitter
    C. Telegraphy produced by on/off keying of the carrier amplitude
    D. Telegraphy produced by an on/off keyed audio tone fed into an FM transmitter

3AH-2-5.1 What is the emission designated as "MCW"?
A. Frequency-modulated telegraphy using audio tones
B. Frequency-modulated telephony
C. Frequency-modulated facsimile using audio tones
D. Phase-modulated television

3AH-2-5.2 In an ITU emission designator like A1A, what does the first symbol describe?
A. The nature of the signal modulating the main carrier
B. The type of modulation of the main carrier
C. The speed of a radiotelegraph transmission
D. The type of the information to be transmitted

3AH-2-5.3 What emission type results when an on-off keyed audio oscillator is connected to the microphone jack of an FM phone transmitter?
A. SS
B. RTTY
C. MCW
D. Image

3AH-2-6.1 In an ITU emission designator like F3B, what does the second symbol describe?
A. The nature of the signal modulating the main carrier
B. The type of modulation of the main carrier
C. The type of information to be transmitted
D. The frequency modulation index of a carrier

3AH-2-6.2 How would you transmit packet using an FM 2-meter transceiver?
A. Use your telegraph key to interrupt the carrier wave
B. Modulate your FM transmitter with audio tones from a terminal node controller
C. Use your mike for telephony
D. Use your touch-tone (DTMF) key pad to signal in Morse code.

3AH-2-7.1 What type of emission results when speaking into the microphone of a 2-meter FM hand-held transceiver?
A. Amplitude modulated phone
B. Code telegraphy
C. An unmodulated carrier wave
D. Frequency modulated phone

3AH-2-7.2 What emission type do most 2-meter FM transmitters transmit?
A. Interrupted pure carrier wave
B. Frequency modulated phone
C. Single-sideband voice emissions
D. Amplitude modulated carrier waves

*3AH-2-8.1 What is the most important consideration when installing a 10-meter dipole inside an attic?
A. It will exhibit a low angle of radiation
B. The dipole must always be run horizontally polarized
C. It will be covered by an insulation to prevent fire and high enough to prevent being accidentally touched during transmission
D. Dipoles usually don't work in attics

*There is a problem with the answer (C) to question 3AH-2-8.1, as released by the VEC Question Pool Committee. The most important consideration is that an indoor antenna should be treated with respect because of the possibility of adverse biological effects due to near-field radiation. Another point to keep in mind is that insulated wire does *not* reduce or eliminate the risk of RF burns. Finally, a dipole does not pose a fire hazard from RF, whether it uses insulated or uninsulated wire.

3AH-2-8.2 Which type of transmitter will produce a frequency modulated carrier wave?
A. A CW transmitter
B. An amplitude modulated transmitter
C. A single-sideband transmitter
D. A phase modulated transmitter

3AH-3.1 What is the term used to describe a constant-amplitude radio-frequency signal?
A. An RF carrier
B. An AF carrier
C. A sideband carrier
D. A subcarrier

3AH-3.2 What is another name for an unmodulated radio-frequency signal?
A. An AF carrier
B. An RF carrier
C. A sideband carrier
D. A subcarrier

3AH-4.1 What characteristic makes FM telephony especially well-suited for local VHF/UHF radio communications?
A. Good audio fidelity and intelligibility under weak-signal conditions
B. Better rejection of multipath distortion than the AM modes
C. Good audio fidelity and high signal-to-noise ratio above a certain signal amplitude threshold
D. Better carrier frequency stability than the AM modes

3AH-5.1 What emission is produced by a transmitter using a reactance modulator?
A. CW
B. Unmodulated carrier
C. Single-sideband, suppressed-carrier phone
D. Phase modulated phone

3AH-5.2 What other emission does phase modulation most resemble?
A. Amplitude modulation
B. Pulse modulation
C. Frequency modulation
D. Single-sideband modulation

3AH-6.1 Many communications receivers have several IF filters that can be selected by the operator. Why do these filters have different bandwidths?
A. Because some ham bands are wider than others
B. Because different bandwidths help increase the receiver sensitivity
C. Because different bandwidths improve S-meter readings
D. Because some emission types occupy a wider frequency range than others

3AH-6.2 List the following signals in order of increasing bandwidth (narrowest signal first): CW, FM voice, RTTY, SSB voice.
A. RTTY, CW, SSB voice, FM voice
B. CW, FM voice, RTTY, SSB voice
C. CW, RTTY, SSB voice, FM voice
D. CW, SSB voice, RTTY, FM voice

3AH-7-1.1 To what is the deviation of an FM transmission proportional?
   A. Only the frequency of the audio modulating signal
   B. The frequency and the amplitude of the audio modulating signal
   C. The duty cycle of the audio modulating signal
   D. Only the amplitude of the audio modulating signal

3AH-7-2.1 What is the result of overdeviation in an FM transmitter?
   A. Increased transmitter power consumption
   B. Out-of-channel emissions (splatter)
   C. Increased transmitter range
   D. Inadequate carrier suppression

3AH-7-2.2 What is *splatter*?
   A. Interference to adjacent signals caused by excessive transmitter keying speeds
   B. Interference to adjacent signals caused by improper transmitter neutralization
   C. Interference to adjacent signals caused by overmodulation of a transmitter
   D. Interference to adjacent signals caused by parasitic oscillations at the antenna

SUBELEMENT 3AI—Antennas and Feed Lines
(3 Exam Questions)

3AI-1-1.1 What antenna type best strengthens signals from a particular direction while attenuating those from other directions?
   A. A beam antenna
   B. An isotropic antenna
   C. A monopole antenna
   D. A vertical antenna

3AI-1-1.2 What is a *directional antenna*?
   A. An antenna whose parasitic elements are all constructed to be directors
   B. An antenna that radiates in direct line-of-sight propagation, but not skywave or skip propagation
   C. An antenna permanently mounted so as to radiate in only one direction
   D. An antenna that radiates more strongly in some directions than others

3AI-1-1.3 What is a *Yagi* antenna?
   A. Half-wavelength elements stacked vertically and excited in phase
   B. Quarter-wavelength elements arranged horizontally and excited out of phase
   C. Half-wavelength linear driven element(s) with parasitically excited parallel linear elements
   D. Quarter-wavelength, triangular loop elements

3AI-1-1.4 What is the general configuration of the radiating elements of a horizontally polarized Yagi?
   A. Two or more straight, parallel elements arranged in the same horizontal plane
   B. Vertically stacked square or circular loops arranged in parallel horizontal planes
   C. Two or more wire loops arranged in parallel vertical planes
   D. A vertical radiator arranged in the center of an effective RF ground plane

3AI-1-1.5 What type of parasitic beam antenna uses two or more straight metal-tubing elements arranged physically parallel to each other?
   A. A delta loop antenna
   B. A quad antenna
   C. A Yagi antenna
   D. A Zepp antenna

3AI-1-1.6 How many directly driven elements does a Yagi antenna have?
   A. None; they are all parasitic
   B. One
   C. Two
   D. All elements are directly driven

3AI-1-1.7 What is a *parasitic beam antenna*?
   A. An antenna where the director and reflector elements receive their RF excitation by induction or radiation from the driven element
   B. An antenna where wave traps are used to assure magnetic coupling among the elements
   C. An antenna where all elements are driven by direct connection to the feed line
   D. An antenna where the driven element receives its RF excitation by induction or radiation from the directors

3AI-1-2.1 What is a *cubical quad antenna*?
A. Four parallel metal tubes, each approximately 1/2 electrical wavelength long
B. Two or more parallel four-sided wire loops, each approximately one electrical wavelength long
C. A vertical conductor 1/4 electrical wavelength high, fed at the bottom
D. A center-fed wire 1/2 electrical wavelength long

3AI-1-2.2 What kind of antenna array is composed of a square full-wave closed loop driven element with parallel parasitic element(s)?
A. Delta loop
B. Cubical quad
C. Dual rhombic
D. Stacked Yagi

3AI-1-2.3 Approximately how long is one side of the driven element of a cubical quad antenna?
A. 2 electrical wavelengths
B. 1 electrical wavelength
C. 1/2 electrical wavelength
D. 1/4 electrical wavelength

3AI-1-2.4 Approximately how long is the wire in the driven element of a cubical quad antenna?
A. 1/4 electrical wavelength
B. 1/2 electrical wavelength
C. 1 electrical wavelength
D. 2 electrical wavelengths

3AI-1-3.1 What is a *delta loop antenna*?
A. A variation of the cubical quad antenna, with triangular elements
B. A large copper ring, used in direction finding
C. An antenna system composed of three vertical antennas, arranged in a triangular shape
D. An antenna made from several coils of wire on an insulating form

3AI-2-1.1 To what does the term *horizontal* as applied to wave polarization refer?
A. The magnetic lines of force in the radio wave are parallel to the earth's surface
B. The electric lines of force in the radio wave are parallel to the earth's surface
C. The electric lines of force in the radio wave are perpendicular to the earth's surface
D. The radio wave will leave the antenna and radiate horizontally to the destination

3AI-2-1.2 What electromagnetic wave polarization does a cubical quad antenna have when the feed point is in the center of a horizontal side?
A. Circular
B. Helical
C. Horizontal
D. Vertical

3AI-2-1.3 What electromagnetic wave polarization does a cubical quad antenna have when all sides are at 45 degrees to the earth's surface and the feed point is at the bottom corner?
A. Circular
B. Helical
C. Horizontal
D. Vertical

3AI-2-2.1 What is the polarization of electromagnetic waves radiated from a half-wavelength antenna perpendicular to the earth's surface?
A. Circularly polarized waves
B. Horizontally polarized waves
C. Parabolically polarized waves
D. Vertically polarized waves

3AI-2-2.2 What is the electromagnetic wave polarization of most man-made electrical noise radiation in the HF-VHF spectrum?
A. Horizontal
B. Left-hand circular
C. Right-hand circular
D. Vertical

3AI-2-2.3 To what does the term *vertical* as applied to wave polarization refer?
A. The electric lines of force in the radio wave are parallel to the earth's surface
B. The magnetic lines of force in the radio wave are perpendicular to the earth's surface
C. The electric lines of force in the radio wave are perpendicular to the earth's surface
D. The radio wave will leave the antenna and radiate vertically into the ionosphere

3AI-2-2.4 What electromagnetic wave polarization does a cubical quad antenna have when the feed point is in the center of a vertical side?
A. Circular
B. Helical
C. Horizontal
D. Vertical

3AI-2-2.5 What electromagnetic wave polarization does a cubical quad antenna have when all sides are at 45 degrees to the earth's surface and the feed point is at a side corner?
A. Circular
B. Helical
C. Horizontal
D. Vertical

3AI-3-1.1 What is meant by the term *standing wave ratio*?
A. The ratio of maximum to minimum inductances on a feed line
B. The ratio of maximum to minimum resistances on a feed line
C. The ratio of maximum to minimum impedances on a feed line
D. The ratio of maximum to minimum voltages on a feed line

3AI-3-1.2 What is *standing wave ratio* a measure of?
A. The ratio of maximum to minimum voltage on a feed line
B. The ratio of maximum to minimum reactance on a feed line
C. The ratio of maximum to minimum resistance on a feed line
D. The ratio of maximum to minimum sidebands on a feed line

3AI-3-2.1 What is meant by the term *forward power*?
A. The power traveling from the transmitter to the antenna
B. The power radiated from the front of a directional antenna
C. The power produced during the positive half of the RF cycle
D. The power used to drive a linear amplifier

3AI-3-2.2 What is meant by the term *reflected power*?
- A. The power radiated from the back of a directional antenna
- B. The power returned to the transmitter from the antenna
- C. The power produced during the negative half of the RF cycle
- D. Power reflected to the transmitter site by buildings and trees

3AI-3-3.1 What happens to the power loss in an unbalanced feed line as the standing wave ratio increases?
- A. It is unpredictable
- B. It becomes nonexistent
- C. It decreases
- D. It increases

3AI-3-3.2 What type of feed line is best suited to operating at a high standing wave ratio?
- A. Coaxial cable
- B. Flat ribbon "twin lead"
- C. Parallel open-wire line
- D. Twisted pair

3AI-3-3.3 What happens to RF energy not delivered to the antenna by a lossy coaxial cable?
- A. It is radiated by the feed line
- B. It is returned to the transmitter's chassis ground
- C. Some of it is dissipated as heat in the conductors and dielectric
- D. It is canceled because of the voltage ratio of forward power to reflected power in the feed line

3AI-4-1.1 What is a *balanced line*?
- A. Feed line with one conductor connected to ground
- B. Feed line with both conductors connected to ground to balance out harmonics
- C. Feed line with the outer conductor connected to ground at even intervals
- D. Feed line with neither conductor connected to ground

3AI-4-1.2 What is an *unbalanced line*?
- A. Feed line with neither conductor connected to ground
- B. Feed line with both conductors connected to ground to suppress harmonics
- C. Feed line with one conductor connected to ground
- D. Feed line with the outer conductor connected to ground at uneven intervals

3AI-4-2.1 What is a *balanced antenna*?
- A. A symmetrical antenna with one side of the feed point connected to ground
- B. An antenna (or a driven element in an array) that is symmetrical about the feed point
- C. A symmetrical antenna with both sides of the feed point connected to ground, to balance out harmonics
- D. An antenna designed to be mounted in the center

3AI-4-2.2 What is an *unbalanced antenna*?
- A. An antenna (or a driven element in an array) that is not symmetrical about the feed point
- B. A symmetrical antenna, having neither half connected to ground
- C. An antenna (or a driven element in an array) that is symmetrical about the feed point
- D. A symmetrical antenna with both halves coupled to ground at uneven intervals

3AI-4-3.1 What device can be installed on a balanced antenna so that it can be fed through a coaxial cable?
- A. A balun
- B. A loading coil
- C. A triaxial transformer
- D. A wavetrap

3AI-4-3.2 What is a *balun*?
- A. A device that can be used to convert an antenna designed to be fed at the center so that it may be fed at one end
- B. A device that may be installed on a balanced antenna so that it may be fed with unbalanced feed line
- C. A device that can be installed on an antenna to produce horizontally polarized or vertically polarized waves
- D. A device used to allow an antenna to operate on more than one band

3AI-5-1.1 List the following types of feed line in order of increasing attenuation per 100 feet of line (list the line with the lowest attenuation first): RG-8, RG-58, RG-174 and open-wire line.
- A. RG-174, RG-58, RG-8, open-wire line
- B. RG-8, open-wire line, RG-58, RG-174
- C. open-wire line, RG-8, RG-58, RG-174
- D. open-wire line, RG-174, RG-58, RG-8

3AI-5-1.2 You have installed a tower 150 feet from your radio shack, and have a 6-meter Yagi antenna on top. Which of the following feed lines should you choose to feed this antenna: RG-8, RG-58, RG-59 or RG-174?
- A. RG-8
- B. RG-58
- C. RG-59
- D. RG-174

3AI-5-2.1 You have a 200-foot coil of RG-58 coaxial cable attached to your antenna, but the antenna is only 50 feet from your radio. To minimize feed-line loss, what should you do with the excess cable?
- A. Cut off the excess cable to an even number of wavelengths long
- B. Cut off the excess cable to an odd number of wavelengths long
- C. Cut off the excess cable
- D. Roll the excess cable into a coil a tenth of a wavelength in diameter

3AI-5-2.2 How does feed-line length affect signal loss?
- A. The length has no effect on signal loss
- B. As length increases, signal loss increases
- C. As length decreases, signal loss increases
- D. The length is inversely proportional to signal loss

3AI-5-3.1 What is the general relationship between frequencies passing through a feed line and the losses in the feed line?
A. Loss is independent of frequency
B. Loss increases with increasing frequency
C. Loss decreases with increasing frequency
D. There is no predictable relationship

3AI-5-3.2 As the operating frequency decreases, what happens to conductor losses in a feed line?
A. The losses decrease
B. The losses increase
C. The losses remain the same
D. The losses become infinite

3AI-5-3.3 As the operating frequency increases, what happens to conductor losses in a feed line?
A. The losses decrease
B. The losses increase
C. The losses remain the same
D. The losses decrease to zero

3AI-6-1.1 You are using open-wire feed line in your amateur station. Why should you ensure that no one can come in contact with the feed line while you are transmitting?
A. Because contact with the feed line while transmitting will cause a short circuit, probably damaging your transmitter
B. Because the wire is so small they may break it
C. Because contact with the feed line while transmitting will cause parasitic radiation
D. Because high RF voltages can be present on open-wire feed line

3AI-6-2.1 How can you minimize exposure to radio frequency energy from your transmitting antennas?
A. Use vertical polarization
B. Use horizontal polarization
C. Mount the antennas where no one can come near them
D. Mount the antenna close to the ground

─── ELEMENT 3A ANSWER KEY ───

SUBELEMENT 3AA

Numbers in this section refer to pages in *Now You're Talking!*

3AA-1.1	A	2-19
3AA-1.2	B	2-19
3AA-2.1		(withdrawn)
3AA-2.2	C	2-20
3AA-2.3	B	2-20
3AA-2.4	A	2-20
3AA-2.5	B	2-20
3AA-3.1	A	2-20
3AA-3.2	A	2-20
3AA-3.3	A	2-20
3AA-4.1	B	2-19
3AA-4.2	A	2-20
3AA-4.3	A	2-25
3AA-5.1	D	2-21
3AA-5.2	C	2-21
3AA-6-1.1	C	2-20
3AA-6-1.2	D	2-20
3AA-6-2.1	C	2-20
3AA-6-3.1	D	2-20
3AA-6-4.1	B	2-20
3AA-7-1.1	C	2-20
3AA-7-1.2	B	2-20
3AA-7-1.3	D	2-20
3AA-7-2.1	C	2-20
3AA-7-2.2	C	2-20
3AA-7-3.1	A	2-20
3AA-7-3.2	D	2-20
3AA-7-3.3	D	2-20
3AA-8-1.1	B	2-24
3AA-8-2.1	B	2-24
3AA-8-3.1	C	2-24
3AA-9-1.1	A	2-22
3AA-9-2.1	A	2-22
3AA-10.1	A	2-22
3AA-10.2	C	2-22
3AA-10.3	D	2-22
3AA-10.4	B	2-22
3AA-11-1.1	A	2-21
3AA-11-1.2	B	2-21
3AA-11-1.3	A	2-21
3AA-11-2.1	D	2-21
3AA-11-2.2	A	2-21
3AA-11-2.3	C	2-21
3AA-11-2.4	A	2-21
3AA-12.1	A	2-23
3AA-12.2	C	2-24
3AA-12.3	B	2-24
3AA-12.4	D	2-24
3AA-12.5	C	2-24
3AA-13.1	B	2-22
3AA-13.2	D	2-22

3AA-13.3	D	2-22
3AA-13.4	C	2-22
3AA-14.1	D	2-23
3AA-14.2	C	2-23
3AA-14.3	D	2-24
3AA-15.1	A	2-24
3AA-15.2	C	2-24
3AA-15.3	D	2-24
3AA-15.4	B	2-24
3AA-16.1	B	2-24
3AA-16.2	D	2-24
3AA-16.3	C	2-24
3AA-17.1	A	2-21

SUBELEMENT 3AB

3AB-1.1	A	9-14
3AB-1.2	C	9-14
3AB-1.3	D	9-14
3AB-2-1.1	B	9-19
3AB-2-1.2	C	9-19
3AB-2-1.3	A	9-19
3AB-2-1.4	D	9-19
3AB-2-1.5	B	9-18
3AB-2-1.6	B	9-19
3AB-2-1.7	D	9-19
3AB-2-2.1	C	9-19
3AB-2-2.2	C	2-24
3AB-2-3.1	D	9-18
3AB-2-3.2	B	9-18
3AB-2-3.3	A	9-18
3AB-2-3.4	C	9-18
3AB-2-4.1	D	2-21
3AB-3.1	A	2-24
3AB-3.2	B	9-12
3AB-3.3	C	9-9
3AB-4.1	A	2-21
3AB-4.2	D	2-21
3AB-5-1.1	C	2-22
3AB-5-1.2	B	2-22
3AB-5-2.1	D	2-22
3AB-6-1.1	A	2-22
3AB-6-1.2	B	2-22
3AB-6-2.1	D	2-22
3AB-6-3.1	B	2-22
3AB-6-3.2	C	2-22

SUBELEMENT 3AC

3AC-1-1.1	A	9-3
3AC-1-1.2	D	9-3
3AC-1-1.3	C	9-41
3AC-1-2.1	A	9-41
3AC-1-2.2	B	9-41
3AC-1-3.1	B	9-41
3AC-1-4.1	D	9-42

3AC-1-4.2	B	9-42
3AC-1-4.3	C	9-42
3AC-2.1	D	9-41
3AC-2.2	B	9-41
3AC-2.3	A	9-41
3AC-2.4	B	9-41
3AC-3.1	D	9-42
3AC-3.2	C	9-42
3AC-3.3	A	9-42
3AC-3.4	B	9-42
3AC-4.1	D	9-44
3AC-4.2	C	9-44
3AC-4.3	A	9-44
3AC-5.1	C	9-45
3AC-5.2	C	9-45
3AC-6.1	A	9-46
3AC-6.2	B	9-46
3AC-7.1	C	9-46
3AC-7.2	A	9-46
3AC-7.3	D	9-46
3AC-7.4	A	9-46
3AC-7.5	B	9-46
3AC-7.6	D	9-46

SUBELEMENT 3AD

3AD-1-1.1	C	8-13
3AD-1-1.2	D	8-13
3AD-1-1.3	B	8-13
3AD-1-1.4	B	8-13
3AD-1-2.1	A	8-14
3AD-1-2.2	A	8-14
3AD-1-2.3	A	8-14
3AD-1-3.1	C	8-14
3AD-2-1.1	B	8-15
3AD-2-2.1	C	8-15
3AD-3-1.1	A	8-15
3AD-3-2.1	D	8-15
3AD-4.1	D	8-16
3AD-5-1.1	A	8-16
3AD-5-1.2	C	8-16
3AD-5-1.3	B	8-16
3AD-5-1.4	A	8-16
3AD-5-2.1	B	8-16
3AD-5-2.2	C	8-16
3AD-6.1	A	8-17
3AD-6.2	D	8-17
3AD-6.3	A	8-17
3AD-7.1	C	8-17
3AD-7.2	B	8-17
3AD-8-1.1	D	8-17
3AD-8-1.2	D	8-17
3AD-8-2.1	A	8-17
3AD-8-2.2	C	8-17
3AD-9.1	D	8-18

3AD-9.2	B	8-18
3AD-9.3	C	8-18
3AD-9.4	B	8-18
3AD-9.5	A	8-18
3AD-9.6	A	8-18
3AD-10.1	C	8-18
3AD-10.2	A	8-18
3AD-11-1.1	B	8-18
3AD-11-1.2	A	8-18
3AD-11-2.1	D	8-19
3AD-11-2.2	B	8-19
3AD-11-2.3	B	8-19
3AD-11-2.4	D	8-19
3AD-11-2.5	B	8-19
3AD-11-3.1	C	8-19

SUBELEMENT 3AE

3AE-1-1.1	D	3-6
3AE-1-2.1	A	3-6
3AE-1-2.2	D	3-6
3AE-1-3.1	B	3-9
3AE-1-3.2	D	3-9
3AE-1-4.1	B	3-9
3AE-1-4.2	C	3-9
3AE-2.1	D	3-8
3AE-2.2	A	3-8
3AE-2.3	C	3-8
3AE-2.4	D	3-10
3AE-2.5	B	3-8
3AE-2.6	D	3-8
3AE-2.7	D	3-8
3AE-2.8	A	3-8
3AE-2.9	A	3-8
3AE-3-1.1	C	3-15
3AE-3-2.1	C	3-16
3AE-3-2.2	C	3-16
3AE-3-2.3	B	3-16
3AE-3-2.4	C	3-16
3AE-3-3.1	B	3-16
3AE-3-3.2	C	3-16
3AE-3-4.1	A	3-16
3AE-3-4.2	B	3-16
3AE-4-1.1	A	3-16
3AE-4-2.1	A	3-16
3AE-4-2.2	B	3-16
3AE-4-2.3	A	3-16
3AE-4-2.4	B	3-16
3AE-4-3.1	C	3-17
3AE-4-3.2	B	3-17
3AE-4-4.1	A	3-17
3AE-4-4.2	A	3-17

SUBELEMENT 3AF

3AF-1-1.1	B	4-7
3AF-1-2.1	D	4-7
3AF-1-2.2	C	4-9
3AF-1-3.1	A	4-9
3AF-1-3.2	B	4-9

3AF-1-3.3	B	4-10
3AF-1-3.4	C	4-9
3AF-1-4.1	A	4-10
3AF-1-4.2	C	4-10
3AF-1-5.1	B	4-2
3AF-1-5.2	C	4-2
3AF-2-1.1	D	4-10
3AF-2-1.2	A	4-10
3AF-2-1.3	D	4-10
3AF-2-1.4	C	4-11
3AF-2-2.1	D	4-10
3AF-2-2.2	C	4-10
3AF-2-3.1	D	4-10
3AF-2-3.2	B	4-10
3AF-2-3.3	A	4-10
3AF-2-3.4	B	4-10
3AF-2-4.1	A	4-11
3AF-2-4.2	B	4-11
3AF-2-4.3	C	4-11
3AF-3-1.1	D	4-12
3AF-3-1.2	A	4-12
3AF-3-1.3	C	4-14
3AF-3-1.4	C	4-13
3AF-3-2.1	B	4-12
3AF-3-2.2	D	4-11
3AF-3-2.3	A	4-12
3AF-3-2.4	B	4-12
3AF-3-3.1	A	4-12
3AF-3-3.2	B	4-12
3AF-3-3.3	D	4-12
3AF-3-4.1	D	4-13
3AF-3-4.2	A	4-14

SUBELEMENT 3AG

3AG-1-1.1	A	5-7
3AG-1-1.2	D	5-7
3AG-1-2.1	C	5-8
3AG-1-2.2	B	5-7
3AG-2-1.1	B	5-8
3AG-2-2.1	A	5-8
3AG-2-2.2	B	5-8
3AG-3-1.1	A	5-8
3AG-3-1.2	D	5-8
3AG-3-2.1	A	5-8
3AG-4-1.1	C	5-11
3AG-4-1.2	D	5-9
3AG-4-1.3	B	5-9
3AG-4-1.4	B	5-12
3AG-4-1.5	D	5-9
3AG-4-2.1	D	5-12
3AG-4-2.2	C	5-10

SUBELEMENT 3AH

3AH-1.1	A	5-9
3AH-2-1.1	A	5-9
3AH-2-1.2	B	9-46
3AH-2-2.1	C	5-9

3AH-2-2.2	A	5-9
3AH-2-3.1	B	9-21
3AH-2-3.2	A	9-21
3AH-2-4.1	B	9-41
3AH-2-4.2	D	9-41
3AH-2-5.1	A	9-41
3AH-2-5.2	B	9-41
3AH-2-5.3	C	9-41
3AH-2-6.1	A	9-41
3AH-2-6.2	B	9-41
3AH-2-7.1	D	9-41
3AH-2-7.2	B	9-41
3AH-2-8.1	C	8-18
3AH-2-8.2	D	9-41
3AH-3.1	A	9-41
3AH-3.2	B	9-41
3AH-4.1	C	9-41
3AH-5.1	D	5-10
3AH-5.2	C	5-9
3AH-6.1	D	9-47
3AH-6.2	C	9-47
3AH-7-1.1	D	9-47
3AH-7-2.1	B	9-47
3AH-7-2.2	C	9-47

SUBELEMENT 3AI

3AI-1-1.1	A	7-19
3AI-1-1.2	D	7-19
3AI-1-1.3	C	7-19
3AI-1-1.4	A	7-24
3AI-1-1.5	C	7-19
3AI-1-1.6	B	7-19
3AI-1-1.7	A	7-25
3AI-1-2.1	B	7-27
3AI-1-2.2	B	7-27
3AI-1-2.3	D	7-27
3AI-1-2.4	C	7-27
3AI-1-3.1	A	7-28
3AI-2-1.1	B	7-24
3AI-2-1.2	C	7-27
3AI-2-1.3	C	7-27
3AI-2-2.1	D	7-25
3AI-2-2.2	D	7-25
3AI-2-2.3	C	7-24
3AI-2-2.4	D	7-27
3AI-2-2.5	D	7-27
3AI-3-1.1	D	7-5
3AI-3-1.2	A	7-5
3AI-3-2.1	A	7-6
3AI-3-2.2	B	7-6
3AI-3-3.1	D	7-23
3AI-3-3.2	C	7-23
3AI-3-3.3	C	7-23
3AI-4-1.1	D	7-5
3AI-4-1.2	C	7-5
3AI-4-2.1	B	7-5
3AI-4-2.2	A	7-5
3AI-4-3.1	A	7-5

3AI-4-3.2	B	7-5
3AI-5-1.1	C	7-24
3AI-5-1.2	A	7-24

3AI-5-2.1	C	7-24
3AI-5-2.2	B	7-24
3AI-5-3.1	B	7-24
3AI-5-3.2	A	7-24

3AI-5-3.3	B	7-24
3AI-6-1.1	D	7-10
3AI-6-2.1	C	7-21

Helpful Data Tables

Standard Resistance Values

Numbers in **bold** type are ±10% values. Others are 5% values.

Ohms

1.0	3.6	**12**	43	**150**	510	**1800**	6200	**22000**	75000
1.1	**3.9**	13	47	160	**560**	2000	**6800**	24000	**82000**
1.2	4.3	**15**	51	**180**	620	**2200**	7500	**27000**	91000
1.3	**4.7**	16	**56**	200	**680**	2400	**8200**	30000	**100000**
1.5	5.1	**18**	62	**220**	750	**2700**	9100	**33000**	110000
1.6	**5.6**	20	**68**	240	**820**	3000	**10000**	36000	**120000**
1.8	6.2	**22**	75	**270**	910	**3300**	11000	**39000**	130000
2.0	**6.8**	24	**82**	300	**1000**	3600	**12000**	43000	**150000**
2.2	7.5	**27**	91	**330**	1100	**3900**	13000	**47000**	160000
2.4	**8.2**	30	**100**	360	**1200**	4300	**15000**	51000	**180000**
2.7	9.1	**33**	110	**390**	1300	**4700**	16000	**56000**	200000
3.0	**10.0**	36	**120**	430	**1500**	5100	**18000**	62000	**220000**
3.3	11.0	**39**	130	**470**	1600	**5600**	20000	**68000**	

Megohms

0.24	**0.62**	1.6	4.3	11.0
0.27	**0.68**	1.8	4.7	12.0
0.30	0.75	2.0	5.1	13.0
0.33	**0.82**	2.2	5.6	15.0
0.36	0.91	2.4	6.2	16.0
0.39	**1.0**	2.7	6.8	18.0
0.43	1.1	3.0	7.5	20.0
0.47	**1.2**	3.3	8.2	22.0
0.51	1.3	3.6	9.1	
0.56	1.5	3.9	10.0	

Resistor Color Code

Color	Sig. Figure	Decimal Multiplier	Tolerance (%)	Color	Sig. Figure	Decimal Multiplier	Tolerance (%)
Black	0	1		Violet	7	10,000,000	
Brown	1	10		Gray	8	100,000,000	
Red	2	100		White	9	1,000,000,000	
Orange	3	1,000		Gold	—	0.1	5
Yellow	4	10,000		Silver	—	0.01	10
Green	5	100,000		No color	—		20
Blue	6	1,000,000					

Standard Values for 1000-V Disc-Ceramic Capacitors

pF	pF	pF	pF
3.3	39	250	1000
5	47	270	1200
6	50	300	1500
6.8	51	330	1800
8	56	360	2000
10	68	390	2500
12	75	400	2700
15	82	470	3000
18	100	500	3300
20	120	510	3900
22	130	560	4700
24	150	600	5000
25	180	680	5600
27	200	750	6800
30	220	820	8200
33	240	910	10000

Common Values for Small Electrolytic Capacitors

μF	V*	μF	V*
33	6.3	10	35
33	10	22	35
100	10	33	35
220	10	47	35
330	10	100	35
470	10	220	35
10	16	330	35
22	16	470	35
33	16	1000	35
47	16	1	50
100	16	2.2	50
220	16	3.3	50
470	16	4.7	50
1000	16	10	50
2200	16	33	50
4.7	25	47	50
22	25	100	50
33	25	220	50
47	25	330	50
100	25	470	50
220	25	10	63
330	25	22	63
470	25	47	63
1000	25	1	100
2200	25	10	100
4.7	35	33	100

*Working voltage

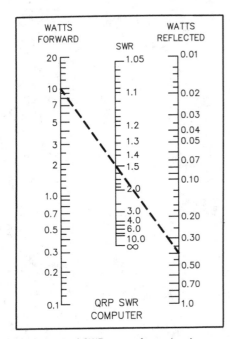

Nomograph of SWR versus forward and reflected power for levels up to 20 watts. Dashed line shows an SWR of 1.5:1 for 10 W forward and 0.4 W reflected.

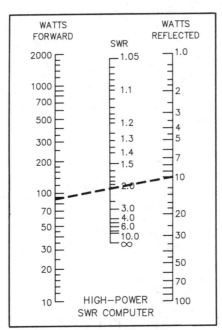

Nomograph of SWR versus forward and reflected power for levels up to 2000 watts. Dashed line shows an SWR of 2:1 for 90 W forward and 10 W reflected.

Fractions of an Inch with Metric Equivalents

Fractions Of An Inch		Decimals Of An Inch	Millimeters	Fractions Of An Inch		Decimals Of An Inch	Millimeters
	1/64	0.0156	0.397		33/64	0.5156	13.097
1/32		0.0313	0.794	17/32		0.5313	13.494
	3/64	0.0469	1.191		35/64	0.5469	13.891
1/16		0.0625	1.588	9/16		0.5625	14.288
	5/64	0.0781	1.984		37/64	0.5781	14.684
3/32		0.0938	2.381	19/32		0.5938	15.081
	7/64	0.1094	2.778		39/64	0.6094	15.478
1/8		0.1250	3.175	5/8		0.6250	15.875
	9/64	0.1406	3.572		41/64	0.6406	16.272
5/32		0.1563	3.969	21/32		0.6563	16.669
	11/64	0.1719	4.366		43/64	0.6719	17.066
3/16		0.1875	4.763	11/16		0.6875	17.463
	13/64	0.2031	5.159		45/64	0.7031	17.859
7/32		0.2188	5.556	23/32		0.7188	18.256
	15/64	0.2344	5.953		47/64	0.7344	18.653
1/4		0.2500	6.350	3/4		0.7500	19.050
	17/64	0.2656	6.747		49/64	0.7656	19.447
9/32		0.2813	7.144	25/32		0.7813	19.844
	19/64	0.2969	7.541		51/64	0.7969	20.241
5/16		0.3125	7.938	13/16		0.8125	20.638
	21/64	0.3281	8.334		53/64	0.8281	21.034
11/32		0.3438	8.731	27/32		0.8438	21.431
	23/64	0.3594	9.128		55/64	0.8594	21.828
3/8		0.3750	9.525	7/8		0.8750	22.225
	25/64	0.3906	9.922		57/64	0.8906	22.622
13/32		0.4063	10.319	29/32		0.9063	23.019
	27/64	0.4219	10.716		59/64	0.9219	23.416
7/16		0.4375	11.113	15/16		0.9375	23.813
	29/64	0.4531	11.509		61/64	0.9531	24.209
15/32		0.4688	11.906	31/32		0.9688	24.606
	31/64	0.4844	12.303		63/64	0.9844	25.003
1/2		0.50000	12.700	1		1.0000	25.400

US Customary to Metric Conversions

US Customary—Metric Conversion Factors

International System of Units (SI)—Metric Units

Prefix	Symbol			Multiplication Factor
exa	E	10^{18}	=	1 000 000 000 000 000 000
peta	P	10^{15}	=	1 000 000 000 000 000
tera	T	10^{12}	=	1 000 000 000 000
giga	G	10^{9}	=	1 000 000 000
mega	M	10^{6}	=	1 000 000
kilo	k	10^{3}	=	1 000
hecto	h	10^{2}	=	100
deca	da	10^{1}	=	10
(unit)		10^{0}	=	1
deci	d	10^{-1}	=	0.1
centi	c	10^{-2}	=	0.01
milli	m	10^{-3}	=	0.001
micro	μ	10^{-6}	=	0.000001
nano	n	10^{-9}	=	0.000000001
pico	p	10^{-12}	=	0.000000000001
femto	f	10^{-15}	=	0.000000000000001
atto	a	10^{-18}	=	0.000000000000000001

Linear
1 metre (m) = 100 centimetres (cm) = 1000 millimetres (mm)

Area
$1\ m^2 = 1 \times 10^4\ cm^2 = 1 \times 10^6\ mm^2$

Volume
$1\ m^3 = 1 \times 10^6\ cm^3 = 1 \times 10^9\ mm^3$
$1\ litre\ (l) = 1000\ cm^3 = 1 \times 10^6\ mmm^3$

Mass
1 kilogram (kg) = 1 000 grams (g)
  (Approximately the mass of 1 litre of water)

1 metric ton (or tonne) = 1 000 kg

US Customary Units

Linear Units
12 inches (in) = 1 foot (ft)
36 inches = 3 feet = 1 yard (yd)
1 rod = 5½ yards = 16½ feet
1 statute mile = 1 760 yards = 5 280 feet
1 nautical mile = 6 076.11549 feet

Area
$1\ ft^2 = 144\ in^2$
$1\ yd^2 = 9\ ft^2 = 1\ 296\ in^2$
$1\ rod^2 = 30¼\ yd^2$
$1\ acre = 4840\ yd^2 = 43\ 560\ ft^2$
$1\ acre = 160\ rod^2$
$1\ mile^2 = 640\ acres$

Volume
$1\ ft^3 = 1\ 728\ in^3$
$1\ yd^3 = 27\ ft^3$

Liquid Volume Measure
$1\ fluid\ ounce\ (fl\ oz) = 8\ fluidrams = 1.804\ in^3$
1 pint (pt) = 16 fl oz
$1\ quart\ (qt) = 2\ pt = 32\ fl\ oz = 57¾\ in^3$
$1\ gallon\ (gal) = 4\ qt = 231\ in^3$
1 barrel = 31½ gal

Dry Volume Measure
$1\ quart\ (qt) = 2\ pints\ (pt) = 67.2\ in^3$
1 peck = 8 qt
$1\ bushel = 4\ pecks = 2\ 150.42\ in^3$

Avoirdupois Weight
1 dram (dr) = 27.343 grains (gr) or (gr a)
1 ounce (oz) = 437.5 gr
1 pound (lb) = 16 oz = 7 000 gr
1 short ton = 2 000 lb, 1 long ton = 2 240 lb

Troy Weight
1 grain troy (gr t) = 1 grain avoirdupois
1 pennyweight (dwt) or (pwt) = 24 gr t
1 ounce troy (oz t) = 480 grains
1 lb t = 12 oz t = 5 760 grains

Apothecaries' Weight
1 grain apothecaries' (gr ap) = 1 gr t = 1 gr a
1 dram ap (dr ap) = 60 gr
1 oz ap = 1 oz t = 8 dr ap = 480 gr
1 lb ap = 1 lb t = 12 oz ap = 5 760 gr

Multiply $\longrightarrow$

Metric Unit = Conversion Factor × US Customary Unit

$\longleftarrow$ **Divide**

Metric Unit ÷ Conversion Factor = US Customary Unit

Metric Unit	Conversion Factor × US Unit	
(Length)		
mm	25.4	inch
cm	2.54	inch
cm	30.48	foot
m	0.3048	foot
m	0.9144	yard
km	1.609	mile
km	1.852	nautical mile
(Area)		
mm²	645.16	inch²
cm²	6.4516	in²
cm²	929.03	ft²
m²	0.0929	ft²
cm²	8361.3	yd²
m²	0.83613	yd²
m²	4047	acre
km²	2.59	mi²
(Mass)	(Avoirdupois Weight)	
grams	0.0648	grains
g	28.349	oz
g	453.59	lb
kg	0.45359	lb
tonne	0.907	short ton
tonne	1.016	long ton

Metric Unit	Conversion Factor × US Unit	
(Volume)		
mm³	16387.064	in³
cm³	16.387	in³
m³	0.028316	ft³
m³	0.764555	yd³
ml	16.387	in³
ml	29.57	fl oz
ml	473	pint
ml	946.333	quart
l	28.32	ft³
l	0.9463	quart
l	3.785	gallon
l	1.101	dry quart
l	8.809	peck
l	35.238	bushel
(Mass)	(Troy Weight)	
g	31.103	oz t
g	373.248	lb t
(Mass)	(Apothecaries' Weight)	
g	3.387	dr ap
g	31.103	oz ap
g	373.248	lb ap

US Amateur Frequency and Mode Allocations

160 METERS

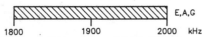

E,A,G

1800   1900   2000   kHz

Amateur stations operating at 1900–2000 kHz must not cause harmful interference to the radiolocation service and are afforded no protection from radiolocation operations.

80 METERS

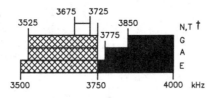

3675   3725
3525   3775   3850

N,T †
G
A
E

3500   3750   4000   kHz

5167.5 kHz (SSB only): Alaska emergency use only.

40 METERS

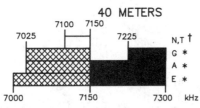

7100   7150
7025   7225

N,T †
G *
A *
E *

7000   7150   7300   kHz

* Phone operation is allowed on 7075–7100 kHz in Puerto Rico, US Virgin Islands and areas of the Caribbean south of 20 degrees north latitude; and in Hawaii and areas near ITU Region 3, including Alaska.

30 METERS

E,A,G

10,100   10,150   kHz

Maximum power on 30 meters is 200 watts PEP output. Amateurs must avoid interference to the fixed service outside the US.

20 METERS

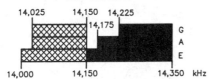

14,025   14,150   14,225
          14,175

G
A
E

14,000   14,150   14,350   kHz

17 METERS

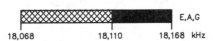

E,A,G

18,068   18,110   18,168   kHz

15 METERS

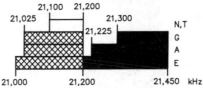

21,100   21,200
21,025   21,300
       21,225

N,T
N
G
A
E

21,000   21,200   21,450   kHz

12 METERS

E,A,G

24,890   24,930   24,990   kHz

10 METERS

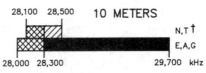

28,100   28,500

N,T †
E,A,G

28,000   28,300   29,700   kHz

Novices and Technicians are limited to 200 watts PEP output on 10 meters.

6 METERS

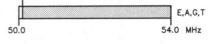

50.1

E,A,G,T

50.0   54.0   MHz

2 METERS

144.1

E,A,G,T

144.0   148.0   MHz

1.25 METERS

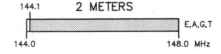

222.1   223.91

N
E,A,G,T

222.0   225.0   MHz

Novices are limited to 25 watts PEP output from 222.1 to 223.91 MHz.

70 CENTIMETERS **

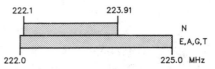

E,A,G,T

420.0   450.0   MHz

33 CENTIMETERS **

E,A,G,T

902.0   928.0   MHz

23 CENTIMETERS **

1270   1295

N
E,A,G,T

1240   1300   MHz

Novices are limited to 5 watts PEP output from 1270 to 1295 MHz.

US AMATEUR BANDS

Revised Sept 1, 1991

US AMATEUR POWER LIMITS

At all times, transmitter power should be kept down to that necessary to carry out the desired communications. Power is rated in watts PEP output. Unless otherwise stated, the maximum power output is 1500 W. Power for all license classes is limited to 200 W in the 10,100–10,150 kHz band and in all Novice subbands below 28,100 kHz. Novices and Technicians are restricted to 200 W in the 28,100–28,500 kHz subbands. In addition, Novices are restricted to 25 W in the 222.1–223.91 MHz subband and 5 W in the 1270–1295 MHz subband.

Operators with Technician class licenses and above may operate on all bands above 50 MHz. For more detailed information see The FCC Rule Book.

KEY

▨	= CW, RTTY and data
▤	= CW, RTTY, data, MCW, test, phone and image
■	= CW, phone and image
▨	= CW and SSB
▨	= CW, RTTY, data, phone, and image
☐	= CW only

E = AMATEUR EXTRA
A = ADVANCED
G = GENERAL
T = TECHNICIAN
N = NOVICE

† Only Technician–class licensees who have passed a 5 – WPM code test may use these frequencies.

** Geographical and power restrictions apply to these bands. See The FCC Rule Book for more information about your area.

Above 23 Centimeters:

All licensees except Novices are authorized all modes on the following frequencies:
2300–2310 MHz
2390–2450 MHz
3300–3500 MHz
5650–5925 MHz
10.0–10.5 GHz
24.0–24.25 GHz
47.0–47.2 GHz
75.5–81.0 GHz
119.98–120.2 GHz
142–149 GHz
241–250 GHz
All above 300 GHz

For band plans and sharing arrangements, see *The ARRL Operating Manual.*

Schematic Symbols

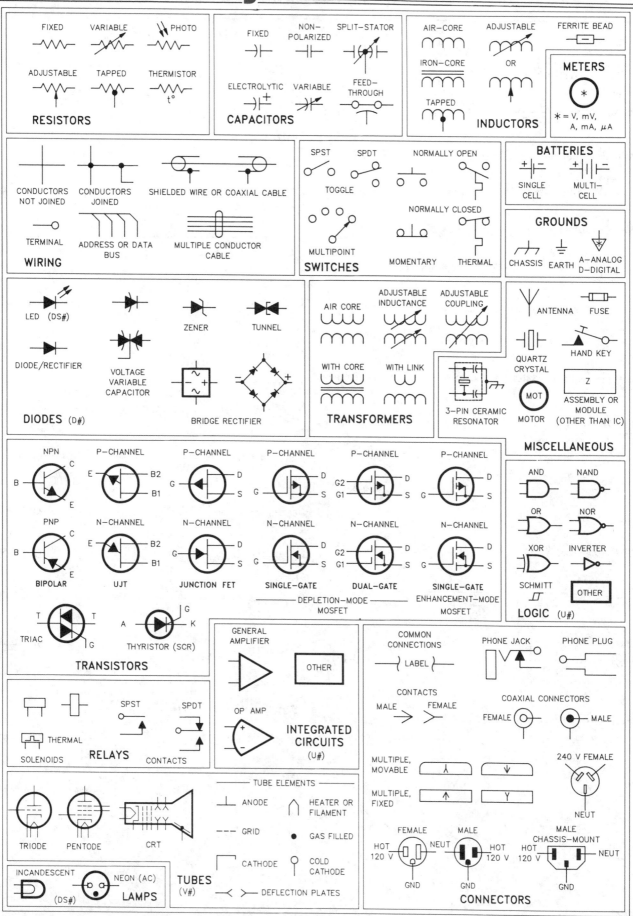

Equations Used in This Book

$$\text{current} = \frac{\text{voltage}}{\text{resistance}} \qquad \text{(Eq 3-1)}$$

$$\text{resistance} = \frac{\text{voltage}}{\text{current}} \qquad \text{(Eq 3-2)}$$

$$\text{voltage} = \text{current} \times \text{resistance} \qquad \text{(Eq 3-3)}$$

$$E = IR \ (\text{volts} = \text{amperes} \times \text{ohms}) \qquad \text{(Eq 3-4)}$$

$$I = \frac{E}{R} \ (\text{amperes} = \text{volts divided by ohms}) \qquad \text{(Eq 3-5)}$$

$$R = \frac{E}{I} \ (\text{ohms} = \text{volts divided by amperes}) \qquad \text{(Eq 3-6)}$$

$$P = IE \ (\text{watts} = \text{amperes} \times \text{volts}) \qquad \text{(Eq 3-7)}$$

$$I = \frac{P}{E} \ (\text{amperes} = \text{watts divided by volts}) \qquad \text{(Eq 3-8)}$$

$$E = \frac{P}{I} \ (\text{volts} = \text{watts divided by amperes}) \qquad \text{(Eq 3-9)}$$

$$c = f\lambda \qquad \text{(Eq 3-10)}$$

$$f = \frac{c}{\lambda} \qquad \text{(Eq 3-11)}$$

$$\lambda = \frac{c}{f} \qquad \text{(Eq 3-12)}$$

$$R_{TOTAL} = R_1 + R_2 + R_3 + \ldots + R_n \qquad \text{(Eq 3-13)}$$

$$R_{TOTAL} = \frac{1}{\dfrac{1}{R_1} + \dfrac{1}{R_2} + \dfrac{1}{R_3} + \ldots + \dfrac{1}{R_n}} \qquad \text{(Eq 3-14)}$$

$$R_{TOTAL} = \frac{R_1 \times R_2}{R_1 + R_2} \qquad \text{(Eq 3-15)}$$

$$L_{TOTAL} = L_1 + L_2 + L_3 + \ldots + L_n \qquad \text{(Eq 3-16)}$$

$$L_{TOTAL} = \frac{1}{\dfrac{1}{L_1} + \dfrac{1}{L_2} + \dfrac{1}{L_3} + \ldots + \dfrac{1}{L_n}} \qquad \text{(Eq 3-17)}$$

$$L_{TOTAL} = \frac{L_1 \times L_2}{L_1 + L_2} \qquad \text{(Eq 3-18)}$$

$$C_{TOTAL} = C_1 + C_2 + C_3 + \ldots + C_n \qquad \text{(Eq 3-19)}$$

$$C_{TOTAL} = \frac{1}{\dfrac{1}{C_1} + \dfrac{1}{C_2} + \dfrac{1}{C_3} + \ldots + \dfrac{1}{C_n}} \qquad \text{(Eq 3-20)}$$

$$C_{TOTAL} = \frac{C_1 \times C_2}{C_1 + C_2} \qquad \text{(Eq 3-21)}$$

$$\lambda \ (\text{in feet}) = \frac{984}{f \ (\text{in MHz})} \qquad \text{(Eq 7-1)}$$

$$\text{Length (in feet)} = \frac{468}{f \ (\text{in MHz})} \qquad \text{(Eq 7-2)}$$

$$\text{Length (in feet)} = \frac{234}{f \ (\text{in MHz})} \qquad \text{(Eq 7-3)}$$

$$L_{director} = L_{driven} \times 0.95 \qquad \text{(Eq 7-4)}$$

$$L_{reflector} = L_{driven} \times 1.05 \qquad \text{(Eq 7-5)}$$

$$C_{driven\ element} \ (\text{ft}) = \frac{1005}{f(\text{MHz})} \qquad \text{(Eq 7-6)}$$

$$C_{director} \ (\text{ft}) = \frac{975}{f(\text{MHz})} \qquad \text{(Eq 7-7)}$$

$$C_{reflector} \ (\text{ft}) = \frac{1030}{f(\text{MHz})} \qquad \text{(Eq 7-8)}$$

$$Bw = 2 \times (D + M) \qquad \text{(Eq 9-1)}$$

Glossary of Key Words

AC power-line filter—A filter connected in the power line to an amateur transmitter or transceiver. It keeps RF energy from entering the power line and radiating from power lines near a house. A line filter in the power line to other electronic devices will keep unwanted RF energy from entering them as well.

Alternating current (ac)—Electrical current that flows first in one direction in a wire and then in the other. The applied voltage is also changing polarity. This direction reversal continues at a rate that depends on the frequency of the ac.

Alternator—A machine used to generate alternating-current electricity.

Amateur operator—A person holding a written authorization to be the control operator of an amateur station.

Amateur service—A radiocommunication service for the purpose of self-training, intercommunication and technical investigations carried out by amateurs, that is, duly authorized persons interested in radio technique solely with a personal aim and without pecuniary interest. (*Pecuniary* means payment of any type, whether money or other goods.)

Amateur station—A station licensed in the amateur service, including necessary equipment, used for amateur communication.

Ampere (A)—The basic unit of electrical current, equal to 6.24×10^{18} electrons moving past a point in one second.[1] We abbreviate amperes as *amps*.

Amplifier—A device usually employing electron tubes or transistors to increase the voltage, current or power of a signal. The amplifying device may use a small signal to control voltage and/or current from an external supply. A larger replica of the small input signal appears at the device output.

Amplitude modulation (AM)—A method of combining an information signal and an RF (radio-frequency) carrier. In double-sideband voice AM transmission, we use the voice information to vary (modulate) the amplitude of an RF carrier. Shortwave broadcast stations use this type of AM, as do stations in the Standard Broadcast Band (540-1600 kHz). Few amateurs use double-sideband voice AM, but a variation, known as *single sideband*, is very popular.

AMTOR (Amateur Teleprinting Over Radio)—A form of **radioteletype** that provides error-detecting capabilities. See **Automatic Repeat Request, Forward Error Correction** and **Selective-call identifier**.

Antenna—A device that picks up or sends out radio waves.

Antenna switch—A switch used to connect one transmitter, receiver or transceiver to several different antennas.

ASCII (American National Standard Code for Information Interchange)—A seven-bit digital code used in computer and radioteleprinter applications.

Atom—A basic building block of all matter. Inside an atom there is a positively charged, dense, central core surrounded by a "cloud" of negatively charged electrons. There are the same number of negative charges as there are positive charges, so the atom is electrically neutral.

Attenuate—To reduce in amplitude.

Audio frequency (AF)—The range of frequencies that the human ear can detect. Audio frequencies are usually listed as 20 Hz to 20,000 Hz.

Audio-frequency shift keying (AFSK)—A method of transmitting radioteletype information. Two switched audio tones are fed into the microphone input. AFSK RTTY is most often used on VHF.

Automatic Repeat reQuest (ARQ)—An AMTOR communication mode. In ARQ, also called Mode A, the two stations constantly confirm each other's transmissions. If information is lost, it is repeated until the receiving station confirms correct reception.

Autopatch—A device that allows repeater users to make telephone calls through a repeater.

A1A emission—The FCC emission designator used to describe Morse code telegraphy (CW) by on/off keying of a radio-frequency signal.

Backscatter—A small amount of signal that is reflected from the Earth's surface after travelling through the ionosphere. The reflected signal may go back into the ionosphere along several paths and be refracted to Earth again. Backscatter can help provide communications into a station's **skip zone**.

Balun—Contraction for *bal*anced to *un*balanced. A device to couple a balanced load to an unbalanced source, or vice versa.

Band-pass filter—A circuit that allows signals to go through it only if they are within a certain range of frequencies. It attenuates signals above and below this range.

Band spread—A receiver quality used to describe how far apart stations on different nearby frequencies will seem to be. We usually express band spread as the number of kilohertz that the frequency changes per tuning-knob rotation. Band spread and frequency **resolution** are related. The amount of band spread determines how easily signals can be tuned.

Bandwidth—The range of frequencies that will pass through a given filter. For a signal, bandwidth is the width of the frequency band outside of which the mean power of the total emission is attenuated at least 26 dB below the mean power of the total emission, including allowances for transmitter drift or Doppler shift.

Battery—A device that stores electrical energy. It provides excess electrons to produce a current and the voltage or EMF to push those electrons through a circuit.

Baud—The unit used to describe the transmission speed of a digital signal. For a single-channel signal, one baud is equal to one digital bit per second.

Baudot—A five-bit digital code used in teleprinter applications.

---

[1]Numbers written as a multiple of some power are expressed in *exponential notation*. This notation is explained in detail on page 3-2.

Beacon station—An amateur station transmitting communications for the purposes of observation of propagation and reception of other related experimental activities.

Beam antenna—A directional antenna. A beam antenna must be rotated to provide coverage in different directions.

Beat-frequency oscillator (BFO)—An oscillator that provides a signal to the product detector. In the product detector, the BFO signal and the IF signal are mixed to produce an audio signal.

Bleeder resistor—A large resistor connected across the output of a power supply. The bleeder discharges the filter capacitors when the supply is turned off.

Block diagram—A drawing using boxes to represent sections of a complicated device or process. The block diagram shows the connections between sections.

Breakdown voltage—The voltage that will cause a current in an insulator. Different insulating materials have different breakdown voltages. Breakdown voltage is also related to the thickness of the insulating material.

Broadcasting—Transmissions intended to be received by the general public, either direct or relayed.

Calling frequencies—Frequencies set aside for establishing contact. Once two stations are in contact, they should move their QSO to an unoccupied frequency.

Capacitor—An electronic component composed of two or more conductive plates separated by an insulating material.

Carbon-composition resistor—An electronic component designed to limit current in a circuit; made from ground carbon mixed with clay.

Carbon-film resistor—A resistor made by depositing a gaseous carbon deposit on a round ceramic form.

Ceramic capacitor—An electronic component composed of two or more conductive plates separated by a ceramic insulating material.

Centi—The metric prefix for 10^{-2}, or divide by 100.

Characteristic impedance—The opposition to electric current that an antenna feed line presents. Impedance includes factors other than resistance, and applies to alternating currents. Ideally, the characteristic impedance of a feed line is the same as the transmitter output impedance and the antenna input impedance.

Chassis ground—The common connection for all parts of a circuit that connect to the negative side of the power supply.

Chirp—A slight shift in transmitter frequency each time you key the transmitter.

Coaxial cable—coax (pronounced ko′-aks). A type of feed line with one conductor inside the other.

Color code—A system in which numerical values are assigned to various colors. Colored stripes are painted on the body of resistors and sometimes other components to show their value.

Communications terminal—A computer-controlled device that demodulates RTTY and CW for display by a computer or ASCII terminal. The communications terminal also accepts information from a computer or terminal and modulates a transmitted signal.

Computer-Based Message System (CBMS)—A system in which a computer is used to store messages for later retrieval. Also called a RTTY mailbox.

Conductor—A material that has a loose grip on its electrons, so that an electrical current can pass through it.

Connected—The condition in which two packet-radio stations are sending information to each other. Each is acknowledging when the data has been received correctly.

Contests—On-the-air operating events. Different contests have different objectives: contacting as many other amateurs as possible in a given amount of time, contacting amateurs in as many different countries as possible or contacting an amateur in each county in one particular state, to name only a few.

Continuous wave (CW)—Morse code telegraphy.

Control operator—An amateur operator designated by the licensee of a station to be responsible for the transmissions of an amateur station.

Control point—The place where the control function takes place.

Coordinated Universal Time (UTC)—A system of time referenced to time at the prime meridian, which passes through Greenwich, England.

Core—The material used in the center of an inductor coil.

CQ—The general call when requesting a conversation with anyone.

Critical angle—If radio waves leave an antenna at an angle greater than the critical angle for that frequency, they pass through the ionosphere instead of returning to earth.

Critical frequency—The highest frequency at which a vertically incident radio wave returns from the ionosphere. Above the critical frequency, radio waves pass through the ionosphere into space.

Cubical quad antenna—An antenna built with its elements in the shape of four-sided loops.

Current—A flow of electrons in an electrical circuit.

Cutoff frequency—In a high-pass, low-pass or band-pass filter, the cutoff frequency is the frequency at which the filter output is reduced to ½ of the power available at the filter input.

D layer—The lowest layer of the ionosphere. The D layer contributes very little to short-wave radio propagation. It acts mainly to absorb energy from radio waves as they pass through it. This absorption has a significant effect on signals below about 7.5 MHz during daylight.

Detector—The stage in a receiver in which the modulation (voice or other information) is recovered from the RF signal.

Delta loop antenna—A variation of the cubical quad with triangular elements.

Deviation ratio—The ratio between the maximum change in RF-carrier frequency and the highest modulating frequency used in an FM transmitter.

Dielectric—The insulating material used between the plates in a capacitor.

Dielectric constant—A number used to indicate the relative "merit" of an insulating material. Air is given a value of 1, and all other materials are related to air.

Digipeater—A packet-radio station used to retransmit signals that are specifically addressed to be retransmitted by that station.

Dipole antenna—See **Half-wave dipole**. A dipole need not be ½ wavelength long.

Direct-conversion receiver—A receiver that converts an RF signal directly to an audio signal with one mixing stage.

Direct current (dc)—Electrical current that flows in one direction only.

Directivity—The ability of an antenna to focus transmitter power into certain directions. Also its ability to enhance received signals from specific directions.

Director—An element in front of the **driven element** in a Yagi and some other directional antennas.

Direct waves—Radio waves that travel directly from a transmitting antenna to a receiving antenna. Also called "line-of-sight" communications.

Double-pole, double-throw (DPDT) switch—A switch that has six contacts. The DPDT switch has two center contacts. The two center contacts can each be connected to one of two other contacts.

Driven element—The part of an antenna that connects directly to the feed line.

Duct—A radio waveguide formed when a temperature inversion traps radio waves within a restricted layer of the atmosphere.

Dummy load (dummy antenna)—A device used when you want to test or tune a transceiver without sending a signal out over the air. Instead of sending the signal to an antenna, you send it to the dummy load, which dissipates (gets rid of) the output power.

DX—Distance; foreign countries.

DX Century Club (DXCC)—A prestigious award given to amateurs who can prove contact with amateurs in at least 100 DXCC countries.

E layer—The second lowest ionospheric layer, the E layer exists only during the day. Under certain conditions it may refract radio waves back to Earth.

Earth ground—A circuit connection to a cold-water pipe or to a ground rod driven into the earth.

Earth station—An amateur station located on, or within 50 km of, the Earth's surface intended for communications with space stations or with other Earth stations by means of one or more objects in space.

Electric field—An invisible force of nature. An electric field exists in a region of space if an electrically charged object placed in the region is subjected to an electrical force.

Electrolytic capacitor—A polarized capacitor formed by using thin foil electrodes and chemical-soaked paper.

Electromotive force (EMF)—The force or pressure that pushes a current through a circuit.

Electron—A tiny, negatively charged particle, normally found in an area surrounding the nucleus of an atom. Moving electrons make up an electrical current.

Electronic keyer—A device that generates Morse code dots and dashes electronically.

Emission—The transmitted signal from an amateur station.

Emission privilege—Permission to use a particular emission type (such as Morse code or voice).

Energy—The ability to do work; the ability to exert a force to move some object.

False or deceptive signals—Transmissions that are intended to mislead or confuse those who may receive the transmissions. For example, distress calls transmitted when there is no actual emergency are false or deceptive signals.

F layer—A combination of the two highest ionospheric layers, the F1 and F2 layers. The F layer refracts radio waves and returns them to Earth. The height of the F layer varies greatly depending on the time of day, season of the year and amount of sunspot activity.

Feed line—The wires or cable used to connect your transceiver to an antenna. See **Transmission line**.

Field Day—An annual event in which amateurs set up stations in outdoor locations. Emergency power is also encouraged.

Field-effect transistor volt-ohm-milliammeter (FET VOM)—A type of multimeter. The meter circuit uses an FET amplifier to provide more accurate readings than can be obtained with a VOM. The FET VOM is the solid-state equivalent of a VTVM.

Fills—Repeats of parts of a previous transmission—usually requested because of interference.

Filter—A circuit that will allow some signals to pass through it but will greatly reduce the strength of others.

Fixed resistor—A resistor with a fixed nonadjustable value of resistance.

Forward Error Correction (FEC)—A mode of AMTOR communication. In FEC mode, also called Mode B, each character is sent twice. The receiving station checks the mark/space ratio of the received characters. If an error is detected, the receiving station prints a space to show that an incorrect character was received.

Frequency—The number of complete cycles of an alternating current that occur per second.

Frequency bands—A group of frequencies where communications of a particular service, such as the amateur service, are authorized.

Frequency Coordinator—A volunteer who keeps records of repeater input, output and control frequencies.

Frequency deviation—The amount the carrier frequency in an FM transmitter changes as it is modulated.

Frequency modulation—The process of varying the frequency of an RF carrier in response to the instantaneous changes in the modulating signal.

Frequency privilege—Permission to use a particular group of frequencies.

Frequency-shift keying (FSK)—A method of transmitting radioteletype information by switching an RF carrier between two separate frequencies. FSK RTTY is most often used on HF.

Fundamental frequency—The desired operating frequency of an oscillator.

Fuse—A thin strip of metal mounted in a holder. When too much current passes through the fuse, the metal strip melts and opens the circuit.

F1B emission—The FCC emission designator used to describe frequency-shift keyed (FSK) digital communications.

F2B emission—The FCC emission designator used to describe audio-frequency shift keyed (AFSK) digital communications.

F3E emission—The FCC emission designator used to describe FM voice communications.

Gain—A measure of the directivity of an antenna.

Gamma match—A method of matching coaxial feed line to the driven element of a multielement array.

General-coverage receiver—A receiver used to listen to a wide range of frequencies. Most general-coverage receivers tune from frequencies below the standard-broadcast band to at least 30 MHz. These frequencies include the shortwave-broadcast bands and the amateur bands from 160 to 10 meters.

Giga—The metric prefix for 10^9, or times 1,000,000,000.

Grace period—The time FCC allows following the expiration of an amateur license to renew that license without having to retake an examination. Those who hold an expired license may not operate an amateur station until the license is reinstated.

Grid—The control element (or elements) in a vacuum tube.

Ground connection—A connection made to the earth for electrical safety.

Ground waves—Radio waves that travel along Earth's surface.

Guided propagation—Radio propagation by means of ducts in the atmosphere.

Half-wave dipole—A basic antenna used by radio amateurs. It consists of a length of wire or tubing, opened and fed at the center. The entire antenna is ½ wavelength long at the desired operating frequency.

Ham-bands-only receiver—A receiver designed to cover only the bands used by amateurs. Usually refers to the bands from 80 to 10 meters, sometimes including 160 meters.

Hand key—A simple switch used to send Morse code.

Harmonics—Signals from a transmitter or oscillator occurring on whole-number multiples of the desired operating frequency.

Hertz (Hz)—An alternating-current frequency of one cycle per second. The basic unit of frequency.

High-pass filter—A filter designed to pass high-frequency signals, while blocking lower-frequency signals.

Horizontally polarized wave—An electromagnetic wave with its electric lines of force parallel to the ground.

Impedance-matching network—A device that matches the impedance of an antenna system to the impedance of a transmitter or receiver. Also called an antenna-matching network or Transmatch.

Input frequency—A repeater's receiving frequency.

Insulator—A material that maintains a tight grip on its electrons, so that an electrical current cannot pass through it.

Intermediate frequency (IF)—The output frequency of a mixing stage in a superheterodyne receiver. The subsequent stages in the receiver are tuned for maximum efficiency at the IF.

Inverted-V dipole—A half-wave dipole antenna with its center elevated and the ends drooping toward the ground. Often called an inverted V.

Ion—An electrically charged particle. An electron is an ion. Another example of an ion is the nucleus of an atom that is surrounded by too few or too many electrons. An atom like this has a net positive or negative charge.

Ionosphere—A region of charged particles about 30 to 260 miles above the Earth. The ionosphere bends radio waves as they travel through it, returning them to Earth.

J3E emission—The FCC emission designator used to describe single-sideband, suppressed-carrier voice communications.

Key clicks—A click or thump at the beginning or end of a CW signal.

Kilo—The metric prefix for 10^3, or times 1000.

Ladder line—Parallel-conductor feeder with insulating spacer rods every few inches.

Line of sight—The term used to describe VHF and UHF propagation in a straight line directly from one station to another.

Lower sideband (LSB)—The common single-sideband operating mode on the 40, 80 and 160-meter amateur bands.

Low-pass filter—A filter designed to pass low-frequency signals, while blocking higher-frequency signals.

Major lobe—The shape or pattern of field strength that points in the direction of maximum radiated power from an antenna.

Malicious Interference—Intentional, deliberate obstruction of radio transmissions.

Matching network—A device that matches one impedance level to another. For example, it may match the impedance of an antenna system to the impedance of a transmitter or receiver. Amateurs also call such devices a Transmatch, impedance-matching network or match box.

Maximum usable frequency (MUF)—The greatest frequency at which radio signals will return to a particular location from the ionosphere. The MUF may vary for radio signals sent to different destinations.

MAYDAY—From the French "m'aider" (help me), MAYDAY is used when calling for emergency assistance in voice modes.

Mega—The metric prefix for 10^6, or times 1,000,000.

Metal-film resistor—A resistor formed by depositing a thin layer of resistive-metal alloy on a cylindrical ceramic form.

Metric prefixes—A series of terms used in the metric system of measurement. We use metric prefixes to describe a quantity as compared to a basic unit. The metric prefixes indicate multiples of 10.

Metric system—A system of measurement developed by scientists and used in most countries of the world. This system uses a set of prefixes that are multiples of 10 to indicate quantities larger or smaller than the basic unit.

Mica capacitor—A capacitor formed by alternating layers of metal foil with thin sheets of insulating mica.

Micro—The metric prefix for 10^{-6}, or divide by 1,000,000.

Microphone—A device that converts sound waves into electrical energy.

Milli—The metric prefix for 10^{-3}, or divide by 1000.

Mixer—A circuit used to combine two or more audio- or radio-frequency signals to produce a different output frequency.

Modem—Short for modulator/demodulator. A modem modulates a radio signal to transmit data and demodulates a received signal to recover transmitted data.

Modulate—To vary the amplitude, frequency, or phase of a radio-frequency signal.

Modulation index—The ratio between the maximum carrier frequency deviation and the frequency of the modulating signal at a given instant in an FM transmitter.

Monitor mode—One type of packet-radio receiving mode. In monitor mode, everything transmitted on a packet frequency is displayed by the monitoring TNC. This occurs whether the transmissions are addressed to the monitoring station or not.

Multiband antenna—An antenna that will operate well on more than one frequency band.

Multimeter—An electronic test instrument used to measure current, voltage and resistance in a circuit. Describes all meters capable of making these measurements, such as the **VOM, VTVM** and **FET VOM**.

Multimode transceiver—Transceiver capable of SSB, CW and FM operation.

Mutual coupling—When coils display mutual coupling, a current flowing in one coil will induce a voltage in the other. The magnetic flux of one coil passes through the windings of the other.

Negative Charge—One of two types of electrical charge. The electrical charge of a single electron.

Nets—Groups of amateurs who meet on the air to pass traffic or communicate about a specific subject. One station (called the *net control station*) usually directs the net.

Network—A term used to describe several packet stations linked together to transmit data over long distances.

Neutral—Having no electrical charge, or having an equal number of positive and negative charges.

Neutralization—A method of preventing oscillation in an amplifier stage.

Nucleus—The dense central portion of an atom. The nucleus contains positively charged particles.

Offset—The 300- to 1000-Hz difference in transmitting and receiving frequencies in a transceiver. For a repeater, offset refers to the difference between its transmitting and receiving frequencies.

Ohm—The basic unit of electrical resistance, used to describe the amount of opposition to current.

Ohm's Law—A basic law of electronics. Ohm's Law gives a relationship between voltage, resistance and current ($E = IR$).

Omnidirectional—Antenna characteristic meaning it radiates equal power in all compass directions.

One-way communications—Transmissions that are not intended to be answered. The FCC strictly limits the types of one-way communications allowed on the amateur bands.

Open circuit—An electrical circuit that does not have a complete path, so current can't flow through the circuit.

Open-wire feed line—Parallel-conductor feeder with air as its primary insulation material.

Operator license—The portion of an Amateur Radio license that gives permission to operate an amateur station.

Oscillator—A circuit built by adding positive feedback to an amplifier. It produces an alternating current signal with no input except the dc operating voltages.

Output frequency—A repeater's transmitting frequency.

Packet Bulletin-Board System (PBBS)—A computer system used to store packet-radio messages for later retrieval by other amateurs.

Packet radio—A communications system in which information is broken into short bursts. The bursts (packets) also contain addressing and error-detection information.

Paper capacitor—A capacitor formed by sandwiching paper between thin foil plates, and rolling the entire unit into a cylinder.

Parallel circuit—An electrical circuit where the electrons follow more than one path.

Parallel-conductor feed line—Feed line with two conductors held a constant distance apart.

Parasitic element—Part of a directive antenna that derives energy from mutual coupling with the driven element. Parasitic elements are not connected directly to the feed line.

Parasitics—Oscillations in a transmitter amplifier that are not related to the operating frequency.

Peak envelope power (PEP)—The average power supplied to the antenna transmission line during one RF cycle at the crest of the modulation envelope. Transmitter power is measured in terms of PEP.

Phase modulation—Varying the phase of an RF carrier in response to the instantaneous changes in the modulating signal.

Pico—The metric prefix for 10^{-12}, or divide by 1,000,000,000,000.

Plastic-film capacitor—A capacitor formed by sandwiching thin sheets of Mylar™ or polystyrene between thin foil plates, and rolling the entire unit into a cylinder.

Polarization—Describes the electrical-field characteristic of a radio wave. An antenna that is parallel to the surface of the earth, such as a dipole, produces horizontally polarized waves. One that is perpendicular to the earth's surface, such as a quarter-wave vertical, produces vertically polarized waves.

Positive charge—One of two types of electrical charge. A positive charge is the opposite of a negative charge. Electrons have a negative charge. The nucleus of an atom has a positive charge.

Potentiometer—Another name for a variable resistor. The value of a potentiometer can be changed without removing it from a circuit.

Power—The rate of energy consumption. We calculate power in an electrical circuit by multiplying the voltage applied to the circuit times the current through the circuit.

Power supply—That part of an electrical circuit that provides excess electrons to flow into a circuit. The power supply also supplies the voltage or EMF to push the electrons along. Power supplies convert a power source (such as the ac mains) to a useful form.

Procedural signal (prosign)—One or two letters sent as a single character. Amateurs use prosigns in CW QSOs as a short way to indicate the operator's intention. Some examples are K for "Go Ahead," or A̅R̅ for "End of Message." (The bar over the letters indicates that we send the prosign as one character.)

Propagation—The means by which radio waves travel from one place to another.

Q signals—Three-letter symbols beginning with "Q." Q signals are used in amateur CW work to save time and for better communication.

QSL card—A postcard sent to another radio amateur to confirm a contact.

QSO—A conversation between two radio amateurs.

Quarter-wavelength vertical antenna—An antenna constructed of a quarter-wavelength long radiating element placed perpendicular to the earth.

Radiate—To convert electric energy into electromagnetic (radio) waves. An antenna radiates radio waves.

Radio frequency (RF)—The range of frequencies that can be radiated through space in the form of electromagnetic radiation. We usually consider RF to be those frequencies higher than the audio frequencies, or above 20 kilohertz.

Radio-frequency interference (RFI)—Disturbance to electronic equipment caused by radio-frequency signals.

Radio-path horizon—The point where radio waves are returned by tropospheric bending. The radio-path horizon is 15 percent farther away than the geometric horizon.

Radioteletype (RTTY)—Radio signals sent from one teleprinter machine to another machine. Anything that one operator types on his teleprinter will be printed on the other machine.

Ragchew—A lengthy conversation (or QSO) between two radio amateurs.

Random-length wire antenna—An antenna having a length that is not necessarily related to a wavelength for which it is used.

Reactance—The property of an inductor or capacitor (measured in ohms) that impedes current in an ac circuit without converting power to heat.

Reactance modulator—A device capable of modulating an ac signal by varying the reactance of a circuit in response to the modulating signal. (The modulating signal may be voice, data, video, or some other kind depending on what type of information is being transmitted.)

Receiver—A device that converts radio signals into audio signals.

Receiver incremental tuning (RIT)—A transceiver control that allows for a slight change in the receiver frequency without changing the transmitter frequency. Some manufacturers call this a clarifier (CLAR) control.

Receiver overload—Interference to a receiver caused by a strong RF signal that forces its way into the equipment. A signal that overloads the receiver RF amplifier (front end) causes *front-end overload*.

Reflected wave—A radio wave whose direction is changed when it bounces off some object in its path.

Reflector—An element behind the driven element in a Yagi and some other directional antennas.

Refract—To bend. Electromagnetic waves are refracted when they pass through a boundary between two different types of material, such as into or out of an ionospheric layer.

Repeater station—An amateur station that automatically retransmits the signals of other stations.

Resistance—The ability to oppose an electric current.

Resistor—Any material that opposes a current in an electrical circuit. An electronic component especially designed to oppose current.

Resolution—The space between markings on a receiver dial. The greater the frequency resolution, the easier it is to separate signals that are close together. Frequency resolution and **band spread** are related.

Resonant frequency—The desired operating frequency of a tuned circuit. In an antenna, the resonant frequency is one where the feed-point impedance contains only resistance.

RF burn—A flesh burn caused by exposure to a strong field of RF energy.

Rig—The radio amateur's term for a transmitter, receiver or transceiver.

Rotary switch—A switch that connects one center contact to several individual contacts. An antenna switch is one common use for a rotary switch.

Rotor—The movable plates in a variable capacitor.

RST—A system of numbers used for signal reports: R is readability, S is strength and T is tone.

Safety interlock—A switch that turns off ac power to a piece of equipment when someone removes the top cover.

Schematic symbol—A drawing used to represent a circuit component on a wiring diagram.

Secondary station identifier (SSID)—A number added to a packet-radio station's call sign so that one amateur call sign can be used for several packet stations.

Selective-call identifier—A four-character AMTOR station identifier.

Selectivity—The ability of a receiver to separate two closely spaced signals.

Semiconductor—Material that has some properties of a conductor and some properties of an insulator.

Sensitivity—The ability of a receiver to detect weak signals.

Series circuit—An electrical circuit where the electrons must all flow through every part of the circuit. There is only one path for the current to follow.

Shack—The room where an Amateur Radio operator keeps his or her station equipment.

Short circuit—An electrical circuit where the current does not take the desired path, but finds a shortcut instead. Often the current goes directly from the negative power-supply terminal to the positive one, bypassing the rest of the circuit.

Simplex operation—A term normally used in relation to VHF and UHF operation. Simplex means you are receiving and transmitting on the same frequency.

Sine wave—A smooth curve, usually drawn to represent the variation in voltage or current over time for an ac signal.

Single-pole, double-throw (SPDT) switch—A switch that connects one center contact to one of two other contacts.

Single-pole, single-throw (SPST) switch—A switch that only connects one center contact to another contact.

Single sideband (SSB)—A common mode of voice operation on the amateur bands. SSB is a form of amplitude modulation.

Skip—Radio waves that are bent back to Earth by the ionosphere. Skip is also called **sky-wave** propagation.

Skip zone—An area past the maximum range of ground waves and before the range of waves returned from the ionosphere. An area where radio communications between stations is not possible on a certain frequency.

Sky waves—Radio waves that travel through the ionosphere and back to Earth. Sky-wave propagation is sometimes called **skip**.

Sloper—A ½-wave dipole or ¼-wave end-fed antenna that has one end elevated and one end nearer the ground.

Solar-flux index—A measure of solar activity. The solar-flux index is a measure of the 2800-MHz radio noise from the sun.

Solid-state devices—Circuit components that use semiconductor materials. Semiconductor diodes, transistors and integrated circuits are all solid-state devices.

sos—A Morse code call for emergency assistance.

Space station—An amateur station located more than 50 km above the Earth's surface.

Space wave—A radio wave arriving at the receiving antenna made up of a direct wave and one or more reflected waves.

Speech processor—A device that increases the average power of a sideband signal, making the voice easier to understand under weak signal conditions.

Splatter—The term used to describe a very wide-bandwidth signal. Splatter is usually caused by an improperly adjusted sideband transmitter.

Spurious emissions—Signals from a transmitter on frequencies other than the operating frequency.

Stability—A measure of how well a receiver or transmitter will remain on frequency without drifting.

Standing-wave ratio (SWR)—Sometimes called VSWR. A measure of the impedance match between the feed line and the antenna. Also, with a Transmatch in use, a measure of the match between the feed line from the transmitter and the antenna *system*. The system includes the Transmatch and the line to the antenna. VSWR is the ratio of maximum voltage to minimum voltage along the feed line. Also the ratio of antenna impedance to feed-line impedance when the antenna is a purely resistive load.

Station license—The portion of an Amateur Radio license that authorizes an amateur station at a specific location. The station license also lists the call of that station.

Stator—The stationary plates in a variable capacitor.

Subatomic particles—The building blocks of atoms. Electrons, protons and neutrons are the most common subatomic particles.

Sunspots—Dark spots on the surface of the sun. When there are few sunspots, long-distance radio propagation is poor on the higher-frequency bands.

Superheterodyne receiver—A receiver that converts RF signals to an intermediate frequency before detection.

Superimposed hum—A low-pitched buzz or hum on a radio signal.

Switch—A device used to connect or disconnect electrical contacts.

SWR meter—A measuring instrument that can indicate when an antenna system is working well.

Teleprinter—A machine that can convert keystrokes (typing) into electrical impulses. The teleprinter can also convert the proper electrical impulses back into text. Computers have largely replaced teleprinters for amateur radioteletype work.

Television interference (TVI)—Interruption of television reception caused by another signal.

Temperature inversion—A condition in the atmosphere in which a region of cool air is trapped beneath warmer air.

Temporary state of communications emergency—When a disaster disrupts normal communications in a particular area, the FCC can declare this type of emergency. Certain rules may apply for the duration of the emergency.

Terminal node controller (TNC)—A TNC accepts information from a computer and converts the information into packets. The TNC also receives packets and extracts information to be displayed by a computer.

Third-party communications—Messages passed from one amateur to another on behalf of a third person.

Third-party participation—The way an unlicensed person can participate in amateur communications. A control operator must ensure compliance with FCC rules.

Ticket—Commonly used name for an Amateur Radio license.

Toroidal inductor—A coil wound on a donut-shaped ferrite or powdered-iron form.

Traffic—Messages passed from one amateur to another in a relay system; the amateur version of a telegram.

Transceiver—A radio transmitter and receiver combined in one unit.

Transformer—A devic that changes ac voltage levels.

Transmatch—See **Matching network**.

Transmission line—The wires or cable used to connect a transmitter or receiver to an antenna.

Transmit-receive (TR) switch—A device that allows you to connect one antenna to a receiver and a transmitter. The switch connects the antenna to the receiver or transmitter as you operate the switch.

Transmitter—A device that produces radio-frequency signals.

Triode—A vacuum tube with three active elements: cathode, plate and control grid.

Troposphere—The atmospheric region just above the Earth's surface and below the ionosphere.

Tropospheric bending or **enhancement**—A weather-related phenomenon. A Tropo can produce unusually long-distance propagation on the VHF and UHF bands.

True or **Geometric Horizon**—The most distant point one can see by line of sight.

Twin lead—Parallel-conductor feed line with wires encased in insulation.

Unidentified communications or signals—Signals or radio communications in which the transmitting station's call sign is not transmitted.

Upper sideband (USB)—The common single-sideband operating mode on the 20, 17, 15, 12 and 10-meter HF amateur bands, and all the VHF and UHF bands.

Vacuum-tube voltmeter (VTVM)—A type of multimeter that includes a vacuum-tube amplifier to provide more accurate readings than can be obtained with a VOM.

Variable capacitor—A capacitor that can have its value changed within a certain range.

Variable-frequency oscillator (VFO)—A circuit used to control the frequency of an amateur transmitter.

Variable resistor—A resistor whose value can be adjusted over a certain range.

Vertical antenna—A common amateur antenna, usually made of metal tubing. The radiating element is vertical. There are usually four or more radial elements parallel to or on the ground.

Vertically polarized wave—A radio wave that has its electric lines of force perpendicular to the surface of the earth.

Virtual height—The height in the ionosphere from which radio waves appear to be reflected when they are returned to Earth.

Volt (V)—The basic unit of electrical pressure or EMF.

Voltage—The EMF or pressure that causes electrons to move through an electrical circuit.

Voltage source—Any source of excess electrons. A voltage source produces a current and the force to push the electrons through an electrical circuit.

Volt-ohm-milliammeter (VOM)—A type of **multimeter**, a device used to measure voltage, current and resistance. The VOM is the least expensive (and least accurate) type of multimeter. (See also **field-effect transistor VOM** and **vacuum-tube voltmeter**.)

VOX (voice-operated switch)—Circuitry that activates a transmitter when the operator speaks into a microphone.

Watt (W)—The unit of power in the metric system. The watt describes how fast a circuit uses electrical energy.

Wavelength—Often abbreviated λ. The distance a radio wave travels in one RF cycle. The wavelength relates to frequency. Higher frequencies have shorter wavelengths.

Wire-wound resistor—A resistor made by winding a length of wire on an insulating form.

Yagi antenna—The most popular type of amateur directional (beam) antenna. It has one driven element and one or more additional elements.

Zero beat—When two operators in a QSO are transmitting on the same frequency.

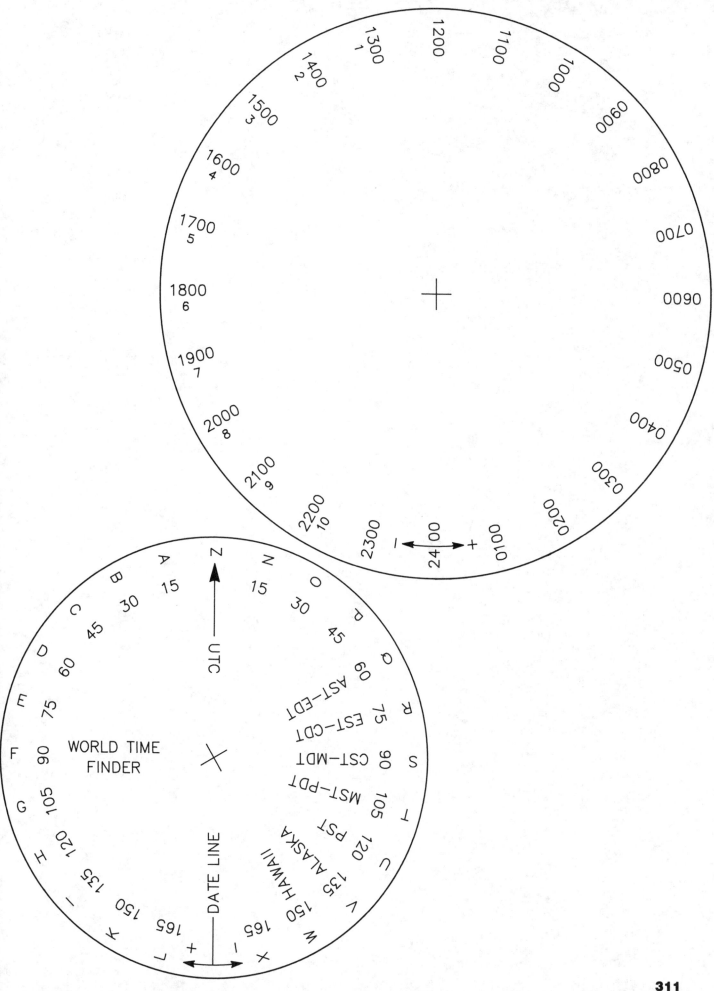

Index

BEST OF MFJ

MFJ, Bencher and Curtis team up to bring you America's most popular keyer in a compact package for smooth easy CW

MFJ-422B

$134.95

The best of all CW world's -- a deluxe MFJ Keyer using a Curtis 8044ABM chip in a compact package that fits right on the Bencher iambic paddle!

This MFJ Keyer is small in size but big in features. you get iambic keying, adjustable weight and tone and front panel volume and speed controls (8-50 WPM), dot-dash memories, speaker, sidetone and push button selection of automatic or semi-automatic/ tune modes. It's also totally RF proof and has ultra-reliable solid state outputs that key both tube and solid state rigs. Use 9 volt battery or 110 VAC with MFJ-1305, $12.95.

The keyer mounts on a Bencher paddle to form a small (4-1/8 x 2-5/8 x 5½ inches) attractive combination that is a pleasure to look at and use.

The Bencher paddle has adjustable gold plated silver contacts, lucite paddles, chrome plated brass and a heavy steel base with non-skid feet.

You can buy just the keyer assembly, MFJ-422BX, for only $79.95 to mount on **your** Bencher paddle.

Deluxe 300 W Tuner

MFJ-949D

$149.95

MFJ-949D is the world's most popular 300 watt PEP tuner. It covers 1.8-30 MHz, gives you a new peak and average reading Cross-Needle SWR/Wattmeter, built-in dummy load, 6 position antenna switch and 4:1 balun -- in a compact 10 x 3 x 7 inch cabinet. Meter lamp uses 12 VDC or 110 VAC with MFJ-1312, $12.95.

SWR Analyzer

MFJ-207
$99.95

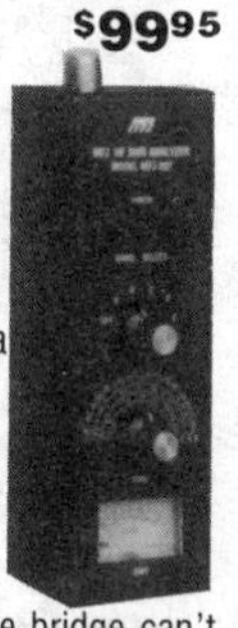

MFJ's innovative new SWR Analyzer gives you a complete picture of your antenna SWR over an entire band -- without a transmitter, SWR meter or any other equipment.!

Simply plug your antenna into the coax connector, set your SWR Analyzer to the frequency you want and read your SWR. You can instantly find your antenna's true resonant frequency, something a noise bridge can't do. Covers 1.8-30 MHz (or choose **MFJ-208**, $89.95 for 2 Meters). Use 9 V battery or 110 VAC with MFJ-1312, $12.95.

Super Active Antenna

"**World Radio TV Handbook**" says MFJ-1024 is a "first rate easy-to-operate active antenna ... quiet ... excellent dynamic range ... good gain ... very low noise ... broad frequency coverage ... excellent choice."

Mount it outdoors away from electrical noise for maximum signal, minimum noise. Covers 50 KHz to 30 MHz.

Receives strong, clear signals from all over the world. 20 dB attenuator, gain control, ON LED. Swtich two receivers and aux. or active antenna.6x3x5 in. Remote unit has 54 inch whip, 50 ft. coax and connector. 3x2x4 in. Use 12 VDC or 110 VAC with MFJ-1312, $12.95.

MFJ-1024 **$129.95**

VHF SWR/Wattmeter

MFJ-812B
$29.95

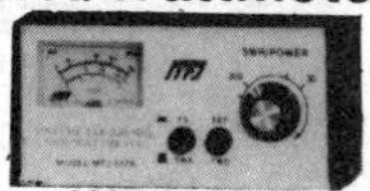

Covers 2 Meters and 220 MHz. 30 or 300 Watt scales. Also reads relative field strength 1-170 MHz and SWR above 14 MHz. 4½x2¼x3 in.

MFJ Coax Antenna Switches

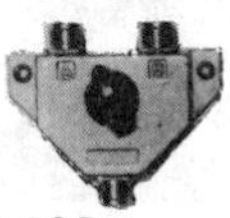

$34.95 MFJ-1701 **$21.95** MFJ-1702B **$59.95** MFJ-1704

Select any of several antennas from your operating desk with these MFJ Coax Switches. They feature mounting holes and automatic grounding of unused terminals. They come with MFJ's one year **unconditional** guarantee.
MFJ-1701, $34.95. Six position antenna switch. SO-239 connectors. 50-75 ohm loads. 2 KW PEP, 1 KW CW. Covers 1.8-30 MHz. 10x3x1½ inches.
MFJ-1702B, $21.95. 2 positions plus new Center Ground. 2.5 KW PEP, 1 KW CW. Insertion loss below .2 dB. 50 dB isolation at 450 MHz. 50 ohm. 3x2x2 in.
MFJ-1704, $59.95. 4 position cavity switch with lightening/surge protection device. Center ground. 2.5 KW PEP, 1 KW CW. Low SWR. Isolation better than 50 dB at 500 MHz. Negligible loss. 50 ohm. 6¼x4¼x1¼ in.

"Dry" Dummy Loads for HF/VHF/UHF

MFJ-260B **$28.95** MFJ-262 **$69.95** MFJ-264 **$64.95**

MFJ has a full line of dummy loads to suit your needs. Use a dummy load for tuning to reduce needless (and illegal) QRM and save your finals.
MFJ-260B, $28.95. VHF/HF. Air cooled, non-inductive 50 ohm resistor. SO-239 connector. Handles 300 Watts. Run full load for 30 seconds, derating curve to 5 minutes. SWR less than 1.3:1 to 30 MHz, 1.5:1 to 150 MHz. 2½x2½x7 in.
MFJ-262, $69.95. HF.1 KW. SWR less than 1.5:1 to 30 MHz. 3x3x13 in.
MFJ-264, $64.95. Versatile UHF/VHF/HF 1.5 KW load. Low SWR to 650 MHz. Run 100 watts for 10 minutes, 1500 watts for 10 seconds. SWR is 1.1:1 to 30 MHz, Below 1.3:1 to 650 MHz. 3x3x7 inches.

MFJ Ham License Upgrade Theory Tutor

MFJ Theory Tutor practically guarantees you'll pass the theory part of any FCC ham license exam. Versatile MFJ software is the best computer tutor ever tailor-made for ham radio. You can study the entire FCC question pool, selected areas and take (or print) sample tests. Auto. saves each study session (ex. sample tests), gives you all FCC test graphics (ex. mono.), explanations of hard questions, pop-up calculator, weighted scoring analysis, color change option and more. **Order** MFJ-1610-**Novice**; MFJ-1611-**Tech.**; MFJ-1612-**Gen.**; MFJ-1613-**Adv.**; MFJ-1614-**Ex.** For **Macintosh**: MFJ-1630-N; MFJ-1631-T; MFJ-1632-G; MFJ-1633-A; MFJ-1634-E. **$29.95** per license class.

MFJ Speaker Mics

MFJ-284 or MFJ-286
$24.95

MFJ's compact Speaker/Mics let you carry your HT on your belt and never have to remove it to monitor calls or talk.
You get a wide range speaker and first-rate electret mic element for superb audio on both transmit and receive.
Earphone jack, handy lapel/pocket clip, PTT. lightweight retractable cord. Gray. One year **unconditional** guarantee.
MFJ-284 fits ICOM, Yaesu, Santec. MFJ-286 fits Kenwood.

MFJ-1278 Multi-Mode Data Controller

MFJ-1278
$279.95

Use computer to transmit/ receive in **all 9** digital modes: Packet, AMTOR, ASCII, CW, RTTY, FAX, SSTV, Contest Memory Keyer and Navtex receive. Automatic Signal Analysis™ (ASA™), Easy-Mail™ Personal Mailbox, built-in printer port. 20 LED tuning indicator, AC power supply, Host/KISS, 32K RAM, Multi-gray level FAX/SSTV modem, CW key paddle jack and tons more. Options include 2400 baud modem (MFJ-2400, $69.95) and software with computer cables. for IBM compatible. Commodore 64/128, Macintosh and VIC-20.

12/24 Hour LCD Clocks

$19.95 MFJ-108B **$9.95** MFJ-107B

Huge 5/8 inch bold LCD digits let you see the time from anywhere in your shack. Choose from the dual clock that has separate UTC/local time display or the single 24 hour ham clock.

Mounted in a brushed aluminum frame. Easy to set. The world's most popular ham clocks for accurate logs. MFJ-108B 4½x1x2; MFJ-107B 2¼x1x2 in.

Cross-Needle SWR Meter

MFJ-815B
$69.95

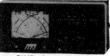

MFJ Cross-Needle SWR/ Wattmeter has a new **peak** reading function! It shows you SWR, forward and reflected power in 2000/500 and 200/50 watt ranges. Covers 1.8-30 MHz.

Mechanical zero adjusts for movement. SO-239 connectors. Lamp uses 12 VDC or 110 VAC with MFJ-1312, $12.95.

Deluxe Code Practice Oscillator

MFJ-557
$24.95

MFJ-557 Deluxe Code Practice Oscillator has a Morse key and oscillator unit mounted together on a heavy steel base so it stays put on your table. Portable because it runs on a 9-volt battery (not included) or an AC adapter ($12.95) that plugs into a jack on the side.

Earphone jack for private practice, Tone and Volume controls for a wide range of sound. Speaker. Key has adjustable contacts and can be hooked to your transmitter. Sturdy. 8½x2¼x3¾ in.

MFJ Multiple DC Outlet

MFJ-1112
$29.95

New MFJ DC Power Outlet saves you space **and** money. Hook it to your 12 VDC power supply and get 6 DC outlets for connecting your accessories. RF bypassing keeps RF out of power supply from DC line outlet. 13½x2¾x2½ in.

Prices and specifications subject to change without notice or obligation.

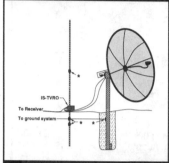

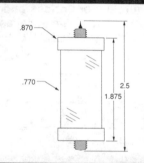

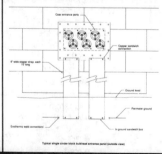
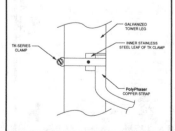

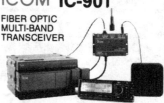

HENRY RADIO...
64 years of providing the amateurs of 50 states and 100 countries with the honest, reliable service they deserve. Through good times and bad the Henry family never wavered from this commitment.

There are a lot of good reasons. We know that we have provided the kind of equipment and service that thousands of amateurs have come to expect. They keep coming back. We'll do our best to see to it that they, and you have every reason for coming back.

☆ **A large inventory of fine equipment from the world's leading manufacturers** ☆ **A knowledgeable staff dedicated to amateur radio** ☆ **A complete line of accessories** ☆ **A well stocked repair shop staffed by experienced technicians** ☆ **We take trade-ins and sell used equipment** ☆ **Generous discounts on cash purchases** ☆ **We carry our own financing & accept most credit cards**

Some of the names we stock include:
HENRY ● TEMPO ● KENWOOD ● ICOM ● YAESU ● ACE ● ADVANCED RECEIVER RESEARCH ● AEA ● AIM ● ALEXANDER ● ALPHA DELTA ● AMECO ● ANTRONIC ● ARRL ● ASTRON ● B&K ● B&W ● BECKMAN ● BENCHER ● BIRD ● BUDWIG ● BUTTERNUT ● CAL CHASSIS ● CALRAD ● CALTRONICS ● CES ● CENTURION ● COMET ● COMMUNICATIONS SPECIALISTS ● CONNECT SYSTEMS ● CREATE ● CUSHCRAFT ● DAIWA ● DIAMOND ● DIGIMAX ● DIGITAR ● DOW KEY ● DURACELL ● EASCO ● EAVESDROPPER ● EIMAC ● ● ELENCO ● FANON ● GC ● GORDON WEST ● GRUNDIG ● HAL ● HEIL ● HOXAN ● HUSTLER ● HY GAIN ● ICOM ● JABRO ● JAPAN RADIO ● KANTRONICS ● LANDWEHR ● LARSEN ● LITTELFUSE ● LMB ● MAG INSTRUMENTS ● MARK ● MAXON ● MFJ ● MIDIAN ● MILLEN ● MIRAGE/KLM ● MOTOROLA RADIUS ● MULTICORE ● MULTIPLIER ● WM. M. NYE ● OUTBACKER ● PALOMAR ● PANAVISE ● PHILMORE ● PIPO ● PORTASOL ● RADIO AMAT CALLBOOKS ● RAWN ● RF CONCEPTS ● ROHN ● SANGEAN ● SELECTONE ● SGC ● SHURE ● SIMPSON ● SONY ● STANDARD ● SWITCHCRAFT ● TEN TEC ● TRI-EX ● TRIPPLITE ● TUBES ● UNADILLA ● UNIDEN ● VAN GORDEN ● VIBROPLEX ● WACOM ● X-10

Henry Radio

2050 S. BUNDY DR.   LOS ANGELES, CA 90025   (213) 820-1234
Toll free order number: (800) 877-7979   TELEX: 67-3625(Henradio)   FAX(213) 826-7790

AMSAT

Dedicated to Keeping Amateur Radio in Space!

AMSAT — *The Radio Amateur Satellite Corporation* is an organization of Radio Amateurs who design, build and launch satellites for use by Radio Amateurs around the world.

Your new Amateur Radio License will be your ticket to a whole world of exciting opportunities. Why not expand your horizons even further by becoming a member of AMSAT and participating in space aged Amateur Radio?

Join the Excitement! Join the Fun! Join AMSAT!

Yearly Membership dues: $30 U.S., $36 Canada/Mexico, $45 Elsewhere   JOIN NOW!

Name_____ Call_____

Address_____

City_____ State_____ Zip_____

$15 of membership dues goes toward a subscription to *The AMSAT Journal*

Post Office Box 27, Washington, DC 20044
Telephone 301-589-6062   Fax 301-608-3410

FLYWEIGHT BODY
with HEAVYWEIGHT FEATURES

Alinco's New DJ-F1/F4T Realized Super Compact Body and Plenty of Features including:

*40 Memory Channels store Frequency, Shift direction, Split operation Setting, Tone encoder/Tone decoder setting (with optional Tone squelch unit), DSQ setting, Tone frequency and Offset frequency independently.

*Digital Signal Display and Memory Function

The DJ-F1T/F4T has special memory channels for transmitting, receiving, and store "Two Digit" DTMF Tones, for communication messages. This feature allows for the DJ-F1T/F4T to receive a "Two Digit" message and display it at any later time, at the convenience of the operator.

*Wide Band Receiving range
F1T:140-170MHz(AM Mode 118-136MHz after modification)
F4T:430-460MHz

*Battery Pack Lock
*Pager and Code Squelch
*Triple Stage Selective Power Output
*5W Output Power with Optional Battery Pack EBP-18N
*8 Scan Modes
*Programmable VFO Range Function
*Battery Save Function
*Six Channel Steps - 5, 10, 12.5, 15, 20, and 25KHz
*Priority Function (Dual Watch)
*Automatic Power Off (Programmable Timed)
*Automatic Dialer Function
*Illuminated DTMF Keypad
*Many Optional Accessories such as:
EMS-8:Remote Control Speaker/Mic.
EME-11:Earphone/Mic. with PTT/VOX
EME-10:Headset with PTT/VOX
EJ-2U:Tone squelch Unit
EDC-33:Quick Charger (Compatible with standard battery pack)

and many more. . . . .

DJ-S1T/S4T is Simple Type and Low-Priced But Offers Features such as:
* 5W Output Power with Optional Battery Pack EBP-18N
* Triple Stage Slective Power Output
* Dry Cell Battery Case Lock
* Programmable VFO Range Function
* Frequency Lock, PTT Lock Function
* One Touch Squelch De-Activation Function
* 8 Scan Modes
* Wide Band Receiving Range

Available Features with Optional DTMF Unit (DJ-10U) and DTMF Keypad (ESK-1) Include:
* Pager and Code Squelch
* Digital Signal Display and Memory Function
* Automatic dialer Function
* Many Optional Accessories Available

•Specifications
Frequency Range:
DJ-F1T/S1T
TX:144-148MHz
RX:140-170MHz (AM Mode 118-136MHz after Modification)
DJ-F4T/S4T
TX:440-450MHz
RX:430-460MHz

Output Power:
* with Battery Pack EBP-16N (Standard for F1T/F4T)
Hi:2W(F1T/S1T) 1.5W(F4T/S4T)
Mid:1W   Low:0.1W
* with Optional Battery Pack EBP-18N
Hi:5W Mid:1W   Low:0.1W
* at 9V
Hi:2.5W(F1T/S1T)   2W(F4T/S4T)
Mid:1W   Low:0.1W

Weight:
DJ-F1T/F4T Approx.:13.2 oz.:
with Standard Battery Pack
DJ-S1T/S4T Approx.:13 oz.:
with Dry Battery case

Dimensions:
4.3(H) × 2.1(W) × 1.5(D) inch (Without Projections)

Specifications and features are guaranteed for amateur bands only and subject to change without notice.

ALINCO ELECTRONICS INC.
438 AMAPOLA AVE. LOT 130
TORRANCE, CALIFORNIA 90501
Phone: 213-618-8616
FAX   : 213-618-8758

STAY TUNED with

DJ-F1T

DJ-S4T

Now You're Talking!: Discover the World of Ham Radio covers everything you need to know to earn your first Amateur Radio license. More than a study guide, it will help you select equipment for your ham radio station and even explain how to set it up!

Now You're Talking! is the successor to the immensely popular *Tune in the World with Ham Radio*. Information every beginning ham needs is presented in bite-sized pieces and easy-to-understand terms.

Whether you're interested in the new codeless Technician license or the traditional Novice ticket, with *Now You're Talking!*, it's easier than ever to become a ham radio operator! If you're starting with the Novice license you should also purchase audio cassettes or computer software to learn Morse code (described below).

Upgrade Your License the Easy Way!

After you receive your license and get on the air, you'll probably want to explore additional operating privileges. The *ARRL License Manual Series* represents the best study material for the Technician, General, Advanced and Extra Class Amateur Radio exams. Each book is carefully revised and updated as new exam questions are released by the VEC Question Pool Committee. The appropriate examination question pool, complete with an answer key, is included for easy reference. The answer key contains page references so you can locate appropriate text explanations as you review the questions before your exam. Our *FCC Rule Book* should be used along with each publication in the series.

Now You're Talking!: Discover the World of Ham Radio .... #3525 **$19**

ARRL License Manual Series
Technician Class (current edition good through June 30, 1993) .... #2375 **$6**
General Class .... #2383 **$6**
Advanced Class .... #3274 **$6**
Extra Class .... #3282 **$8**
FCC Rule Book .... #2456 **$9**

Code Proficiency
When it comes to the code, whether you're just starting out, or you're working on your Extra Class upgrade, practice makes perfect!

The ARRL produces five sets of Morse code tapes to get you from 0 to 22 words per minute. Each set includes two C-90 cassettes. *GGTE Morse Tutor* software for IBM PCs and compatibles teaches you the code, provides plenty of practice for exams and helps keep your code skills sharp in easy, self-paced lessons. Features include code speeds from 1 to more than 100 words per minute, standard or Farnsworth modes and random QSOs. The *Advanced Morse Tutor* has even more features.

Your Introduction to Morse Code, our cassette program for beginners, makes learning the code fun. It teaches you all the characters and provides plenty of practice .... #3487 **$10**

ARRL Code Practice Cassettes. Each set of two C-90 tapes provides three hours of practice.
Set 1: 5 to 10 WPM .... #2227 **$10**
Set 2: 10 to 15 WPM .... #2235 **$10**
Set 3: 15 to 22 WPM .... #2243 **$10**
Set 4: 13 to 14 WPM .... #2251 **$10**
GGTE Morse Tutor (5.25-inch) .... #2081 **$20**
GGTE Morse Tutor (3.5-inch) .... #2936 **$22**
Advanced Morse Tutor (5.25-inch) .... #3231 **$30**
Advanced Morse Tutor (3.5-inch) .... #3258 **$30**

For Instructors

In addition to ham radio study guides for students, we also produce instructor's guides to help you teach license courses. These are for use with *Now You're Talking!* and **ARRL License Manuals**. The *Instructor's Manual* is a valuable aid for those teaching Amateur Radio classes at any level.

Proceedings of the ARRL National Educational Workshop presents ideas from top instructors to help you motivate your students and increase their enjoyment.
ARRL Novice/Technician Class
Instructor's Guide .... #3649 **$6**
ARRL General Class Instructor's Guide .... #2669 **$5**
ARRL Instructor's Manual .... #2448 **$6**
Proceedings of the ARRL National Education

Help for Beginners

Operating an Amateur Radio Station. This booklet answers the basic Amateur Radio questions often posed by newcomers: How do I decide what equipment to buy? What kind of antenna do I need? What procedures do I use, and what do I say when I make my first contact? How do I QSL? and many others .... #226X **$1**

Novice Notes: The Book is a selection of articles for the beginner from the popular *QST* series. It's filled with useful information: What you should do before your license arrives; how to buy used gear; all about antenna tuners and antennas, logging and QSLing; awards chasing; tips on phone, Morse code and digital operating and much more .... #2561 **$6**

W1FB's Help for New Hams by Doug DeMaw offers sound advice on getting started in Amateur Radio after you get your license. This book acts as your personal Elmer, covering such topics as selecting equipment, station layout and accessories, constructing and using antennas, and operating .... #2871 **$10**

First Steps in Radio by Doug DeMaw, W1FB, is a tutorial on electronics principles tailored to the beginner. Reprinted from the popular *QST* series, this book will help you learn the electronics theory helpful for licensing exams and to gain some insight into how radio equipment works .... #2286 **$5**

- new information on using the Microsats
- updated operating information on AMTOR and RTTY
- a discussion on the latest bioeffects findings
- a detailed examination of direct digital synthesis

An indispensable reference for hams and engineers alike, *The ARRL Handbook*, with its 1200 pages and 2100 charts and illustrations, is an exceptional value ....#1697 **$25**

Every chapter of the 4th edition of *The ARRL Operating Manual* has been updated to include the latest information about every aspect of our dynamic hobby. It's simply the best book available covering on-the-air amateur operating practices. How do I operate on a repeater or on PacketCluster? How can I snare a contact through a DXpedition pileup? What satellites are available and how can I use them? You'll find the answers to all of these questions and many more in *The ARRL Operating Manual*!

One impressive and colorful section features dozens of US and overseas operating awards, and a handy reference section includes an ARRL DXCC Countries List, beam-heading information, a series of maps, US counties, sunrise/sunset tables, and much, much more. No shack is complete without this valuable reference ....#1086 **$18**

The ARRL Radio Buyer's Sourcebook is for anyone who buys, sells or owns Amateur Radio equipment. The *Sourcebook* includes *QST* reviews of HF and VHF transceivers, accessories and power amplifiers from 1981-1991 (plus a few "golden oldies"). It tells what the radios do, how well they do it, where to get them serviced and where to find articles about modifications. Comparative feature and performance charts provide ammunition for your next flea market visit. Newcomers will love the glossary of radio features and terms. You'll find the *Sourcebook* a vital part of your ham radio library! ....#3452 **$15**

The ARRL Electronics Data Book is a valuable aid to the radio amateur, RF design engineer, technician and experimenter. All those commonly used tables, charts, and those hard-to-remember formulas and semiconductor pin-out diagrams are found in one handy source. You'll also find hundreds of popular circuits and "building blocks," including oscillators, mixers, amplifiers, other devices and their operating parameters. By Doug DeMaw, W1FB ....#2197 **$12**

Hints and Kinks for the Radio Amateur is a popular compilation of hundreds of ideas contributed by individual authors. This edition includes ideas on setting up your gear for comfortable and efficient operation, solving interference problems and tailoring your equipment to your individual operating preferences. You're sure to find the answer to that tricky problem or a simple project you can build ....#3002 **$8**

The 1991-1992 ARRL Repeater Directory lists more than 18,000 VHF/UHF repeaters and more than 2200 digipeaters located around the US, Canada, Mexico and several other countries. This edition also lists more than 500 beacons from 14 MHz to 24 GHz. You'll also find band plans, a CTCSS (PL™) tone chart and a list of frequency coordinators and ARRL Special Service Clubs. The *Repeater Directory* comes in a handy pocket size for your operating convenience ....#3533 **$6**

Passport to World Band Radio is the "TV Guide" of shortwave listening. Updated annually, *Passport* contains comprehensive schedules for hundreds of international shortwave broadcast stations—when they're on, who they're targeting and what languages they're using—in an easy-to-understand format.

Increase your knowledge of today's changing world with *Passport to World Band Radio* and make the most of your listening ....#3337 **$17**

Handy References

The 1992 ARRL Handbook

We're proud of the 69th edition of *The ARRL Handbook for Radio Amateurs*. That's right—the 69th edition! *The Handbook* has been the "ham's bible" since 1926, and each new edition brings you the latest on what's new in Amateur Radio state of the art. *The Handbook* is many things:

- **a reference guide**, with updated lists of parts and equipment suppliers and other indispensable data on solid-state components and transmitting tubes

- **a guide to radio theory every ham should know**, including the latest digital modes and hundreds of explanatory and practical circuits

- **a goldmine of construction projects** that will allow all hams—beginners, old-timers and everyone in between —to build useful amateur gear for their stations.

What's new in the 1992 edition? Plenty! Here's some of what you'll find:

- a 1500-watt linear amplifier that uses inexpensive 3-500Z tubes

- a laboratory-grade directional HF wattmeter usable from 1.5 to 1500 watts

- the latest version of the popular "Cubic Incher," an easy-to-build QRP transmitter that now covers three bands

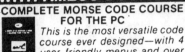

FEDERAL COMMUNICATIONS COMMISSION
GETTYSBURG, PA 17326

Approved OMB
3060-0003
Expires 12/31/92
See instructions for information
regarding public burden estimate

APPLICATION FOR AMATEUR RADIO STATION AND/OR OPERATOR LICENSE

ADMINISTERING VEs' REPORT			EXAMINATION ELEMENTS							
Applicant is credited for: ➡			1(A)	1(B)	1(C)	2	3(A)	3(B)	4(A)	4(B)
A. CIRCLE CLASS OF FCC AMATEUR LICENSE HELD: N T G A	**Class** ➡		(NT)	(GA)		(NTGA)	(TGA)	(GA)	(A)	
B. CERTIFICATE(S) OF SUCCESSFUL COMPLETION OF AN EXAMINATION HELD: ➡			Date Issued	Date Issued	Date Issued	Date Issued	Date Issued	Date Issued	Date Issued	Date Issued
C. FCC COMMERCIAL RADIOTELEGRAPH OPERATOR LICENSE HELD:	Number:									
	Exp. Date:									
D. EXAMINATION ELEMENTS PASSED THAT WERE ADMINISTERED AT THIS SESSION: ➡										

E. APPLICANT IS QUALIFIED FOR OPERATOR LICENSE CLASS: ☐ NONE:

E1. ☐ NOVICE   (Elements 1(A), 1(B), or 1(C) and 2)

E2. ☐ TECHNICIAN   (Elements 1(A), 1(B), or 1(C), 2 and 3(A))
 ☐ GENERAL   (Elements 1(B) or 1(C), 2, 3(A), and 3(B))
 ☐ ADVANCED   (Elements 1(B) or 1(C), 2, 3(A), 3(B) and 4(A))
 ☐ AMATEUR EXTRA   (Elements 1(C), 2, 3(A), 3(B), 4(A), and 4(B))

H. Date of VEC coordinated examination session:

I. VEC Receipt Date:

F. NAME OF VOLUNTEER-EXAMINER COORDINATOR: (VEC coordinated sessions only)

G. EXAMINATION SESSION LOCATION: (VEC coordinated sessions only)

SECTION I

1. IF YOU HOLD A VALID LICENSE ATTACH THE ORIGINAL LICENSE OR PHOTOCOPY ON BACK OF APPLICATION. IF THE VALID LICENSE OR CERTIFICATE OF SUCCESSFUL COMPLETION OF AN EXAMINATION WAS LOST OR DESTROYED, PLEASE EXPLAIN.

2. CHECK ONE OR MORE ITEMS, NORMALLY ALL LICENSES ARE ISSUED FOR A 10 YEAR TERM.

2A. ☐ RENEW LICENSE—NO OTHER CHANGES ➡ EXPIRATION DATE (Month, Day, Year)

2B. ☐ REINSTATE LICENSE EXPIRED LESS THAN 2 YEARS ➡

2C. ☐ EXAMINATION FOR NEW LICENSE

2D. ☐ EXAMINATION TO UPGRADE OPERATOR CLASS   FORMER LAST NAME   SUFFIX (Jr., Sr., etc.)

2E. ☐ CHANGE CALL SIGN (Be sure you are eligible—See Inst. 2E)

2F. ☐ CHANGE NAME (Give former name) ➡   FORMER FIRST NAME   MIDDLE INITIAL

2G. ☐ CHANGE MAILING ADDRESS

2H. ☐ CHANGE STATION LOCATION

3. CALL SIGN (If you checked 2C above, skip items 3 and 4)

4. OPERATOR CLASS OF THE ATTACHED LICENSE:

5. CURRENT FIRST NAME | M.I. | LAST NAME | SUFFIX (Jr., Sr., etc.)

6. DATE OF BIRTH __/__/__ MONTH DAY YEAR

7. CURRENT MAILING ADDRESS (Number and Street) | CITY | STATE | ZIP CODE

8. CURRENT STATION LOCATION (Do not use a P.O. Box No., RFD No., or General Delivery. See Instruction 8) | CITY | STATE

9. Would a Commission grant of your application be an action which may have a significant environmental effect as defined by Section 1.1307 of the Commission's Rules? See instruction 9. If you answer yes, submit the statement as required by Sections 1.1308 and 1.1311. ☐ YES ☐ NO

10. Do you have any other amateur radio application on file with the Commission that has not been acted upon? If yes, answer items 11 and 12.   ☐ YES ☐ NO

11. PURPOSE OF OTHER APPLICATION

12. DATE SUBMITTED (Month, Day, Year)

CERTIFICATION

I CERTIFY THAT all statements herein and attachments herewith are true, complete, and correct to the best of my knowledge and belief and are made in good faith; that I am not a representative of a foreign government; that I waive any claim to the use of any particular frequency regardless of prior use by license or otherwise; and that the station to be licensed will be inaccessible to unauthorized persons.

**WILLFUL FALSE STATEMENTS MADE ON THIS FORM OR ATTACHMENTS ARE PUNISHABLE BY FINE AND IMPRISONMENT
U.S. CODE TITLE 18, SECTION 1001**

13. SIGNATURE OF APPLICANT: (Must match Item 5)

14. DATE SIGNED:

SECTION II—EXAMINATION INFORMATION

SECTION II-A FOR NOVICE OPERATOR EXAMINATION ONLY. To be completed by the Administering VEs after completing the Administering VE's Report on the other side of this form.

CERTIFICATION

I CERTIFY THAT I have complied with the Administering VE requirements stated in Part 97 of the Commission's Rules; THAT I have administered to the applicant and graded an amateur radio operator examination in accordance with Part 97 of the Commission's Rules; THAT I have indicated in the Administering VE's Report the examination element(s) the applicant passed; THAT I have examined documents held by the applicant and I have indicated in the Administering VE's Report the examination element for which the applicant is given examination credit in accordance with Part 97 of the Commission's Rules.

1A. VOLUNTEER EXAMINER'S NAME: (First, MI, Last, Suffix) *(Print or Type)*

1B. VE'S MAILING ADDRESS: (Number, Street, City, State, ZIP Code)

1C. VE'S OPERATOR CLASS:
☐ GENERAL ☐ ADVANCED ☐ AMATEUR EXTRA

1D. VE'S STATION CALL SIGN

1E. LICENSE EXPIRATION DATE:

1F. IF YOU HAVE AN APPLICATION PENDING FOR YOUR LICENSE, GIVE FILING DATE:

1G. SIGNATURE: (Must match Item 1A)

DATE SIGNED

2A. VOLUNTEER EXAMINER'S NAME: (First, MI, Last, Suffix) *(Print or Type)*

2B. VE'S MAILING ADDRESS: (Number, Street, City, State, ZIP Code)

2C. VE'S OPERATOR CLASS:
☐ GENERAL ☐ ADVANCED ☐ AMATEUR EXTRA

2D. VE'S STATION CALL SIGN

2E. LICENSE EXPIRATION DATE:

2F. IF YOU HAVE AN APPLICATION PENDING FOR YOUR LICENSE, GIVE FILING DATE:

2G. SIGNATURE: (Must match Item 2A)

DATE SIGNED

SECTION II-B FOR TECHNICIAN, GENERAL, ADVANCED, OR AMATEUR EXTRA OPERATOR EXAMINATION ONLY. To be completed by the Administering VEs after completing the Administering VE's Report on the other side of this form.

CERTIFICATION

I CERTIFY THAT I have complied with the Administering VE requirements stated in Part 97 of the Commission's Rules; THAT I have administered to the applicant and graded an amateur radio operator examination in accordance with Part 97 of the Commission's Rules; THAT I have indicated in the Administering VE's Report the examination element(s) the applicant passed; THAT I have examined documents held by the applicant and I have indicated in the Administering VE's Report the examination element(s) for which the applicant is given examination credit in accordance with Part 97 of the Commission's Rules.

1A. VOLUNTEER EXAMINER'S NAME: (First, MI, Last, Suffix) *(Print or Type)*

1B. VE'S STATION CALL SIGN:

1C. SIGNATURE: (Must match Item 1A)

DATE SIGNED:

2A. VOLUNTEER EXAMINER'S NAME: (First, MI, Last, Suffix) *(Print or Type)*

2B. VE'S STATION CALL SIGN:

2C. SIGNATURE: (Must match Item 2A)

DATE SIGNED:

3A. VOLUNTEER EXAMINER'S NAME: (First, MI, Last, Suffix) *(Print or Type)*

3B. VE'S STATION CALL SIGN:

3C. SIGNATURE: (Must match Item 3A)

DATE SIGNED:

FCC Form 610
February 1990

BE A PART OF THE TRADITION

Your decision to become a radio amateur will bring you much enjoyment throughout your life. Make another great decision. Join the American Radio Relay League.

The League is a democratic organization of, by and for its members (there are more than 150,000 worldwide). America's ham organization for more than 75 years, the League provides you with services every radio amateur wants and needs, and leads the fight to preserve and expand amateur frequencies. The ARRL is a strong voice for every member.

As a member, you'll have access to our "all-risk" ham radio equipment insurance program. You'll find this program less expensive and with broader coverage than similar plans.

You'll also receive our monthly membership journal, *QST*. With more than 170 pages per issue, *QST* guides you to great equipment bargains in our Ham Ads section. You can obtain essential consumer information from our New Products announcements and Product Review articles. And there's much more of interest to you: feature, technical and "how-to" articles...the list goes on.

So, if you want to make another great decision, just turn the page, and accept our invitation to membership. You'll be glad you did!

THE AMERICAN RADIO RELAY LEAGUE
Serving Amateur Radio for more than 75 years.

Invitation to Membership

YOU'VE GOT QUESTIONS? WE'VE GOT ANSWERS!

Now you've got what you need to go after your own Amateur Radio license and call sign! But you've probably still got a question or two. Does anyone in my area teach classes? Where can I find a person who can give me my exam? Where in my area can I buy equipment? Which is better from my location, a dipole antenna or a vertical antenna? If I decide to learn Morse code, where can I find someone to help me practice? Can someone check my station to see if I've set up everything correctly? Who do I turn to for the answers? The American Radio Relay League's Educational Activities Department can send you a list of Amateur Radio clubs, instructors, examiners and Elmers who live in your area and enjoy helping newcomers. Here's your first question and answer: What's an Elmer? An Elmer is a person who helps you with whatever you need; an Elmer is another Amateur Radio tradition of hams helping others. For your list, send a postcard to ARRL EAD, 225 Main St, Newington, CT 06111, or call us at 203-666-1541.

"IF I JOIN A CLUB, I'LL BE ABLE TO MAKE NEW FRIENDS AND HAVE FUN WHILE LEARNING ABOUT HAM RADIO."